FORESTRY COMMISSION BOOKLET NO. 33

Conifers in the British Isles

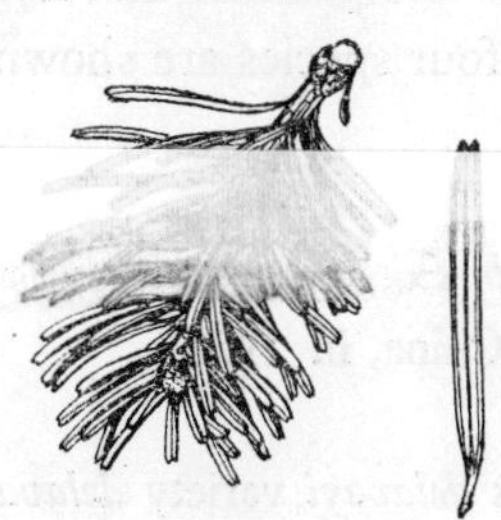

A Descriptive Handbook

by ALAN F. MITCHELL, B.A., B.Agric.(For.)

Forestry Commission

with drawings by

CHRISTINE DARTER, B.Sc.(Hort.)

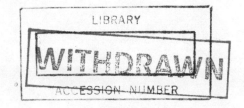

LONDON: HER MAJESTY'S STATIONERY OFFICE

1972

A NOTE ON THE DRAWINGS AND TEXT

All the 203 drawings have been made by Mrs. Christine Darter from living specimens identified by Mr. Alan Mitchell.

Most are reproduced at exactly two-thirds natural size, the few exceptions and the enlarged detail being noted; the magnifications for the latter are shown in their respective captions.

The text describes 43 genera, 270 species and a further 217 varieties or cultivars. It mentions 526 arboreta and gardens that have been visited by the author. Twenty-four species are shown in full-page photographs.

Cover Picture: Cone and foliage of *Abies delavayi* variety *georgei*, a Silver fir introduced from Yunnan, China, in 1923.

Title Page Decoration: Foliage of *Abies delavayi* variety *delavayi*.

SBN 11 710012 9

Contents

ACKNOWLEDGMENTS

Except for the two subjects noted below, all the photographs are drawn from the Forestry Commission's official collection, and were taken by its own staff photographers.

Plate 22 was kindly provided by Mr. H. Girling, and Plate 5 by Mr. Maurice Nimmo. Mr. N. D. G. James and Messrs. Blackwells, publishers, of Oxford kindly assisted with information on trees at the Bicton Gardens in South Devon.

Introduction

The British Isles hold a uniquely important position in the history of the cultivation of conifers and taxads as exotics. This position has been brought about by three main factors. Firstly, British plant-collectors have been the pioneers or among the most active workers in every area of the world important for conifer species. In the second half of the seventeenth century Bishop Compton at Fulham Palace was inspiring collection in eastern North America by Tradescant and receiving plants from Bartram. From 1827 David Douglas was sending back the first conifers from western North America, and his collecting was greatly augmented by the Veitchian collectors and those from the Oregon Society from 1853 to 1856. J. G. Veitch and Robert Fortune were sending plants from Japan in 1860 and 1861, Fortune having already sent some from southern China in 1843. William Lobb and William Archer had followed Menzies's pioneer introduction (*Araucaria araucana*) from South America by many more species in 1847 and 1854. From 1899, Wilson and Forrest were sending a multitude of species from China and later, Formosa. In India, amateur collectors acquired Himalayan species from 1818 onwards. Hence the gardens in Great Britain had unrivalled opportunities to receive the earliest and subsequent imports, and thus to contain a high proportion of the oldest, and often the original plants in cultivation. The second factor is the extraordinary number of people interested in the new conifers and willing and able to plant them. Arboreta and garden-collections were established by the hundred. In parts of Scotland where many conifers flourish best, it became the fashion to plant the policies with conifers and it was to facilitate this and increase supplies that the Oregon Society was founded. The result was a great number of small, and some large, collections, made from the earliest seed in areas of very good growth, and thus a wealth of very big trees. The interest has continued, and there is hardly a county without at least one good collection and in some counties there are fifty or more garden-collections with good specimens. The last factor is the climate of these islands which allows, somewhere or other, good growth of the majority of temperate-world conifers, and growth somewhere of some sort, in nearly every species. There are five regions where most of the larger growing species of *Abies*, *Picea*, *Pseudotsuga*, *Thuja* and *Tsuga* make remarkably rapid growth, and these regions are peculiarly distributed. They are the South-west Peninsula of England and, to some extent, the New Forest; Eastern Ireland; the coast of Argyll; Central Perthshire; and near the coast north of Inverness. In Devon, Cornwall and Ireland, growth in girth is more notable than that of height, whereas in Argyll, Perthshire, Inverness and Ross, growth in height is also sustained and notable. Another difference among these regions is that in Devon and Cornwall, the trees tend to mature and degenerate relatively early and many trees of these genera have died when about 120 years old. In Argyll, gales seem to be the only hazard and here, as in Perth, Inverness and Ross-shire, trees of 120 years of age are usually in full health and even still increasing in height.

It is both natural and important that such a vast collection of the older specimens of conifer as is found in the British Isles should attract a series of reports on the progress of their growth. The first reports were those from individual estates or short summaries of particular species, published at short intervals in the Gardeners' Chronicle and the Transactions of the Highland and Agricultural Society and, later the Transactions of the Arboricultural and Agricultural Society, from about 1840 to 1890.

The first general summary attempted was in the Report of the Conifer Conference of 1891, (Wilks and Weathers, 1892). This featured particularly the trees sent by David Douglas, by then about 60 years in cultivation; the Himalayan species, deodar and Morinda spruce, and the species from the intensive collection of species in Oregon and California in 1853–4, but some European, Japanese and other species were included by many contributors. This gave a good indication of the sort of growth of many of the North-west American species after 35 years, and some after 60 years of growth, within these islands, with a preponderance of Scottish estates.

From 1906 to 1913 Elwes and Henry published their unsurpassed work, *The Trees of Great Britain and Ireland** The dimensions of about 1,000 specimens of conifers are given, nearly all from the travels of the two authors during the time the book was written, with a very even spread and wide cover of the regions.

The next summary was far more comprehensive, (Chittenden, 1932). The data gathered for the Conifer Conference in 1931 included some 4,500 specimens. At this time, the original trees from Douglas's seed were 100 years old, and those from the Oregon Association and Veitchian collectors were 75 years old. A valuable addition was the data for the Chinese species from Wilson's collecting, many of which were then 25–30 years old and showing something of their form.

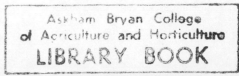

The present work is the next in the series. About a third of the specimens of conifers given by Elwes and Henry, half those of the 1932 Report, and many also in the 1891 Report, have been found and remeasured. From a total of over 18,000 recent measurements by the author, only a selection can be included. Trees recorded in the previous works are given some precedence and are included if they have made good, or occasionally, exceptionally little, growth. Some 580 estates, gardens, parks and collections have been visited by the author and some outstanding trees not hitherto recorded have been found. The best of these are all included. Specimens outside the general range of their species in this country are also given precedence even if of no great size. The coverage is thus intended to show, as well as possible, the range of the species and of the larger specimens; the largest, the finest and those of the most rapid growth. Special attention has been paid to the oldest or original trees surviving, as, in many cases, this is likely to be the last survey in which they will appear as living trees.

It will presumably also be the last with the measurements in feet and inches. This has been adhered to in order to show the growth of the trees in the form in which it is, at present, most easily comprehended, and to mark the final state of many well-known trees in a form consistent with their earlier records. Concurrently with this, the appropriate section of the Report of the Conifer Conference of 1970 will include most of these trees in metric measure to start the next phase of recording.

Every species of conifer that the author has found growing in these countries has been included. He is aware that there are one or two collections which may have a species which has escaped him, but has tried to eliminate as many as is possible. Among the cultivars, only those reaching, or apparently going to reach, tree-size, say 20 feet, have been included.

Every species and cultivar has been described as found, from living foliage. In a few cases the foliage was sent from Northern Ireland and from Finland, through the kind co-operation of Mr. R. Sherwood of the Northern Ireland Forestry Division and Professor M. Hagman of the Finnish Tree-Breeding Station, respectively. In a few other cases, a few features, mainly cones, could not be found fresh and the descriptions have been taken (and noted as taken) from *The Handbook of Conifers* by W. Dallimore and A. B. Jackson (revised by J. Harrison, 1966) or from the *Manual of Conifers* by P. den Ouden and B. K. Boom, (1965).

References

CHITTENDEN, F. J. (1932). *Conifers in Cultivation. The Report of the Conifer Conference held by the Royal Horticultural Society, Nov.* 10–12, 1931. Royal Horticultural Society, Vincent Square, London, S.W.1. (Out of print).

DALLIMORE, W., JACKSON, A. B., and HARRISON, S. G. (1966). *A Handbook of the Coniferae and Ginkgoaceae.* 4th edition. Arnold, London, £8·40.

ELWES, H. J., and HENRY, A. (1906–1913). *The Trees of Great Britain and Ireland.* Seven vols. and index, many illustrations. Privately printed, Edinburgh, 1906–1913. Now out of print; a facsimile edition is currently being published for the Royal Forestry Society of England, Wales, and Northern Ireland, 102 Hight St., Tring, Hertfordshire.

OUDEN, P. DEN, and BOOM, B. K. (1965). *Manual of Cultivated Conifers Hardy in the Cold and Warm Temperate Zone,* Martinus Nijhoff, The Hague, Holland, £5·40.

WILKS, REV. W., and WEATHERS, JOHN, (1892). Report of the Conifer Conference (1891). *Journal of the Royal Horticultural Society,* London, Vol. XIV, 1892.

The Keys

A key has been provided for each major genus. These are not strictly botanical, in that closely related species may emerge widely separated. The author is quite unrepentant about this as the keys are designed to be simple and to work primarily with leaves and shoots alone. Other characters are sometimes used secondarily. If they do work, then the ability to use easily acquired foliage and to dispense with the seldom available cones or flowers justifies, in the author's view this botanical licence.

The aim has been to avoid features which require drawing a line between intergrades or features which are variable within one species. The need to separate, early in the key, groups of species showing well-defined features regardless of their relationships, is the cause of the departure from strict botanical lines.

New Species

In two hybrids of the x *Cupressocyparis* group, the descriptions, and even the mention, of the trees are new. These have been named and described in the Journal of the Royal Horticultural Society, October 1970. See pp. 96-95.

Descriptions of Genera and Species with Line Drawings:

Abies Miller (Pinaceae)

A genus of about fifty species in the northern hemisphere, occurring in nearly all parts south to Mexico, North Africa, the Himalaya and South-west China. They are botanically rather uniform and most have very restricted ranges, few anywhere ranging across a continent and several, like the Mediterranean species, being shrinking montane relicts. Nearly all are tall, straight growing trees of moderate to very large ultimate size but a few are low and bushy trees. The leaves are firm and leathery, rarely spine-tipped, and arise from circular bases which leave small round depressions on the shoot when the leaves are shed. Male flowers are small globular or conic, usually crowded along the underside of the young shoots. Female flowers are erect, green or red, cylindrical, often confined to few shoots around the apex of the tree. The cones are cylindrical or barrel-shaped, from small to very large, erect, green, brown or blue-purple often encrusted with resin and with bracts either hidden or exserted. They are composed of many flat scales, and break up on the tree when ripe, leaving a tall narrowly conic spike and base-plate on the tree. Monoecious. A few Mexican species are only doubtfully hardy even in mildest areas and some northern Asiatic species are damaged by late frosts, but otherwise all are hardy.

Key to the species of Abies

Notes (1) Pubescence is often shown more on side-shoots.
(2) Shoot colour in the key refers to the underside of the shoot as it is more readily seen and is usually brighter coloured.

---

1. Shoots uniformly and conspicuously pubescent (without use of lens) — 2
   Shoots glabrous or with pubescence scattered; confined to grooves or exceedingly fine — 9
2. Leaves all round the shoot, crowded forwards, brilliant white beneath; pubescence on shoot orange-brown — *delavayi* v. *georgei*
   Leaves pectinate beneath, or distinctly parted — 3
3. Leaves pectinate or widely parted above shoot — 4
   Leaves not parted above shoot; lying forward or standing above — 6
4. Pubescence white; leaves 1·5–2 cm, curved inwards, often upswept; foliage yellow-green, strongly fragrant (cedarwood oil) — *sibirica*
   Pubescence pale or dark brown, leaves 3 cm +, scarcely curved in, not upswept; scarcely fragrant — 5
5. Pubescence pale coffee-brown, short, dense; leaves parallel, slender, not notched — *borisii-regis*
   Pubescence dark brown, long; leaves variously forward, broad, notched — *delavayi* v. *fabri*
6. Leaves with bright white bands beneath only; no stomata above — 7
   Leaves with pale bands above and below — 8
7. Leaf to 3 cm; 2nd year shoot grey-brown, foliage strong scent of tangerines (bark smooth, blistered) — *amabilis*
   Leaf to 2 cm; 2nd year shoot red-purple, foliage with warm slight scent (bark freckled grey) — *mariesii*

8\. Leaves densely covering shoot; flat, grooved (branches level) — *procera*
Leaves more open, showing shoot; rounded, keeled, can be rolled (branches short ± upswept) — *magnifica*

9\. Pubescence on shoots in grooves only or in lines; — 10
Pubescence uniform and very fine, or scattered, or absent — 15

10\. Leaves 4 cm + long; white or bright white banded beneath; shoot stout; bud big, 1 cm — 11
Leaves 2–4 cm, thinly white or greenish bands beneath; shoot seldom stout, bud 5–6 mm — 12

11\. Leaves widely pectinate; brilliant white bands beneath; deep blue-green above — *spectabilis*
Leaves scarcely parted above, white bands beneath not brilliant; yellow-green above — *pindrow* v. *intermedia*

12\. Leaves broad thick, narrowly stalked; distant, perpendicular to shoot; 2 broad bands beneath, greenish or white; yellowish green above — *firma*
Leaves not broad, seldom thick, obscurely stalked, forward — 13

13\. Buds dark red, whorled, foliage densely parallel forward on 5–6 years of shoot, grass-green readily fragrant, leaves 3–4 cm, 2nd year shoot dark grey — *sachalinensis*
Buds deep purple, not whorled; leaves variously forward; deep green, not readily fragrant — 14

14\. Shoot golden brown, 2nd year pale pink-grey, leaves curved in, pale-tipped 2·5–3 cm — *delavayi* v. *faxoniana*
Shoot pale orange or pink-brown; 2nd year shoot dark orange-brown; lower leaves dense parallel rows, blackish-green, to 2·5 cm — *kawakamii*

15\. Leaves not pectinate below; a proportion beneath the shoot — 16
Leaves pectinate below, spreading each side or curved upwards — 28

16\. Leaves radiating all round the shoot perpendicular to it; stiff; rigid — 17
Leaves below shoot lying forwards; flexible — 21

17\. Leaves with stomata above and below — 18
Leaves with stomata below only — 19

18\. Stomata below in bright white bands; stomata above grey; leaf 1–2 cm, straight, broad — *numidica*
Stomata grey-green both sides; leaf 0·5–1 cm, some curved backwards, moderately broad. — *pinsapo*

19\. Leaves ± equally above and below shoot, well spaced to 3 cm long — *cephalonica*
Leaves fewer below than above, 2·5 cm — 20

20\. Leaves crowded above shoot, partly forwards; white bands beneath — *cephalonica* v. *apollinis*
Leaves well spaced; perpendicular; pale grey bands beneath — x *vilmoriniana*

21\. Leaves without stomata above — 22
Leaves with stomata above — 23

22\. Leaves slender, pale bright green, densely parallel; shoot pale brown, bands beneath very narrow, grey, sometimes white — *sachalinensis*
Leaves not slender; deep bluish-green, inner leaves upright or forward; shoot orange or brown; bands beneath broad bright white — *delavayi* v. *forrestii*

23\. Stomata on upper surface in two bands or irregularly banded — 24
Stomata on upper surface in one central band or at tip or completely dusted all over — 26

24\. Leaves shiny pale green both sides (stomata visible under lens), shoot pink-brown — *pindrow brevifolia*
Leaves brilliantly white banded beneath; or dull grey-green both sides; stomata above readily visible — 25

25\. Leaves brilliantly white beneath, very dark above, 1–2 cm long — *koreana*
Leaves dull grey-green each side; 2–4 cm long — *lasiocarpa*

26\. Stomata above, in one central band from the tip; those beneath blue-white, inner leaves reversed along shoot; leaves acute-pointed — *vejari*
Stomata above dusted over leaf, those beneath brilliant chalky white; leaves truncate notched — 27

27. Shoot glabrous, rough; cone barrel-shaped, bracts exserted 1–5 mm — ***delavayi* v. *forrestii***
Shoot smooth, glabrous or densely pubescent; cone cylindric, bracts exserted 5–10 mm — ***delavayi* v. *georgei***

28. Leaves pectinate above also; lying ± flat each side of shoot — **29**
Leaves above shoot rising each side to leave a "V" or all across the shoot vertical or forwards — **34**

29. Inner leaves lying strongly forwards; shoot orange-brown, or purple, ribbed or grooved — 30
Inner leaves parallel with outer, ± perpendicular to shoot; shoot smooth — **31**

30. Pubescence and shoot pale orange-brown; leaves to 2·5 cm — ***kawakamii***
Pubescence white; shoot purple, red-brown and brown on same plant, leaves to 4·5 cm — ***fargesii***

31. Shoot shiny, glabrous, pink or yellow-brown, bud large, pale — ***chensiensis***
Shoot olive, green or grey, pubescent — 32

32. Shoot dull grey or fawn; scattered dark pubescence, leaf 2–3 cm, broad white bands beneath — ***alba***
Shoot olive oı green, very finely pubescent; leaf 3–5 cm, narrow white bands beneath — **33**

33. Shoot olive-brown, 2nd year grey-brown, leaf 3–4 cm (bark grey, cracked into squares) — ***grandis***
Shoot green; 2nd year copper brown, leaf 4–5 cm (bark black or dark purple-grey; widely and shallowly fissured) — ***concolor* v. *lowiana* (N)**

34. Leaves above shoot distinctly parted by a narrow or wide "V" — **35**
Leaves above shoot not parted, lying along or standing above shoot — **49**

35. Bud, slender, fusiform, pointed, 1·5 cm long, pale brown not resinous; leaves stiff, sharply spined, not broad, 4–5 cm long — ***bracteata***
Bud ovoid or globose, blunt, red or purple, resinous; leaves leathery pliant, if rigid, also broad and short — **36**

36. Prominent patch of white stomata on upper tip of leaf; bud shining red — *balsamea*
Stomata absent from upper surface or if present, widely scattered — **37**

37. Leaves with broad, bright white bands beneath — 38
Leaves with greenish, grey or narrow white bands beneath — 41

38. Shoot white or buff, deeply grooved; leaves parallel, slightly forward — ***homolepis***
Shoot dark brown, purple or orange, smooth or ribbed — **39**

39. Shoots purple and brown, leaves slender, shiny — ***sutchuenensis***
Shoots orange-brown; leaves broad, dull. — **40**

40. Shoots roughened; leaves 3–4 cm — *delavayi* v. *forrestii*
Shoots smooth, leaves blue-grey; 1·5–2·5 cm — *delavayi* v. *georgei*

41. Shoot pale yellowish or pinkish-grey — **42**
Shoot green, orange, brown or purple — **46**

42. Shoot pale yellow-brown or buff; finely pubescent — 43
Shoot pink or grey-pink, shiny, glabrous — 45

43. Leaves narrowly stalked widening to very broad; hard, rigid — *firma*
Leaves parallel-sided from base, usually slender, not rigid — 44

44. Bud bright deep purple, leaves forward, parallel, deep green, not arched; shoot ribbed — *delavayi* v. *faxoniana*
Bud red-brown; tips of scales free; lower leaves perpendicular to shoot, upper assurgent or arched forwards; light green; shoot smooth — *cilicica*

45. Shoot pink, shiny, glabrous, ribbed and cracking; leaves to 2 cm long, mid-leaves vertical or bent backwards — *recurvata*
Shoot ashen-pink, very stout, leaves to 5 or 7 cm, arched — *pindrow*

46. Leaves with two blue-grey bands on upper surface; to 5 cm long, perpendicular to shoot, curved upwards; shoot green — *concolor* v. *lowiana* (S)
Leaves without stomata above; to 3·5 cm long — 47

47. Leaves linear-lanceolate to fine, sharp, yellow spine, side leaves curved outwards; shoot green, yellow and red-brown — *religiosa*
Leaves parallel-sided to blunt, usually notched apex — 48

48. Shoot pale orange to buff-orange, pubescent between ribs; lower leaves spreading in dense parallel ranks — *kawakamii*
Shoot brown to rich purple, shiny, usually glabrous, leaves bent down at tips; many curved forwards — *sutchuenensis*

49. Leaves along mid-line of shoot erect; side leaves curved upwards — 50
Leaves along mid-line of shoot lying forwards along shoots; side leaves spread flat — 56

50. Leaves more than 3 cm, usually 4–5 cm long — 51
Leaves 2·5 cm or less — 54

51. Leaves blue-grey above; thick, rounded; shoot yellow-green — *concolor*
Leaves green above, thin, flat; shoots pink or brown, pale or reddish — 52

52. Leaves bright green above without stomata; shoot pink-buff, shiny — *holophylla*
Leaves dark green above with some stomata — 53

53. Shoot red-brown, shining, glabrous; leaves 3–4·5 cm, with prominent stomatal patch at tip and in two bands on upper side of some leaves — *bornmulleriana*
Shoot yellow-brown, side-shoots at least finely pubescent; leaves 2–3 cm, occasionally with one central line of stomata above prominent — *cilicica*

54. Shoot purple-brown or orange-brown; leaf with 2 grey lines above — *squamata*
Shoot yellow-brown or pale brown, no stomatal lines above — 55

55. Leaves banded bright white beneath; blackish green above, pale-tipped, bud resinous, chocolate-purple — *fraseri*
Leaves greenish-white beneath, yellow green to tip above; bud not resinous; red-brown — *nebrodensis*

56. Leaves pale blue-grey above; shoot yellowish-grey — *lasiocarpa* v. *arizonica*
Leaves grey-green or dark green above — 57

57. Leaves sparse, 5–7 cm, hard, arching widely; greenish bands beneath, shoots glabrous — *pindrow*
Leaves dense, to 3·5 cm, leathery, straight, white bands beneath, shoots $\pm$ pubescent — 58

58. Bud pale brown, not resinous, shoot olive-brown — *nordmanniana*
Bud purple or red, very resinous; shoot fawn or grey — 59

59. Leaves brilliantly white beneath; deep, slightly shiny green above (bole deeply fluted) — *veitchii*
Leaves dull grey-white beneath; dull grey-green above (bole smooth) — *nephrolepis*

Fig. 1
Abies alba. Common Silver fir. The leaves and pubescence are rather sparse on the shoot. The single leaf ($\times 1\frac{1}{3}$) shows the white stomatal bands on the underside.

Abies alba Miller. Common silver fir (*A. pectinata* De Candolle)

Pyrenees, France, Corsica, the Alps to the Tatra Mountains south to Balkan Mountains and Calabria. Introduced in 1603. Oldest known surviving tree dates from 1680—very few known from the eighteenth century.

Common in many broadleaved woodland areas in Cornwall and north-west Devon and parts of County Kerry, the Lake District and in Argyll, Wester Ross and Perthshire. Infrequent and largely confined to a few collections and large gardens in South-east England.

Natural regeneration is often abundant and almost always present near old trees.

Bark. Young trees smooth, stippled with leaf-traces, dull brown grey; shallow cracks appearing. Later, pale grey, small plates with wide shallow brown-pink cracks between. Biggest trees, dull grey, cracked into small thick plates, curving away, especially on flutes in the bole.

Crown. Young trees, symmetrically conic with regularly whorled branches rising at a slight angle from horizontal. Very open, sparsely branched; shoots below leader curving strongly upwards around it. Older trees in woods have long, usually slightly sinuous boles bearing numerous stubs of dead branches and lose the main axis at the height of the surrounding canopy-top. Above this there are many stems, two most usually arching away from each other at the top. In Devon and Cornwall this happens fairly low and early and the dead tops have shallow "V's" of slender branches very close together, like bent herring-bones. Elsewhere the tree may be much bigger and the top is composed of heavy branches arching out. Open-grown trees mostly either fork low or have huge low branches, level for many feet from the bole then abruptly turning vertically upwards. The outline is very broadly columnar and the top is thinly foliaged and opens out.

Foliage. Shoot pale brown or dull grey, with variably dense, short, blackish pubescence. Shoot of vigorous young tree, stout, shining pale grey, glabrous but slightly puckered. Bud red-brown, some white resin.

Leaves. 1 to 2 cm; mixed lengths, upper ones short; bent into almost flat ranks each side of shoot; tip rounded, often notched; grooved and dark shining green above; two whitish bands beneath; rather sparse, especially on vigorous shoots and leaders.

Flowers and Cone. Male flowers small, globular, clustered thickly on underside of previous year's shoots over most of crown. Cones clustered on a few branches at very top of tree; pale green, then red-brown, cylindrical, narrowed at base, slightly tapered, 10–15$\times$3·5 cm; bract tip exserted, slender down-curved, 6–7 mm. Scales large and few.

Growth. Flushes very early; side-shoots shed bud-scales and expand in mid-April and suffer damage from late frosts. Leading shoot starts growth in early May and stops by mid-June, damaged only by very late frosts, in frost-pockets. Growth for the first 6 years is very slow in height but side-shoots grow strongly to make a flat, broad crown, especially in shade. Once established, growth of leaders increases rapidly to a maximum of about 3 feet a year. Young, dated trees are hardly known; one at Speech House, Gloucestershire was 58ft$\times$4ft 5in at 43 years, and one at Fenagh House, County Carlow was 52ft$\times$4ft 7in at 67 years, but growth must often be at nearly double the rates shown by these two.

The oldest trees have grown extraordinarily slowly during this century. Very few of the identifiable old silver firs in the 1932 Report have added more than 12 inches to their girth since then. One very marked exception to this slow growth is the four-stemmed tree at Ardkinglas, Argyll. It can now be measured properly only at 3 feet up the bole. In 1905 it was 114ft$\times$21ft. In 1931 it was 110ft$\times$24ft 10in and in 1969 it is 125ft$\times$28ft 9in; a growth of 47 inches in 38 years, and over 90 inches in 64 years.

Specimens. The tree at Kilbride was one of the two tallest trees known in Britain from 1931 (when it was 168 feet) to 1965 (when it had been about 180 feet for 10 years) and it forked at 90 feet into two huge limbs. It has lost one limb for several years and is now nearly dead. The tallest now is a long-boled tree of 154 feet in the Den at Dupplin Castle. A very slender, young tree at Fonthill, was 141ft×7ft 3in in 1965 and remarkably straight. Some of the oldest and biggest are in Table 1.

Table 1. Oldest and Largest Trees of Abies alba

Locality	*Date Planted*	*Dimensions*	
Dawyck	1680	112′ × 15′ 6″ (1909)	120′ × 16″ 8″ (1967)
Alnwick Castle		100′ × 15′ 11″ (1931)	143′ × 16′ 1″ (1956)
Alnwick Castle		120′ × 16′ 7″ (1931)	137′ × 16′ 10″ (1956)
Alnwick Castle			142′ × 16′ 1″ (1956)
Cowdray Park		130′ × 10′ 2″ (1903)	133′ × 12′ 0″ (1967)[1]
Ardkinglas (Strone)		114′ × 21′ 0″ (1905)	125′ × 28′ 9″ (1969)[2]
Ardkinglas (Strone)			140′ × 12′ 8″ (1969)
Ardkinglas		105′ × 20′ 0″ (1931)	140′ × 20′ 11″ (1969)
Ardkinglas		105′ × 17′ 4″ (1931)	120′ × 18′ 6″ (1969)
Lynedoch	1730	× 14′ 8″ (1931)	130′ × 15′ 6″ (1970)
Cortachy Castle	1745		90′ × 14′ 0″ (1962)
Culzean Castle	1780	93′ × 16′ 0″ (1931)	124′ × 18′ 2″ (1970)
Raehills	1790		136′ × 19′ 1″ (1970)
Raehills	1790		131′ × 20′ 1″ (1970)
Dalguise			139′ × 18′ 2″ (1955)
Dunkeld House			144′ × 16′ 3″ (1970)
Dunkeld House (River Walk)		113′ × 15′ 9″ (1931)	121′ × 16′ 2″ (1970)
Blairquhan	1810	118′ × 16′ 0″ (1931)	121′ × 17′ 1″ (1970)
Blairquhan	1810	110′ × 12′ 0″ (1931)	128′ × 13′ 9″ (1970)
Bargany			150′ × 13′ 2″ (1954)
Abercairny		122′ × 12′ 3″ (1931)	128′ × 14′ 3″ (1962)
Abercairny		78′ × 17′ 3″ (1931)	115′ × 19′ 1″ (1955)
Curraghmore	1835	102′ × 14′ 9″ (1931)	110′ × 16′ 2″ (1968)
Powis Castle	1847		151′ × 12′ 2″ (1970)
Dupplin Castle (Garden)		123′ × 15′ 6″ (1931)	153′ × 16′ 9″ (1970)
Dupplin Castle (Lawn)		100′ × 17′ 6″ (1909)	130′ × 19′ 4″ (1970)
Dupplin Castle (Den)			154′ × 12′ 0″ (1970)
Inistioge		120′ × 15′ 4″ (1931)	128′ × 17′ 9″ (1966)
Birr Castle		107′ × 7′ 3″ (1931)	125′ × 11′ 5″ (1966)
Hamwood	prob. 1844	91′ × 10′ 6″ (1931)	100′ × 11′ 4″ (1968)
Killarney House		70′ × 7′ 3″ (1931)	100′ × 11′ 0″ (1968)
Avondale		125′ × 15′ 4″ (1908)	144′ × 16′ 9″ (1968)
Avondale		132′ × 17′ 6″ (1912)	146′ × 18′ 3″ (1968)
Minard Castle			110′ × 19′ 3″ (1969)
Moniack Glen			138′ × 11′ 0″ (1970)

[1] Top snapped off where about 1 foot in diameter
[2] Girth taken at 3 feet

cv. Columnaris. (Found wild in France, Cultivated 1855) Two big trees of this very narrowly columnar form were recorded in 1931 at Durris House, but cannot now be found. The only specimen known now is one 74ft × 3ft 7in (1971) at Tregrehan, Cornwall.

cv. Pendula. (Found wild in France 1835) This curious form is narrow with downswept branches and its stem may bend to horizontal in the upper part. At Tregrehan, the tree 60 feet tall in 1931 is still 60 feet tall, 4 feet 1 inch in girth. At Endsleigh, one is 35ft×3ft 9in and another has a horizontal branch 15 yards long and is about 40ft×3ft 1in (1957).

Uses. No longer planted for ornament, shelter nor timber, the tree which had provided the biggest specimens in Britain for over a hundred years has been replaced by others. This is entirely due to the damage caused by *Adelges nordmannianae* (*nusslini*). If this were avoided, the tree would be planted quite widely for its very big volume-production and its resistance to *Fomes annosus* rot which make it highly attractive. Trials of provenances from throughout the natural range were planted by the Forestry Commission in 1966.

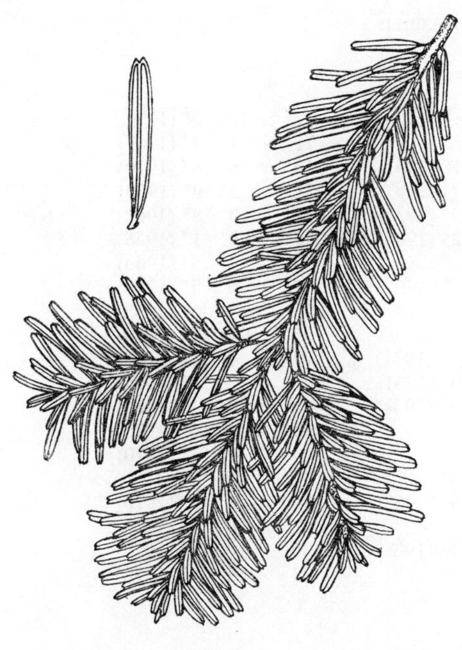

Fig. 2
A short-leafed spray, typical of many *Abies amabilis.* This foliage closely resembles that of *Abies mariesii* but is more spreading and the shoot is much less densely pubescent. Shoots with long leaves to 3 cm, are quite unlike those of *A. mariesii.*

Abies amabilis Douglas ex Forbes. Red fir

Alaskan border along the coast mountains through British Columbia and Washington just in to Oregon. Inland only to Washington Cascades and south through Oregon to Californian border. Introduced in 1830. No original trees known since 1905. Only one tree now known of certain date before 1900. (1898 Hergest Croft) but one at Doldowlod is in a wood planted in 1868. Infrequent: almost confined to large conifer collections and a few trial plantations.

BARK. Young trees—greyish purple, smooth; horizontal resin-blisters. Older trees slightly corky, dark grey, often still blistered.

CROWN. Where flourishing, regular, medium-conic; whorled branches, dense foliage. Where growing slowly, narrowly conic becoming columnar, short, level branches, thin, sparse foliage. Young trees growing vigorously have a slender leading shoot with the middle section bearing small, closely adpressed side-shoots. Shoots at base of leader lie very flat.

FOLIAGE. Juvenile leaves about 2 cm, banded grey beneath, not white, on shoots almost glabrous, and may be borne for 6–8 years from seed. Adult shoot pale greenish brown or grey, grey-brown second year, variably covered in very short, dense, pale pubescence.

BUD small, globular, soon white with resin.

LEAVES very densely set, swept flat each side of shoot, lower rows spreading at right angles and curved at tips, succeeding rows above progressively forward-pointing; parallel-sided, truncate and notched. New leaves often dusty grey-blue; second year always shining rich dark green; grooved above, two broad bright white bands beneath. 3 cm×0·2 cm. When crushed, gives strong aroma of tangerines. Stomatal patch at tips of leaves on some vigorous shoots.

FLOWERS AND CONE. Male flowers abundant, large globules crowded on underside of shoot; female seldom seen, on topmost shoots, red. Cone cylindric, domed rather greyish purple, ripening brown, 10–15 cm, very smooth.

GROWTH. Very variable indeed, the general pattern being slow and thin in South-east England and vigorous and luxuriant trees in the far north and west, but the origin of the seed (unknown in all cases) may be important. It has been very short-lived here so far—none of the 8 mentioned by Elwes and Henry survives, and only 7 of the 23 given in 1931 have been found in Great Britain, but four more in Ireland survive. A few of the biggest trees are dying back. Growth in girth can be remarkably rapid in luxuriant trees—25 inches in 12 years at Benmore. At Headfort, a tree has added 73 inches in 35 years; at Castlewellan, an older tree added 69 inches in 39 years, and at Avondale 47 inches in 22 years. Many trees showing such rapid increases in girth have made relatively slow growth in height so they are singularly stout of bole and taper rapidly. Leading shoots grow from late in May until the end of July.

SPECIMENS. The best trees are remarkably luxuriant and growing very rapidly.

USES. Apart from a few small trial plantations at Crarae and Kyloe this tree has been used only in collections or as a specimen in large gardens which are, in effect, collections like Stourhead and Leonardslee. Where it grows well, few conifers are more attractive, but it should be planted on a sheltered, damp site over deep soil. Two trees at Clunas, Cawdor, Nairn, were over 90 feet tall when blown down in 1953 and there was some interest in using this species on such high, drier sites, but specimens elsewhere do not encourage this view.

TABLE 2. LARGEST TREES OF ABIES AMABILIS

Locality	*Date Planted*	*Dimensions*	
Doldowlod	1868(?)		97′ × 11′ 1″ (1959)
Hergest Croft	1898		71′ × 7′ 7″ (1961)
Keir House	1901	61′ × 3′ 1″ (1931)	66′ × 5′ 8″ (1970)
Westonbirt	1905	17′ (1931)	51′ × 3′ 0″ (1969)
Little Hall	1906	19′ × 1′ 3″ (1931)	57′ × 3′ 8″ (1961)
Avondale	1909	50′ × 5′ 2″ (1946)	90′ × 9′ 1″ (1968)
Dawyck	1909		60′ × 4′ 8″ (1966)
Scone Palace			93′ × 5′ 5″ (1970)
Kyloe Wood	1910		65′ × 3′ 6″ (1958)
Kyloe Wood	1910		55′ × 4′ 10″ (1958)
Derreen	1911	20′ (1931)	77′ × 4′ 3″ (1966)
Wakehurst Place	1914	20′ × 1′ 6″ (1931)	47′ × 3′ 11″ (1964)
Headfort	1914	25′ × 1′ 10″ (1931)	53′ × 7′ 11″ (1966)
Taymouth Castle			(65′) × 13′ 4″ (1970)[1]
Fairburn (Pinetum)	1920		79′ × 9′ 1″ (1970)
Endsleigh		46′ × 9′ 2″ (1957)	60′ × 10′ 2″ (1970)
Benmore		77′ × 6′ 5″ (1958)	90′ × 8′ 6″ (1970)
Stanange Park			73′ × 6′ 9″ (1959)
Castlewellan		52′ × 4′ 3″ (1931)	90′ × 10′ 0″ (1970)
Castlewellan	1939		73′ × 4′ 7″ (1970)

[1] Much died back

Abies balsamea (L.) Miller. Balsam fir

Eastern Canada and U.S.A. from Newfoundland to Virginia. Introduced 1695 or before. Original tree at Saltoun swept away by flood in 1891. Oldest now known was planted in 1906. Very rare; in a few collections.

BARK. Dark grey, at first smooth, with resin-blisters, later deeply cracked vertically. Epicormic sprouts frequent.

CROWN. Young trees splendidly regular conic, narrow, shapely and dark.

FOLIAGE. Shoot dull grey, finely pubescent.

BUD. Red, resinous, shiny.

LEAVES. Arranged flat, pectinate, spreading perpendicular to shoot, 2·5 cm dark green above with triangular white patch of stomata near the tip, two broad grey bands beneath. Strongly aromatic of balsam when crushed.

GROWTH. The original tree, planted at Saltoun, Midlothian in 1697 was 194 years old and 68ft × 7ft 10in when destroyed, but all others have been short-lived and only one recorded previously, in 1931 has been found. Young trees grow slowly but steadily into quite sturdy trees. One planted in Tubney Wood, in 1906 was 62ft × 2ft 4in in 1966. Two trees of 55 and 45 feet were reported at Prested Hall, Essex by Maynard Greville in 1954. A small tree at Warnham Court, is 47ft × 2ft 2in. A tree at Fenagh House, planted in 1918 and 19 feet tall in 1931, is now 42ft × 2ft 10in. In Scotland young trees remain very shapely and appear to be going to make good trees. A young tree in the Pinetum at Scone is 37ft × 2ft 8in (1970). High on Lon Mor, Inverness, some trees were about 46ft × 2ft after 37 years growth, and a plot at Kilmun Arboretum, is very attractive with trees up to 45ft × 2ft 8in after 34 years.

Abies borisii-regis Mattfeld. (*A. alba* var. *acutifolia* Turill)

Pindus, Olympia, Athos and the Isle of Thasor, Greece. Introduced 1883. Rare but in a few collections, usually unrecognised.

BARK. Dark grey, almost black, finely roughened.

CROWN. Rugged, heavily branched and rough, broadly conic with a domed top.

FOLIAGE. Shoot densely covered by pale coffee-brown short pubescence.

LEAVES. densely set in flattened rows each side of shoot; much denser and narrower than in *A. alba*, slender, to 3 cm long, parallel and pointing forwards; rich shining dark green above, sometimes with some stomata near the rounded tip; grooved; below two narrow but bright white bands.

CONE. Tall ovoid, 12 × 4 cm pale green-purple, bracts exserted, spreading.

GROWTH. Complete lack of dated trees makes precision impossible, but evidently a species of great vigour, particularly in growth of a big bole. One tree had increased 6 inches in girth in 4 years. Growth in height seems very moderate.

SPECIMENS. The largest is a tree by Loop Walk, Westonbirt, now 100ft × 11ft 8in. A younger tree at the edge of The Oaks, Wakehurst Place, is 70ft × 9ft 7in. Others are:—by the lake at Smeaton House, 85ft × 8ft 4in. Young trees at Castle Milk, 59ft × 4ft 5in; Blandsfort, 56ft × 7ft 10in; Abbeyleix, 66ft × 7ft 6in and 60ft × 6ft 10in. Fairburn (Orrin Falls), 59ft × 6ft 6in (1970). This vigorous tree deserves to be better known. The dense, pale pubescence combined with narrow leaves and dark bark make it quite distinct.

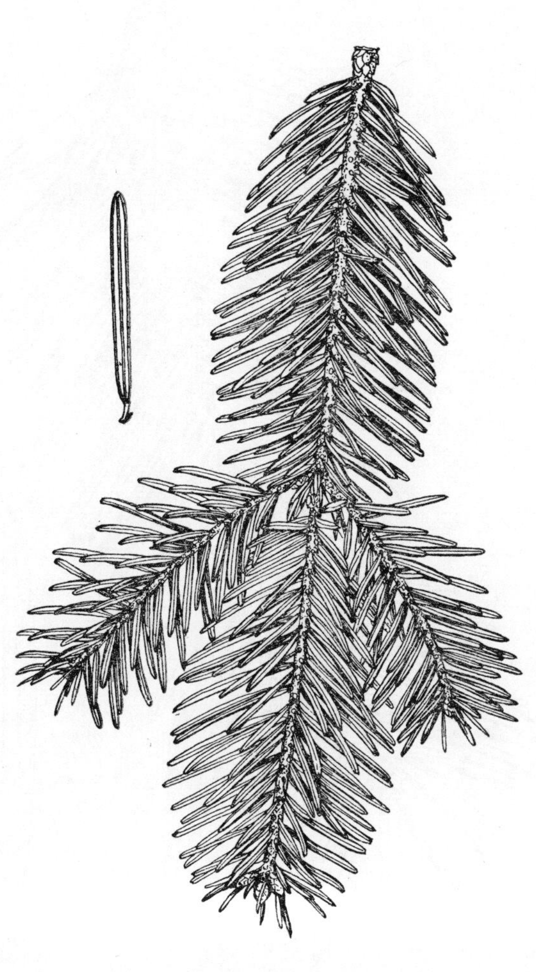

Fig. 3
Abies borisii-regis. A spray of this seldom-recognised, vigorous tree, showing the narrow leaf and densely pubescent shoot.

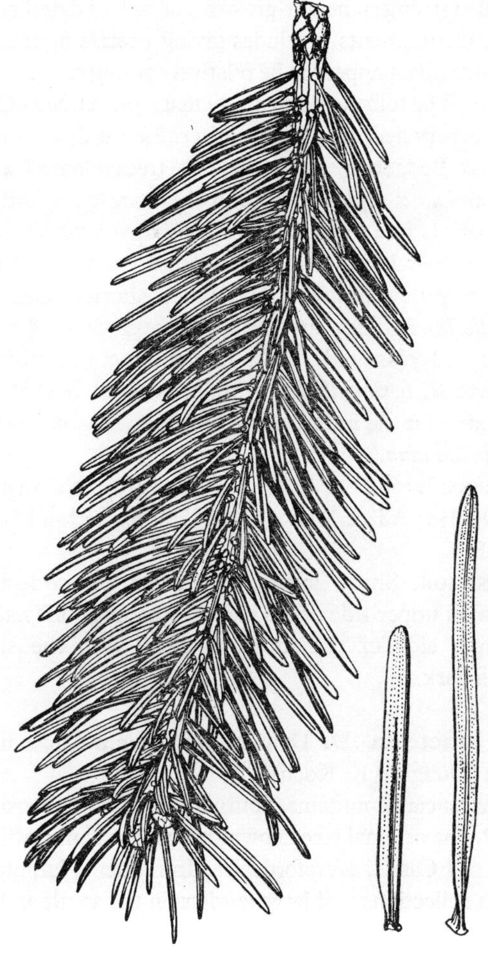

Fig. 4
Abies bornmulleriana. Typically stout, luxuriant shoot. Leaves (×1⅓): left, upper surface showing stomata especially near the tip; right, underside with stomata in two broad bands.

Abies bornmulleriana Mattfield.

Northern Central Asia Minor. Date of introduction unknown. Very rare; in only a few collections and gardens. Intermediate between *A. cephalonica* and *A. cilicica* or as usually stated, but less convincingly *A. nordmanniana.*

BARK. smooth, finely roughened and black.

FOLIAGE. Shoot stout, glabrous, shiny red-brown on green; second year pale orange-brown striped with grey.

BUD. 8–10 mm, ovoid, the scales visible and protruding in thick resin, pale green at base, red-brown at tips.

LEAVES. nearly pectinate below, densely set, pointing forwards but rising strongly from the shoot covering the upper side, stout, stiff, the upper side with stomata either as a broad patch near the tip and tapering down the mid-rib or in two grey bands running the full length of the leaf; blackish green, shiny first year, dark yellow green second year with stomata above more faint; under side with broad grey-white bands; 3–4·5×0·2 cm, bluntly rounded, some slightly notched.

GROWTH. This very vigorous tree rapidly makes a stout bole

and is also strong in height-growth but lack of dated trees or earlier measurements precludes giving precise figures. The Specimens given appear to be relatively young trees.

GENERAL. The foliage, particularly that from a tree at Castlewellan, is very near that of the *Abies cilicica* at Speech House (q.v.). At Bedgebury there are two trees planted as "*A. nordmanniana x cephalonica*" and these are quite different. Their bark is like that of *A. cephalonica*, smooth and pink-grey and their leaves radiate all round the shoot, and are hard and yellowish-green, and much shorter than in *A. bornmulleriana*. They are both just over 50ft×4ft when probably 42 years old. These circumstances reinforce the view that *A. bornmulleriana* proper is more related to *A. cilicica* and not the intermediate between *A. cephalonica* and *A. nordmanniana*.

SPECIMENS. Dropmore; 92ft×9ft 2in (1970); Welford Park, 84ft×9ft 1in; Adare Manor, 54ft×7ft 5in. Bicton 86ft×7ft 5in 1968.

RECOGNITION. Shiny green-brown shoot and conspicuous stomata on upper side of long leaves standing stiffly all over the upper side of the shoot, together with the smooth blackish bark.

Abies bracteata (D. Don) Nuttall. Santa Lucia fir. (*A. venusta* (Douglas) K. Koch)

Santa Lucia Mountains, Southern California. Introduced in 1852, one original tree known, not planted out until 1865, at Eastnor Castle, Herefordshire. Infrequent; largely confined to collections and large gardens in the south and west, but very occasionally seen in small gardens; very rare in southern Scotland, known north to Deeside.

BARK. Young trees—dark grey, smooth, with wrinkles and black lines around knots. Older trees—black or purplish-black, smooth with small blisters or roughened; big circular cracks around knots.

CROWN. Broad at base narrowing to a long, narrowly conic top; branches very flat and sparse in upper crown; drooping and more dense in lower, with big sprays of shoots fanning out below on each side.

FOLIAGE. Shoot smooth, almost shiny, red-brown, or light greenish purple, stout.

BUD. Pale brown, long (2 cm) and slender, acute.

LEAVES. Parted each side of most shoots, lower rows spreading and somewhat forwards, upper rising from shoot, strongly forward-pointing, sometimes some above the shoot; widely spaced, hard, sharply spined, to 5 cm long, dark, dull green above; 2 bright white bands beneath. All foliage is on a large scale. Leaves are held for 5 years or more.

CONE. Rarely seen, but biggest trees do cone at least in some years. Californian specimen: ovoid 8×5 cm, golden-brown, bracts exserted, linear, to 3 cm, green, grooved strongly decurved.

GROWTH. In the south and east, growth is seldom rapid and the life of the tree is short, but by the west coast growth is fast and trees in the north, west and Midlands can reach a good age, although there have been many losses. Of the eight trees noted by Elwes and Henry in 1908, only the big tree at Eastnor Castle is known to survive. Of the 28 noted in 1931, 16 have been found, but two have died recently and two more were dying. Notable increases in size have been at Leonardslee, Bodnant, and at Smeaton, East Lothian, as will be seen in Table 3. A spontaneous seedling arose at Streatham Hall, Exeter, in about 1945.

Abies bracteata

Fig. 5
Abies bracteata. Santa Lucia fir. A hanging shoot of typical weaker foliage showing the fusiform bud. The leaf (×1⅓) has narrow but bright white stomatal bands beneath, and tapers to a sharp spine.

Specimens. The original tree at Eastnor has been noted so:
1865 Planted out
1889 40ft
1908 78ft × 9ft 0in
1931 112ft × 12ft 9in
1954 116ft × 15ft 2in
1970 122ft × 15ft 10in
Other specimens are given in Table 3.

Recognition. Long, hard, spiny leaves lying forwards; big foliage and pointed bud, are not found together in any other silver fir.

Table 3. Large Trees of Abies bracteata

Locality	*Date Planted*	*Dimensions*	
Eastnor Castle (2)			118′ × 10′ 4″ (1970)
Bodnant	1891	85′ × 8′ 0″ (1931)	114′ × 10′ 7″ (1966)
Bodnant	1909	24′ × 2′ 0″ (1931)	60′ × 7′ 0″ (1966)
Little Hall	1906	40′ × 2′ 7″ (1931)	60′ × 4′ 5″ (1961)
Little Hall	1914	28′ × 2′ 8″ (1931)	65′ × 4′ 10″ (1961)
Tilgate	1907	21′ 4″ (1931)	65′ × 4′ 8″ (1961)[1]
Tilgate	1911	27′ (1931)	(77′) × 5′ 10″ (1961)
Leonardslee		18′ (1931)	78′ × 3′ 4″ (1969)
Stanage Park	1909		77′ × 6′ 9″ (1970)
Wakehurst Place	1911	20′ × 1′ 4″ (1931)	65′ × 4′ 10″ (1957)[2]
Wakehurst Place			66′ × 4′ 6″ (1966)
Mells Park		75′ × 8′ 0″ (1931)	97′ × 8′ 10″ (1962)
Althorp		74′ × 4′ 10″ (1931)	96′ × 8′ 11″ (1962)[3]
Smeaton House		30′ × 2′ 2″ (1931)	81′ × 6′ 3″ (1971)
Streatham Hall			105′ × 11′ 1″ (1967)
Streatham Hall			85′ × 11′ 10″ (1967)[4]
Hergest Croft	1922		61′ × 5′ 11″ (1969)
Hergest Croft	1922		54′ × 5′ 7″ (1969)
Hergest Croft			62′ × 4′ 11″ (1969)
Mount Usher			77′ × 6′ 10″ (1966)
Castlewellan		55′ × 8′ 3″ (1931)	80′ × 9′ 0″ (1966)
Nr. Colemans Hatch			69′ × 6′ 3″ (1968)
Holkham Hall	1923		77′ × 5′ 11″ (1968)
Edinburgh R.B.G.	1931		34′ × 2′ 6″ (1967)
Edinburgh R.B.G.	1937		25′ × 1′ 7″ (1967)
Doune House			46′ × 3′ 10″ (1970)
Durris House			36′ × 1′ 10″ (1970)

[1] Dying back fast
[2] Died 1963
[3] Two stems, both × 8ft 11in
[4] Forked from 0 to 12ft

Abies cephalonica Loudon. Grecian fir

Mountains of southern Greece. Introduced 1824. Earliest plantings fully recorded and one original tree known. Most of the dated biggest trees were planted in or soon after 1849. Uncommon but in many big gardens everywhere.

Bark. Until very large, distinctively tinged pink or brown on grey; smooth but finely flaking. Old trees grey; wide shallow fissures dark grey; small plates partly lifting away.

Crown. Young tree sturdy, somewhat broadly conic, often bushy lower part, spiky above. Old trees in the open, hugely branched low on bole, flat-topped, irregularly very wide-domed with long wandering branches. Grown among other trees, it has long, stout, slightly sinuous bole, big level branches and usually multiple leading-shoots.

Foliage. Shoot stout, pale brown, shiny; second year bright red-brown or orange.

Bud. Ovoid, resinous, scales prominent.

Leaves. Spreading all round shoot but more above than below; arising from large, sucker-like bases and a narrow stalk; broadening to 0·2 cm; stiff, leathery, usually spined at tip; 2–3 cm long; grooved and dark, shiny green above; two narrow bright white bands beneath. Young plants more rigid and spiny.

Flowers and Cone. Males densely clustered beneath shoots over much of the crown; globular. Cone cylindric, to 15 cm often crowded densely on branches at the top of the crown, green-brown; bract-tips exserted and decurved.

Growth. The first *Abies* in leaf, and frequently damaged by frost, this tree may take years to become established. Once established, however, it soon makes a sturdy tree of moderate growth in height, but rapid in girth for many years. Old trees increase very slowly in girth in the south and east but,

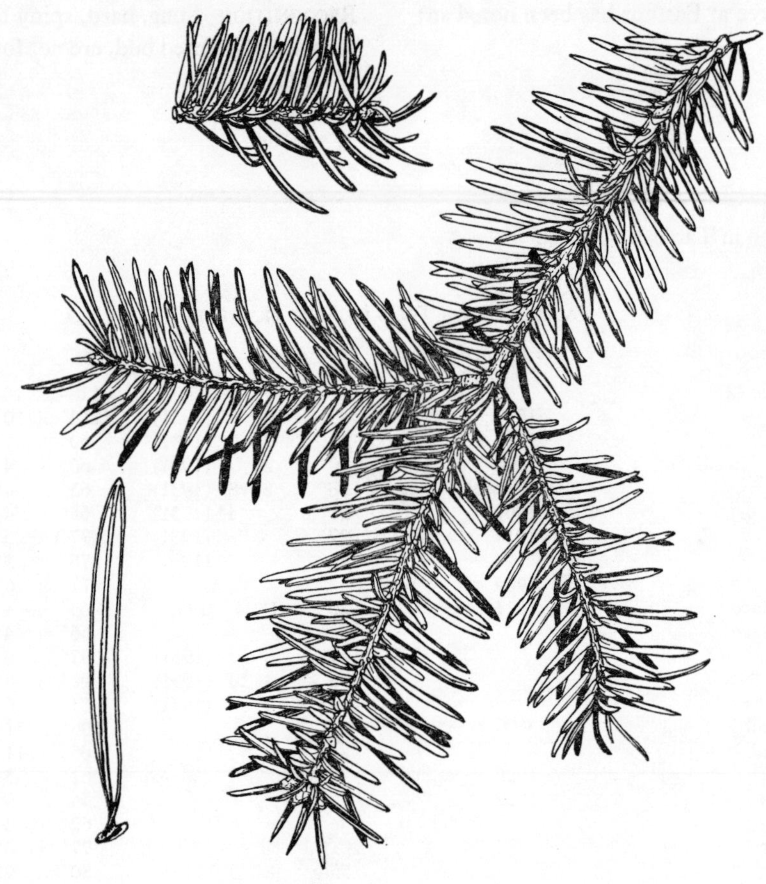

Fig. 6
Abies cephalonica. Grecian fir. The radiating leaves, spiny in young plants, are hard and give a spiky appearance. The underside of the leaf (×2) has white stomatal bands, and the second-year wood is red-brown.

equally big, much rougher trees grow more rapidly in the damp west and north.

The increases in height since earlier measurement have been mostly 20–25 feet in about 60 years and, on younger trees, from about 10 to 40 feet in 30–40 years. A tree at Wakehurst Place has grown 82 inches in girth in 40 years. Several fairly young trees have added 30 to 50 inches in around 35 years, but old trees are growing at less than half this rate.

SPECIMENS. Some of the oldest and biggest trees, together with some younger trees of good growth are given in Table 4.

var. apollinis (Link) Beissner. Within the natural range of the type. Introduced at an unknown date, before 1876.

This differs from the type only in the more densely set leaves being rounded at the tips and almost entirely lying forward or rising from the upper side of the shoot. It seems at least as vigorous as the type and there are big trees at: Tilgate, Sussex, planted 1876, 84ft × 10ft 4in (1961); Hergest Croft, Hereford, planted 1900, 88ft × 10ft 5in (1961), Haffield House, Hereford, 90ft × 13ft 3in (1966); Ormidale, 103ft × 9ft 5in (1969); Bicton 106ft × 8ft 9in (1968) Headfort, pl. 1914, 65ft × 6ft 10in (1966); Fairburn, 92ft × 6ft 9in (1970); Oakley Park (Pinetum), 105ft × 10ft 7 in (1971).

RECOGNITION. The hard, acute leaves radiating from the stout shining brown shoot distinguish the type, and var. *apollinis* differs only in the arrangement of blunter leaves; the orange-brown second-year shoot and narrow white bands beneath the leaves are shared with the type and are distinctive.

TABLE 4. SPECIMENS OF ABIES CEPHALONICA

Locality	*Date Planted*	*Dimensions*	
Hampton Park	1824 (seed)		85′ × 13′ 3″ (1969)
Stanage Park	1840	80′ × 10′ 3″ (1931)	82′ × 12′ 10″ (1970)
Highnam Court	1846		85′ × 10′ 5″ (1970)
Bayfordbury	1847	70′ × 6′ 11″ (1905)	75′ × 8′ 10″ (1968)
Castle Kennedy	1849	59′ × 9′ 8″ (1904)	83′ × 13′ 8″ (1967)
Whittingehame	1849	75′ × 12′ 6″ (1931)	80′ × 16′ 4″ (1957) at 2 feet
Rhinefield Terrace	1861	76′ × 5′ 10″ (1931)	98′ × 7′ 1″ (1971)
Abercairney	1864	50′ × 11′ 2″ (1931)	97′ × 12′ 0″ (1962)
Hergest Croft	1867		80′ × 15′ 0″ (1961)
Blandsfort	1867	54′ × 7′ 2″ (1931)	60′ × 9′ 4″ (1968)
Bodnant	1876	{76′ × 7′ 9″ (1931)}	118′ × 10′ 4″ (1966)
Bodnant	1876		108′ × 11′ 7″ (1966)
Fulmodestone	1880	78′ × 7′ 10″ (1931)	110′ × 10′ 11″ (1969)
Fulmodestone	1880		117′ × 8′ 6″ (1969)
Fulmodestone	1880		110′ × 10′ 10″ (1969)
Albury Park	1891	51′ × 3′ 3″ (1931)	73′ × 7′ 6″ (1968)
Albury Park	1891	51′ × 3′ 11″ (1931)	78′ × 8′ 6″ (1968)
Fenagh House	1896		74′ × 7′ 5″ (1968)
Little Hall	1906	44′ × 4′ 6″ (1931)	72′ × 7′ 1″ (1961)
Wakehurst Place	1913	25′ × 1′ 6″ (1931)	78′ × 8′ 4″ (1971)
Westonbirt	1923		76′ × 5′ 0″ (1967)
Blounts Court		87′ × 10′ 8″ (1907)	112′ × 13′ 1″ (1958)
Highclere		75′ × 11′ 0″ (1903)	105′ × 14′ 4″ (1968)
Melbury			102′ × 14′ 10″ (1971)
Patshull House		75′ × 8′ 4″ (1931)	85′ × 10′ 0″ (1970)
Tendring Hall			100′ × 12′ 6″ (1964)
Woolverstone Hall			110′ × 13′ 6″ (1968)
Heanton Satchville			75′ × 16′ 10″ (1960)
Cortachy Castle			118′ × 14′ 2″ (1962) at 2 feet
Cortachy Castle			110′ × 17′ 0″ (1962) at 3 feet
Powerscourt		55′ × 8′ 9″ (1906)	75′ × 15′ 2″ (1966)
Hamwood House		50′ × 9′ 6″ (1904)	70′ × 15′ 0″ (1968)
Bicton			121′ × 12′ 0½″ (1968)
Tottenham House			110′ × 10′ 11″ (1967)

Abies chensiensis Van Tieghen.

Yunnan and West Szechuan, China. Introduced 1907. Very rare; a few collections only.

BARK. Smooth, lenticelled; a few vertical cracks.

CROWN. Medium to broad conic.

BUD. Grey brown with thin resin over the scales.

FOLIAGE. Shoot stout pink, shiny, glabrous; leaves 2·5–4 cm strongly parted each side of the shoot, but curved upwards, yellowish green above, two greenish bands beneath; acute to sharp point. Another form (Reference number F 30668) has orange-brown shoots, scarcely shiny, whilst a giant-foliaged form has stout fawn shoots and very bifid, spined rigid leaves in flat ranks; very perpendicular, 4–7 cm; hard, thick.

SPECIMENS. A tree with reference number F 30668, at Borde Hill, is 43ft × 2ft 10in (1968). A tree of the very short-leaved form at Headfort, is about 20 feet tall, and another at Annesgrove, is 25 feet. A similar tree at Bayfordbury, is 50ft × 2ft 9in. Another at Burnside was 19ft × 1ft 8in when 20 years old in 1956; now 35 ft tall—giant foliaged form.

Abies cilicica (Antoine and Kotschy) Carriere. Cilician fir

Mount Lebanon and the Antitaurus Mountains. Introduced 1855. An original tree survives at Castle Kennedy. Rare; almost confined to collections.

BARK. Dark grey, smooth, conspicuously wrinkled and cracked into black rings around knots; outermost ring may be 3 feet across.

CROWN. Narrow-conic; rather open, occasionally dense and luxurious.

FOLIAGE. Peculiarly variable, with two extreme forms, one with very short leaves, the other with very long and dense foliage approaching closely *A. bornmulleriana* in all features. Normal foliage; shoot pale brown, glabrous, slightly pubescent side-shoots, slender, or olive-green slightly cracked with pale brown. Second year light orange-brown.

BUD. Red-brown, paling to orange-brown, the scales covered in resin and protruding bluntly.

LEAVES. All pointing forwards, those above ascending and bending straight forward, rather sparse, slightly curved, tapering to rounded or slightly notched point, dark green, rather shiny above, an obscure white line toward the tip; two narrow, greenish bands below, 1–2 cm. One variant (Jermyns House) has stout shoots with pale brown short pubescence; large buds (8×5 mm) purple with some white resin; leaves along the upper side very short in inner rows, 1·5 cm stiff and upright leaving a narrow open "V"; blunt rounded tip, with a patch of grey-white stomata at the tip, dark green above; outer leaves to 2·5 cm; all with white bands below separated by a broad shiny midrib. The very vigorous tree at Speech House is almost *A. bornmulleriana*. Its bark is much darker grey and shallowly fissured into squares. The main shoot is stout, yellowish-brown and glabrous, side-shoots pubescent. The leaves stand densely above the shoot, curving up nearly to the vertical, those below are pectinate. They are hard, 3×0·15 cm, uniform in length, rich dark green, to pale rounded or obtuse points, with grey stomatal bands on the upper side, brighter white bands beneath.
GROWTH. Usually a slow-growing tree, but the atypical tree at Speech House is singularly vigorous, and a tree which died at Bedgebury in 1968 when it was 92ft×7ft 3in was found to be only 75 years old. The growth made by some other trees over various periods can be seen from Table 5.
RECOGNITION. Like *A. nordmanniana*, but thinner crown, distinctive bark and more distant, assurgent leaves, pale or stomatic at the tips.

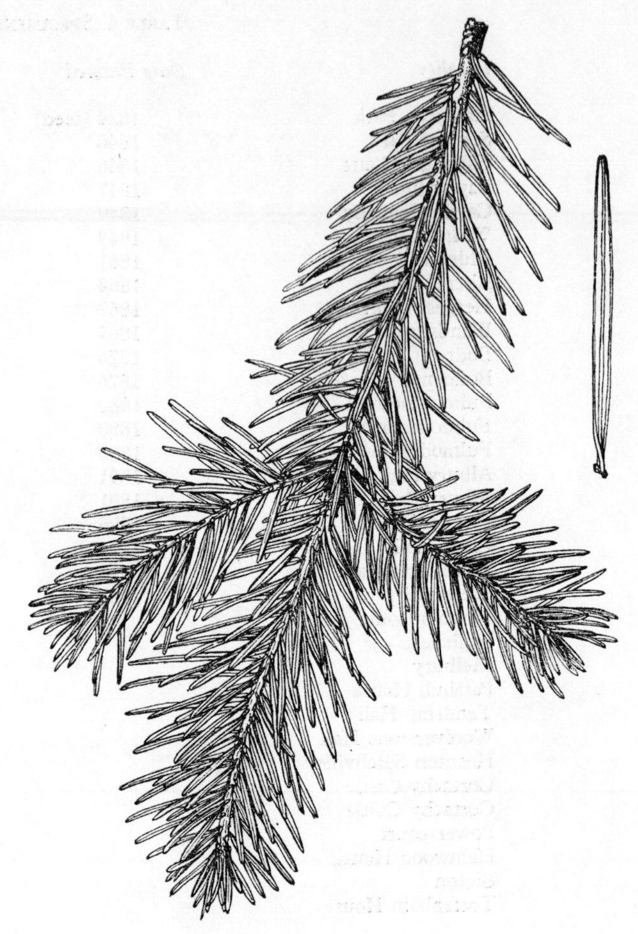

Abies cilicica

Fig. 7
***Abies cilicica*. A spray of the most usually-seen form with slender, rather sparse leaves. Single leaf (right ×2) showing stomatal bands on underside.**

TABLE 5. LARGEST TREES OF ABIES CILICICA

Locality	*Date Planted*	*Dimensions*	
Castle Kennedy	1859	48′ × 5′ 1″ (1904)	75′ × 7′ 5″ (1967)
Castle Kennedy			75′ × 5′ 11″ (1967)
Rhinefield Drive	1861		95′ × 7′ 9″ (1970)
Headfort	1914	25′ × 1′ 9″ (1931)	60′ × 4′ 3″ (1966)
Speech House	1916	56′ × 6′ 1″ (1959)	77′ × 7′ 11″ (1970)
Wakehurst Place	1915	25′ × 1′ 8″ (1931)	58′ × 5′ 5″ (1964)
Fulmodestone		65′ × 5′ 0″ (1931)	90′ × 6′ 11″ (1969)
Adhurst St. Mary			73′ × 7′ 0″ (1964)
Powerscourt		37′ × 2′ 8″ (1906)	89′ × 6′ 5″ (1966)
Powerscourt			67′ × 6′ 9″ (1966)
Smeaton House			62′ × 6′ 9″ (1966)
Glenapp			100′ × 6′ 2″ (1970)
Birr Castle			39′ × 5′ 7″ (1966)
Westonbirt	1923	7′ 9″ (1931)	50′ × 3′ 7″ (1971)

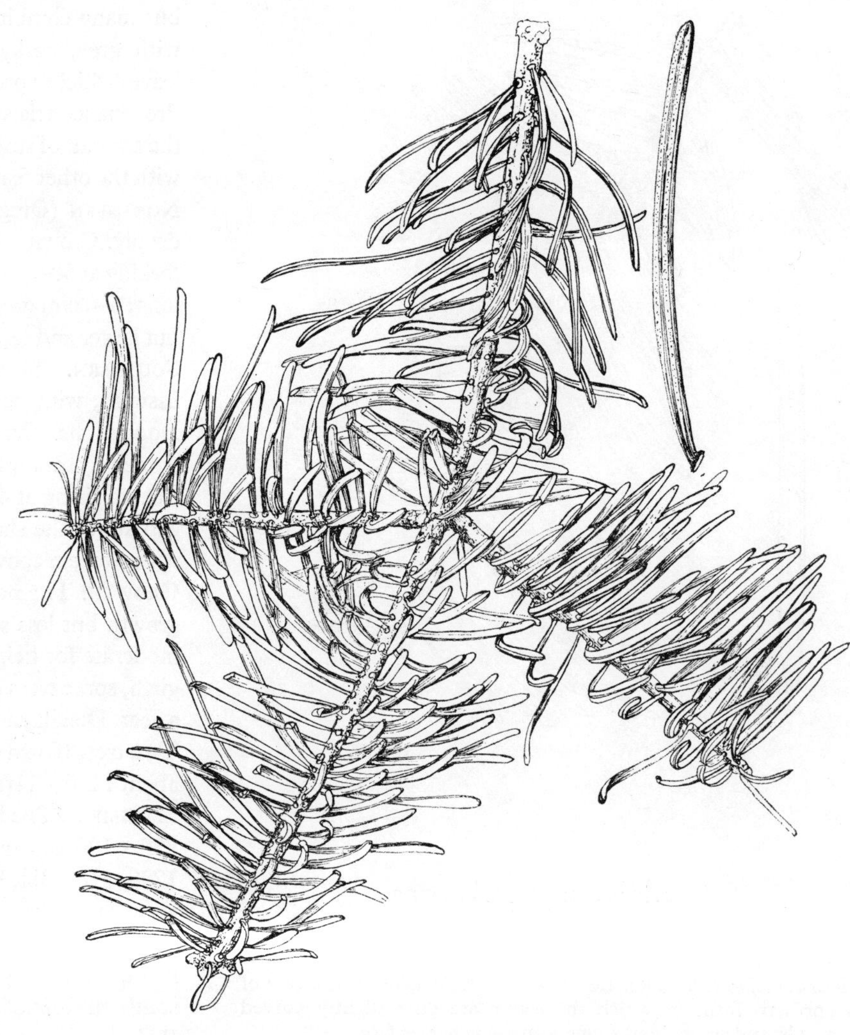

Fig. 8
Spray of *Abies concolor*, White fir, showing the thick, upstanding leaves with stomata on each side. The single leaf (×1⅓) shows the underside with midrib.

Abies concolor (Gordon) Hildebrand. White fir

Southern California, Utah, Colorado to Mexico. Introduced 1873. The type tree is less common than the var. *lowiana*, and is mainly in collections and a few large gardens.

BARK. Dark grey, smooth, with resin-blisters. Oldest trees dark grey, finely fissured or cracked.

CROWN. Conic, open; branches markedly whorled; apex becoming domed with age then broken and irregular with level, curved branches and much dead wood.

FOLIAGE. Shoot stout, yellow-green; second year grey-brown; bud globular, very resinous.

LEAVES. Dull uniform blue-grey both sides except for green midrib beneath; thick, leathery, to 5·5×0·2 cm, well-spaced, upswept, standing vertically from shoot. Crushed foliage or broken shoots emit a strong lemony scent.

CONE. 12–15 cm×4 cm, smooth, apple-green in summer; on branches around apex only, cylindrical tapering to a point.

GROWTH. Leading shoots grow from mid-May to July. In south and east rarely a good tree, being thin in crown and soon losing the top. In the south-west it grows with better health and vigour but also loses shape fairly early, but in the northeast (Northumberland) and north (Argyll and Perthshire) it grows vigorously and maintains a good shape to the largest sizes. Very few of the trees given in 1931 survive.

SPECIMENS. In the south-east there is only one big tree: Albury Park, 102ft×6ft 8in (1966). At Bedgebury, planted

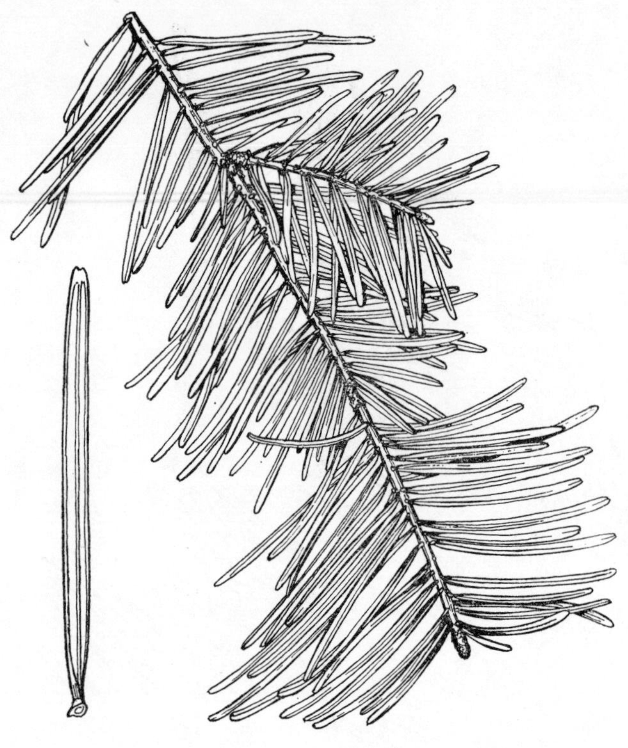

Abies concolor v. lowiana

Fig. 9
Abies concolor v. *lowiana*. Low's White fir. A shoot from a tree of a northern form in which the leaves are only slightly curved upwards, and are without stomata on the upper surface.

in 1925 is 62ft×3ft 10in (1969). In the south-west, one at Heanton Satcheville, is 115ft×7ft 7in (1960).

The finest tree is at Cragside, Northumberland, 131ft×11ft 6in (1958). Comparable trees stood at Blair Atholl, to 127ft×9ft 8in (1955), but have blown down. At Benmore, in 1956 the best were 131ft×9ft 5in, and 124ft×9ft 9in, but by 1969 the largest left was 130ft×8ft 5in. One at Brahan Castle, planted in 1901 was 75ft×7ft 8in at 54 years of age, and at Capenoch, one planted in 1926 is 69ft×6ft 0in (1970).

var. lowiana (Gordon) Lemmon. Low's fir

Mid-Oregon to the southern end of the Sierra Nevada, California. Introduced 1851. Uncommon but in many large gardens and some smaller. This is an intermediate between *A. grandis* in the north and *A. concolor* in the south, and is usually quite distinct from both. There are two extreme forms in cultivation which can be placed geographically by their correlated features of bark, crown-form and foliage, but many combine features from both, particularly a form with grey, corky but unfissured bark and bluish, raised leaves which is presumably from the northern Sierra Nevada. Provenance trials show a good positive connection between the amount of stomata and southern origin and this combines with the other features as below.

NORTHERN (Oregon). Bark black, rough, fissured but not deeply. Crown columnar but flat topped, almost invariably forking at 50–60 feet. Leaves laid very flat each side of shoot, long, 5–6 cm, green above without stomata. (Like *A. grandis* but larger and second year shoot coppery-brown).

SOUTHERN. (Sierra Nevada). Bark brown, corky, deeply fissured, with pale brown, open, corky-sided fissures, like Douglas fir. Crown conic, rather broad, in biggest trees domed by multiple leaders from near the top, but not forked. Leaves rising at 45° or more in a curve, leaving a U-shaped gap above the shoot, 3–4 cm, pale blue-grey or green-grey with stomata above, two whiter bands beneath.

GROWTH. The northern forms are very vigorous in height-growth but less so in girth whereas the southern forms are moderate for height increment, but remarkably vigorous in girth, some trees exceeding a mean increase of two inches in a year. Details can be found in the table under "Specimens". Two trees blown down in 1953 at Guisachan, Inverness were about 143ft×11ft 6in and 135ft×11ft 2 in when 90 years old.

SPECIMENS. The big tree at Linton Park, planted in 1862 and 85ft×10ft 6in in 1902 was last seen in 1956 when it was 120ft×16ft 3in, but could not be found in 1965. No tree is known to be from the original seed.

USES. With the increasing interest in planting *A. grandis* for its high volume production, there may be sites on which the southern form of *A. lowiana* would yield as well. The plot at Bedgebury contains a mixed lot but it had a total volume production of 2,340 cubic feet per acre (quarter-girth measure) at 29 years on a poor soil and is growing very fast.

cv. Violacea. A slim, tree of narrowly conic, open crown and rather shorter leaves than the type, but of bright blueish grey. It is fairly frequent in parks and smaller gardens. It seems to grow better in the south-east than does the type.

SPECIMENS. At Little Hall, planted in 1906, and 48ft×3ft 6in in 1931, now 66ft×5ft 1in (1966); Bedgebury, planted 1925, 57ft×3ft 8in (1967); Westonbirt, Willesley Drive, 50ft×2ft 2in (1969); Holkham, 64ft×3ft 11in (1968); Powerscourt, 60ft×5ft (1966).

cv. Wattezii. Leaves emerge creamy white, later like cv. Violacea but whiter, this is properly identifiable only in May and June. A tree at Borde Hill, was 58ft×4ft 6in in 1957 but no other has been noted.

TABLE 6. SPECIMENS OF ABIES CONCOLOR VARIETY LOWIANA

Locality	*Date Planted*	*Type*	*Dimensions*	
Durris		S	74′ × 7′ 6″ (1904)	153′ × 15′ 7″ (1970)
Durris		S	57′ × 5′ 9″ (1904)	105′ × 13′ 8″ (1970)
Durris		S	58′ × 5′ 4″ (1904)	118′ × 15′ 0″ (1970)
Fairburn		S		124′ × 12′ 7″ (1970)
Scone Palace	1860	N		111′ × 11′ 10″ (1970)
Glamis Castle	1861	N		128′ × 7′ 4″ (1970)
Youngsbury	1866	N	68′ × 5′ 6″ (1907)	108′ × 7′ 8″ (1966)
Powerscourt	1869	N	92′ × 9′ 3″ (1931)	118′ × 11′ 0″ (1966)
Dawyck	1870	S	77′ × 8′ 0″ (1930)	115′ × 13′ 0″ (1961)
Dupplin Castle		S	91′ × 7′ 9″ (1931)	98′ × 12′ 6″ (1970)
Dupplin Castle				120′ × 10′ 11″ (1970)
Castle Milk	1886		64′ × 6′ 8″ (1931)	113′ × 9′ 2″ (1966)
Bodnant	1888	S	78′ × 7′ 6″ (1931)	133′ × 11′ 6″ (1966)
Bodnant	1901	S		78′ × 8′ 0″ (1966)
Blair Atholl (St. Brides)		S	80′ × 9′ 0″ (1931)	111′ × 13′ 6″ (1970)
Blair Atholl (Diana's Grove)				132′ × 11′ 2″ (1970)
Rammerscales		N		123′ × 9′ 2″ (1954)
Inchmarlo		N		119′ × 6′ 5″ (1956)
Londesborough Hall		N		111′ × 6′ 6″ (1958)
Cragside		S		128′ × 10′ 3″ (1958)
Fulmodestone		N		108′ × 7′ 8″ (1969)†
Oakley Park		N		121′ × 9′ 5″ (1971)
Monk Coniston		N		118′ × 10′ 7″ (1971)
Brockhall		N		115′ × 8′ 7″ (1964)
Tottenham House		S		126′ × 13′ 3″ (1967)
Trentham Park		N		110′ × 8′ 9″ (1968)
Westonbirt		S	99′ × 9′ 5″ (1931)	129′ × 12′ 7″ (1971)
Kilravock Castle		S		98′ × 18′ 9″ (1970)
Warnham Court		S	69′ × 7′ 3″ (1931)	105′ × 9′ 2″ (1969)
Patshull House		N	98′ × 8′ 5″ (1931)	123′ × 10′ 5″ (1970)
Bicton		N		132′ × 9′ 4″ (1968)
Dunkeld (Cathedral)				115′ × 9′ 1″ (1970)
Longleat				120′ × 7′ 6″ (1971)
Leonardslee	ca.1905			105′ × 6′ 11″ (1969)
Leonardslee		N	79′ × 5′ 1″ (1931)	124′ × 7′ 6″ (1969)
Vernon Holme	1907		37′ × 1′ 3″ (1931)	64′ × 5′ 4″ (1961)
Fenagh House	1920	S	8′ (1931)	52′ × 5′ 8″ (1968)
Bedgebury	1926	S	77′ × 7′ 11″ (1957)	92′ × 9′ 4″ (1970)
Ffrwdgrech	1931	S		77′ × 3′ 4″ (1960)
Exbury		S	47′ × 5′ 0″ (1955)	75′ × 7′ 1″ (1968)
Strathallan	1939	S		48′ × 3′ 11″ (1962)
Redleaf Wood	1942	S		56′ × 4′ 3″ (1967)
Monk Hopton				118′ × 10′ 7″ (1971)

†Clear bole for 71 feet

Abies delavayi Franchet.

South China. Introduced in various forms in 1901, 1910 and 1923. Largely confined to collections but widely distributed and thriving particularly in those in the west and north. One form, var. *forrestii,* is more frequent in large gardens than are the other varieties.

BARK. Smooth, dark or pale grey, with a few deep, wide black vertical fissures, or dark brown and flaking.

CROWN. Regularly conic but rather sparse and spiky from strong, ascending, straight branches rather far apart, bearing short shoots on their upper surface, making a crown of tilted, plate-like masses of foliage.

FOLIAGE. Shoots stout, ridged or smooth, shades of red-brown, orange-brown or pale, with or without pubescence.

BUD. Globular, resinous, red, purple, brown or white.

LEAVES. All round the shoot and curved, or pectinate above and below and straight, 1–4 cm long broad, bluntly rounded and notched, shades of deep blue-green above, sometimes bloomed, usually brillaintly white in two bands beneath.

CONE. Barrel-shaped or cylindric, dark purple-blue or deep blue, with bracts exserted minutely as curved spines or exserted far with broad bases.

The naming of the various forms in cultivation is rendered difficult, or impossible, by the wide variations met with and the difficulty of aligning these with the type specimens. The type specimens at the Kew Herbarium are shrivelled and brown.

That of *A. delavayi* (*sensu stricto*) is a short length of shoot

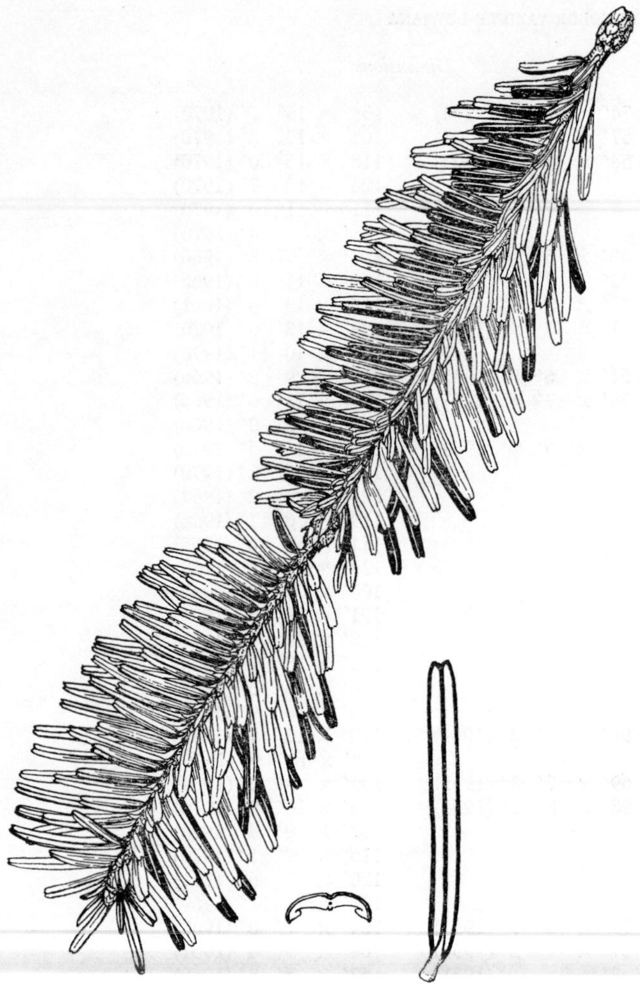

Fig. 10
Abies delavayi v. *fabri*. In this variety the shoot is brown or red-brown and pubescent, especially on side-shoots. The underside of the leaf ($\times 1\frac{1}{3}$) is thickly banded bright white. The leaves have variably revolute margins (transverse section $\times 5\frac{1}{3}$).

in a small envelope half full of shed leaves. The type specimen at Kew of var. *faxoniana* (ref. no. W. 4060) shows none of the features shown by the trees grown under this name, but it is of fertile cone-bearing shoots which have short, curved, sharply pointed leaves. In the absence of fresh specimens from seed of known numbers of each variety, the type specimens can be of limited use only and that mainly with the cones. From an examination of the type specimens and from a study of growing trees and fresh foliage, the following descriptions are given in an attempt to typify the most marked varieties seen and allocate them to the names which seem to accord best with the types where these suffice, or to stabilise the names accepted for those where the type is not adequate.

var. delavayi Franchet. Tali Range. The type has a description written later, which states that the shoots are dark brown and glabrous. The cones are distinctive in their smoothly curved scale-margins and complete lack of exserted bracts; they are ovoid and 9×4 cm. The feature most remarked upon, but difficult to assess on shrivelled material, is the strongly revolute leaves, the margins curling right underneath. This variety has been found only at Edinburgh and Benmore. It has strikingly bright green leaves all round, short upright shoots with prominent red-brown buds. The leaves are 1·5–1·8 cm, the margins rolled right under, almost concealing bright silver white bands but showing the broad bright green midrib. The shoot is bright orange and very finely pubescent. For illustration, see title page.

var. fabri (Masters) Hunt. Mount Omei, Szechuan. Introduced in 1901.

The type is described as having minutely pubescent shoots. This is the specimen Faber 984, collected in 1887. A specimen collected by Fang has very short leaves, only 7 mm long, but Faber's type has leaves of 2×0·2 cm, very revolute, and cones long-ovoid, 5×2·5 cm, with the spines of the bracts exserted 2–3 mm. Many trees labelled "*A. delavayi*" in Britain have pale brown shoots, pubescent in shallow grooves and varyingly revolute but largely pectinately arranged leaves. These are here regarded as var. *fabri*. The bark is most distinctive, dark orange-brown with many shallow fissures—separating this form safely from v. *forrestii* at a distance.

Specimens. Abbotswood, planted 1916, 47ft×2ft 10in; 43ft×3ft 8in (1966); Abbeyleix, 36ft×2ft 7in (1968) Fenagh House, 41ft×3ft 0in (1968); Crarae, planted 1939, 37ft×3ft 10in (1969); East Bergholt, 58ft×3ft 5in (1965); Headfort, 52ft×5ft 6in (1966); Westonbirt, 39ft×3ft 7in (1968), Edinburgh Royal Botanic Garden, (W 4078) 52ft×4ft 9in (1970) Stourhead, planted 1924, 51ft×4ft 10in (1970); Wakehurst Place, 42ft×3ft 5in (1970) Pencarrow 42ft×3ft 1in (1970); Benmore planted 1937, 53ft×5ft 10in (1970); Dawyck, 62ft×3ft 5in; 56ft×4ft 3in (1970).

var. faxoniana (Rehder and Wilson) Jackson. West Szechuan to Upper Burma.

Introduced in 1910. The type, specimen W4060, is described on the sheet as having hairy young shoots. The cones from this and several other specimens in the Kew Herbarium are notably small and cylindric, 4·5×2·5 cm, but specimen W 4069 has a cone 7 cm×3 cm and another, not numbered is 10cm×4 cm. The bracts are exserted as spines 2–3 mm, some with the base showing. The leaves still show chalky undersides. In cultivation, trees planted under this name are distinguished by:

Bark. Patches of shiny plum-purple (Powerscourt) or shiny pink-brown (Castlewellan).

SHOOT. Golden-brown or yellowish, grooved, sometimes cracked and rough, usually with a short pale pubescence in the grooves; second year pale pink-grey.
BUD. Deep purple or dark red.
LEAVES. Pectinate below, standing above the upper side, rising densely and curved inwards and forwards leaving a "V", usually narrow; 2·5–3 cm × 0·2 cm, thick, deep grey-green to a noticeably pale whitish blunt tip; underside banded greenish-white but sometimes bright white. (This character is useful but dangerously variable in many *Abies* species—cf *A. firma; A. pindrow*. The type var. *faxoniana* and all the other herbarium material show bright white, but most cultivated trees have greenish bands). In some the leaves are more slender and lie flatter.
SPECIMENS. Abbotswood planted 1916, 44ft × 3ft 1in (1966); Speech House planted 1916, 39ft × 3ft 7in (1963); Powerscourt, 54ft × 4ft 4in (1966); Castlewellan, 44ft × 4ft 0in (1966); Dawyck, 57ft × 4ft 0in (1970); Stanage Park, 33ft × 2ft 0in (1970).

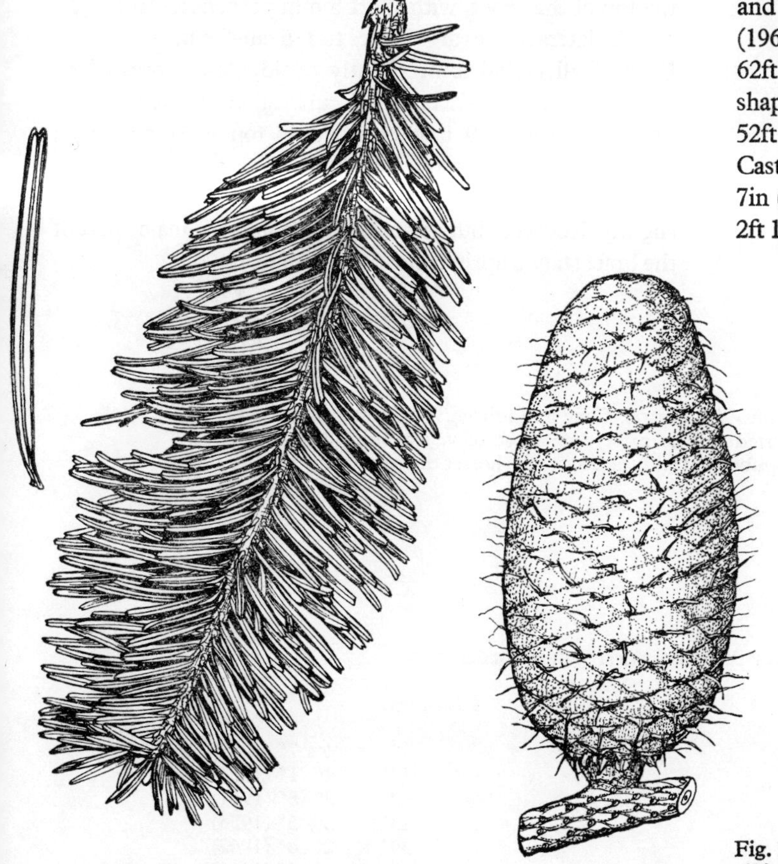
Abies delavayi v. forrestii

var. forrestii (Rogers) Jackson. Yunnan, Szechuan. Introduced in 1910.

Type bears the collectors reference number F 6744; F 10152, and Rock 24957 are from the same area (Likiang Range). The commonest form; distinguished by:
FOLIAGE. Shoot bright orange-brown to reddish brown, glabrous, finely roughened. Second year shoot deep mahogany purple with small white striae.
BUD. 3 mm, globular, smooth dark red, thick with resin, white in patches.
LEAVES. Spreading all round the shoot, those below curved sharply forwards, those above crowded forwards, some curled over to show white underside; often parted in a marked "V", 2 cm (mid-line) to 4 cm (laterals) truncate, deeply notched, dark blue-green, slightly shiny above, brilliantly white-banded beneath. Some trees have leaves dusted grey above at first.
CONE. Barrel-shaped, broad, 9 × 4·5 cm, flat-topped, deep blue, bracts exserted to 0·5 cm, a spreading filament, curved down in those at the base of the cone, the broad base of the bract, deeply toothed, showing, or, when exserted only 3 mm, the base not showing.
SPECIMENS. Stanage Park, seed 1912, 50ft × 6ft 7in (1967) and 66ft × 5ft 2in (1951); Werrington Park, 50ft × 4ft 7in (1969); Walcot Park, 60ft × 4ft 10in (1959); Tregullow, 62ft × 4ft 3in (1959); Cortachy Castle, many vigorous and shapely trees to 60ft × 4ft 4in (1962); Headfort planted 1930, 52ft × 6ft 1in (1966); Hawick, 50ft × 3ft 4in (1958); Birr Castle, planted 1942, 38ft × 3ft 8in (1966); Bicton, 62ft × 3ft 7in (1968); Stourhead, 63ft × 5ft 6in (1970); Durris, 59ft × 2ft 11in (1970); Dawyck, 60ft × 3ft 4in (1970).

Fig. 11
Abies delavayi v. *forrestii*, Forrest's fir. A shoot from a form with long leaves, showing the roughened but glabrous shoot. Leaf (× 1⅓) showing thickly white-coated underside. The cone has bracts exserted further than those of v. *fabri*, but mainly not so far as in v. *georgei*.

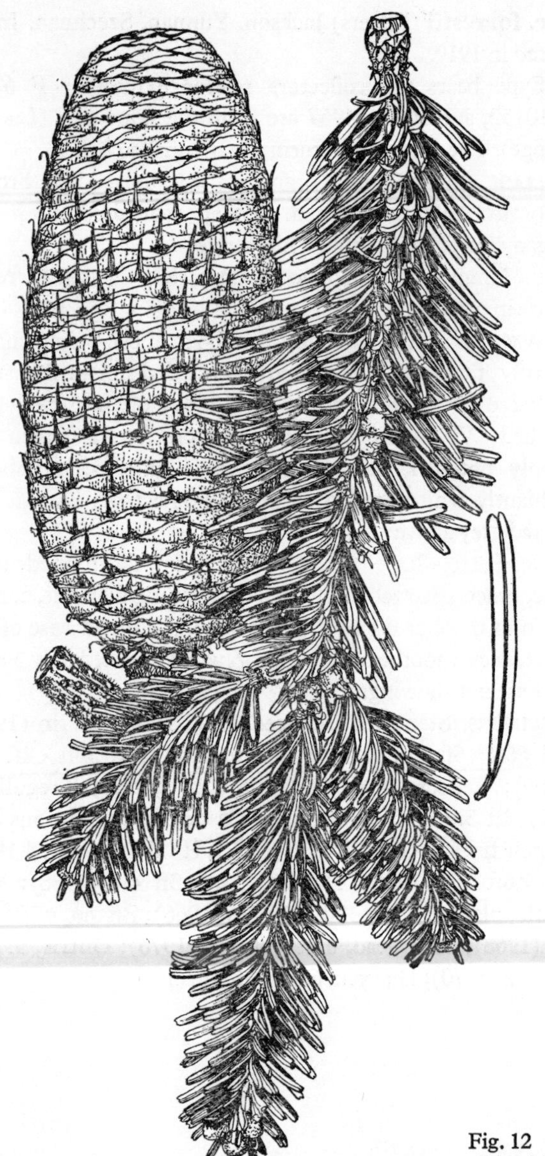

var. georgei (Orr) Melville. Yunnan. Introduced in 1923.

Type is specimen W 30853 from Chuza Yan. This is almost var. *forrestii*, traditionally separated by densely pubescent shoots and by "long exserted" bracts on the cones (without noting that in var. *forrestii* they can also be regarded as "long exserted"). The cone in the type specimen is squashed somewhat and would appear to be immature so the bracts would be more prominent than on a mature cone. They extend 1–1·2 cm, about half of which is the base. Mature cones in cultivated trees have bracts exserted up to 8–9 mm, showing the bases of the bracts in the lower cone but often only the filaments 5 mm long or so, higher on the cone. However, the cone shape is consistently different from var. *forrestii* and the following distinctions can be made.

FOLIAGE. Shoot brownish orange, slightly grooved, with a dense, short pubescence of the same colour. (Trees with glabrous shoots identified as v. *georgei* by the exserted cone bracts, seen coning in 1970 by the author, were v. *forrestii*.)

BUD. Globular 8 mm and usually pure white with thick resin.

LEAVES. As in var. *forrestii* except that they are pale blue-grey above for the first year, being densely bloomed white on very dark blue-green, and they tend to close more over the top of the shoot, with short 8 mm perpendicular leaves, and the lateral leaves are shorter to 1·5 cm–2 cm.

CONE. Tall cylindric or slightly ovoid, flat, depressed or domed at the top, 9–12 cm × 4–5 cm bright dark blue-purple, bracts exserted 8–9 mm crowded at top in some cones; bases exposed when more than 5 mm exserted, and they are bright blue-purple, edged light brown; the tips of the bracts slightly decurved, but in most of the cones the major part of the bract stands upright close to the cone.

Fig. 12
Abies delavayi v. *georgei*. Cone and foliage. The bracts of the cone are exserted a little more than those of v. *forrestii*. The shoot is densely pubescent and the leaves are shorter than in most v. *forrestii*.

Abies delavayi v. georgei

TABLE 7. SPECIMENS OF ABIES DELAVAYI VARIETY GEORGEI

Locality	*Date Planted*	*Dimensions*
Lamellan	ca.1927	35′ × 4′ 7″ (1963)
Hergest Croft		43′ × 4′ 1″ (1963)
Wakehurst Place		50′ × 2′ 8″ (1964)
Burnside	1936	43′ × 2′ 3″ (1956)
Strathallan Castle	1939	39′ × 2′ 4″ (1962)
Vivod Arboretum	1942	35′ × 2′ 3″ (1964)
Birr Castle	1945 (Rock)	26′ × 1′ 11″ (1966)
Borde Hill (Tolls)		49′ × 1′ 11″ (1968)
Borde Hill (Gores Wood)		42′ × 1′ 8″ (1961)
Powis Castle (Pinetum)	post 1932	55′ × 3′ 7″ (1970)

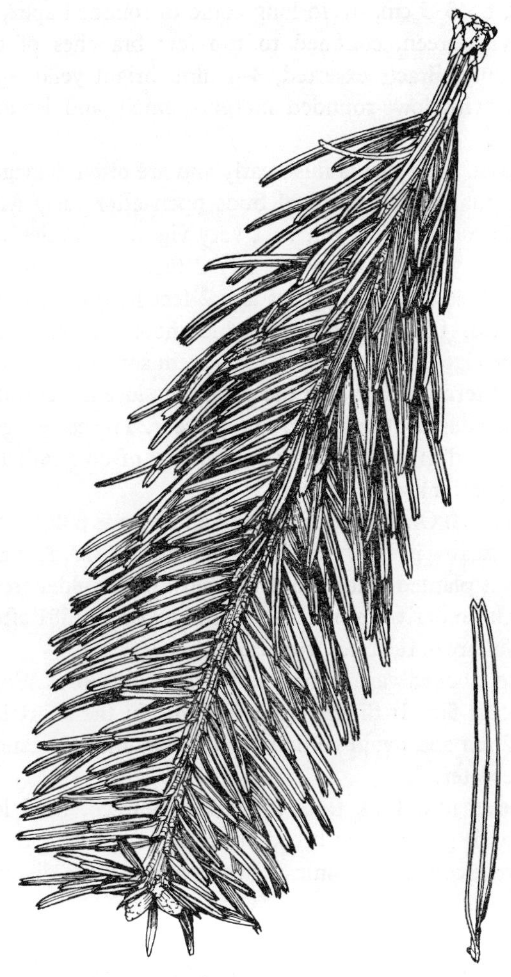

Fig. 13
Abies fargesii. A spray of this rare but distinctive fir. The leaves are leathery and the shoot purple or red. The single leaf ($\times 1\frac{1}{3}$) shows the deeply bifid tip and the broad bands of dull grey-white stomata beneath.

Abies fargesii Franchet.

West China. Introduced to the U.S.A. in 1901 but probably not to Britain before 1907. Rare. In a few collections. A most handsome and distinct tree, whose foliage is different from others of the *A. delavayi* complex; it may be regarded as a giant form of *A. sutchuenensis.*

BARK. Smooth, grey-pink.

CROWN. Narrowly conic, branches level, gently upturned tips.

FOLIAGE. On a large scale. Shoot from purple to pale brown on the same tree, mostly shades of deep red-brown; faintly ribbed beneath, with a short curly white pubescence (visible under a lens). Second year shining pale orange-brown, with traces of black pubescence between broad broken white streaks.

BUD. Ovoid, 5–6 mm, yellowish brown with the scales making bumpy the resinous outside.

LEAVES. Mainly pectinate below, but a few spreading straight down then curved forwards, somewhat pectinate above, inner leaves well forward; inner leaves 2 cm, outer, 4–4·5 cm leathery, hard, very glossy deep yellowish green, grooved narrowly and tapering slightly to a deeply bifid tip. Margins slightly revolute, underside with large green midrib and a dull grey band each side.

A tree at Dawyck planted 1923, 53ft × 2ft 7in (1961); two young, vigorous trees at Jermyns House (from which the description has been taken), planted 1954, one 21ft × 1ft 7in (1969); one at Westonbirt with the same foliage, 39ft × 3ft 1in (1969). One at Bicton 48ft × 3ft 0in (1968).

RECOGNITION. The absence of blue coloration in the deep green leaves and the glossy, leathery, long leaves distinguish this tree from the *A. delavayi* group. The purple and brown shoots and large leathery leaves are together distinct from all others.

Abies firma Siebold and Zuccarini. Momi fir

Southern Japan. Introduced in 1861. The oldest tree was undoubtedly one at Pencarrow, Cornwall, which was undated but must have been from original seed. No original trees seem to have been explicitly recorded. Confined to collections and the largest gardens, but found in these in all parts.

BARK. Young trees, pink-grey with horizontal resin-blisters; becoming finely flaked. Old trees pale grey with orange-pink tints in places; thick corky, overall smooth but roughened finely.

CROWN. Conic with level branches; sturdy, often broad at base, rather open. Young trees have straight ascending branches.

FOLIAGE. Shoot pale grey-brown or yellow-buff, grooved, sometimes with fine pale pubescence in the grooves. Second year shining pink-brown; stout.

BUD. Broadly conic, pale brown or shining red and green.

LEAVES. Vigorous young trees; to 5·0 × 0·3 cm hard, rigid, broadening rapidly from a very marked stalk and tapering to two short spines. Older trees sometimes bear these on shoots among other shoots with the more usual foliage. Older trees—2·5 × 0·2 cm leathery, stiff, broadly rounded tips, yellowish green, pale or dark, above; bands beneath usually pale green but may be grey or whitish; in several dense rows rather flat each side of shoot and spreading at right-angles. Distinctive foliage both to the touch (hard, leathery, thick) and against the light, where the densely overlapping broad blades of the leaves and the shoot are opaque, but a broad band of light comes through between these where the relatively slender stalks are. Young trees distinctive by spiky, yellow-green growth.

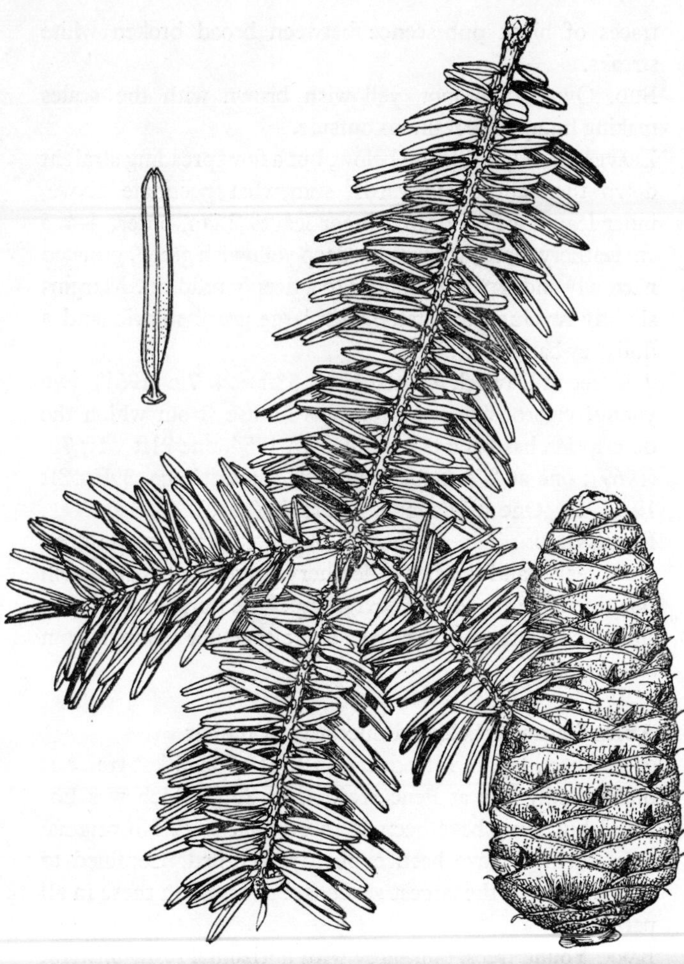

Abies firma

Fig. 14
Abies firma. A spray and cone of a mature tree. Young trees have longer and deeply bifid, spined leaves. The cone is a livid yellowish-green. Mature foliage leaf ($\times 1\frac{1}{3}$) shows stomatal bands beneath which are usually green but sometimes white.

CONE. 8×3·5 cm, ovoid long conic to rounded apex, deep yellowish-green, confined to top few branches of oldest trees only. Bracts exserted, 3–4 mm, bright yellow-green. Scales with low, rounded margins, finely and irregularly toothed.

GROWTH. Side shoots flush early and are often damaged by frost, but the big terminal buds open after early May so usually escape. This can be a very vigorous species with 2 year +2 year transplants nearly 2 feet tall and 4–5 years later 8 feet tall, growing leaders 2 feet long of remarkable thickness. Unfortunately the side shoots are of equal or greater vigour and their big buds seem sometimes to crowd out the terminal bud and the plant may lose its central axis, until a side-shoot bends up to replace it. The early vigour is maintained in growth in circumference of bole rather than in height, for a good 50 years.

SPECIMENS. One, a probable original tree was 88ft×10ft 0in at Pencarrow in 1957 but was not found in 1970. At Bagshot one was planted before 1881 but most of the older trees are thought to derive from a later introduction in 1881 after the near failure of the trees from earlier seed.

A tree labelled var. *tardina* at Borde Hill (Gores Wood) is 59ft×4ft 5in. It differs from the type in the short leaves, 1·5–2 cm and ovoid-conic purple buds, and it presumably flushes later.

RECOGNITION. Pink tints in bark and thick, hard leaves, yellowish green, very broad from narrow stalks; the dark yellow-green ovoid-conic cones are also very distinctive.

TABLE 8. LARGE TREES OF ABIES FIRMA

Locality	*Date Planted*	*Dimensions*	
Bagshot Park	1880	36′ × 3′ 11″ (1907)	72′ × 9′ 9″ (1960)
Borde Hill	1890	50′ × 4′ 0″ (1931)	86′ × 7′ 1″ (1968)
Borde Hill	1890		80′ × 6′ 9″ (1968)
Westonbirt		60′ × 6′ 9″ (1931)	80′ × 9′ 1″ (1970)
Hergest Croft	1904		59′ × 5′ 5″ (1961)
Hergest Croft	1916		50′ × 5′ 5″ (1961)
Little Hall	1906	35′ × 2′ 5″ (1931)	65′ × 4′ 7″ (1961)
Dropmore	1906		64′ × 6′ 1″ (1970)
Vernon Holme	1907	32′ × 1′ 2″ (1931)	57′ × 5′ 3″ (1961)
Stourhead	1911	25′ × 1′ 9″ (1931)	82′ × 8′ 4″ (1970)
Wakehurst Place	1914	18′ × 1′ 0″ (1931)	53′ × 3′ 7″ (1964)
Tregrehan		50′ × 7′ 0″ (1931)	111′ × 10′ 7″ (1971)
Bicton		71′ × 6′ 10″ (1927)	118′ × 8′ 7″ (1968)
Bicton			104′ × 8′ 5″ (1968)
Bicton	ca.1916		76′ × 7′ 5″ (1968)
Curraghmore		28′ × 3′ 2″ (1931)	48′ × 7′ 0″ (1968)
Fenagh House	1918		58′ × 7′ 8″ (1968)
Bedgebury	1926		63′ × 6′ 2″ (1969)
Bedgebury	1926		53′ × 5′ 6″ (1967)

Abies fraseri (Pursh) Poiret. Fraser's Balsam fir

Virginia, North Carolina and East Tennessee, U.S.A. Introduced in 1871. Very rare; confined to a few collections.

BARK. Rich brown, densely covered in resin-blisters, becoming pinkish-grey, pimpled and shredding.

CROWN. Narrowly conic, open with spiky shoots.

FOLIAGE. Shoot pale yellow-brown, finely pubescent.

BUD. Ovoid lumpy with scales in thick resin, deep chocolate brown and blackish purple.

LEAVES. Like *A. numidica* but more assurgent, those below curved strongly upwards, those on top standing densely on all the upper surface, all perpendicular, not forward, 1–1·5 cm broadest near the blunt, often notched tip, very dark green prominently pale-tipped; broad white bands below.

FLOWERS. Female flowers bright pale green.

CONES. 8×4 cm, cylindrical tapered; dark purple, largely hidden by well exserted, slightly decurved, waved broad-based pale brown, bracts. Numerous on quite small trees in 1970.

SPECIMENS. At Dupplin Castle, an old tree, reported as 42 feet tall in about 1880, was found, labelled in 1954 when it was 58ft×4ft 5in, but, at that time the identity was not checked. In Tubney Wood, one planted in 1906 was 50ft×2ft 1in in 1966. At Birr Castle, a tree planted in 1921 was 32ft×3ft 1in in 1966. At Castlewellan, there was, in 1966, a tree 32ft×2ft 5in. At Crarae, two trees in a young plot were 16ft×1ft 4in in 1956. A small tree at Bedgebury is 20ft×1ft 5in (1970).

GROWTH. Young trees can be vigorous and handsome—in two years one grew 3 feet 10 inches—but the size of the specimens given suggests that this rate of growth does not last long.

Abies grandis Lindley. Grand fir

Coast, from northern end of Vancouver Island south to Navarro River, California. Inland from central Southern British Columbia, through Idaho, Western Montana and Oregon. Introduced by D. Douglas 1831. One original tree survives, at Curraghmore, County Waterford, and possibly another at Lochanhead, Dumfries. Next oldest known was planted in 1852 (at Murthly Castle) but nearly all the biggest trees were planted after 1870. Common in large gardens, policies and increasingly in plantations, but not in towns or near cities.

BARK. At first brownish-grey with large resin-blisters. Big trees, dull grey or brown or purple-grey, cracked into small square plates in places, especially around scars of branches.

CROWN. Regularly narrow-conic, whorled and rather open until some 100 feet tall, then broadly columnar more dense, fanning out at the top with age. Trees in the open usually have a few low, very large branches which turn sharply upwards some 10–15 feet from the bole. In woodlands, old trees may have long slender hanging branches from the mid-bole. In exposure, tall trees lose their tops and often grow 5 or 6 new trunks close together and vertical, and rapidly regain height. One tree only has been seen in which large branches have layered (Sheffield Park).

FOLIAGE. Shoot olive-green, very finely pubescent at first, second year shoot brown.

BUD. Very small, dark brown becoming bright purple with a little white resin.

LEAVES. Arranged very flat each side of shoot, of roughly three sizes, the shortest row above; 2 to 5 cm, spreading at right angles to shoot; upper surface shiny, grooved, bright mid-green; blunt-ended; margins often somewhat decurved; lower surface with two bright but narrow white bands. When crushed, the leaves give a fruity orange-flavoured aroma.

FLOWERS AND CONE. Male flowers small for *Abies*, 2 mm, ovoid, purple until open, on undersides of shoot on the basal half only; densely on side shoots, a few scattered on main shoots, in the upper crown of old trees, seldom seen from ground. Cone small, 5–10 cm, tapered, light green, on top-most shoots of some old trees, ripening dull grey-brown, much covered in resin.

GROWTH. Side shoots flush in early May only a few days before the leading shoot starts growth. The leader grows until early or mid-July. After a slow start in the nursery, this tree is for a very long period and on a variety of sites, one of very great vigour. At Bedgebury, on poor sands, 97ft×9ft 11in has been grown in 43 years and 82ft×6ft 7in in 29 years. At Westonbirt on shallow clay over limestone, one grew to 106ft×7ft 9in in 36 years and 142 feet in less than 70 years.

The most rapid growth in height was made by some trees at Keltie, Crieff, which blew down in 1953. They were then about 53 years old. One was 167ft×8ft 9in. Increments in girth have been as high as three inches per year for a period of 60 years at Castle Leod, and similar rates elsewhere as can be seen in Table 9.

SPECIMENS. One tree is known to be an original from Douglas's seed. This is at Curraghmore. One other, at Lochanhead, is so much bigger in girth than any other except one (Balmacaan) but on a site without any particular advantages, that it may be an original, also. Some of the largest and most vigorous trees are in Table 9.

TABLE 9. THE LARGEST AND MOST VIGOROUS TREES OF ABIES GRANDIS

Locality	*Date Planted*	*Dimensions*	
Curraghmore	1835	108′ × 14′ 9″ (1931)	105′ × 17′ 5″ (1968)
Lochanhead			110′ × 19′ 9″ (1962)
Murthly Castle	1852	124′ × 10′ 11″ (1931)	133′ × 19′ 8″ (1970)
Abercairny	1861	91′ × 8′ 4″ (1904)	142′ × 16′ 5″ (1962)
Cultoquhey	1861		121′ × 16′ 1″ (1970)
Eastnor Castle	1861	95′ × 7′ 6″ (1908)	144′ × 14′ 6″ (1970)
Blair Atholl (Diana's Grove)	1861		154′ × 14′ 3″ (1970)
Blair Atholl (Diana's Grove)	1861		151′ × 13′ 11″ (1970)
Blair Atholl (Diana's Grove)	1861		157′ × 12′ 3″ (1970)
Oxenfoord Castle	1863	76′ × 7′ 9″ (1931)	140′ × 12′ 2″ (1967)
Glamis Castle	1864	119′ × 12′ 0″ (1931)	148′ × 16′ 6″ (1970)
Glamis Castle			161′ × 14′ 9″ (1970)
Glamis Castle			151′ × 13′ 7″ (1970)
Balmacaan			131′ × 20′ 6″ (1970)[1]
Madresfield Court	1866	95′ × 7′ 6″ (1908)	135′ × 13′ 6″ (1964)
Fonthill		98′ × 8′ 0″ (1906)	149′ × 12′ 5″ (1963)
Inveraray (Frews Br.)		109′ × 12′ 0″ (1931)	157′ × 18′ 3″ (1969)
(Garden)			120′ × 17′ 11″ (1969)
(Lime Kilns)			152′ × 13′ 5″ (1969)
Fota		90′ × 14′ (1931)	107′ × 16′ 1″ (1966)
Shelton Abbey			125′ × 15′ 6″ (1968)
Sheffield Park			110′ × 15′ 2″ (1968)
Eridge Castle	1868	76′ × 6′ 6″ (1908)	151′ × 14′ 2″ (1971)
Brahan Castle	1868	85′ × 13′ 0″ (1931)	143′ × 18′ 1″ (1970)
Golden Grove	1869	80′ (1905)	126′ × 14′ 6″ (1960)
Durris House			117′ × 16′ 4″ (1970)
Durris House			126′ × 15′ 7″ (1970)
Dawyck	1870	114′ × 10′ 0″ (1931)	135′ × 14′ 2″ (1966)
Bradfield House	1875		119′ × 16′ 1″ (1959)
Coollattin	1875	63′ × 6′ 4″ (1906)	115′ × 14′ 4″ (1968)
Ashford Castle			125′ × 14′ 1″ (1968)
Ardkinglas (Strone)	1876	100′ × 11′ 8″ (1931)	175′ × 16′ 8″ (1969)
Fairburn			164′ × 14′ 9″ (1970)
Bedgebury (Cypress Valley)			144′ × 12′ 5″ (1970)
Conon House			127′ × 15′ 10″ (1955)
Taymouth Castle			170′ × 15′ 9″ (1970)
Dupplin Castle (Pinetum)		99′ × 10′ 4″ (1931)	151′ × 16′ 1″ (1970)
Dupplin Castle (Pinetum)		102′ × 8′ 9″ (1931)	151′ × 13′ 6″ (1970)
Dupplin Castle (N. Lodge)			161′ × 12′ 9″ (1970)
Silia			151′ × 14′ 10″ (1970)
Castle Kennedy	1879	78′ × 6′ (1904)	110′ × 12′ 6″ (1967)
Youngsbury		91′ × 9′ 8″ (1907)	118′ × 13′ 6″ (1966)
Petworth House		94′ × 6′ 6″ (1908)	132′ × 11′ 8″ (1971)
Woodhouse			155′ × 10′ 7″ (1970)
Westonbirt (1)	1880	95′ × 9′ 5″ (1926)	154′ × 13′ 11″ (1971)
Castle Milk	1886	94′ × 10′ 7″ (1931)	143′ × 14′ 2″ (1966)
Bodnant (1)	1887	117′ × 11′ (1931)	145′ × 15′ 3″ (1966)
Endsleigh		80′ × 9′ 6″ (1931)	150′ × 15′ 2″ (1970)
Endsleigh			150′ × 14′ 7″ (1970)
Leighton Hall (Park Wood)	1888		176′ × 11′ 1″ (1970)
Leighton Hall (Park Wood)	1888		170′ × 12′ 6″ (1970)
Westonbirt (2)	1890	106′ × 7′ 9″ (1926)	147′ × 10′ 1″ (1971)
Highclere	1897	70′ × 7′ 8″ (1930)	115′ × 14′ 4″ (1968)
Dunkeld Cathedral	1897	59′ × 7′ 6″ (1931)	137′ × 13′ 0″ (1970)
Hergest Croft	1900		130′ × 14′ 1″ (1969)
Bodnant (2)	1902	70′ × 7′ 2″ (1931)	125′ × 13′ 9″ (1966)
Brandon Park	1905		110′ × 8′ 6″ (1964)
Mells Park			141′ × 14′ 9″ (1962)
Castle Leod			110′ × 15′ 6″ (1966)
Castle Leod	1906		100′ × 14′ 6″ (1966)
Inistioge			122′ × 14′ 2″ (1966)
Wakehurst Place	1909	45′ × 2′ 5″ (1931)	96′ × 10′ 6″ (1964)
Avondale	1910	57′ × 5′ 6″ (1931)	120′ × 12′ 8″ (1968)
Strathallan	1911		130′ × 8′ 2″ (1962)
Bedgebury	1926	10′ 2″ (1931)	102′ × 10′ 2″ (1970)

[1] Measured at 6 feet; above a huge limb

Fig. 15
Abies grandis, Grand fir. Spray and (×1⅓) single leaf. The leaf margins of some trees are decurved. The pubescence on the shoot is much too fine to show.

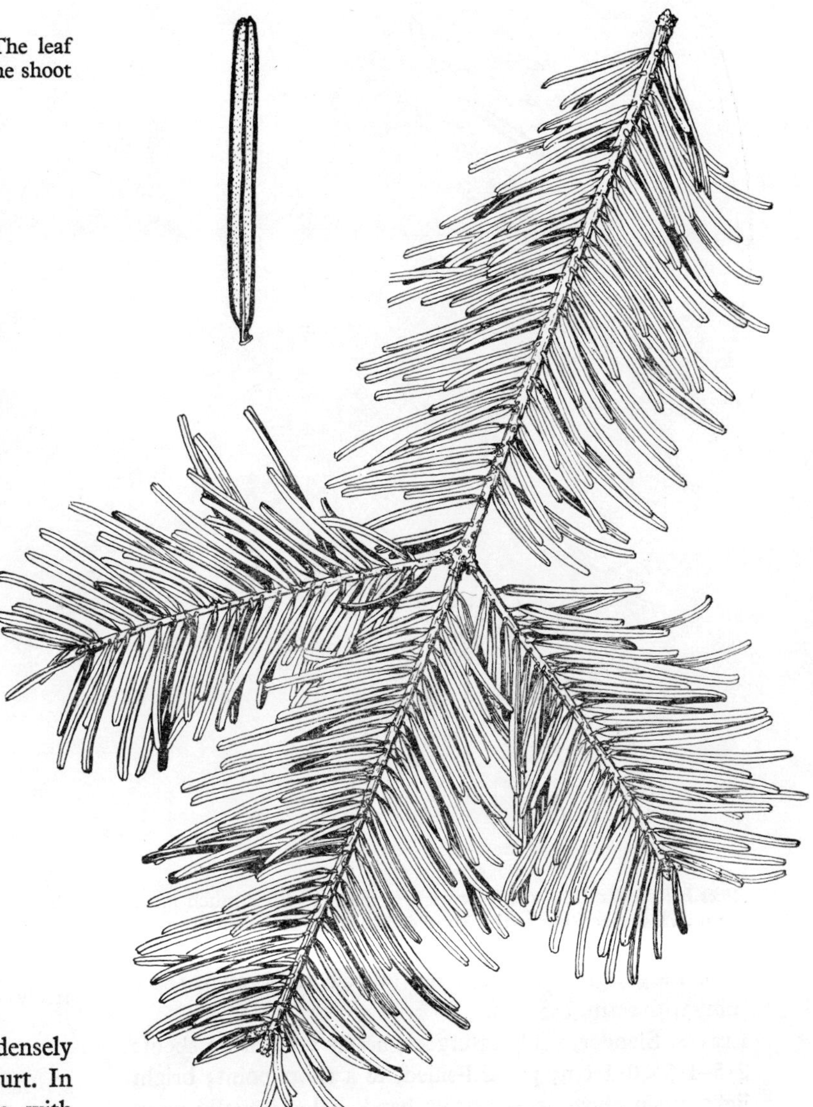

Abies grandis

Cultivar. Several trees of a peculiarly compact, densely columnar form stand in a rock-garden at Powerscourt. In 1966 the best was 65ft×3ft 0in and very handsome, with very short branches holding foliage in level layers.

RECOGNITION. The flat, long and short leaves, perpendicular each side of the olive-green shoot distinguishes this from all other silver firs, except for the Northern form of *Abies concolor* variety *lowiana* (q.v.).

USES. For the past 30 years or so, this species has been planted occasionally on good soils or sheltered sites, and experimentally. Several of these have grown at a rate corresponding to a higher yield class than Sitka spruce. Big specimen trees have shown similar rates of growth even on light, sandy soils, and some of the tallest have re-grown one or many new tops to great heights after damage from wind in exposed sites. It therefore seems that big volumes of timber can be yielded by this species even on sites far less favourable than those hitherto used. Planting is now on an increasing scale on a wider variety of sites. Early growth is as rapid, and establishment is quicker, under light shade in hardwood stands, so there is a considerable amount of under-planting with this species.

Abies holophylla Maximowicz. Manchurian fir

Manchuria and Korea. Introduced in 1904. Rare; in some collections and a few large gardens mainly in the west and in Ireland.

BARK. Shredding into fine, papery scales; usually buff-orange or pink-buff but sometimes grey with light pink or whitish areas, or purplish in parts.

CROWN. Fairly narrowly conic or narrow-topped, but broader at base.

FOLIAGE. Shoot shiny, glabrous light pink-brown or buff-orange.

Fig. 16
Abies holophylla. The rich green leaves may be either much more or much less erect than in this sample. They are pale green beneath.

Fig. 17
Spray, leaf (× 1⅓) and mature cone of *Abies homolepis*, the Nikko fir. The shoot is glabrous, grooved and pink to yellow; the leaves are well parted on most trees but occasionally cover the shoot. The underside has two broad, very white bands. The tree cones rather freely on low branches when old.

BUD. Large, globular, deep red or pale red-brown, some shiny with resin, 7·5 mm.
LEAVES. Slender, stiffly assurgent, nearly vertical on shoot; 2·5–4·5×0·1 cm; parallel-sided, to a short point; bright light green above, two narrow bands below usually grey-green, rarely white.
CONE. 10×5 cm, cylindric, smooth, pale green.
GROWTH AND SPECIMENS. After an initial period of slow growth, most trees enter a period of quite rapid growth in both height and girth. At Westonbirt two trees growing vigorously when 33 years old, increased their girth by 7in and 8in in 5 years. At Crarae, an increase of 20in in 13 years was recorded on a tree 19 years old at the beginning. Borde Hill, Sussex (specimen W 9302) planted about 1925 61ft× 3ft 10in (1968); and 50ft×2ft 3in (1968); Wakehurst Place, 53ft×3ft 2in (1970). Crarae, Argyll planted 1937, 28ft× 3ft 0in (1969) Westonbirt, planted 1930, 46ft×4ft 2in; 52ft×3ft 7in (1970); Birr Castle, planted 1927 40ft×3ft 4in (1966) Bedgebury, planted 1929, 44ft×3ft 5in (1969). Fenagh House, 45ft×3ft 1in (1968) Headfort planted 1929 47ft×5ft 5in. This last tree has very luxuriant foliage.
RECOGNITION. The combination of red, globular shiny buds, upstanding long leaves and shiny, glabrous pink-brown shoot is diagnostic.

Abies homolepis Siebold and Zuccarini. Nikko fir

Central Japan. Introduced in 1861. Uncommon, but in many big gardens and occasional in smaller gardens and parks, where it will grow reasonably well in or near towns.
BARK. Smooth but shredding finely into papery scales; pale grey with distinctive pink shade until old when purplish grey-brown and cracked into fine flakes.
CROWN. Sturdy broad-conic with spiky appearance and rather open, until a big tree when it becomes broad-columnar and domed, with level branches.
FOLIAGE. Shoot shining white to pale buff, grooved into plates. Second year very pale pink-brown.
BUD. Blunt, dark or light chocolate, white with resin later.
LEAVES. Well parted above shoot, somewhat stiff, variable

TABLE 10. NOTABLE TREES OF ABIES HOMOLEPIS

Locality	*Date Planted*	*Dimensions*	
Castle Kennedy	1873	65′ × 6′ 6″ (1931)	78′ × 7′ 4″ (1967)
Bodnant	1876	62′ × 6′ 9″ (1931)	76′ × 7′ 8″ (1966)
Westonbirt (Loop Walk)	1880	59′ × 4′ 9″ (1932)	87′ × 7′ 3″ (1971)
Westonbirt (Willesley)		67′ × 5′ 7″ '1931)	82′ × 7′ 10″ (1970)
Tregrehan		50′ × 6′ 6″ (1931)	84′ × 10′ 2″ (1971)
Keir House			70′ × 7′ 4″ (1970)
Tremough			80′ × 10′ 5″ (1962)
Errol			82′ × 7′ 5″ (1970)
Taymouth Castle			108′ × 10′ 10″ (1970)
Grayswood Hill	1881	41′ × 3′ 3″ (1906)	84′ × 8′ 4″ (1971)
Eridge Castle	1885	32′ × 2′ 0″ (1908)	60′ × 5′ 0″ (1971)
Dropmore	1890	32′ × 2′ (1907)	78′ × 5′ 10″ (1970)
Fenagh House	1897	45′ × 2′ 7″ (1931)	61′ × 7′ 2″ (1968)
Fenagh House	1918	13′ (1931)	80′ × 6′ 2″ (1968)
Sidbury Manor	1898	52′ × 2′ 8″ (1925)	67′ × 7′ 3″ (1959)
Br ahan Castle	1901		66′ × 6′ 7″ (1970)
Tilgate	1905	35′	70′ × 4′ 7″ (1961)
Little Hall	1906	45′ × 4′ 4″ (1931)	66′ × 6′ 8″ (1961)
Pencarrow		40′ × 3′ 10″ (1901)	72′ × 7′ 8″ (1970)
Bicton		47′ (1906)	86′ × 6′ 8″ (1968)
Whittingehame		53′ × 5′ 10″ (1931)	70′ × 8′ 7″ (1957)
Brownscombe			75′ × 8′ 9″ (1969)
Heythrop House			75′ × 8′ 1″ (1969)
Avondale	1907		64′ × 8′ 5″ (1968)
Abbeyleix			58′ × 7′ 2″ (1968)
Endsleigh			80′ × 9′ 1″ (1970)
Endsleigh			60′ × 8′ 11″ (1970)
Stanage Park	1910		85′ × 8′ 2″ (1970)
Cowdray Park	1912	30′ × 2′ 1″ (1931)	70′ × 6′ 3″ (1967)
Wakehurst Place	1916	25′ × 1′ 8″ (1931)	67′ × 5′ 6″ (1964)
Smeaton House		40′ × 3′ 4″ (1931)	63′ × 7′ 6″ (1966)
Yester House			88′ × 8′ 10″ (1955)
Highnam			72′ × 8′ 5″ (1970)
Wansfell			72′ × 8′ 4″ (1957)[1]
Tibberton Court	1912		58′ × 5′ 7″ (1967)
Trentham Park			70′ × 7′ 6″ (1969)
Bedgebury	1926	10′ (1931)	56′ × 6′ 1″ (1969)
Oakley Park			95′ × 8′ 5″ (1971)
Hergest Croft			65′ × 7′ 6″ (1961)
Leighton Park			66′ × 8′ 7″ (1970)
Beauport Park			70′ × 8′ 8″ (1965)
Powerscourt		26′ (1931)	69′ × 6′ 8″ (1966)
Castlewellan		45′ × 7′ 9″ (1931)	61′ × 10′ 1″ (1970)
Exbury		17′ 6″ × 1′ 7″ (1931)	60′ × 4′ 7″ (1968)

[1] At 6 feet. This tree, grafted at 2 feet, was not found in 1971

in length 1–3 cm, at first often glaucous-grey above, later shining green, grooved, narrowed at base, bluntly tipped and notched; two broad, bright white bands beneath; lower rank perpendicular to shoot. Crushed gives minty aroma.
CONE. Borne fairly freely and not confined to the top—even on low branches; barrel-shaped, 12×3·5 cm, flat-domed, purplish-grey encrusted in places with white resin.
GROWTH. This species starts fairly quickly for a Silver fir and soon settles into a steady growth, relatively more rapid in girth than in height. There is some indication from the 1931 figures that this rapid increase in girth culminates at a girth of about 5 feet, at least in the south-east.

Three trees in this area, young in 1931 have increased in girth by an average of more than 50 inches in 36 years, whilst five older trees have a mean increase of only 15 inches in that period.

var. tomomi (Bobbink and Atkins) Rehder. Shorter (1–2 cm) leaves bloomed blue on the upper surface, and more open in the crown; this rare variety is known only from two of the biggest collections:—Borde Hill, (Warren) 54ft×2ft 11in (1970); 63ft×5ft 6in (1968), and Wakehurst Place, 75ft×5ft 9in (1970).
var. umbellata (Mayr) Wilson. Described as differing only in the cone, where the lower bracts protrude and the apex is flattened with a raised centre. The following have been seen and measured, but not checked for variety:

Vernon Holme, Kent	pl. 1908	65′×4′ 1″ (1961)
Bedgebury N.P. Kent	pl. 1925	40′×3′ 3″ (1969)
		37′×2′ 6″ (1969)
Holkham, Norfolk		44′×3′ 2″ (1968)
Dawyck, Peebles	pl. 1924	52′×3′ 6″ (1961)
Edinburgh R.B.G. (W7707)	pl. 1915	25′×4′ 3″ (1970)

Abies kawakamii (Hayata) Ito.

Mount Morrison, Formosa. Introduced in 1919 which failed, and again before 1929. Found only in collections. Closely related to *Abies mariesii*, but very different and easily identified.

BARK. Young trees bright grey coarsely flaking or yellowish-brown flaking grey, becomes corky, pale grey-buff, shredding in vertical strips.

CROWN. Rounded-conic and dense.

FOLIAGE. Shoot pale shining orange-brown with narrow deep grooves above shallower below, crowded with brown hairs.

BUD. Chocolate-red to purple-brown, bumpy.

LEAVES. In dense layers nearly flat each side of shoot, curved down at the tips; very slender and straight, 1–2·5 cm slightly forward pointing, deep rich shining green above, below with two very narrow grey lines. The finest tree is at Birr Castle, where it was planted in 1929 (1930 is usually given as date of reintroduction). In 1966 it was 38ft × 4ft 6in. Other relatively large trees are at Kilmacurragh (52ft × 4ft 9in); Headfort, planted 1931, girth 6ft 8in but top lost in a gale; Crarae 33ft × 3ft 3in 1969; Blauquhan 22ft × 2ft 10in (1970).

RECOGNITION. The dense layers of very narrow, dark leaves, well parted each side of pale brown, grooved shoot are very distinct. In older trees the bark is also a good feature.

Abies koreana Wilson. Korean fir

Qualpaert Island, Korea. Introduced in 1913. Fairly frequent in good gardens of any size and often grown as a flowering shrub in a border.

BARK. Dark olive-brown to black, shiny, conspicuously freckled by pale lenticels.

CROWN. Either a low broad bush or a broadly conic tree, occasionally narrow.

FOLIAGE. Shoot pale fawn slightly pubescent under lens.

BUD. Small, globular but slightly pointed, pale brown, much covered by white resin, becoming conspicuously true white in winter.

LEAVES. Nearly covering the upper side of the shoot where curve upward to nearly vertical and some curving backwards; a few below the shoot pointing forwards; taper to pale green petiole at base, expand to broad, blunt, notched tip. Blackish green above often with white line of stomata near the tip; two very broad, bright white bands below often obscuring the midrib. Usually quite crowded, but sparse on some main shoots, 1·0 to 1·6 × 0·2 cm.

FLOWERS. Male buds on side-shoots only, nearly all round the shoot, crowded among the leaves, ovoid 4–5 mm dark red-brown with some white resin. Female buds spaced along the top of main shoots, squat 6 × 6 mm pale or yellow-brown with some white resin. Open to dark red or any shade of purple, or pink to bright yellow-green flowers 4–5 cm tall. Cones dark blue-purple, white resin blobs exuded here and there, brown bracts pressed down against scale below; 7 × 3 cm.

Abies koreana

Fig. 18
Abies koreana. A fruiting shoot, typical of even very small trees. The leaves show thickly white-coated undersides.

SPECIMENS. This tree is by no means always the dwarf it is often assumed to be. At Hergest Croft, at 34 years, it is 32ft × 3ft 0in. At Borde Hill, 33ft × 2ft 0in (Gores Wood, in 1968); Wakehurst Place, 26ft × 2ft 0in (1964); Edinburgh Royal Botanic Garden, 27ft × 2ft 7in (1970); Dawyck, 31ft × 2ft 11in at 39 years (1970); Crarae, 29ft × 2ft 9in (1969); Headfort, 26ft × 2ft 4in at 37 years (1966); Castlewellan, 27ft × 2ft 3in (1970); Bedgebury, planted 1927, 37ft × 2ft 0in (1970).

Abies lasiocarpa (Hooker) Nuttall. Alpine fir

Alaska to North Arizona on mountains. Introduced 1863. Very rare and scarcely surviving to make a tree. None of the trees mentioned in Elwes and Henry (two) nor the 1932 Report (two more) have been found.

BARK. Dark grey, blistered.

CROWN. Bushy and low in the few old trees. Young trees 13 years planted in a plot at Bedgebury are very variable but mostly ovoid, very dense in the lower parts. Many have main branches ending vertically and close to the main axis, but on the whole they are surprisingly shapely and promising.

FOLIAGE. Shoot shiny light grey-brown; 2nd year more grey.

Fig. 19
Abies lasiocarpa, Alpine fir. A spray of the slender leaves and one leaf (× 1⅓) showing narrow stomatal bands beneath. The swellings at the base of each year's growth are frequently much more pronounced in unhealthy trees.

Bud. Ovoid, scales rough, pale brown with white resin.
Leaves. Densely set, all pointing forwards, those in middle rising in a curve to, and some beyond, the vertical; slight parting on weak shoots only; some bend down, a few much below the shoot, pointing forwards. Slender 2·5 cm × 1·5 mm, shiny grey-green above with two incomplete white stomatal bands, two complete narrow white bands beneath. Shoots on older and some younger plants grossly swollen at joints.
Flowers. Not seen.
Specimens. A poor tree 45ft × 3ft 5in was at Bicton in 1957 but has since died. One at Abbeyleix is now 20ft × 1ft 9in. Several trees in the plot at Bedgebury are 8–10 feet tall, and one is 12ft after 13 years.

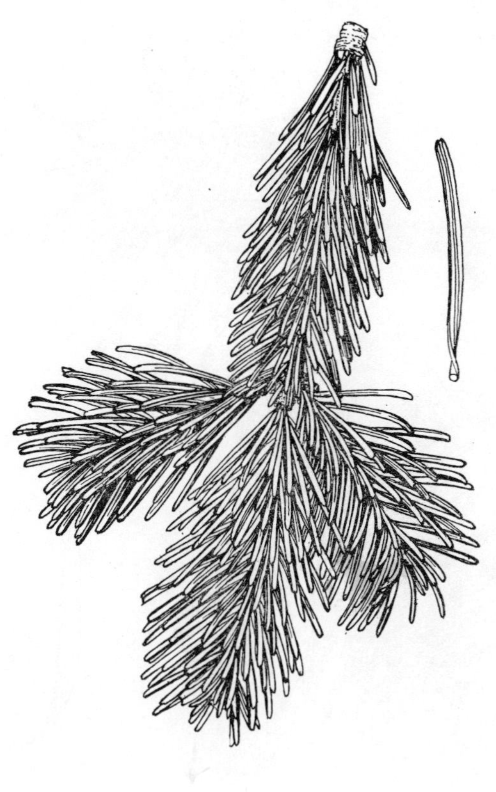

Fig. 20
Abies lasiocarpa var. *arizonica* is a neat, narrow tree, much more healthy than the type. Each leaf has a broad white band on the greyish upper surface, giving a bright blue appearance.

var. arizonica (Merriam) Lemmon.
Bark. When young, grey-green with wide corky-pink fissures soon appearing. Older trees, thick corky, pale brown.
Crown. Narrowly columnar or conic, like *Picea omorika*. Early damage may cause multiple stems in candelabra shapes.
Foliage. Shoot slightly grooved, pale yellowish-brown with scattered pubescence; bud globular, red-brown with a green tip, white in parts, with resin.
Leaves. To 3 cm, similar to the type, densely set, curved forwards, very bluntly rounded or short-pointed, but differ in their striking steely-blue appearance due to broad central white band above. Petiole pale green. Crushed foliage sticky —and giving off a balsam aroma.
Specimens. At Highclere, a tree 20ft × 2ft 0in in 1931 is now 60ft × 5ft 0in and a fine dark blue spire. Similar smaller trees are at Brinkburn Priory (46ft × 2ft 8in 1958) and Bayfordbury (46ft × 3ft 0in 1968). Hergest Croft 52ft × 4ft 1in (1961); 52ft × 5ft 2in 1969 (candelabra crown) and 56ft × 3ft 7in 1961 (candelabra crown).
cv. Nana. Leaves 1·5–2·5 cm all round the shoots. Only small plant, seen, but growing with vigour equal to that of var. *arizonica*.

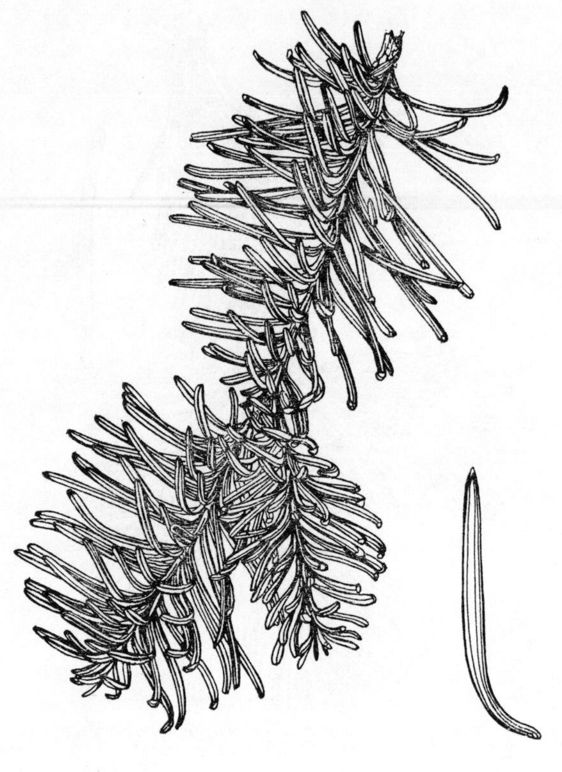

Fig. 21
Abies magnifica. The leaves, sparser and longer than in *Abies procera*, are not always so strongly upswept as in this sample.

Abies magnifica A. Murray. Californian red fir

Cascade Mountains of Oregon, Mount Shasta and Sierra Nevada, California. Introduced 1851. Uncommon, confined to largest gardens and collections.

BARK. Young trees at first with level lines of blisters, soon have thick, corky bark, purple and grey, finely roughened. Older trees purple-grey with curled cracks or narrow vertical fissures; very irregular, prominent dark, black branch-scars.

CROWN. Regularly narrow-conic, prominently whorled, tapering in a curve to a point until very old. Oldest trees with broken, irregular tops but most distinct in regular whorls of short, strongly up-curved branches and big, dark scars on barrel-shaped bole. Much more regular, narrow, upswept and open than *A. procera*.

FOLIAGE. Shoot dark rusty brown with short dense pubescence; 2nd year darker, tinged purplish. End of spray on shoot, rounded.

BUD. Very small chestnut-brown pubescent, hidden by small terminal leaves.

LEAVES. To 3·5 cm long; wide-spreading then curving inwards, upper ones curving upwards to vertical and beyond; nearly round in cross-section, can be rolled; less crowded than in *A. procera.* Dark grey-green with two paler bands slightly depressed on each surface.

CONES. Seldom seen, 20×12 cm, big, smooth, domed barrel, pale golden-green.

GROWTH AND SPECIMENS. Growth in height is not usually rapid. From rather few comparative records, the tree at Borde Hill is quite exceptional in growing from 24ft to 88ft in 37 years. Normal long-term growth is little above 1 foot per year. Growth in girth, however, is very rapid and thus most trees are very sturdy with barrel-like boles which taper sharply from an early age. After some 50 years this rapid growth diminishes sharply and many old trees are adding much less than 1 inch per year. This species seems short-lived here. Eleven of the thirteen given by Elwes and Henry have been sought but only two survive despite some being only 20 years old in 1905. The proportion surviving from the 1931 Report is one half. Borde Hill 88ft×8ft 0in (1968); Foxley, Hereford, 95ft×9ft 7in (1969); Glamis Castle, 112ft×10ft 6in (1955); Taymouth Castle, 120ft×10ft 3in (1970) and 113ft×10ft 11in (1970); Dunkeld Cathedral, 120ft×9ft 11in (1970); Dunkeld House, 123ft×10ft 5in (1970); Blair Atholl (St. Brides), planted 1878, 120ft×14ft 6in (1970) and (Diana's Grove), 118ft×10ft 3in (1970); Aldourie Castle, 95ft×9ft 11in (1956); Walcot Park, 102ft×8ft 11in (1963); Cragside, 105ft×8ft 6in (1958), Rowallane, 70ft×7ft 11in. A very shapely tree is in Bloomer's Valley, Wakehurst Place, 85ft×5ft 11in (1968), others are at Lanrick, 89ft×9ft 3in (1970) and at Culzean Castle (Happy Valley), 70ft×4ft 11in (1970); Fairburn, 80ft×6ft 4in (1970); planted in 1925, 72ft×8ft 1in (1970).

var. shastensis. Lemmon. Mount Shasta region, north. Date of introduction not recorded. Very rare. This differs from the type chiefly in the rather smaller cone (14 cm×7 cm) having long exserted bracts reflexed and thus resembling the cones of *A. procera.* The bark, at Bedgebury, is very smooth, pale grey with a fine pattern of brown stippling and some blisters. The leaves are very blue-grey above with two bands of stomata on each surface and up to 4 cm long. This tree at Bedgebury was planted among type trees in 1926. In 1968 it bore a cone showing it was *var. shastensis.* It is 56ft×5ft 0in and is now making shoots 3 feet long. The trees planted as this variety are miserable grafted specimens and have not coned.

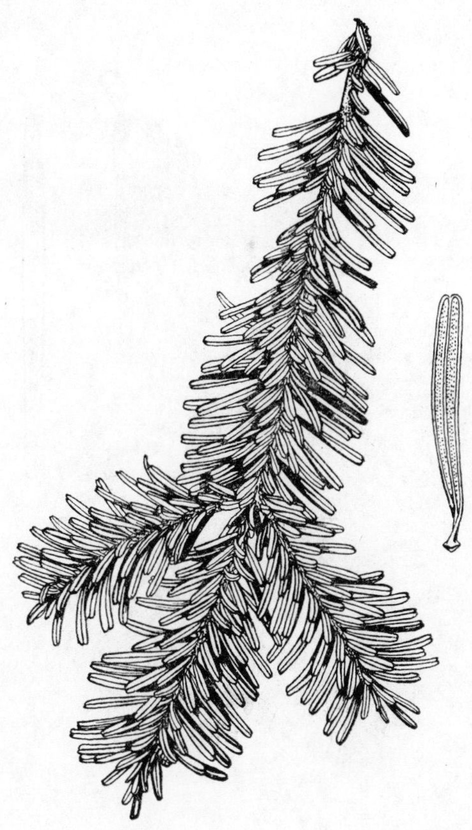

Fig. 22
Abies mariesii, Maries's fir. The foliage can resemble closely that of *Abies amabilis* but the shoot is densely clothed in pale brown hairs and the leaves are usually shorter making a narrower spray. The leaf (×2½) is brightly banded white beneath.

Abies mariesii Masters. Maries' fir

Central Japan. Introduced 1879. Rare. In biggest collection-gardens only.

BARK. Dark silvery grey, prominently freckled by small brown lenticels and marked by large, dark branch-scars.
CROWN. Narrowly conic, regularly whorled light branches, curving downwards then outwards, rather open.
FOLIAGE. Shoot (underside) pink-brown or pale orange from dense pubescence. Second year dark orange to red-brown.
LEAVES. Indistinctly parted, pointing forwards, to 2 cm, rich dark, glossy green, deeply grooved, bluntly square-ended and notched; 2 broad white bands beneath. The expanding buds are tinged crimson. Some trees resemble, in foliage, *A. amabilis* and there is confusion between the species.
FLOWERS AND CONE. Male flowers open to 4–6 cm long, yellow with dark grey ends to the scales. *Cone.* Long ovoid, 10×5 cm, smooth, dark blue-purple.
SPECIMENS. Probable original tree at Tregrehan has not been found since 1931. A shapely tree at Grayswood Hill is 55ft×3ft 6in. The best at Bedgebury planted in 1925 is 48ft×3ft 6in. At Dawyck, one planted in 1910 was 55ft×5ft 0in in 1966, other younger trees were 49ft×3ft 9in and 47ft ×2ft 10in. At Borde Hill there is one 55ft×3ft 9in and at Hergest Croft the largest is 45ft×3ft 7in. A shapely tree at Blairquhan is 38ft×2ft 8in (1970).
RECOGNITION. The typical tree is easily known by bark, crown and short, shiny, blunt and grooved leaves on a shoot with dense pink-brown pubescence. Although compared elsewhere with *A. veitchii* it scarcely resembles that species, but is much confused with *A. amabilis*, which differs in bark, luxuriance (but not always) and, probably best, grey-brown second-year shoots (not orange). Even the aroma of crushed leaves of *A. mariesii*, normally a warm one like ironed linen, can approximate to the tangerines of *A. amabilis*, but the leaves of *A. mariesii* are normally much shorter.

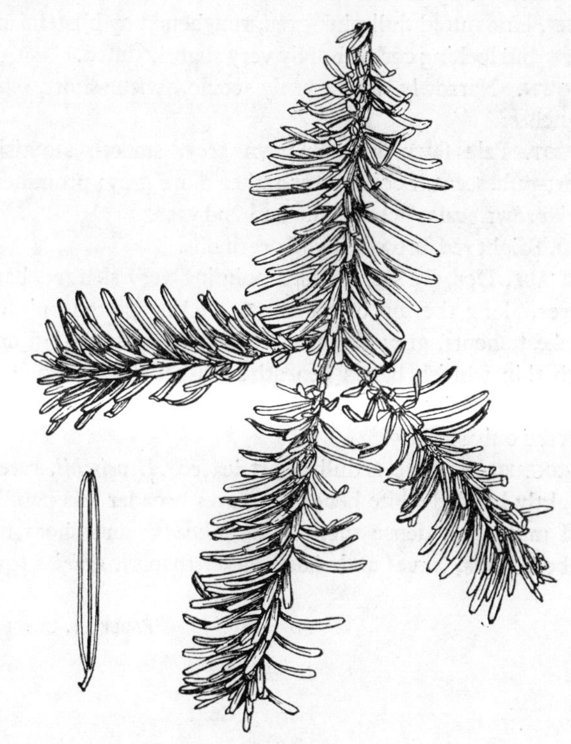

Fig. 23
Abies nebrodensis. From a young plant at Grayswood Hill. The shoot is pale pinkish-brown. Only 21 plants are known in the wild

Abies nebrodensis (Lojacono-Pojero) Mattei.

Sicily, on Monte Scalone where reduced to 21 trees. Very rare. Young plants in a few collections; only 7 known in Italian gardens, and 5 in France. 2 in Britain (Morandini, 1969). Except for one of the Italian trees, those in gardens are all grafted plants.

BARK. Orange and shredding.
BUD. Ovoid conic, pale reddish-brown, 5 mm, not resinous.
SHOOT. Pale corky-pink, glabrous (Borde Hill) yellowish brown with scattered short dark pubescence (Grayswood Hill).
FOLIAGE. Assurgent, all leaves slightly forward then curving up to nearly vertical. Short, and broad, of even lengths (1·5–2·0 cm×0·2 cm); blunt, notched tips, dark yellowish green above, two pale greenish white bands beneath. Said to be an island variety of *A. alba*, but seems remarkably different in bark, and in the arrangement of the leaves. Borde Hill, planted 1940. 25ft× 1ft 3in (1968); Grayswood Hill 5ft (1969).

Abies nephrolepis (Trautvetter) Maximowicz.

North China, East Siberia, Korea. Introduced 1908. Rare. Confined to largest collections.
BARK. Unfissured dull pink-grey, roughened by blisters and warts and looking corky. Rarely very slightly fluted.
CROWN. Narrowly and evenly conic, with short, stiff branches.
SHOOT. Pale fawn-pink or fawn grey, smooth stoutish; short-pubescent. Second year rather more grey; prominent dark brown scales between 1st and 2nd year.
BUD. Bright red-brown, slightly resinous.
FOLIAGE. Densely set, forward pointing very slender, hard leaves, along the top of the shoot, slightly parted only on weakest shoots, grey-green or light green matt, 1–2·5 cm, with thin whitish bands beneath; crushed leaves smell of balsam or paint. The ends of the shoots are 'square', tapered only slightly.
RECOGNITION. Like a dull, short-leaved *A. veitchii*, rarely brightly banded white beneath. Leaves broader less parallel and much less dense than *A. sachalinensis* and shoot not ribbed. Buds, leaves and shoot darker than *A. sibirica* (qv).

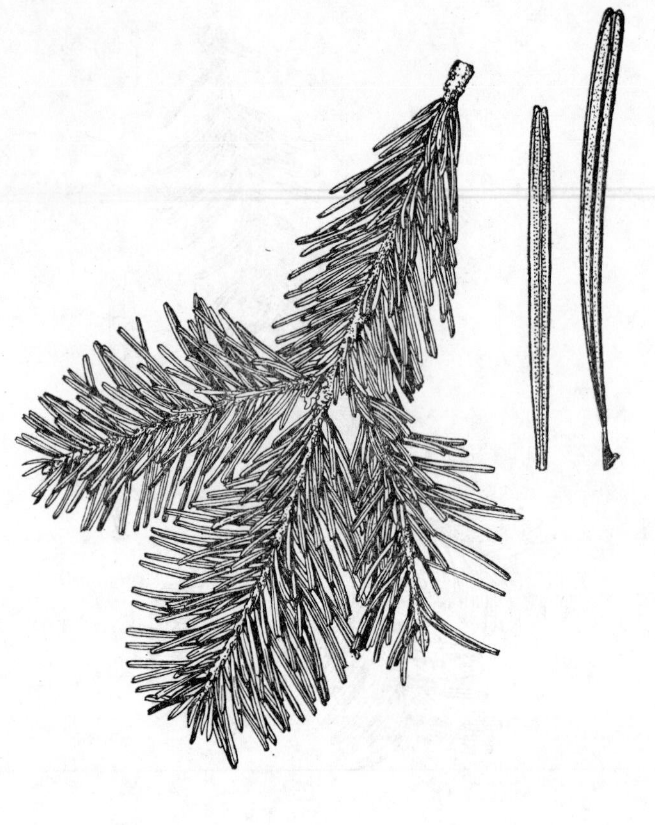
Abies nephrolepis

Fig. 24
A spray and one leaf (left ×2) of *Abies nephrolepis*, which is dull green above with narrow bands of whitish green beneath. The leaf of *Abies veitchii* (right ×2), usually longer, has bright white, broader stomatal bands beneath.

TABLE 11. SPECIMENS OF ABIES NEPHROLEPIS

Locality	*Date Planted*	*Dimensions*
Hergest Croft	1928	30′ × 2′ 6″ (1961)
Dawyck	1931	46′ × 3′ 10″ (1961)
Wakehurst Place		82′ × 5′ 0″ (1971)
Westonbirt	1934	46′ × 2′ 3″ (1967)
Stanage Park		60′ × 2′ 5″ (1970)
Stourhead		63′ × 3′ 6″ (1970)

Abies nordmanniana (Steven) Spach. Caucasian fir

Western Caucasus and North East Asia Minor. Introduced 1848. Common in collections and the larger gardens; quite frequent in smaller gardens and parks.
BARK. Grey and fairly smooth; areas of shallow fissuring into small square plates on older trees; occasionally more fissured and rough.
CROWN. Regularly conic for many years; columnar when older, usually still retaining a pointed top but some flat-topped. Varies between luxurious, dense crown, frequent in the west and in Scotland, and thin unhealthy crown most often seen in Eastern England. Shoots at base of leader of young tree, straight, ascending, not curving up sharply as they do in *A. alba*.
SHOOT. Greenish olive-brown with slight or moderate pale pubescence. On young, vigorous trees usually shiny and glabrous. Second year pink-brown.
BUD. Light brown without resin.

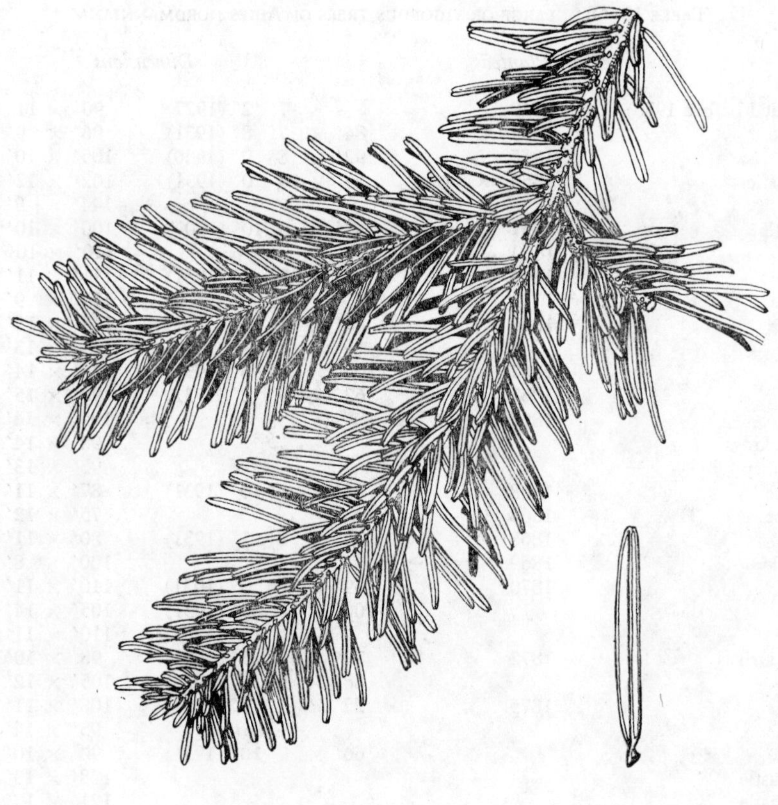

Fig. 25
A fairly typical spray of *Abies nordmanniana*, the Caucasian fir. In this variable species, trees may be found with shorter leaves curled forwards or longer straight and luxuriant leaves.

LEAVES. Very variable in density, length and curvature; pectinate beneath but all forward-pointing, upper ones very forward, low over shoot. Length of lower leaves 3 cm (upper normally 1 to 1·5 cm) but in luxurious specimens leaves exceed 3·5 cm. Usually straight but may be rather twisted inwards and then with down-rolled margins and lower leaves curved sharply forward; abruptly square tipped and notched; hard, leathery, shiny dark green, grooved above, darker second year, two bright white bands below. Crushed leaves emit rather faint aromas of fruity, resinous sorts, sometimes like petrol.

FLOWERS AND CONE. Male flowers prominent small globules, not very common. Cones often abundant but confined to few topmost shoots; 15×5 cm, cylindric pale green becoming brown and resinous, bracts exserted, downward appressed.

GROWTH. Early growth is rather more vigorous than that of *A. alba;* shoots of 2 feet occurring within three years of planting out. This does not increase as much with passing years as does that of *A. alba* and shoots of 3 feet are less common. Growth in height falls off earlier than in *A. alba* and occurs only on favourable sheltered sites, with deep, moist soils. It takes place between mid-May and early July. Table 12 shows that 100 feet is often exceeded. Girth increase is rapid only in a few very vigorous individuals and usually becomes very slow on trees of 8–10 feet in girth.

SPECIMENS. Two outstanding trees for luxuriance of foliage, splendid shapely crowns to the ground and combined dimensions are at Taymouth Castle Gardens. One of them has the twisted leaves with decurved margins mentioned above. Outstanding stems include those at Glamis (second tree; East Drive, not found 1970) Mells Park and Poltimore. The remarkably tall tree at Cuffnells has a long, conic apex.

TABLE 12. OLD, LARGE OR VIGOROUS TREES OF ABIES NORDMANNIANA

Locality	*Date Planted*	*Dimensions*	
Pencarrow (died before 1970)	1848	× 7′ 2″ (1927)	90′ × 11′ 3″ (1957)
Fota	1852	84′ × 7′ 8″ (1931)	96′ × 9′ 2″ (1966)
Dawyck	1855	92′ × 8′ 9″ (1930)	105′ × 10′ 7″ (1966)
Buchanan Castle	1856	75′ × 10′ 0″ (1931)	102′ × 12′ 10″ (1971)
Cuffnells			144′ × 9′ 10″ (1970)
Penrhyn Castle	1857	80′ × 6′ 10″ (1907)	100′ × 10′ 0″ (1959)
Scone Palace	1860		110′ × 10′ 5″ (1970)
Glamis Castle	1864	82′ × 9′ 2″ (1931)	111′ × 11′ 9″ (1970)
Glamis Castle			117′ × 9′ 6″ (1955)
Curraghmore	1866	80′ × 7′ 4″ (1931)	115′ × 13′ 8″ (1968)
Curraghmore			115′ × 13′ 0″ (1968)
Powerscourt	1867	104′ × 7′ 6″ (1931)	134′ × 14′ 3″ (1966)
Powerscourt	1867	62′ × 9′ 2″ (1931)	90′ × 15′ 1″ (1966)
Powerscourt	1867		105′ × 14′ 10″ (1966)
Road by Muckross			90′ × 14′ 7″ (1968)
Muckross Abbey			95′ × 13′ 5″ (1968)
Fenagh House	1868	65′ × 6′ 10″ (1931)	87′ × 11′ 5″ (1968)
Fenagh House	1868		75′ × 12′ 0″ (1968)
Blackmoor	1868	73′ × 9′ 1″ (1931)	80′ × 11′ 11″ (1968)
Cowdray Park	1869		100′ × 8′ 6″ (1967)
Stourhead	1870	49′ × 6′ 0″ (1931)	110′ × 11′ 2″ (1970)
Endsleigh		100′ × 10′ 0″ (1931)	105′ × 14′ 11″ (1970)
Endsleigh			110′ × 11′ 7″ (1970)
Blair Castle (Drive)	1872	78′ × 7′ 5″ (1931)	98′ × 10′ 3″ (1970)
Boconnoc		88′ × 6′ 0″ (1927)	105′ × 12′ 1″ (1970)
Coollattin	1875	22′ × 1′ 6″ (1891)	108′ × 11′ 9″ (1968)
Coollattin			95′ × 14′ 0″ (1968)
Blandsfort		66′ × 7′ 10″ (1931)	90′ × 10′ 3″ (1968)
Taymouth Castle			128′ × 13′ 4″ (1970)
Taymouth Castle			121′ × 13′ 5″ (1970)
Sidbury Manor	1880	75′ × 6″ 2″ (1925)	100′ × 9′ 3″ (1959)
Derreen	1880	60′ × 8′ 0″ (1931)	86′ × 10′ 11″ (1966)
Ashford Castle			89′ × 12′ 3″ (1968)
Inistioge			100′ × 13′ 9″ (1966)
Woodhouse		108′ × 6″ 11′ (1931)	129′ × 8′ 7″ (1970)
Kirkennan	1886	90′ × 6′ 8″ (1931)	117′ × 9′ 11″ (1970)
Oakley Park			132′ × 9′ 8″ (1971)
Cortachy Castle			103′ × 12′ 6″ (1962)
Mells Park			113′ × 9′ 5″ (1962)
Dunans			112′ × 9′ 10″ (1969)
Benmore			125′ × 11′ 0″ (1970)
Vivod			117′ × 7″ 5″ (1964)
Bodnant			108′ × 11′ 3″ (1957)
Luxborough			102′ × 12′ 2″ (1959)
Leaton Knolls		96′ × 4′ 11″ (1931)	115′ × 6′ 0″ (1970)
Durris House		62′ × 5′ 4″ (1904)	128′ × 13′ 0″ (1970)
Durris House		66′ × 6′ 2″ (1931)	115′ × 10′ 11″ (1970)
Poltimore			102′ × 10′ 10″ (1964)
Vernon Holme	1908	38′ × 2′ 6″ (1931)	62′ × 4′ 8″ (1961)
Wakehurst Place	1911	30′ × 2′ 2″ (1931)	85′ × 5′ 7″ (1964)
Westonbirt	1919		69′ × 4′ 3″ (1967)

cv. Aurea. A slow-growing variety with yellow leaves.

Only seen at Little Hall, planted 1916, 20ft×1ft 6in (1931), 35ft×2ft 7in (1961).

var. equi-trojani Guinier and Maire. Western Turkey in a small area near the West coast, south of the Bosphorus. Only nursery-plants seen, where the shining red-brown shoot is noticeable and the leaves (possibly juvenile) were more widely spaced, stiffer and larger than in the type.

FOREST USE. This species seems promising as a robust alternative to *A. alba* but trial plots have not borne this out. At Bedgebury damage from *Adelges nüsslini* has been extensive and necessitated spraying with insecticide, and frost has destroyed many leading shoots, causing misshapen crowns. Provenance may be important, but since the really vigorous trees are all in the western parts of the country, it is more likely that plantations there could be more successful. Cool, damp summers are probably required.

Abies numidica De Lannoy. Algerian fir

Mount Babor, Algeria at 5–6,000ft above sea level. Introduced 1862. Uncommon; seldom in ordinary gardens however large. No regional limits.

BARK. Purplish-grey, sometimes pinkish-grey; smooth; fine roughening from lenticels; with age becomes broken into small nearly circular plates sometimes in a regular fish-scale pattern. In oldest trees the plates start to lift away. The basal 1–2 feet usually more coarsely cracked into larger plates.

CROWN. Rather densely conic, usually narrowly but some broadly, with abruptly pointed top. Branches numerous, very heavily clothed, level then bent slightly down for outer half. Pink bark of upper bole, seen in a few gaps, contrasts with very dark blackish green and grey of foliage.

SHOOT. Scarcely visible among crowded broad leaf-bases, shining greenish-brown. Second year pale orange-brown.

BUD. Small, ovoid, conic, pale red-brown to chocolate brown; basal scales long pointed, appressed.

LEAVES. On main shoots, only slightly parted beneath in first year; second year all round shoot. Crowded, short, thick, stiff leathery, broad and blunt, make a very distinctive spray and very attractive. Perpendicular to shoot all over upper half, from 1–2 cm; broadly rounded tip. Dark blue-green; vertical leaves have two complete, broad white or

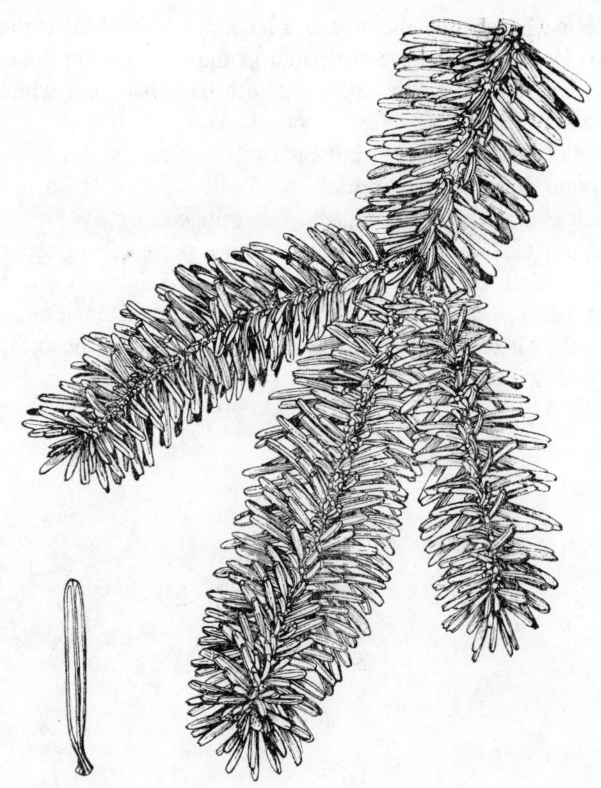

Fig. 26
A typically densely leafed shoot of *Abies numidica*, the Algerian fir, with short, thick leaves. The single leaf (×1⅓) shows the broad white bands of stomata beneath.

Abies numidica

TABLE 13. SPECIMENS OF ABIES NUMIDICA

Locality	*Date Planted*	*Dimensions*	
Pampisford	1876	37′ × 3′ 2″ (1909)	60′ × 7′ 5″ (1969)
Pampisford		44′ × 4′ 6″ (1931)	63′ × 6′ 1″ (1969)
Pampisford			90′ × 6′ 11″ (1969)
Castlewellan		44′ × 5′ 6″ (1931)	69′ × 10′ 8″ (1970)
Cowerne Court			66′ × 10′ 7″ (1956)
Tubney Wood	1906		70′ × 3′ 5″ (1966)
Little Hall	1906	27′ × 1′ 10″ (1931)	55′ × 3′ 7″ (1961)
Leighton Hall			73′ × 6′ 10″ (1970)
Chiltley Place			67′ × 6′ 7″ (1957)
Broxwood Court			80′ × 6′ 10″ (1957)
Castle Kennedy			85′ × 6′ 4″ (1967)
Blandsfort			70′ × 7′ 6″ (1968)
Inveraray (Lime Kilns)		65′ × 7′ 8″ (1956)	72′ × 8′ 6″ (1969)
Trentham Park			70′ × 6′ 5″ (1968)
Abbeyleix			53′ × 7′ 6″ (1968)
Borde Hill	1907	46′ × 4′ 1″ (1931)	84′ × 8′ 3″ (1968)
Westonbirt	1910	25′ × 2′ 0″ (1926)	88′ × 6′ 0″ (1971)
Westonbirt	1925		42′ × 5′ 1″ (1967)
Wakehurst Place	1912	25′ × 1′ 10″ (1931)	57′ × 6′ 0″ (1971)
Dawyck	1919	7′ 9″ (1930)	55′ × 5′ 4″ (1966)
Blackmoor (road)			62′ × 6′ 3″ (1969)
Glasnevin		58′ × 7′ 0″ (1931)	75′ × 9′ 2″ (1966)
Kilmacurragh			54′ × 6′ 0″ (1966)
Birr Castle	1933		42′ × 4′ 2″ (1966)
Nuneham Court		47′ × 4′ 8″ (1931)	69′ × 6′ 5″ (1970)
Bicton			60′ × 5′ 4½″ (1968)

green-white bands above; and a large patch of white at the tip; lateral leaves have the patch at the tip tapering down the mid-line to about half way. Both have two very white bands beneath.

Cone. Often numerous but restricted entirely to branches around the apex; cylindric, 15×5 cm with short abrupt beak at apex; smooth, whitish-green tinged lilac.

Growth. A very sturdy species with a period from about tenth to fiftieth years of steady growth in height, to 2 feet annually, and very rapid increase in girth. Remarkably healthy, luxuriant tree in most areas; probably the most resistant of the genus to polluted air.

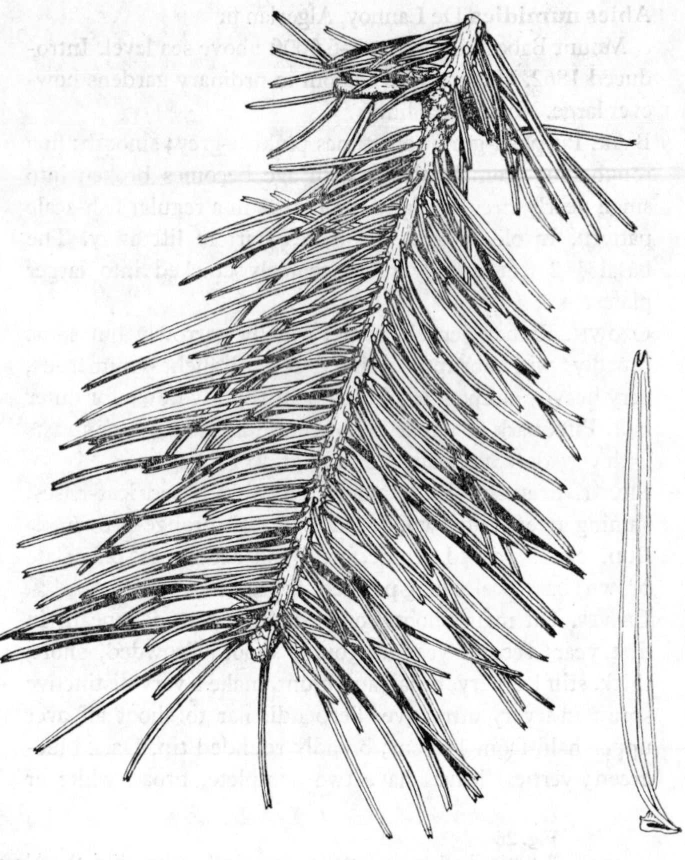

Fig. 27
A typically stout shoot of *Abies pindrow* with long, hard leaves arching forwards and downwards. A leaf (×1⅓) showing the large size, notched tip and the stomatal bands, which are usually pale green, on the underside.

Abies pindrow

Abies pindrow (Royle) Spach. West Himalayan fir

Afghanistan to Nepal at 5–7,000ft above sea level. Introduced 1837. Rare; most trees are in the larger collections, but a few are found in unexpected places.

Bark. Dark grey, rough with a few paler smooth areas; shallowly fissured into irregular broad, flat ridges.

Crown. Usually narrowly columnar with a domed top; upper branches become rather heavy with age, and crown may open out; some fork several times and are broad and irregular.

Shoot. Stout, smooth, glabrous ashen-pink or fawn. Second year pale grey.

Bud. Globular, to 8 mm or more on vigorous young shoots; dark red base, pale green-brown centre, covered thickly with white resin, or only slightly resinous.

Foliage. Leaves sparse over the top of the shoot, slightly parted, pointing forward, inner lines more so; at side of shoot less sparse, arching over, many below shoot, down-curved, pointing forward; 5–7 cm. Dark, shiny green, slender, parallel-sided to abrupt pale yellowish point of two minute spines. Two thin greenish white bands beneath.

Cones. Rarely produced in this country. 12×6 cm ovoid-cylindric, smooth, rounded scales slate-blue with grey margin.

Growth. Early growth is very subject to damage from late frosts, and the species needs high shade to be established quickly. The south and east of England do not suit it; few exceed 40 years in age and crowns remain thin and poor. In the north west and in the far north east of Scotland the tree flourishes. By far the finest is at Castle Leod, north of Dingwall. It would seem to require a high rainfall or a cool summer with the latter the more important.

Specimens. The tree at Castle Leod is quite outstanding, being very much larger in both dimensions than any other. It forks at 40 feet, but retains a shapely crown and extremely rich, healthy foliage. Original trees survive at Dropmore, (just alive), Smeaton Hepburn, and probably at Monk Coniston.

TABLE 14. NOTEWORTHY TREES OF ABIES PINDROW

Locality	Date Planted	Dimensions	
Dropmore	1844	48′ × 3′ 10″ (1905)	83′ × 5′ 11″ (1958)[1]
Smeaton House	1844	56′ × 4′ 1″ (1908)	82′ × 5′ 8″ (1966)
Castle Kennedy	1856	72′ × 5′ 0″ (1931)	89′ × 6′ 5″ (1967)
Castle Kennedy			85′ × 5′ 0″ (1967)
Hewell Grange	1861	78′ × 6′ 4″ (1931)	85′ × 7′ 5″ (1963)[3]
Monk Coniston		69′ × 4′ 9″ (1906)	93′ × 9′ 10″ (1971)
Leighton Hall (Died 1970)		50′ (1908)	105′ × 10′ 3″ (1968)
Tregrehan		40′ × 5′ 0″ (1931)	100′ × 8′ 6″ (1971)
Castle Leod			117′ × 13′ 3″ (1966)
Whittingehame		76′ × 7′ 10″ (1931)	88′ × 9′ 0″ (1956)
Inchmarlo			84′ × 11′ 7″ (1956)[2]
Aldourie Castle			90′ × 8′ 5″ (1956)
Wansfell			73′ × 7′ 6″ (1957)
Eastnor Castle			90′ × 6′ 0″ (1969)
Kilmacurragh			93′ × 10′ 6″ (1966)
Borde Hill	1908	46′ × 3′ 1″ (1931)	68′ × 4′ 6″ (1961)
Fenagh House	1916	8′ (1931)	43′ × 3′ 7″ (1968)
Fenagh House	1918		40′ × 2′ 1″ (1968)
Hergest Croft	1918		57′ × 5′ 1″ (1961)
Fota			82′ × 4′ 4″ (1966)
Headfort	1931		40′ × 2′ 8″ (1966)
Castlewellan (KW 1040)			39′ × 4′ 1″ (1970)

1 Died in 1970
2 Forks at 5ft 6in; ×7ft 6in+6ft 10in
3 Died back to 65ft

var. brevifolia Dallimore and Jackson. (*Abies gamblei* Hickel).

Very rare. Shoot stout, shiny, glabrous pale pinkish fawn. Second year darker. Bud blunt, ovoid, dark red-brown with white resin. Leaves all round the shoot, spreading perpendicular to it, slightly forward, 2 cm long, shiny above, shiny but paler below; abruptly pointed with or without short spine. Pencarrow, planted 1905, 65ft×2ft 10in (1957), (not seen 1970); Durris House, 49ft×5ft 6in (1970); Castle Milk, 45ft×2ft 10in (1966); Jermyns House, 15ft (1970).

var. intermedia Henry. Intermediate between *A. pindrow* and *A. spectabilis*; stout shoot pale pinkish-brown, grooved, hairs in grooves on underside; buds large, squat, conic, resinous pale brown, bumpy 5–10 mm. Leaves 4 cm, spread slightly forward each side leaving a "V", tips curved outwards ending in two widely separated spines; shiny, yellowish green above, bands beneath greenish-white, rarely bright.

Abies pinsapo Boissier. Spanish fir; Hedgehog fir. Sierra de Ronda, Southern Spain in three small groves widely scattered. Introduced in 1839. Frequent all over the country in larger gardens, parks and churchyards.

BARK. Young trees; dark grey, roughly freckled, becoming irregularly fissured into plates which lift away at the edges. Oldest trees often more smooth, black, dark grey-black or purplish-black, finely roughened, especially around branch scars surrounded by folds.

CROWN. Young trees rather regular, narrow-conic, older trees usually irregular, asymmetrical, leaning at the top, dense, twiggy with much dead wood. Oldest trees nearly always with dead, flat fans of dense, slender twigs, spraying out from the top. Fairly old, large trees are regularly columnar.

BUD. Ovoid-conic, greenish to purple-brown, very resinous, 3–5 mm.

SHOOT. Greenish-brown to orange-brown, glabrous; second year dark orange.

LEAVES. All round shoot, perpendicularly from broad sucker-like bases, those below especially bend backwards; 1–1·8 cm leathery, stiff, broad, bluntly rounded; dull grey-green or blue-grey with two broad bands of grey green or dull bluish white on each side. Older leaves dull grey-green.

FLOWERS AND CONE. Male flowers abundant, big, about 6 mm, globular, crowded along underside of shoot, dark brown, opening bright cherry-red in May. Female confined to upper branches. Cone, cylindric, abruptly narrowed to apex, 10–15 cm purplish-brown.

GROWTH. Rather slow in height and, except for occasional trees, in girth; height-growth ceasing fairly early and growth in girth reducing to remarkably little in old trees. One which died at Pampisford in 1969 had added only 4 inches to its girth since 1909; one inch since 1931.

Specimens. The finest tree seen is at Lydhurst, which despite its large size is of regular broad-columnar form and a single stem to 60 feet. A remarkable tree with a long clean bole is that at The Frythe. The trees at Dropmore are original trees.

Table 15 gives only trees which may be measured at 5 feet, or forked trees with one stem much the larger. There are many big trees which are multiple stems from near the ground. A few of the biggest are in Table 16.

Table 15. Specimens of Abies pinsapo

Locality	*Date Planted*		*Dimensions*
Dropmore	1843		80′ × 7′ 1″ (1970)
Dropmore	1843		75′ × 6′ 11″ (1961)
Longleat		65′ × 7′ 9″ (1906)	83′ × 10′ 3″ (1971)
Lydhurst			78′ × 11′ 11″ (1971)
The Frythe			110′ × 10′ 1″ (1969)
Keir House	1851	45′ × 8′ (1931)	65′ × 9′ 2″ (1970)
Clonmannon			80′ × 11′ 9″ (1968)
Poltimore			89′ × 10′ 0″ (1964)
Rhinefield Drive	1861	80′ × 5′ 2″ (1931)	95′ × 6′ 7″ (1970)
Rhinefield Drive	1861		98′ × 5′ 8″ (1971)[1]
Bodnant	1876	71′ × 8′ 0″ (1931)	95′ × 9′ 5″ (1966)
Eridge Castle	1886		82′ × 6′ 2″ (1971)
Madresfield Court		40′ × 7′ 10″ (1931)	45′ × 8′ 5″ (1964)
Warnham Court		62′ × 5′ 3″ (1931)	76′ × 6′ 2″ (1955)
Borde Hill	1890	51′ × 3′ 5″ (1931)	80′ × 4′ 7″ (1957)
Borde Hill	1890		75′ × 4′ 3″ (1961)
Fenagh House	1896		65′ × 5′ 11″ (1968)
Patshull House		64′ × 5′ 10″ (1931)	75′ × 6′ 10″ (1970)
Garnons			80′ × 8′ 8″ (1969)[2]
Powerscourt			92′ × 8′ 6″ (1966)[1]
Pitt House		72′ (1931)	85′ × 9′ 6″ (1960)[1]
Monk Hopton			80′ × 7′ 4″ (1962)
Wansfell			78′ × 7′ 9″ (1957)
Conon House			80′ × 6′ 11″ (1956)
Murthly Castle			73′ × 7′ 8″ (1970)
Leonardslee	c1905		82′ × 4′ 11″ (1969)
Wakehurst Place	1915	25′ × 2′ 4″ (1931)	57′ × 4′ 7″ (1964)

[1] Main stem
[2] Main stem broken out at 35ft

Table 16. Trees of Abies pinsapo with multiple stems

Locality	*Dimensions*
Minard Castle	57′ × 7′ 8″ (1969) + 5 more stems
Holme Park	60′ × 9′ 10″ at 2ft (1968)
Clonmannon	65′ × 19′ 9″ at 2ft (1968)

cv. Glauca. Trees differ in the blue-ness of foliage, bluish trees being frequent at one natural site near Grazalema. The bluest are perhaps distinguishable and the brightest are given below. The tree at Headfort has grown remarkably rapidly.

Specimens.

Vernon Holme	52ft × 4ft 7in	(1961)
The Hendre	65ft × 5ft 10in	(1962)
Headfort, planted 1914	60ft × 9ft 10in	(1966)

Abies procera Rehder. Noble fir (*A. nobilis* Lindley)

Washington, Oregon and North California. Introduced 1830, and 2 original trees known until 1968. Common in large gardens and some smaller; a few forest plantations in west and north; particularly frequent in policies of Scottish castles.

BARK. Silvery grey on many old trees, dark purple and grey on others; smooth but with a few big black fissures and many fine wandering cracks.

CROWN. Young trees sparsely whorled, very regularly conic, narrow when thriving, broader where not. Oldest trees broad-columnar, flat-topped, often with heavy, twisted dead branches at the top.

BUD. Hidden by surrounding small leaves, very small, 2 mm, pointed, dark purplish red-brown.

SHOOT. Largely occupied by sucker-like bases of leaves; dark orange with fine, dense pubescence; second year dark purple brown.

LEAVES. Strongly parted beneath shoot and curve upwards a little, then down to below shoot, perpendicular to shoot; upper leaves point forwards at base then curve up sharply to nearly vertical or slightly beyond. Upper leaves 1 cm, lower to 3·5 cm×0·1–0·2 cm, springy. Upper surface dark grey-green with two broad bands of scattered, white stomata on outer end tapering to nothing before reaching the base; underside with two rather narrow grey-white bands, becoming greenish-grey in second year. Flat; grooved, parallel sided to truncate, notched ends.

FLOWERS AND CONE. Males often very numerous beneath all shoots, crowded small globules, enlarging and rich purple-red before shedding pollen. Cones numerous every year, largely around the tops of the trees, but beginning early in life so may be on trees scarcely 20 feet tall; broad cylinders 15–25 cm, green with yellow exserted bracts strongly depressed.

GROWTH. This is not one of the most rapid growing *Abies*, but where well suited, mainly in Scotland, shoots of nearly 3 feet are seen. From about 80 feet upwards, growth is slow. Old trees are usually of less girth than equivalent trees of *Abies alba* or *A. grandis*, or *A. concolor* var. *lowiana*, but some have made very rapid increases in middle age and a few are still doing so, whereas most of the older trees are now adding very slowly to their girth. Exposure seems to limit growth in height severely in southern and eastern regions but much less so in areas of high rainfall like North Wales and Argyll. Height growth starts late, in early June and ceases before August.

cv. Glauca. Trees of *A. procera* differ considerably in the blue-grey tint of foliage. In some, an extra bright colour is derived from two broad bands of blue-white on the upper surface, coalescing at the tip. In the second year the lines break into four narrow ones or remain as two. Specimens are marked (1) in Table 17.

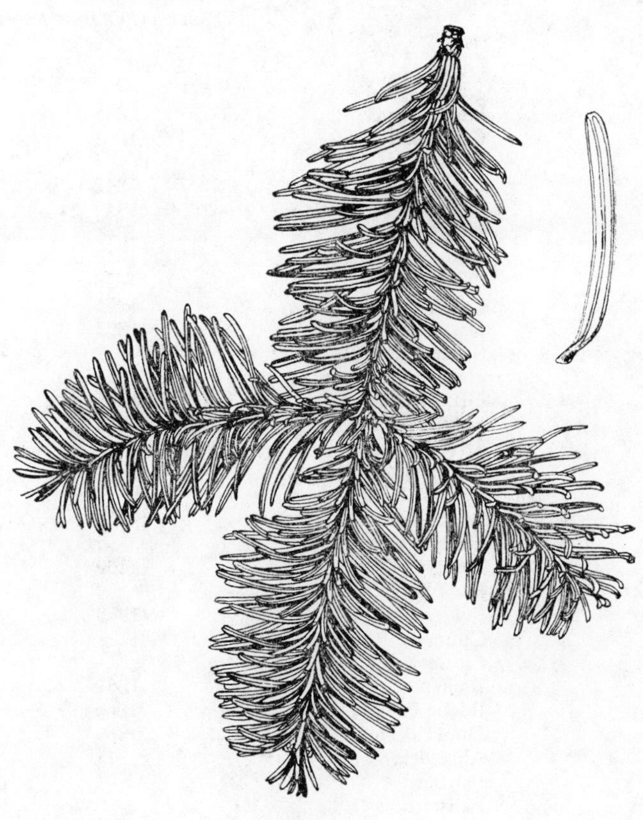

Abies procera

Fig. 28
Abies procera. Noble fir. A spray showing the leaves closely appressed, at their bases, to the shoot. The leaf (×1⅓) shows the underside where the stomata are in two bands. On the upper surface they are uniformly spread.

TABLE 17. OLDEST AND BEST TREES OF ABIES PROCERA

Locality	*Date Planted*	*Dimensions*	
Dropmore (1)	1835		85′ × 11′ 2″ (1961)[2]
Stourhead (1)	1841	100′ × 12′ 0″ (1931)	142′ × 14′ 5″ (1970)[1]
Upcott			115′ × 13′ 3″ (1970)
Pencarrow	1842	65′ × 9′ 4″ (1927)	80′ × 11′ 3″ (1970)
Whitfield (Northumb.)	c1840	18′ (1853)	115′ × 12′ 5″ (1958)
Linton Park	1844	90′ × 8′ 6″ (1902)	97′ × 11′ 5″ (1970)
Whittingehame	1846	94′ × 9′ 3″ (1931)	100′ × 11′ 1″ (1957)
Castle Milk	c1850	83′ × 10′ 5″ (1931)	80′ × 12′ 3″ (1966)[1]
Castle Kennedy	1851	80′ × 7′ 10″ (1904)	109′ × 12′ 8″ (1967)
Scone Palace	1852	84′ × 11′ 9″ (1931)	119′ × 14′ 1″ (1970)
Scone Palace			120′ × 13′ 11″ (1970)
Hewell Grange	1856	98′ × 10′ 6″ (1931)	103′ × 12′ 5″ (1963)
Glamis Castle	1856	103′ × 9′ 3″ (1931)	118′ × 13′ 1″ (1970)
Herriard Park	1858		100′ × 13′ 8″ (1961)
Strete Ralegh			105′ × 13′ 10″ (1970)
Ballindalloch	1860	94′ × 9′ 11″ (1907)	107′ × 13′ 4″ (1961)[1]
Durris House		69′ × 7′ 2″ (1904)	131′ × 14′ 0″ (1970)
Durris House		80′ × 7′ 9″ (1904)	134′ × 15′ 5″ (1970)
Eastnor Castle		95′ × 9′ 9″ (1931)	128′ × 13′ 8″ (1970)
Dupplin Castle (Garden)	1859	129′ × 9′ 9″ (1931)	134′ × 13′ 1″ (1970)
Dupplin Castle			131′ × 12′ 11″ (1970)
Bolderwood	1860		135′ × 13′ 10″ (1970)[3]
Cuffnells			118′ × 12′ 6″ (1970)
Castle Leod (1)			95′ × 15′ 3″ (1966)
Brahan	1861	89′ × 11′ 0″ (1931)	108′ × 13′ 10″ (1970)
Rossie Priory	1866		108′ × 13′ 1″ (1970)
Dunkeld House	1869		111′ × 11′ 6″ (1970)
Abbeyleix	1871	60′ × 9′ (1931)	85′ × 13′ 3″ (1968)
Fairburn			105′ × 16′ 11″ (1970)
Fairburn			136′ × 13′ 6″ (1970)
Raehills			98′ × 14′ 6″ (1970)
Kilkerran			128′ × 14′ 9″ (1970)
Melbury Park			118′ × 15′ 3″ (1971)
Inchmarlo			124′ × 14′ 2″ (1956)
Buchanan Castle			98′ × 14′ 6″ (1962)
Patshull Ho.		82′ × 8′ 4″ (1931)	85′ × 11′ 10″ (1970)
Dunans			127′ × 12′ 7″ (1969)
Woodhouse			131′ × 8′ 6″ (1970)[1]
Cortachy Castle	1872	112′ × 11′ 5″ (1931)	110′ × 15′ 11″ (1962)
Langholm	1872	69′ × 8′ 0″ (1931)	120′ × 10′ 2″ (1954)
Cowdray Park	1872	114′ × 7′ 8″ (1931)	132′ × 10′ 1″ (1967)
Blair Atholl (St. Brides)	1872	88′ × 11′ 6″ (1931)	105′ × 16′ 5″ (1970)
Blair Atholl (Drive)	1872	78′ × 11′ 0″ (1931)	92′ × 15′ 2″ (1970)
Taymouth Castle	ca.1872	76′ × 11′ 6″ (1931)	140′ × 15′ 6″ (1970)[1]
Taymouth Castle	ca.1872		131′ × 15′ 4″ (1970)
Taymouth Castle	ca.1872		147′ × 15′ 6″ (1970)
Blandsfort	1875	75′ × 9′ 6″ (1931)	95′ × 12′ 6″ (1968)
Kirkennan	1875	110′ × 7′ 8″ (1931)	135′ × 12′ 6″ (1970)
Inveraray (Dubh Loch)	1878		147′ × 11′ 3″ (1969)
Inveraray (Frews Bridge)			100′ × 14′ 0″ (1969)
Stourhead (2)			130′ × 12′ 3″ (1970)
Yester	1884		95′ × 12′ 0″ (1967)
Castle Milk (2)	1886	74′ × 10′ 3″ (1931)	100′ × 12′ 3″ (1966)
Westonbirt		95′ × 9′ 4″ (1931)	112′ × 11′ 0″ (1971)
Dropmore (2)	1906	45′ × 3′ 4″ (1931)	70′ × 6′ 2″ (1961)
Castle Leod (2)	1911		98′ × 10′ 0″ (1966)
Headfort	1914		55′ × 10′ 3″ (1966)[1]
Capenoch	1926		66′ × 7′ 1″ (1970)
Bedgebury	1926	10′ 6″ (1931)	78′ × 8′ 8″ (1967)

[1] var. *glauca*
[2] Died 1968
[3] Grafted on *A. alba* at ground level

Abies recurvata Masters.

Western Szechuan, China. Introduced 1910. Original trees in several collections. Confined to conifer collections.

BARK. Pink-brown or pale orange-brown covered in small (1 cm) papery flakes, often grey-centred and rolling off vertically.

CROWN. Narrowly conic; open with small, level branches and dark yellow-green foliage. Epicormic shoots frequent on bole.

BUD. Ovoid, light red-brown, without resin, scales forming bumps in the resin-covering.

SHOOT. Shiny, glabrous, light-brown above, reddish beneath, slightly ribbed, sometimes cracking. Second year fawn, breaking open on ribs, third year pale dull brown roughly cracked.

FOLIAGE. Leaves thick, hard, shiny yellowish green, grooved at base, strongly parted beneath, spreading perpendicular to shoot; upper leaves also perpendicular, rising from shoot slightly curved to nearly vertical or recurved, especially on second year shoots; leaving a narrow "V" between two ranks; very small "sucker" base; blunt and rounded at tip, hard but springy, deep glossy green both sides, pale green bands beneath. 2×0·2 cm.

CONES. Ovoid to obovoid, tapering to base, broadly domed, 6×3 cm deep blue-purple, tips of bracts exserted only 1–2 mm closely appressed vertically.

SPECIMENS. Tilgate, planted 1913, 66ft×3ft 4in (1961). Abbotswood, Forest of Dean, planted 1916, best tree 56ft×4ft 1in. These are from the original seed. Other trees: Borde Hill, 42ft×2ft 10in (1967). Wakehurst Place planted 1919 42ft×2ft 8in (1970) and 58ft×2ft 10in (1964). Edinburgh Royal Botanic Garden. 41ft×2ft 5in (1970). Westonbirt planted 1934, 39ft×2ft 7in (1967), Gordon Castle, 52ft×4ft 1in (1970). Tilgate Forest Lodge 40ft×3ft 0in (1961). Powerscourt, 42ft×4ft 11in (1966). Tibberton Court, planted 1920 (original seed), 35ft×2ft 3in (1967); Holkham, planted 1921, 49ft×3ft 4in (1968); Fenagh House, planted 1921, 50ft×2ft 1in (1968); Bicton, planted 1918, 60ft×4ft 0in (1968).

RECOGNITION. Only like *A. firma*, and bark is most constant difference. 2nd year leaves of *A. firma* also recurved but usually much longer. *A. recurvata* shoot very smooth and shiny, also differs.

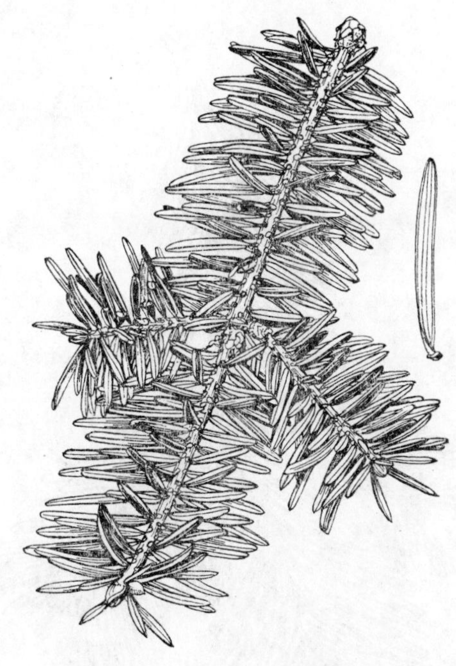

Abies recurvata

Fig. 29
Abies recurvata. The short, thick leaves have pale green stomatal bands beneath. Strongly recurved leaves, bending back above the shoot, are seen usually only on older wood.

Abies religiosa (Humboldt, Bonpland and Kunth) Schlechtendal and Chamisso. Sacred fir.

Central and Southern Mexico, Northern Guatemala. Introduced in 1838. Extremely rare; almost extinct before a large import of seed in 1962 from which young plants were sent to many collections in the south-west. Two big trees were recorded in 1931; one at Fota, County Cork was blown down soon after; one at Binsted, Ryde, could not be seen in 1968.

SHOOT. Shiny brown, partly yellow-brown, partly rich red-brown; minutely downy especially on the slight ribs.

BUD. Purple; thin white resin, blunt, broadly conic, often pale green in places.

LEAVES. Parted on top, all lying forward, side leaves slightly, upper leaves more so; lower leaves arch over and bend below shoot; to 3·5 cm; upper leaves curve outwards, inner ones straight, to 2 cm. All deeply grooved at base only—flat before mid-way. Broadest between ¼ and ½ length; tapering gradually, then abruptly to pale, yellowish fine point. Dark rather shiny green above; bands below variable in width and brightness; can be very white. (Young plants).

CONE. (10×5 cm conical, blue ripening brown; bracts long exserted, with long points reflexed—Dallimore and Jackson).

RECOGNITION. Foliage more like Douglas fir than is any other *Abies*, due to purple buds and arrangement. Groove failing before half way and outward curved tapering leaves on shiny brown shoot are diagnostic, but *A. vejari* (qv) differs only in minor ways.

GROWTH. Young plants are very vigorous and have a long season of growth. One in Surrey in its first year grew 22 inches largely between July and October. In west Devon, shoots 26 inches long were grown in the third year.

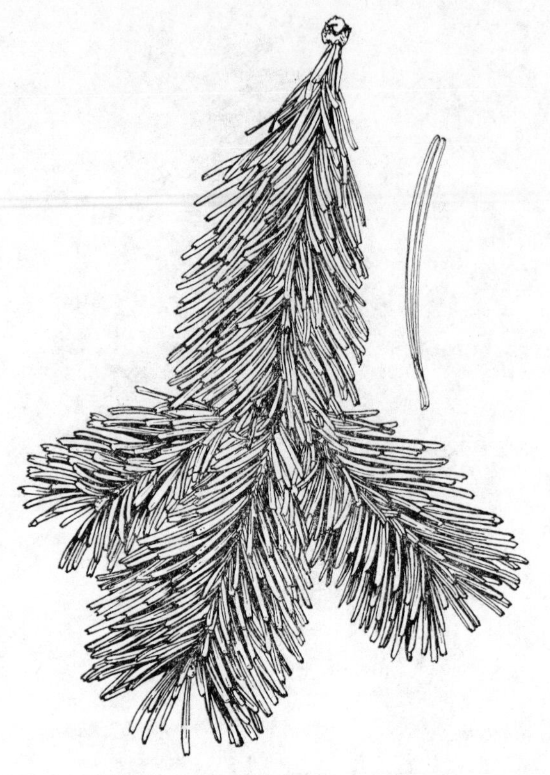

Abies sachalinensis

Fig. 30
Abies sachalinensis, Sakhalin fir. A spray of the very dense, bright green, narrow leaves, with one leaf (×1⅓) showing the moderately narrow white stomatal bands beneath.
This tree is sometimes grown as "*Abies sibirica*" in collections.

Abies sachalinensis Masters.

Kurile Islands, Sakhalin and Hokkaido. Introduced 1879. Rare. A few collections.

BARK. Blackish grey, smooth except for lines of rough lenticels.

CROWN. Fairly narrowly conic.

BUD. Dark shiny red, and purple-brown thickly encrusted with white resin, purplish in parts; whorled; side buds vertical beside terminal bud.

SHOOT. Shiny grey-brown, shallowly but plainly ribbed, a fine curly pubescence, of the same colour chiefly in the folds between the ribs. Second year (above) dark grey slightly purplish; pubescence now black.

FOLIAGE. Dense, all round main shoots, slightly parted above on weaker shoots where nearly pectinate below; all lying forward, except occasionally those by the buds along the shoot which may spread widely, those above the shoot stand upward and forwards, some showing their undersides, slender, straight parallel-sided to truncate notched tip with minute area of white stomata between 2 ovoid points; 3–3·5 cm long, 1 mm broad, grooved; underside with narrow grey-green or white bands; crushed foliage is sticky and smells of cedarwood-oil.

CONE. Cylindric, 6×4 cm, pinkish-purple, many scales; tips reflexed to perpendicular.

GROWTH. The few large trees have grown quite rapidly, but young plants are extremely slow to establish. This species flushes very early and is damaged by late frosts, but even on a slope near the sea in South West Devon, small plots after 5 years growth have no plants bigger than little dense bushes of 2–3 feet.

SPECIMENS. Duffryn House, ca. 75ft (1964 J. Harrison), Murthly Castle, planted 1897, 53ft×4ft 0in (1970); Castlewellan, 43ft×3ft 4in (1966); Hergest Croft, planted 1929, 41ft×3ft 5in (1963); Castle Milk, planted 1921, 50ft×4ft 6in (1966); Scone Palace, 38ft×1ft 4in (1970); Borde Hill, (Warren) 50ft×1ft 10in (1957).

var. nemorensis. (Japan, 1914.) Smaller cone. A specimen at Borde Hill, 48ft×2ft 3in (1970) differs in pale orange-brown shoot; leaves shorter 1.3–1.5cm with very white bands beneath.

RECOGNITION. Similar to and somewhat resembling *A. nephrolepis*, *A. sibirica* and *A. veitchii* but with paler green, very dense, more slender leaves not so brilliantly white below, and a smoothly rounded bole. See *A. nephrolepis* and *A. sibirica* for distinctions among these three.

Abies sibirica Ledebour. Siberian fir

North Russia and eastwards across mid-Siberia and south to Turkestan (now Turkmen) and China. Introduced in 1820. Very rare, probably not in cultivation. Some so labelled are *A. sachalinensis*, in fact. The description of the foliage is from fresh material from 10 trees in Finland, grown from seed collected at Kdirinsk, Siberia and is mainly points of difference from *A. sachalinensis*.

BUD. Clustered, forward; pale yellow-brown, usually joined by pearly resin-coat.

SHOOT. Smooth (not ribbed) pale, slightly shiny fawn or honey-coloured, evenly and densely covered in short, fine, white pubescence. Second year dull grey slightly cracking, black scattered pubescence.

FOLIAGE. Arising all round the shoot, hiding it from above, forward, slightly or strongly upswept each side but usually many below pointing forwards, upper leaves curved inwards, some laterals curved outwards, 1·5–2 cm long, 1 mm broad, fresh yellowish-green, sometimes dark by second year; stomata above (under lens) in broad ill-defined band from tip 2–10 mm down leaf; two narrow white bands below separated by broad pale midrib. From beneath the foliage is distinctively pale whitish yellow-green in general.

SPECIMENS. None found. Trees so labelled have been found to be *A. sachalinensis*.

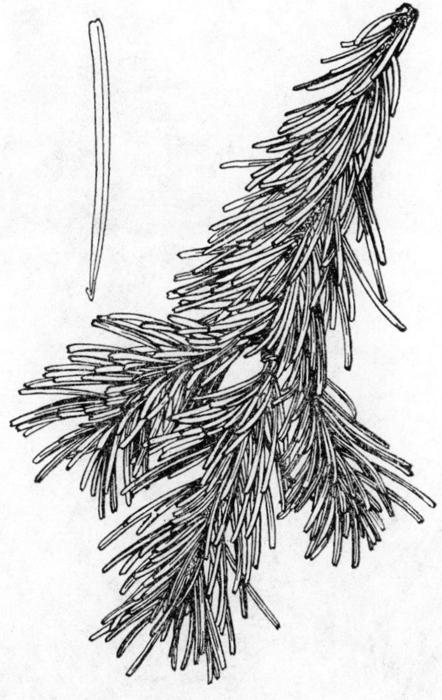

Fig. 31
Abies sibirica (from fresh foliage sent from Finland). The Siberian fir may not now be in cultivation. The shoot has a dense, fine, white pubescence and the leaves are more curved, less regular and whiter beneath than those of *A. sachalinensis*.

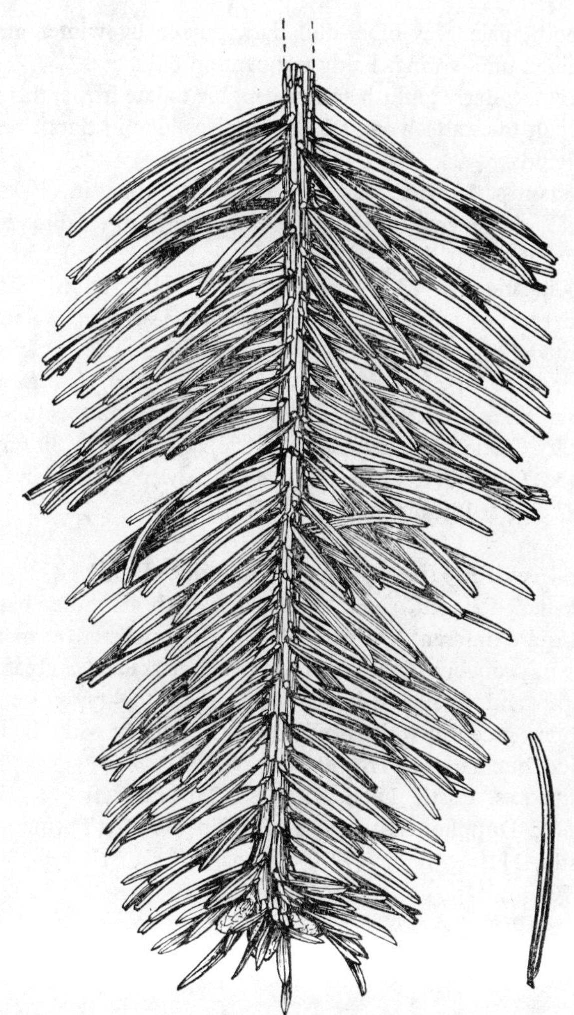

Fig. 32
Abies spectabilis. A typically stout shoot, which has pale pinkish-brown hairs in the furrows. The leaf (×1) can be 6 cm long and has brilliant white stomatal bands beneath.

Recognition. From *A. sachalinensis*, yellow-brown, pearly bud; smooth shoot, white pubescence, much shorter, curved leaves; denser above, more all round the shoot, narrower sprays, paler below. From *A. nephrolepis* pale bud; yellowish shoot, pale green curved leaf.

Abies spectabilis (D. Don) Spach. (*A. webbiana*) East Himalayan fir

Afghanistan to Bhutan, at 8,000–13,000ft above sea level 1–2,000ft above *A. pindrow* which, although so different in cultivation, is a very closely related species. Introduced 1822. Infrequent and mostly in collections in western areas, but also in North East Scotland

Bark. Distinctively rough, pink and grey; young trees pink-grey shredding finely. Old trees dull grey, rough, craggy, with brown or pink irregular deep fissures.

Crown. Broad-columnar, gaunt, with few, heavy level branches, upturned at ends. Soon flat-topped; old trees carrying some dead wood. Large epicormic shoots usual.

Shoot. Stout, grey or light brown, rarely orange-brown, glabrous except in the deep grooves which have red or orange hairs, sometimes very few. Second year pale yellow; third year pale brown.

Bud. Ovoid, large, 1 cm, thick with white resin, yellow-brown, scales protrude as bumps.

Foliage. On a large scale. Leaves dense, parallel, lying slightly forward in two ranks parted by a "V", inner leaves rising, all slightly curved inwards; deep green above tapering to blunt yellow tip, hard, 3–6 cm long. Two broad bright silvery white bands beneath. Outer leaves arched; inner curled downwards at tips.

Cone. Flat-topped, or domed, cylindrical, 12×7 cm,

smooth, pale grey-blue, dull dark purple by winter and retained until spring. Fairly frequent on old trees.
GROWTH. Early to flush and susceptible to late frosts, this is difficult to establish and seldom survives long in South east England.
SPECIMENS. Howick, planted 1841, 78ft × 10ft 1in (1958), Pencarrow, planted 1842, 83ft × 8ft 1in (1970), Fulmodestone, 65ft × 8ft 3in (1969), Keir House, planted 1850, 83ft × 8ft 0in and 64ft × 9ft 0in (1970), Little Hall, raised from Keir trees, planted 1911, 64ft × 5ft 10in (1961); Highclere, planted 1887, 78ft × 8ft 2in (1969, dying back), Westonbirt, planted 1918, 60ft × 5ft 3in (1967, new top), Inveraray (Lime Kilns) planted 1876, 88ft × 9ft 3in and 52ft × 6ft 3in (1969), Castle Kennedy, planted 1856, largest 85ft × 8ft 6in; Castle Leod, 87ft × 12ft 1in (1966); Powerscourt planted 1867, 92ft × 10ft 8in and 96ft × 8ft 7in (1966).

var. brevifolia (Henry) Rehder. Introduced 1879.

A dark-foliaged, short leaved form with smoother bark and quite different, narrowly conic, level-branched, shapely crown, probably slightly more hardy as it reaches a greater height and retains a better shape than the type. Leaf, 3–4 cm, greenish white bands beneath; narrow white band above; bud dark red-brown.
SPECIMENS. Castle Leod, 85ft × 8ft 2in and 84ft × 6ft 1in (1966); Dupplin Castle, 95ft × 8ft 0in (1970); Taymouth Castle, 111ft × 9ft 6in (1970); Stanage Park, 51ft × 3ft 3in (1970).

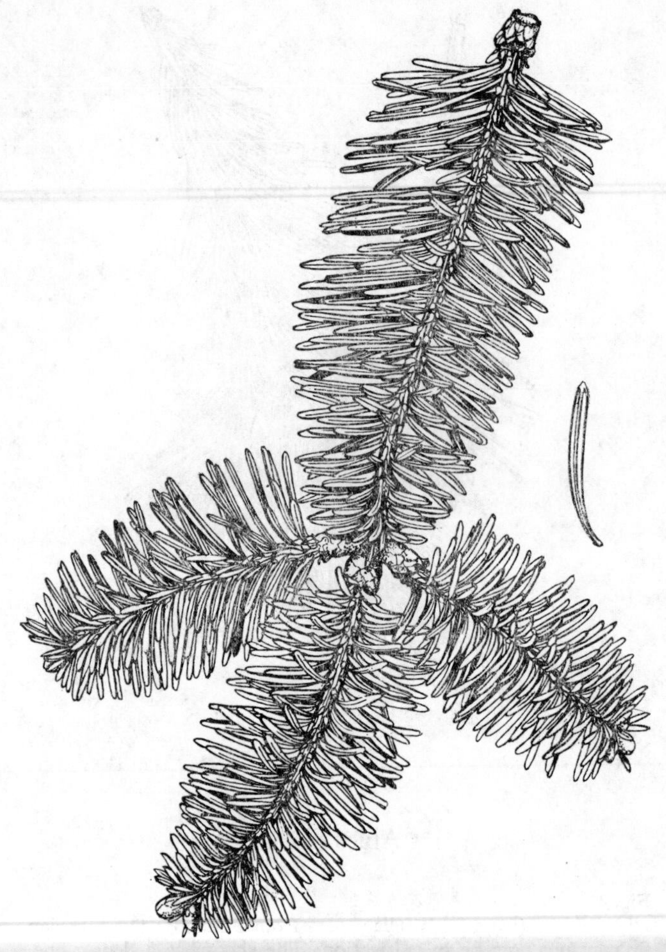

Abies squamata

Fig. 33
Abies squamata. Flaky fir. The densely set leaves are stiff; their upper surfaces well dusted with grey stomata. The taper of the spray towards the tip of each year's growth is typical.

Abies squamata Masters. Flaky fir

West Szechuan at 12,000–14,000 feet above sea level. Introduced 1910. Rare—large collections only.
BARK. Rich orange from distance; pink-brown at close quarters flaking with large papery rolls of orange, hanging especially under the branches.
CROWN. Conic, often rather broad, a few trees narrow; sturdy.
SHOOT. Purple-orange-brown smooth and glabrous.
BUD. Globular, covered in thick white resin; purple red beneath, ovoid, 6 mm.
FOLIAGE. Leaves almost pectinate below, densely standing above the shoot, hard, stiff, 1–1·5 cm on side-shoots; 1·5–2·5 cm on main shoots; perpendicular, parallel-sided to an abrupt, short, rounded point; dark grey-green above, many tips dusted in the centre with white stomata; beneath with two greyish bands. The leaves decrease in length towards the end of each year's growth.
CONES. Ovoid-cylindric, dark blue-purple, 6 × 3 cm, numerous bracts long exserted spreading or decurved.

GROWTH AND SPECIMENS. A slow-growing tree, so the earliest recorded plantings in 1920 and 1921 are probably from the original 1910 seed. These are at Bicton, 1920, which was 36ft × 2ft 3in in 1968, and Hergest Croft, where two trees, planted in 1921 were 44ft × 2ft 10in and 40ft × 2ft 5in by 1961. The most vigorous tree is in Ireland, planted in 1930 at Birr; by 1966 it was 37ft × 3ft 2in. At Dawyck a tree planted in 1931 was 27ft × 1ft 9in in 1966. Other trees are—Ripley Castle 34ft × 2ft 8in (1958); Borde Hill, the biggest of three was 19ft × 8in in 1957; Hillier's, Chandlers Ford, 27ft × 1ft 6in (1961); Durris, 41ft × 3ft 0in (1970) a very fine tree.

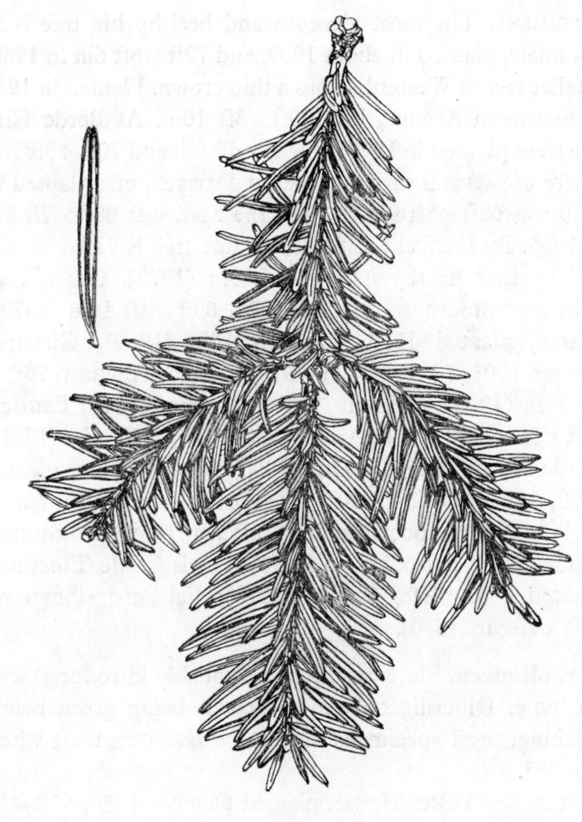

Abies sutchuenensis

Fig. 34
The rare *Abies sutchuenensis* is identified by the purple or mahogany-red shoot bearing glossy, deep green leaves.

Abies sutchuenensis (Franchet) Rehder and Wilson.

West Kansu, China. Introduced 1911. Rare—confined to the larger collections.

BARK. Pink-grey, rather oak-like, with shallow fissures and small plates.

CROWN. Conic, rather narrow when thriving.

SHOOT. Shiny, rich mahogany-red or purple-red, and (on the same tree) orange-brown.

BUD. Purplish red-brown, ovoid, the scales making lumps in the resin; 6 mm long.

LEAVES. Pectinate below, slightly forwards, parted above leaving a "V", less marked on main shoots; a few curving below; some bent sideways and forwards so they stand vertical with the underside to one side—on edge—; tips bent down; very dark green, shiny, grooved, notched; two bright white bands below, 1–2·5 cm.

CONE. 7×3·5 cm bluntly domed cylinder; small spines exserted.

Although this is closely connected with the *A. delavayi* group, it is a distinctive tree and a small-foliaged form of *A. fargesii.* The foliage is handsome, the very dark, glossy leaves set off by the purple shoot.

GROWTH AND SPECIMENS. Growth is very slow in the eastern half of the country, but in the west, and in Ireland there are some quite vigorous trees now making good leading shoots. The earliest planting seems to be in 1923 and these could be from the original seed. In 1926 Rock sent seed under his numbers which have turned out to be this species. Some trees from this seed are at Westonbirt (East of Broad Drive) and, were planted in 1932. The largest is 30ft×1ft 11in. The best trees are at: Dawyck, planted 1924, 44ft×3ft 7in (1966); Wakehurst Place, 44ft×3ft 6in (1970); Hergest Croft, planted 1923, 38ft×3ft 6in (1969); Birr Castle, planted 1933, 33ft×3ft 4in and 35ft×2ft 6in (1966); and Abbeyleix, three vigorous young trees, the largest 29ft×1ft 8in. One at Headfort has grown as a low bush, 8 feet tall and spreading widely. At Bedgebury the tree is most unhappy and after 44 years is only 18ft×1ft 4in.

Abies veitchii Lindley.

Central Japan. Introduced 1879. Grown in almost all collections and large gardens all over the country, but seems to be confined to these and not found in small gardens, churchyards or parks.

BARK. Dark grey or greenish grey; smooth; whitish patches on old trees. Bole deeply fluted; large pockets under each branch and ribs between—a reliable distinction from *Abies amabilis* and *Abies nephrolepis,* but less marked perhaps in var. *nikkoensis.*

CROWN. Conic, rather broad with upswept lower branches, but narrow in upper parts. Some trees have lower branches so upcurved at the ends that the silvery undersides of the leaves show from a distance.

SHOOT. Pale buff, pink-brown or grey, slightly ribbed, short brown curly pubescence on many trees; often glabrous on vigorous young growth. Second year shiny pale brown.

BUD. Small ovoid 2–3 mm, red-purple or brown-purple, shiny and smooth with resin.

LEAVES. Parted beneath, where lowest rank curves downwards, and all pointing forwards at about 45°; no parting above or narrow "V"; leaves forward covering shoot or standing nearly vertical (making a usually much narrower spray than in *A. amabilis*); sub-shiny, dusted faintly with white, crowded, 2·5–3 cm; broadest towards the tip and abruptly square-ended; notched; two brilliantly white bands beneath.

MALE FLOWERS. Visible from July as minute orange-red buds beneath shoot. Enlarge to globular, red-brown buds and shed pollen in June.

Female Flowers. Borne early in life, may be before the tree is 20 feet tall; near the apex; bright red, narrowly cyclindrical, about 5 cm tall.
Cone. Very cyclindrical, 7–8 cm purple-blue, ripening brown, flat topped with rounded spike in centre.
Growth. Among the fastest of all *Abies* in the first 5 years, this species will grow shoots of 2–2½ft two years after planting out. It remains of rapid height-growth for about 20 years, with shoots as long as 3 feet but then slows rapidly almost to a halt and soon after, usually dies. A very short-lived species. The two largest trees in 1957 were dead soon after and few planted before 1900 survive. An original tree at Eridge Castle, planted in 1881 died in 1957 when 68ft× 7ft 8in. Growth in girth is not great, and none much exceeding one inch increase per year has been noted except for that at Avondale which has averaged about two inches a year for 50 years. The best trees are in the north and west and in Ireland.

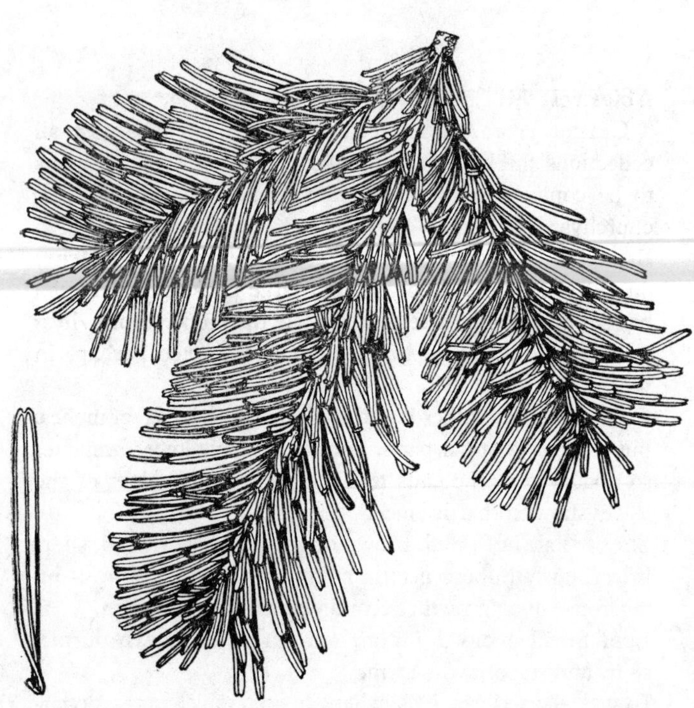

Fig. 35
Abies veitchii, Veitch's Silver fir. The branch-ends are often upswept and thus show the bright white stomatal bands on the underside of the leaf, as shown left (×1⅓).

Specimens. The most vigorous and healthy big tree is at Avondale, planted in about 1909, and 72ft×8ft 6in in 1968. A taller tree at Westonbirt has a thin crown. Planted in 1916 in Specimen Avenue, it is 79ft×3ft 10in. At Borde Hill, two trees planted in 1890 are 69ft×4ft 8in and 70ft×3ft 1in. There are several thriving trees at Dawyck, one planted in 1910 was 68ft×5ft 9in in 1970, the best, was 68ft×7ft 0in in 1966. By Dunkeld Cathedral, a fine tree is 71ft×7ft 5in and another nearby is 77ft×5ft 5in (1970). Other large trees are: Stourhead, planted 1924, 69ft×4ft 10in (1970); Crarae, planted 1919, 60ft×5ft 10in (1969); Glenapp, planted 1901, 74ft×6ft 0in (1970); Scone (Pinetum) 75ft× 6ft 10in (1970); Keir Ho, 73ft×5ft 10in (1970); Lanrick, 66ft×6ft 8in (1970); Arley Castle, 73ft×3ft 3in (1961); Castle Milk, 54ft×6ft 11in (1966); Castlewellan, planted 1898, 66ft×6ft 5in (1970); Headfort, planted 1914, 68ft× 7ft 9in (1966); Abbeyleix, 55ft×6ft 7in (1968). Blairquhan, planted 1909, 54ft×5ft 1in (1970); Powis Castle (Pinetum), planted 1932, 51ft×3ft 7in (1970); Fairburn (Pinetum), 84ft×7ft 5in (1970).

var. olivacea. Shirasawa. Japan. Probably introduced with the type. Differing only in the cones being green before ripening, most specimens have to be taken on trust where labelled.
Specimens. Yester House, planted October 1886, 55ft×5ft 6in (1966); Edinburgh Royal Botanic Garden, 30ft×2ft 11in (1970); Bedgebury planted 1925, 48ft×2ft 9in; 43ft×2ft 4in (1969).

Abies vejari Martinez.

Mexico. Introduced 1962 and plants sent to several estates in South West England in 1965 and planted in small trials, and at Bedgebury and Westonbirt. Shoot, greenish-brown or orange, glabrous smooth, shiny beneath especially.
Bud. Ovoid, 5 mm, deep purple-red covered in white resin, raised in bumps by the scales.
Leaves. Arise all round strong shoots and lie well forwards, 2·5–3·0 cm, slightly grooved tapering to a fine yellow point; upper side dark blue green with a central line of grey stomata, underside with two narrow blueish white bands. In lying forwards the upper leaves are not twisted over, so their white-banded under side becomes the upper side. This feature, together with the tapering leaves and pale orange shoots make a very distinct plant.
Growth. Young plants have shown good vigour, shoots of 12–15 inches being grown two years after planting out.
Recognition. This may be only a geographical form of *A. religiosa*. Young plants differ in their rather shorter leaves with stomata on the upper surface, and in the undersides of some leaves showing along the upper side of the shoot.

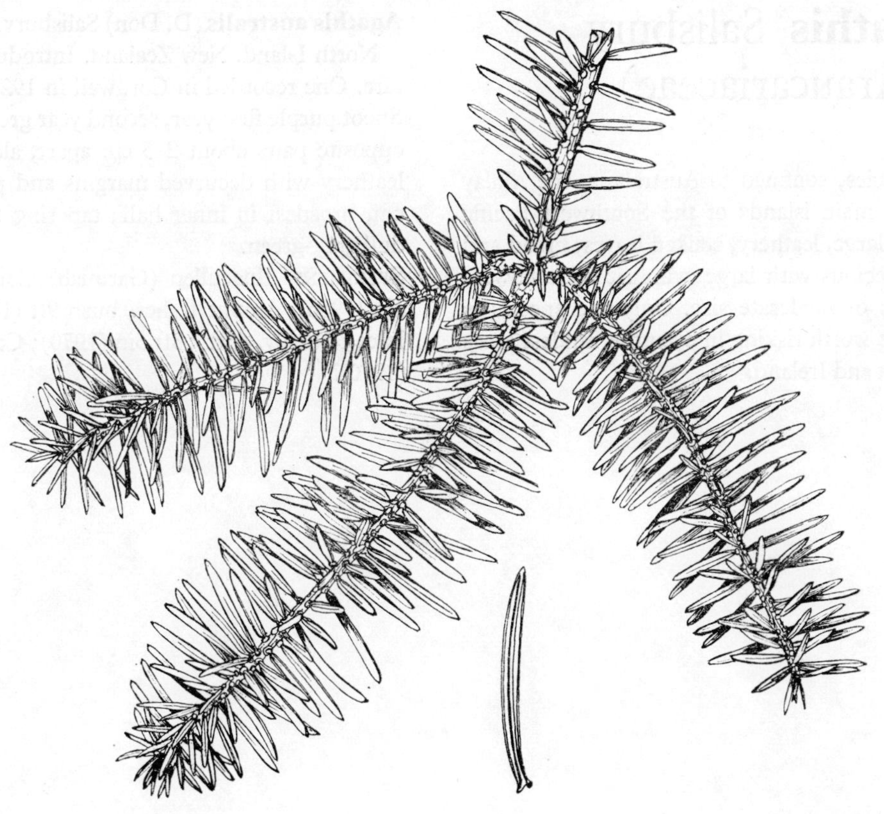

Abies x vilmoriniana

Fig. 36
***Abies* x *vilmoriniana*, a hybrid between *A. cephalonica* and *A. pinsapo*, occurred as a single seedling, and grafts of it are occasionally seen. The foliage is intermediate in most features between those of the parent species. The leaf (×1⅓) shows the two pale green bands beneath.**

Abies x vilmoriniana Masters.

A hybrid between *A. pinsapo* and *A. cephalonica*. A controlled pollination was made in 1867 and one plant resulted. This is propagated by grafting, but is found only in a few collections.

Bark. Dark grey-pink, flaking finely between coarse curving cracks.

Crown. Wide and open; irregularly placed heavy branches in lower crown; Upper branches level then arching downward.

Shoot. Green; second year bright orange-brown.

Bud. Small, pale brown, resinous.

Leaves. Spreading, mostly more or less vertically above shoot, a few straight below, all rather widely spaced (cf. *A. pinsapo*); rigid, thick with a thick rounded keel below, rounded at apex to a short very sharp point; narrowing at base to pale "suckers"; dark shiny green above, two pale green bands below; 2·5 cm.

Specimens. Westonbirt (Morley Ride), planted 1923, 14ft 6in×10in (1931) now 56ft×2ft 8in. Bedgebury, planted 1925, 52ft×5ft 8in mis-shapen at the top and no longer increasing in height but still increasing rapidly in girth: Hergest Croft, planted 1923, 35ft×2ft 7in (1969).

Recognition. Nearest to *A. cephalonica* var. *apollinis* but with distant leaves, not crowded, and bands beneath greenish not white; also small buds.

Agathis Salisbury (Araucariaceae)

A genus of 21 species, confined to Australasia, the Malay Peninsula and the main islands of the Southwest Pacific Ocean. They have large, leathery, stalked leaves, broad and flat, and are monoecious with large cylindric male flowers and globular cones of moderate size. Only one species is hardy enough to be worth risking in even the mildest areas of the far southwest and Ireland.

Agathis australis (D. Don) Salisbury. Kauri pine

North Island, New Zealand. Introduced 1823. Extremely rare. One recorded in Cornwall in 1927 but not seen since. Shoot purple first year, second year grey or white. Leaves in opposite pairs about 2·5 cm apart, along the shoot, thick, leathery with decurved margins and parallel veins 8×1·7 cm, broadest in inner half; tapering to a blunt point and dull grey-green.

SPECIMENS. Ilnacullen (Garinish) County Cork, 18ft×1ft 1in (1966); Mount Usher, bush 9ft (1966); Tresco Abbey, Isles of Scilly, 65ft×3ft 3in (1970); Casa di Sole, 15ft×9in (1970).

Araucaria Jussieu (Araucariaceae)

Fourteen species from the southern hemisphere, confined to South America, Australasia and a few of the larger islands immediately to the north. Symmetrical, tall or very tall, these trees have hard, sharp, overlapping scale-like leaves varying much in size. Usually dioecious, the female trees bear large to very large, globular cones. One species is completely hardy; two others survive in Cornwall as one tree, and several now grown indoors have been tried outside and failed.

Araucaria araucana. (Molina) K. Koch. Chile pine; Monkey-puzzle.

Chile and West Argentina. Introduced 1795. Very common all over these islands and thriving particularly near the western seaboard from Cornwall and Devon to Ayrshire, Kirkcudbrightshire, Argyll and Wester Ross. A few of the very large specimens are found further east from Sussex, Berkshire and Buckinghamshire to Perthshire and Inverness-shire, but away from the west most trees look less healthy and lose branches more readily.

BARK. Dark grey, smooth on young trees but partly hidden by adhering leaves until the bole is about 1 foot through. In old trees, bark is dull grey with vertical smooth wrinkles or cracked into small, rough, square plates.

CROWN. Variably broad-columnar with a smoothly domed top. In narrow trees the crown is dense; in broad trees it may be more open. Exceptional trees may be as broad as high, with long gently descending branches.

Very large and dense bunches of epicormic shoots may fill the middle of the crown.

FOLIAGE. Shoots bright green formed by plates at the bases of the leaves, each plate 1·5 cm wide, 1 cm long by third year.

BUD. Quite concealed by the leaves, which crowd closely at the tips of shoots, pointing forwards and decreasing in size towards the centre of the rosette.

LEAVES. Triangular, 3–4 cm long, 1 cm across at base, hard, dark yellow-green except newest which are bright green; finely marked with parallel lines of white stomata, margin yellow; terminal spine brown; lying forward then curving outwards to nearly vertical.

FLOWERS AND CONE. Male flowers on separate trees, indistinguishable other than by the flowers, from female trees, either by vigour or by shape of crown. In the avenue at Bicton, 19 of the old trees are male, 20 female and three have not been seen flowering. The mean height and mean girth of male and female trees are the same to within one foot in height and one inch in girth. The large tree at Nymans was bearing flowers of both sexes in 1931 but has been only male when seen in three different recent years. Male flowers drooping at the ends of most shoots in the

Araucaria araucana

Fig. 37
Araucaria araucana, Chile pine or Monkey-puzzle. A shoot showing the closely spaced, spine-tipped leaves.

upper crown, about 12 cm long, cylindric, tapering, round-ended, shedding pollen in June and remaining on the tree, dark brown until autumn, or the New Year.

Female flowers globular, on the upper side of upper branches; green; expanding during the third year to 20 cm × 15 cm dark green with long yellowish spines. They break up at the end of the year and shed some 200 large seed, 3 × 1 cm and highly fertile if a male tree be very near but otherwise small and empty.

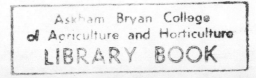

GROWTH. The whorls are not always annual whorls, as some trees have only one for each two years of growth, some have two for each three years and others do have one whorl per year. Growth often ceases in autumn without any terminal buds and restarts next season continuing the main axis. Trees are also often seen with growth stopped when a whorl is developing and the axis has grown on above it for 5–10 cm. Height growth begins late, in late June and stops by September. It is seldom more than 1 foot in a year and no old tree has a mean growth of as much as this, but of the few young trees of known date about half have slightly exceeded it. The first 5–10 years are spent reaching to above grass-height and it is only after that that shoots of about 15 inches occur. Growth in girth has often well exceeded 1 inch per year, and is still at about that rate in the best old trees, but in many others it has decreased to less than half of this.

SPECIMENS. The last known original tree (1796) died at Kew Royal Botanical Gardens in 1892; a reputed original is at Holker.

TABLE 18. OLDEST AND LARGEST TREES OF ARAUCARIA ARAUCANA

Locality	*Date Planted*	*Sex*	*Dimensions*	
Holker	? 1796			79′ × 11′ 0″ (1971)[1]
Duns	1830	♀	38′ × 5′ 3″ (1882)	× 9′ 8″ (1961)
Dropmore (1)	1830			64′ × 6′ 5″ (1961)
Dupplin Castle	1833			77′ × 10′ 4″ (1970)
Hafodunos	1836			59′ × 9′ 7″ (1960)
Cairnsmore	1837	♂		65′ × 11′ 0″ (1960)
Bicton (Garden)	1837			67′ × 9′ 11½″ (1968)
Keir House (1)	1838			45′ × 9′ 3″ (1970)
Highnam	1839	♂		66′ × 9′ 7″ (1970)[1]
Dropmore	1840			72′ × 10′ 5″ (1970)
Bury Hill	1841		68′ × 7′ 7″ (1931)	80′ × 9′ 1″ (1971)
Dropmore (2)	1843			75′ × 8′ 6″ (1970)[1]
Dropmore	1843			52′ × 7′ 8″ (1961)
Taymouth Castle	1843		63′ × 7′ 0″ (1931)	72′ × 9′ 1″ (1970)
Taymouth Castle		♂	× 8′ 1″ (1931)	79′ × 9′ 7″ (1970)
Bicton (Avenue)	1844	♂	71′ × 10′ 8″ (1931)	83′ × 12′ 3″ (1968)
Bicton (Avenue)	1844			85′ × 11′ 4½″ (1968)
Bicton (Avenue)	1844			83′ × 10′ 7½″ (1968)[1]
Keir House (2)	1845		57′ × 6′ 1″ (1931)	67′ × 8′ 2″ (1970)
Curraghmore	1846	♂	62′ × 7′ 10″ (1931)	63′ × 9′ 10″ (1968)
Endsleigh		♀		87′ × 11′ 11″ (1970)
Dunans			72′ × 9′ 10″ (1954)	78′ × 10′ 4″ (1969)
Whittingehame	1846		55′ × 7′ 6″ (1931)	60′ × 9′ 5″ (1955)
Fota	1847			57′ × 8′ 7″ (1966)
Sandling Park	1848			70′ × 7′ 11″ (1965)
Castle Kennedy	1849		50′ × 6′ 2″ (1904)	70′ × 9′ 4″ (1967)
Castle Kennedy	1849		67′ × 7′ 6″ (1931)	74′ × 8′ 4″ (1967)
Watcombe	1850			75′ × 9′ 0″ (1970)
Oxenfoord	1851		64′ × 6′ 2″ (1931)	72′ × 8′ 6″ (1967)[2]
Dunkeld House	1851		58′ × 5′ 0″ (1904)	74′ × 6′ 4″ (1970)
Scorrier House	1853		69′ × 7′ 5″ (1928)	83′ × 10′ 5″ (1965)
Inveraray Castle	1856		65′ × 7′ 6″ (1931)	75′ × 9′ 6″ (1969)
Blairquhan	1856		70′ × 7′ 0″ (1931)	82′ × 8′ 9″ (1970)
Blairquhan	1856			74′ × 9′ 4″ (1970)
Blairquhan	1856	♀		59′ × 9′ 5″ (1970)
Coollattin	1856	♂	50′ × 8′ 0″ (1931)	68′ × 10′ 6″ (1968)
Coollattin		♀		66′ × 9′ 5″ (1968)
Nymans		♂	65′ × 8′ 3″ (1931)	79′ × 9′ 3″ (1970)
Bowood		♀	68′ × 8′ 0″ (1931)	80′ × 10′ 0″ (1968)[1]
Penjerrick			80′ × 8′ 0″ (1928)	65′ × 9′ 3″ (1965)
Trevarrick Hall		♀	× 8′ 0″ (1929)	77′ × 9′ 7″ (1965)
Trevarrick Hall		♂	× 7′ 10″ (1929)	72′ × 9′ 3″ (1965)
Minard Castle		♂	54′ × 8′ 0″ (1931)	73′ × 9′ 10″ (1969)
Rossdhu			50′ × 7′ 3″ (1931)	65′ × 9′ 2″ (1969)
Glenapp	1871		31′ × 6′ 4″ (1931)	51′ × 8′ 2″ (1970)
Bedgebury (Dallimore Avenue)				64′ × 9′ 3″ (1970)
Bedgebury (Farm Road)				77′ × 8′ 3″ (1970)
Glasserton		♀		58′ × 9′ 5″ (1954)
Rossie Priory		♀	59′ × 5′ 11″ (1931)	71′ × 7′ 10″ (1970)
Lochnaw		♀		84′ × 9′ 2″ (1954)
Exbury				62′ × 9′ 2″ (1968)
Pencarrow				72′ × 9′ 1″ (1970)
Lexden Manor				76′ × 9′ 6″ (1952MG)
Coldrennick				66′ × 9′ 1″ (1970)
Melfort House				51′ × 9′ 11″ (1956)
Eggesford				78′ × 9′ 2″ (1970)
Newton St. Cyr		♀		70′ × 10′ 4″ (1967)[1]
Poltimore				60′ × 9′ 10″ (1964)
Killiow		♂		59′ × 10′ 6″ (1959)

Locality	*Date Planted*	*Sex*	*Dimensions*
Arlington Court			70′ × 9′ 3″ (1959)
Enys			67′ × 9′ 2″ (1962)
Sharpham		♀	75′ × 10′ 9″ (1965)[1]
Mamhead		♂	76′ × 8′ 11″ (1970)[1]
Scone Palace		♂	74′ × 8′ 11″ (1970)
Biel			73′ × 8′ 11″ (1967)[1]
Kilkerran		♀	53′ × 10′ 0″ (1970)
Windsor Great Park		♂	74′ × 10′ 0″ (1967)
Nuneham Court		♂	79′ × 9′ 1″ (1970)
Shelton Abbey			56′ × 10′ 1″ (1968)
Crowthorne			70′ × 9′ 10″ (1969)[1]
Old Castle, Wardour		♀	71′ × 8′ 10″ (1959)[1]
Tremough			83′ × 8′ 6″ (1962)
Powerscourt	1867	♂	63′ × 10′ 10″ (1966)
Hamwood		♂	70′ × 10′ 9″ (1968)
Inistioge		♀	80′ × 10′ 0″ (1966)
Inistioge			65′ × 10′ 1″ (1966)
Cortachy Castle	1872	♂	71′ × 8′ 5″ (1962)
Gask House		♀	72′ × 9′ 5″ (1962)
Tregothnan		♀	66′ × 10′ 2″ (1971)[1]
Auchinellan	1875		60′ × 9′ 5″ (1956)
Howick			81′ × 7′ 7″ (1958)
Sidbury Manor	1880		48′ × 7′ 10″ (1959)
Luscombe Castle			86′ × 9′ 1″ (1970)

1 Outstanding trees for fine boles
2 Thin and dying

Araucaria bidwillii Hooker.

Queensland. Introduced 1843. One tree known, another blew down in 1929 and a third recorded long ago at Mount Edgcumbe. The known tree is at Glendurgan and was 35ft × 3ft 5in in 1965. It has a more open crown and looser foliage than *A. araucana*, but the foliage could not be seen closely. The only other difference notable was the deep horizontal wrinkles in the grey bark.

Araucaria heterophylla (Salisbury) Franco.
(*A. excelsa* (Lambert) Brown.) Norfolk Island pine.

The only specimen growing out of doors seems to be one at Tresco Abbey in the Scilly Islands, estimated by Major Darrien Smith to be 100 feet tall, and measured as 7ft 3in in girth.

Athrotaxis Don
(Taxodiaceae)

Three closely related species confined to western Tasmania. Two are small trees and one quite large. The foliage is scale-like, close or spreading at the tips, or completely, and the cones are small, globular and woody. They are monoecious and generally hardy but two only marginally so in the coldest areas.

Athrotaxis

The three species are easily separable by their foliage:

cupressoides—terete scale-leaves.

laxifolia—leaves free only at incurved points; green all round.

selaginoides—leaves spreading, incurved, spined, blue-white bands on inner surface.

A. cupressoides has foliage resembling that of a species of *Cupressus*. *A. laxifolia* is more like *Sequoiadendron* and *A. selaginoides* resembles some species of *Juniperus*. All have shredding bark, which, especially in the last two, hangs in shaggy strips.

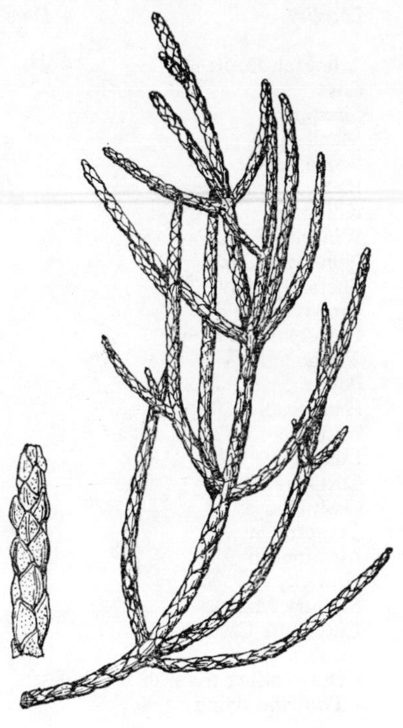

Athrotaxis cupressoides

Fig. 38
Athrotaxis cupressoides. Spray of branchlets in whorls of three. The leaves are fleshy, close-pressed scales. Detail of shoot ×2.

Athrotaxis cupressoides Don.

Western Tasmania. Introduced 1857. Rare. Found in only a few collections and growing well only in the far South West and in Ireland.

BARK. Brownish-grey, slightly shredding.

CROWN. Rather broadly columnar, domed; open especially in lower parts.

FOLIAGE. Distant branchlets in whorls of three, with only occasional further branchlets. Scale-leaves small, hard, slightly shiny, bright green, closely appressed to shoot, bluntly pointed.

CONES. Terminal on side-shoots, globular, 1×1 cm bright pale green turning orange.

GROWTH AND SPECIMENS. Growth is very slow in England, the few trees remeasured since 1931 having increased in height by 5 to 12 feet in 26–35 years. In Ireland, growth must be more rapid although there is only one dated tree and no earlier measurements to show this, but the size and health of some trees indicate it.

Only two specimens are known in Scotland; Edinburgh Royal Botanic Garden. 17ft×1ft 2in (1970) and Riccarton, 25ft×1ft 7in (1967). At Bedgebury the largest is 15 feet tall after 43 years growth. Two trees at Borde Hill were 18ft and 12ft in 1958. Others are: Tregrehan 28ft×2ft 6in (1957), Bicton 27ft×1ft 11in (1967); Leonardslee 20ft×1ft 0in (1960); Hergest Croft, 20ft×1ft 8in and 6ft (1961). In Ireland, the biggest are at Kilmacurragh; 45ft×5ft 2in+3ft 6in; and two of 36ft×4ft 7in (1966). One at Mount Usher is 19ft×1ft 3in (1966), one at Headfort, planted 1914 is 30ft×3ft 3in (1966) and one of 8ft on Garinish Island.

Athrotaxis laxifolia Hooker.

Western Mountains, Tasmania. Introduced in 1857. By far the most frequent of the three, and found in many collections and in a few large gardens, at least as far north and east as Ross-shire.

BARK. Coppery-brown, deeply fissured into shaggy, pale red-brown strips and coarse flakes, shredding and peeling.

CROWN. Ovoid-conic or broadly conic, moderately dense.

FOLIAGE. Branchlets rather sparse without further division or with single short further branchlets irregularly placed. New shoots are strikingly pale yellow or even bright yellow. Scale leaves 1–2 mm convex, ribbed, curving out then inwards, hard and acutely pointed.

CONES. Very freely borne, densely clustered singly on the ends of short shoots, bright yellow or pale, becoming brown and opening wide, when they are 2 cm across, ovoid.

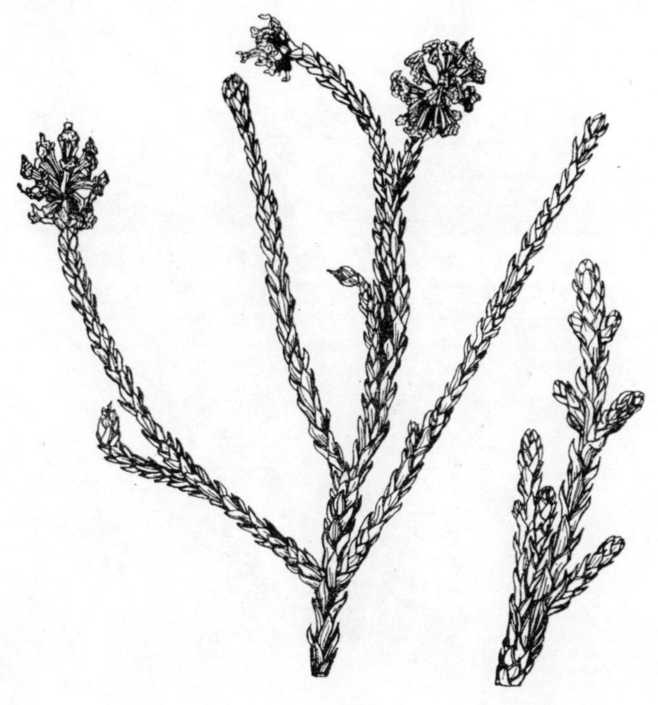

Fig. 39
Athrotaxis laxifolia. A spray with opened cones. The leaves are hard scales which are pale yellow when first grown. The cones are orange, ripening brownish-orange. Shoot-tip $\times 1\frac{1}{3}$.

Fig. 40
Athrotaxis selaginoides, King William pine. The foliage resembles that of *Cryptomeria japonica* but each leaf is brightly marked with white on the interior face. (right $\times$ 2).

GROWTH AND SPECIMENS. The oldest tree known, planted at Scorrier House in 1871, has been measured over two long intervals and shows steady growth: 38ft × 3ft 9in at 40 years; 45ft × 5ft at 57 years and 63ft × 7ft 6in after 94 years. Away from the far South West and Ireland growth is much slower and no large trees are known. The other large trees are: Tregrehan, 55ft × 2ft 11in and 41ft × 3ft 5in (1971), Trevarrick Hall 50ft × 4ft 4in (1965); Trewidden 45ft × 4ft 7in (1959); Lynhales (Hereford) 41ft × 5ft 1in at 4ft (1961); Garinish Island, 35ft × 4ft 4in (1966); Headfort, planted 1914, 35ft × 4ft 4in (1966); Kilmacurragh, 50ft × 5ft 11in + 4ft 11in (1966); Castlewellan, 41ft × 3ft 9in (1970).

Athrotaxis selaginoides Don. King William pine

Western Mountains, Tasmania. Introduced in 1857. Fairly rare, confined to collections and a few large gardens in southern England and in Ireland, the most northerly being noted at Bodnant, North Wales.

BARK. Dull red-brown with long strips shredding and peeling downwards.

CROWN. Rounded conic, uneven with a bunched top.

SHOOT. Visible, unlike in the two preceding species; smooth and bright apple-green.

LEAVES. Spirally arranged, stout, hard, convex above, acute to a short sharp point, pointing forwards and incurved, to 1·2 cm; rich shining green on outer surface; 2 broad white bands on inner surface.

CONES. Orange-brown, globular, to 2·5 cm across, in pairs.

GROWTH AND SPECIMENS. There are only a few specimens of known date and these have grown very slowly except for the one in Ireland. From the increase in the size of trees with their distance west it is evident that the further west the more rapid the growth. This is well shown in the dated trees: Bedgebury, planted 1925, 13ft; Sandling Park planted 1905, 18ft × 1ft 5in (1965); Wakehurst Place planted 1917, 31ft × 2ft 9in (1965); Headfort planted 1927, 32ft × 2ft 10in (1966). The largest trees are: Tregrehan, 51ft × 3ft 8in (1971); Lamellan 41ft × 3ft 0in (1963); Grayswood Hill, 36ft × 3ft 3in; Mount Usher, 49ft × 5ft 1in; 39ft × 4ft 5in (1966); Killerton, 44ft × 1ft 8in; Kilmacurragh, 48ft × 5ft 7in (1966); Nymans, 36ft × 1ft 7in (1970).

Austrocedrus Florin and Boutelje (Cupressaceae)

A single species from South America with scale-like leaves in two ranks of different sizes and very small cones.

Austrocedrus chilensis (D. Don) Florin and Boutelje. Chilean cedar

Chile and Argentina. Introduced in 1847. Rare; confined to collections mainly in the south and west.

BARK. Dark coppery grey, finely and closely grey-scaled; bole often slightly fluted.

CROWN. Very straight single bole (rarely forked) and small widely up-curved branches form a narrow, slightly rounded conic crown, dense above, becoming open below.

FOLIAGE. Short, flattened sprays clothed in overlapping scales in fours. The facial scales are very small and obtuse, the lateral scales are three times as long, acute with a very blunt, slightly incurved tip, deep green above usually with a narrow white band, and a broad white band below.

Flowers and Cones not seen in the British Isles.

GROWTH AND SPECIMENS. In 1907 a tree at Whiteways, Devon was 47ft × 5ft 6in and must have been an original tree, but it is no longer there. The only dated trees known were planted since 1925, but it is apparent that growth is everywhere slow but least slow in Sussex and Ireland. No specimens have been found in Cornwall and only two in Devon, although some of the best growth could have been expected there. Noteworthy trees are: Nymans, (Rough Ground) 50ft × 3ft 7in and 44ft × 3ft 1in (1970); Wakehurst Place, eight good trees; the best 44ft × 2ft 10in, 36ft × 2ft 6in, 36ft × 2ft 1in (1964) and 43ft × 2ft 11in (1971); Wisley Royal Horticultural Society Garden, 43ft × 2ft 11in + 2ft 10in (1970); Mount Usher, 38ft × 4ft 6in (1966); Birr Castle, planted 1933, 28ft × 2ft 6in (1966). In Scotland there are small trees at Blairquhan, Dawyck and Edinburgh Royal Botanic Garden (planted 1926, 21ft × 1ft 3in 1970).

RECOGNITION. The bark and neat foliage, very dark green, prettily marked white above and below, are distinctive.

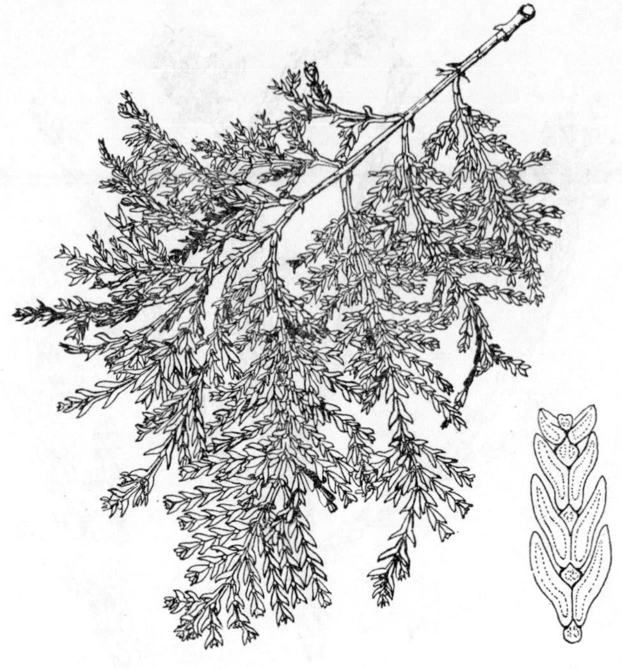

Austrocedrus chilensis

Fig. 41
The foliage of *Austrocedrus chilensis* is deep green with a broad white band on the underside of each leaf (inset × 2⅝) and a narrower white band on the upper surface of many leaves. The bark is copper-grey and finely flaking.

Callitris Ventenat (Cupressaceae)

Fourteen species from Australia and Tasmania, with minute scale-leaves in whorls of three.

Callitris oblonga Richard.

Tasmania. Introduced before 1893. Very rare indeed, in a few collections in South England and in Ireland.

A wiry bush with fine, bright green branchlets.

SHOOT. Pink-brown striped between green, 1 cm-long appressed scales. Long narrow slightly sinuous sprays; ultimate shoots at various angles with long bright green scale-leaves which have pale, thickened tips. These shoots arise all round longer shoots, spreading forwards.

CONE. Very dark purple and purple-brown with three big, smooth rounded, incurved scales and three smaller ones at the side, globular, 2 cm, very hard, in tightly pressed bunches of 12–15, the bunches roughly globular and 5 cm across. Not seen borne out of doors.

Garinish Island, 11 feet (1966).

Callitris rhomboidalis (Brown) ex Richard (*C. tasmanica* [Bentham] Baker & Smith.) Oyster Bay pine.

Two plants known—Tresco Abbey, 18ft × 5in (1970) and Casa di Sole, 12ft (1970).

Calocedrus Kurz (Cupressaceae)

Three species allied to *Thuja*, from North West America, South West China and Formosa. Tall growing monoecious trees with scale-like foliage in fanned sprays, the leaves in two ranks of equal length. The cones are small, leathery and vase-shaped. One is reliably hardy, one has very seldom been tried and succeeds in Ireland and South England, while the third has not been introduced.

Calocedrus decurrens (Torrey) Florin. Incense cedar. (*Libocedrus decurrens* Torrey).

Oregon to Lower California. Introduced in 1853. Quite common in England in large and smaller gardens, sometimes in boundaries by roads and has been planted as a road tree. Less frequent in Wales and Scotland where confined to policies; uncommon in Ireland.

BARK. Dark red-brown, broken from an early age into big vertical flakes or plates, whose ends curl far out from the bole.

CROWN. In England, especially in the eastern half, typically very narrowly columnar with parallel sides from within a few feet of the ground to the flat-domed top, or broadening slightly when forked, with two or three closely fused tops. Occasional trees in the east, broadly columnar, often through multiple low forking. In the west, broad columnar, especially in Ireland where none is really narrow and unforked trees have relatively wide and open crowns. Short branches, in the narrow trees, curve sharply upwards and divide into sprays of foliage within 3–4 feet of the bole. Foliage high in the crown often obscurely divided into deep horizontal layers about 5 feet thick. On thin soils or in exposure, tall trees typically lose their foliage below the top 3 feet or so, leaving a green tuft on a spray of bare twigs.

FOLIAGE. The shoot, clothed in scales, is soon red-brown. Sprays, nearly vertical are a rich deep green outside (or above) and slightly yellower beneath. Scale leaves long, fully appressed to the shoot except for their broadened, pointed tips. When crushed a strong scent of shoe-polish arises.

FLOWERS AND CONES. Male flowers are small (0·4 cm) ovoid and pale yellow, on some of the older trees, rather infrequent, visible from autumn until shedding pollen in May. Cones in some years seen in masses on the oldest trees only, rather patchily distributed over the crown, pale yellow-brown becoming red-brown when ripe. They are about 2·5 cm long, upright, and composed of two leathery, long scales with small out-turned processes at the tip.

GROWTH. A steady grower in height until about 80 feet tall (less in exposure) when height growth practically ceases. Young plants may grow 2 feet between June and early September but over many years the mean increment seldom much exceeds 1 foot a year. A selection of increments in height and girth over long periods is given in the Table 19.

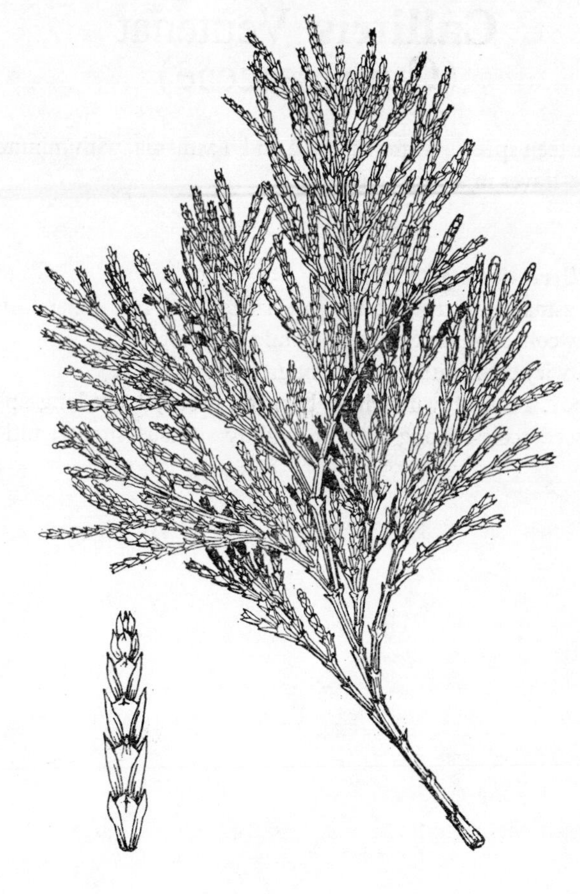

Calocedrus decurrens

Fig. 42
Spray of foliage of *Calocedrus decurrens*, Incense cedar, which is bright green above, and slightly yellower green beneath and highly aromatic. Shoot × 2½.

SPECIMENS. Several original trees are known and a few more are highly probable. The best known is that at Frogmore. One at Bicton was 88ft × 12ft 4in in 1957 but has since been blown down. Others are at Fota and Herriard Park, whilst the biggest at Eastnor Castle, Dropmore and some others are most likely from the first seed imported also. The largest trees known are given in Table 19.

NATURAL REGENERATION. This has been seen only in one place—a 2 foot seedling on the coping of a brick wall below a 77 foot specimen at Huntly Manor, Glos.

TABLE 19. LARGE TREES OF CALOCEDRUS DECURRENS

Locality	*Date Planted*	*Dimensions*		*Remarks*
Fota	1854		82′ × 12′ 3″ (1966)	At 2 feet
Frogmore	1857	65′ × 9′ 0″ (1904)	99′ × 15′ 6″ (1964)	At 6 inches
Herriard	1858		87′ × 8′ 2″ (1961)	
Keir House	1859	42′ × 4′ 10″ (1905)	70′ × 6′ 10″ (1970)	
Scone Palace	1860		93′ × 11′ 8″ (1970)	At 1 foot
Curraghmore	1861	62′ × 11′ 0″ (1931)	95′ × 15′ 11″ (1968)	At 3 feet
Eastnor Castle		53′ × 7′ 6″ (1906)	102′ × 17′ 10″ (1970)	At 6 inches
Fulmodestone		88′ × 5′ 11″ (1905)	102′ × 12′ 1″ (1969)	Good bole
Nuneham Court		58′ × 7′ 0″ (1908)	117′ × 10′ 9″ (1970)	
Nuneham Court		65′ × 10′ 0″ (1931)	109′ × 12′ 0″ (1970)	
Wilton House		78′ × 10′ 6″ (1931)	81′ × 12′ 10″ (1962)	
Stradbally House		53′ × 5′ 6″ (1907)	97′ × 12′ 7″ (1968)	Fine tree
Adare Manor		47′ × 7′ 9″ (1903)	70′ × 15′ 10″ (1968)	Fork at base
Abercairney	1864	60′ × 7′ 9″ (1931)	81′ × 10′ 5″ (1962)	
Pampisford	1865	67′ × 5′ 6″ (1931)	82′ × 7′ 7″ (1969)	Slender
Killerton		55′ × 5′ 5″ (1908)	104′ × 10′ 1″ (1970)	
Penrhyn Castle		60′ × 7′ 4″ (1931)	70′ × 10′ 3″ (1959)	
Doune House			115′ × 16′ 0″ (1970)	4 stems at 8ft.
Monk Hopton			90′ × 15′ 9″ (1970)	At 1 foot
Moor Park		88′ × 10′ 2″ (1954)	96′ × 10′ 11″ (1963)	
Dunorlan Park			76′ × 11′ 10″ (1954)	
Glenlee			93′ × 11′ 8″ (1970)	Double stem
Dropmore			96′ × 9′ 2″ (1970)	Dying back
Eggesford			88′ × 13′ 5″ (1957)	Fork 7 feet
Heckfield Place			90′ × 13′ 5″ (1969)	Fine bole
Lythe Hill			106′ × 12′ 2″ (1969)	Two tops
Tittenhurst Park			116′ × 11′ 5″ (1964)	Forked base
Tittenhurst Park			112′ × 15′ 0″ (1964)	Forked base
Scorrier House	1870	52′ × 8′ 8″ (1928)	66′ × 10′ 10″ (1965)	
Westonbirt (1)		74′ × 8′ 1″ (1931)	102′ × 11′ 0″ (1971)	
Hardwicke	1873	48′ × 4′ 5″ (1908)	99′ × 8′ 9″ (1953)	
Endsleigh			100′ × 12′ 0″ (1970)	Fork at 6 feet
Oakley Park			118′ × 10′ 6″ (1971)	
Broxwood Court			111′ × 10′ 2″ (1957)	
Broxwood Court			107′ × 10′ 2″ (1957)	
Arrow Mill			77′ × 12′ 8″ (1966)	Fork at 6 feet
Holme Lacey			93′ × 11′ 2″ (1962)	Bole 65 feet
Leonardslee		82′ × 8′ 6″ (1931)	80′ × 11′ 5″ (1969)	
Eridge Castle	1886		88′ × 9′ 10″ (1971)	At 1 foot
Highnam			99′ × 10′ 4″ (1970)	
Mells Park			88′ × 10′ 5″ (1963)	
Fenagh House	1901		52′ × 7′ 10″ (1968)	
Little Hall	1906	36′ × 3′ 10″ (1931)	56′ × 6′ 4″ (1951)	
Westonbirt	1910		77′ × 5′ 4″ (1966)	
Bedgebury	1929		56′ × 5′ 0″ (1970)	

cv. Aureovariegata. A very rare form, fortunately, with irregular large patches of bright yellow leaves. At Little Hall, the dated specimen has grown somewhat less vigorously than the type tree, and at Bedgebury very much slower. Little Hall, planted 1906, 49ft×4ft 3in. (1961); Dunloe Castle, 23ft×1ft 10in (1968); Bedgebury, planted 1926, 24ft×1ft 6in (1970).

Cedrus Link (Pinaceae)

Four species, very closely allied, from the Mediterranean and the Western Himalaya. Three grow to be very large trees, two of them in breadth of crown and the third in height. The fourth is a tree of moderate size. Leaves on new shoots are spirally set, while on older wood they arise in whorls on short spur-shoots. Male flowers are erect and pollinate (here) in the autumn; cones, usually on the same trees, are erect and barrel-shaped, taking 2–3 years to ripen and break up on the trees when they leave a long narrow spike and a stout, woody base-plate. All are quite hardy.

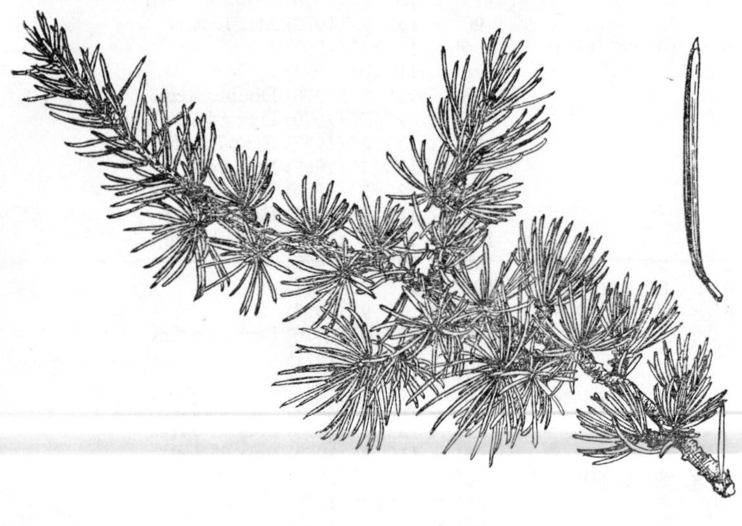

Cedrus atlantica v. glauca

Fig. 43
Spray of foliage of *Cedrus atlantica* var. *glauca*, the Blue Algerian cedar, showing spirally set leaves on the new shoot and leaves in whorls on spurs on older wood. Single leaf ×2.

Cedrus atlantica (Endlicher) Carriere. Atlas cedar; Algerian cedar. Algeria and Morocco. Introduced a few years before 1840. One original tree known and several very probable. Fairly common in large gardens, churchyards and parks, all over the country, but in recent plantings entirely replaced by cv. Glauca.

BARK. Young trees pale grey, smooth, with narrow, dark fissures vertically and fine horizontal cracks. Old trees dark grey fissured into short, narrow plates which flake brown and grey.

CROWN. Young trees broadly conic, very open crowned with few branches all ascending at about 45°, right to the tip. Old trees broadly or very broadly columnar but usually tapering to a conic top; usually single-stemmed to above half the total height, upper branches strongly ascending but lower branches level, their terminal shoots slightly ascending or level.

SHOOT. Grey-green with very short, dense, blackish curly pubescence. Second year dark grey with black pubescence in lines.

BUD. Ovoid, light red-brown, darkening to nearly black at the tips of the scales. 2–3 mm.

FOLIAGE. Leaves on new shoots 2·5 cm long; those on old wood in whorls of 30–45 each on short spurs; 1·5–2 cm long; both kinds very slender, dark green upper surface with 2–8 fine dotted white lines, undersides glossy, round-keeled with or without 2–8 fine white lines; tips with a translucent yellow-white to clear, spine (under lens). Foliage on the tree appears a dark blue-green.

FLOWERS AND CONE. Male flowers numerous on somewhat older trees; erect ovoid-conic about 2 cm; pale whitish green, apparent from about June, shedding pollen in mid-September when they lengthen to 5 cm+, turn brown, bend into a curve and are shed. Female flowers green, 1 cm globular, enlarge to pale green cones with a blue-grey tint, to 8×5 cm, barrel-shaped.

GROWTH AND SPECIMENS. A fast-growing tree, no doubt growing at the same rate as cv. Glauca, but with many fewer planting-dates of young trees to show it. Many mentioned by Elwes and Henry or in the Report of 1932 now seem to be cv. Glauca and if included here, will be found under that cultivar. The *Cedrus atlantica* with the biggest bole, which is probably an original tree, is at Corsham Court, 87ft×21ft 0in (1965). Another fine bole is at Stratfield Saye, 90ft×15ft 3in (1968). The biggest specimen all round is a probable original tree at Bowood, 132ft×18ft 10in (1968). Another not far from it is 112ft×16ft 1in (1968). An original tree at Westonbirt House, planted 1847 is 102ft×15ft 0in (1967) and a slightly later planting in the Arboretum (Jackson Avenue) includes one 100ft×15ft 0in (1971). Another original tree, planted 1846 at Hewell Grange is 95ft×12ft 2in (1963). Other large trees are: Eastnor Castle, 110ft×16ft 8in (1961); Madresfield Court, planted 1866, 86ft×13ft 4in (1964); Pitt House, 95ft×15ft 6in (1960); Gask House, 100ft×14ft 1in (1962); Kinfauns, 87ft×16ft 6in (1970). A very shapely, narrow tree is at Eridge, planted 1889, 90ft×9ft 9in (1971).

RECOGNITION. The distinctions between this and *C. libani* are not absolute, but include habit; angle of branch-ends; length of leaf; translucent spine on leaf; smaller cone and broad cavity on the top of the cone, and grey rather than red-brown bark. The one distinction that is quite invalid is the colour of the leaf; many undoubted (and pre 1840) *C. libani* having much bluer leaves than the type *C.*

atlantica. With several features taken together probably all trees can be distinguished and at present it seems that the translucent spine on the leaf-tip is most constant, but time of shedding pollen might be valuable.

cv. Aurea. The golden-leaved form may be found as a small tree, but all the larger trees seen have been *C. libani* cv. Aurea, except three at Little Hall, planted 1906; the largest 42ft × 2ft 7in in 1961, and one at Poltimore 47ft × 4ft 0in in 1964.

cv. Fastigiata. 1890 Nantes. Very rare. When young, a very narrowly columnar, acutely pointed tree with rather dense, nearly upright branching. With age the lower branches descend to some 50° from horizontal and the crown is relatively broader. The foliage is a light blue-grey so this form presumably arose from a tree of cv. Glauca. A striking tree which should have a valued place in formal planting and as a variation of colour among the green columnar trees.

SPECIMENS. Grayswood Hill, 70ft × 7ft 6in (1969); Highclere 61ft × 4ft 8in (1968); Chiltlee Place, 55ft × 4ft 2in (1961); Wishanger, 50ft × 1ft 6in (1963); Tower Court, 50ft × 3ft 3in (1965); Bedgebury, planted 1926, 52ft × 3ft 9in and 47ft × 3ft 5in (1969).

cv. Glauca. Introduced from a part of the native population, in 1845. Original tree at Eastnor Castle planted by Lord Somers who made the introduction. Now propagated largely by grafting from seedling stock trees selected for bright colour and probably the most widely planted of all ornamental conifers.

BARK. Very pale grey, finely fissured into small squares.

CROWN. Big trees tend to be more pointed and less liable to multiple stems than is the type, and are broadly conic for most of their lives so far.

LEAVES. The blue-white, (almost pink in some forms) arises from the increased number of stomata on the upper surface of the leaf. Under a lens, the difference is very small, but on many leaves the stomatal lines are brighter, a little broader and more numerous, but more important, they spread and join near the tip of some leaves.

GROWTH. The large plants so often used start very slowly,

TABLE 20. SPECIMENS OF CEDRUS ATLANTICA CULTIVAR GLAUCA

Locality	*Date Planted*	*Dimensions*	
Dropmore	1846		90′ × 13′ 5″ (1970)
Eastnor Castle	1847	80′ × 10′ 8″ (1931)	105′ × 13′ 9″ (1970)
Fota	1850	93′ × 10′ (1931)	108′ × 10′ 11″ (1966)
Scone Palace	1852	81′ × 8′ 6″ (1931)	100′ × 11′ 7″ (1970)
Kinnettles	1859	43′ × 5′ 2″ (1931)	92′ × 11′ 6″ (1970)
Hewell Grange	1861	83′ × 10′ (1931)	100′ × 11′ 8″ (1963)
Dupplin Castle	1861		108′ × 12′ 4″ (1970)
Bowood			92′ × 13′ 0″ (1968)
Patshull House		90′ × 10′ 7″ (1931)	105′ × 14′ 7″ (1970)
Poles		70′ × 11′ (1931)	75′ × 12′ 10″ (1969)
Woburn Abbey			82′ × 12′ 5″ (1970)
Westonbirt (1)		93′ × 9′ 0″ (1931)	105′ × 11′ 10″ (1970)
Madresfield Court	1866	80′ × 9′ 6″ (1931)	95′ × 13′ 4″ (1964)
Madresfield Court	1866	75′ × 9′ 2″ (1931)	81′ × 12′ 7″ (1964)
Stourhead	1871	71′ × 5′ 10″ (1931)	100′ × 8′ 11″ (1970)
Bodnant (1)	1876		110′ × 11′ 2″ (1966)
Forde Abbey			101′ × 13′ 7″ (1960)
Luscombe Castle			108′ × 12′ 3″ (1970)
Lydhurst			92′ × 14′ 10″ (1971)
Knightshayes Court			111′ × 12′ 11″ (1970)
Holme Lacey			82′ × 14′ 10″ (1962)
Cuffnells			113′ × 7′ 7″ (1970)
Adhurst St. Mary			83′ × 13′ 5″ (1964)
Woodhouse		97′ × 10′ 1″ (1931)	92′ × 12′ 2″ (1970)
Leaton Knolls		86′ × 11′ 1″ (1931)	95′ × 13′ 11″ (1970)
Tortworth Court		66′ × 10′ 7″ (1931)	72′ × 11′ 9″ (1964)
Nymans	1892	52′ × 6′ 9″ (1931)	92′ × 11′ 8″ (1970)
Fenagh House	1897		55′ × 7′ 6″ (1968)
Wilton House	1901		85′ × 10′ 11″ (1971)
Vernon Holme	1901	27′ × 1′ 5″ (1931)	57′ × 5′ 11″ (1961)
Bodnant (2)	1902		64′ × 7′ 10″ (1966)
Sandon Park	1902		50′ × 7′ 10″ (1969)
Easton Lodge	1903		58′ × 7′ 6″ (1956)
Hamwood	1904	53′ × 5′ 9″ (1931)	70′ × 9′ 3″ (1968)
Little Hall	1906	49′ × 4′ 9″ (1931)	67′ × 7′ 2″ (1961)
Westonbirt (2)	1909		78′ × 8′ 8″ (1966)
Castlewellan	1910		67′ × 6′ 1″ (1970)
Headfort	1912	29′ × 2′ 3″ (1931)	52′ × 5′ 6″ (1966)
Peamore	1923		55′ × 9′ 0″ (1966)
Bedgebury	1926		60′ × 5′ 3″ (1967)

but seedlings soon make shoots of $1\frac{1}{2}$–2ft. Once they are about 15–20 feet tall plants of either kind grow very rapidly, particularly in girth. See Table 20 on previous page.

SPECIMENS. Lord Somers' original tree at Eastnor Castle is still thriving. Another original survives, planted about 1846 at Dropmore.

cv. Glauca Pendula. The trees seen appear to be of this form which may be the same as cv. Pendula which arose in 1900. It is very difficult and slow to establish and one at Westonbirt, nine feet tall 37 years after planting, seems hardly to have grown. Well-grown trees are magnificent, their sinuous branches cascading down on one side and fanning out. They are probably the result of grafting high on a plant of the type. A fine tree in the rock-garden at Glasnevin, is about 7 feet tall. Others are at Little Hall, planted 1906, 45ft × 4ft 0in (1961) and two remarkable groups at Tittenhurst Park, the largest trees being 25ft × 3ft 9in and 24ft × 3ft 8in (1963).

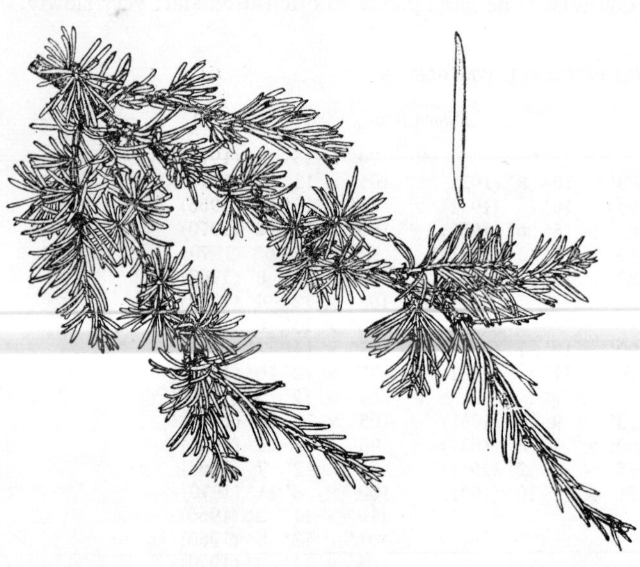

Cedrus brevifolia

Fig. 44
Foliage of *Cedrus brevifolia*, Cyprus cedar, which may be yellowish or deep green but the leaves (right × 2) are always shorter than those of *C. libani*.

Cedrus brevifolia (Hooker fil.) Henry. Cyprus cedar

Paphos Main Forest, Cyprus. Introduced in 1879. Rare, almost confined to collections, but young plants raised in about 1955 are more widespread.

BARK. Dark grey, sometimes purplish, smooth, with widely spaced deep, flat-bottomed blackish fissures, forming square plates.

CROWN. Rather narrowly conic, lower branches soon bearing dense level plate-like masses of deep green foliage, upper branches arching out; open.

SHOOT. Pale greenish-brown, finely pubescent; second year pale pinkish brown. Pulvini pale orange.

LEAVES. On new shoot curved outwards, to 1·5 cm near base of shoot, shorter farther out. Spur-leaves 1–1·2 cm, slender, rich green, occasionally blue-green or yellowish-green; with fine stomatal lines above.

CONE. 12 × 5 cm, tapered at base, lemon-shaped, apex protruded; smooth, pale green.

GROWTH AND SPECIMENS. Although often referred to and grown as a dwarf, this species is not even very slow-growing. Good plants will soon make shoots of 20 inches or more and older trees have usually grown on average a foot for each year of age. The largest is a fine tree in The Warren, Borde Hill. It was 10ft tall in 1931 and 56ft × 3ft 10in in 1968. At Bedgebury, two were 44ft × 2ft 9in and 39ft × 3ft 0in when 41 years planted. At Wakehurst Place the largest of three is 53ft × 4ft 4in (1970) when about 54 years old. One at Bicton is 52ft × 4ft 5in (1970). At Windsor Great Park, (Botany Bay) the larger of two was 44ft × 2ft 11in in 1969. At Edinburgh Royal Botanic Garden a 46-year old tree was 26ft × 2ft 6in.

RECOGNITION. The leaves are so much shorter than *C. libani* that they are distinct even from a very sickly, short-leafed tree and in that case the leaves are yellowish. *C. brevifolia* has a dark yellow-green or sea-green crown which is distinctive even though each leaf under a lens is seen to be bluish green, as are the brownish shoots.

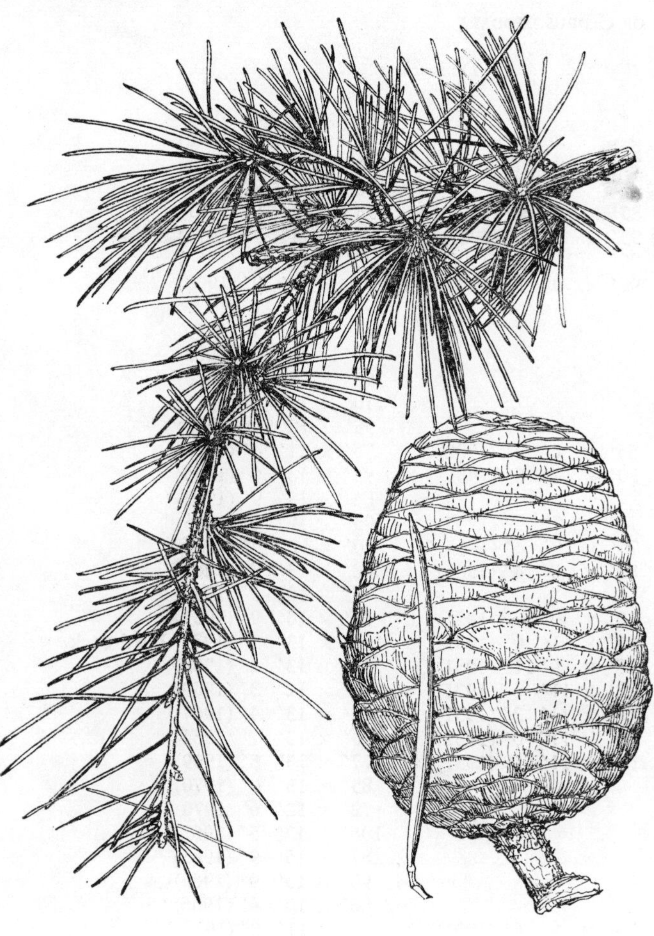

Fig. 45
Foliage and cone of *Cedrus deodara*, Deodar, with spirally set leaves on new shoot. Single leaf × 1⅓.

Cedrus deodara (Roxburgh) D. Don. Deodar

West Himalayas to Afghanistan. Introduced in 1831 and several original trees known. Common all over England and East Scotland in gardens of various sizes, including many small ones on the outskirts of towns; small parks in towns, churchyards, and graveyards, especially. In Wales, West Scotland and Ireland much less common; mainly confined to large gardens.

BARK. Smooth and dark grey on young tree, soon cracking. On old trees, a close pattern of wide, shallow fissures, black and pinkish grey, leaving short, pale grey ridges.

CROWN. Narrowly conic when young, with level branches drooping at the ends and a long narrow spire to a drooping leader; the foliage blue-grey. This colour is lost soon after the tree exceeds 20 feet, and becomes very dark green. Older trees broadly conic to a pointed tip with one or several drooping leaders, either with a single straight bole to the tip or, in open grown trees, more usually many stout branches turning vertically, close to or replacing the central bole. Branches ascending; particularly heavy, low branches on open grown trees.

SHOOT. Pale pinkish-fawn, densely pubescent; cracking open a little in winter to show dark green stripes; second year dull grey-brown, still pubescent.

BUD. Pointed, 1 mm, orange paling to whitish brown on the free tips of the scales.

LEAVES. Spirally arranged, to 5 cm × 0·1 cm on new shoots, curving outwards; on young trees blue-grey due to 4–6 bright stomatal lines on the upper surface. Leaves on spur-shoots, 3–3·5 cm, dark green, narrowing to a clear translucent spine-tip with many inconspicuous stomatal lines on both sides, broader on the underside.

FLOWERS AND CONES. Male flowers erect, 2–3 cm rounded-conic, pale green until lengthening to 8·5 cm to shed pollen in early November. These are found on most large trees but female flowers occur only on relatively few trees. Cones pale grey-green for two years, barrel-shaped 8–12 cm, ripening very dark brown.

GROWTH. Once established, early height-growth is rapid; leading shoots may be over 3 feet long, grown from early May or June until the end of September. This decreases gradually until the tree is about 70 feet tall and then usually sharply so that further growth is very slow. The fastest height-growth found is 70ft in about 50 years at Wakehurst Place, but few younger dated trees have been found. Older trees show their slow height-growth in that none of the 38 trees remeasured since 1931 has added 30 feet and few have added 20 feet, in the 25–38 year interval. Growth in girth can be very rapid but is usually moderate and falls sharply with age.

See Table 21 overleaf.

TABLE 21. FINEST TREES OF CEDRUS DEODARA

Locality	*Date Planted*	*Dimensions*	
Dropmore (1)	1832		80′ × 10′ 6″ (1961)
Dropmore	1832		85′ × 13′ 0″ (1970)
Dropmore	1839	77′ × 8′ 10″ (1905)	101′ × 10′ 10″ (1961)
Walcot Hall	1832		110′ × 12′ 8″ (1959)
Westonbirt House	1832	85′ × 8′ 9″ (1905)	93′ × 11′ 6″ (1967)
Bury Hill (1)	1834	95′ × 9′ 8″ (1931)	90′ × 11′ 1″ (1971) Dying
Bicton	ca.1835	80′ × 11′ 8″ (1902)	103′ × 18′ 2½″ (1968)
Bicton	ca.1835	90′ × 9′ 1″ (1902)	92′ × 13′ 0″ (1968)
Dropmore (2)	1840		90′ × 15′ 11″ (1970)
Powis Castle			95′ × 15′ 5″ (1970)
The Frythe			76′ × 15′ 2″ (1969)
Haffield House			105′ × 15′ 9″ (1966)
Whitfield			110′ × 14′ 4″ (1963)
Adare	1841		95′ × 10′ 0″ (1968)
Smeaton House	1841	55′ × 6′ 7″ (1902)	75′ × 11′ 4″ (1966)
Linton Park	1842	80′ × 11′ 6″ (1931)	95′ × 13′ 0″ (1965)
Linton Park			84′ × 13′ 9″ (1965)
Hamwood	1844	74′ × 7′ 6″ (1905)	95′ × 12′ 0″ (1968)
Highclere Park	1844	75′ × 8′ 4″ (1904)	90′ × 12′ 9″ (1968)
Chart Park		89′ × 8′ 4″ (1905)	80′ × 13′ 8″ (1967)
Dropmore (3)	1845		75′ × 10′ 9″ (1961)
Pencarrow	1845	80′ × 9′ (1927)	88′ × 10′ 9″ (1957)
Bury Hill (2)	1847	96′ × 11′ 0″ (1931)	105′ × 13′ 7″ (1971) Died back
Leondardslee		78′ × 9′ 11″ (1931)	100′ × 13′ 2″ (1968)
New Court		78′ × 11′ 6″ (1931)	70′ × 12′ 3″ (1969)
Tortworth		60′ × 11′ 3″ (1931)	82′ × 13′ 4″ (1964)[1]
Tortworth		90′ × 11′ 0″ (1931)	100′ × 13′ 7″ (1964)[1]
Poles		60′ × 11′ (1931)	77′ × 13′ 8″ (1969)
Woburn Abbey			85′ × 13′ 0″ (1970)
Fairburn			72′ × 12′ 6″ (1970)
Redleaf House			106′ × 13′ 5″ (1963)[1]
Fairlawne			87′ × 15′ 9″ (1965)
Fairlawne			90′ × 13′ 9″ (1965)[1]
Fota	1848		86′ × 10′ 4″ (1966)
Nymans	1850	74′ × 9′ 6″ (1931)	88′ × 11′ 8″ (1970)[2]
Sindlesham (Bear Wood)			62′ × 21′ 0″ (1970) At 6 inches[1]
Highnam			95′ × 12′ 9″ (1970)[1]
Herriard Park	1851		95′ × 11′ 10″ (1961)[3]
Blairquhan	1856	57′ × 9′ 5″ (1931)	79′ × 14′ 2″ (1970)[1]
Blairquhan	1856	47′ × 7′ (1931)	71′ × 10′ 10″ (1970)
Pampisford	1856	63′ × 6′ 3″ (1931)	70′ × 9′ 5″ (1969)
Inveraray Castle	1857		90′ × 11′ 8″ (1969)
Inveraray Castle	1857		75′ × 11′ 8″ (1969)
Taymouth Castle			108′ × 11′ 8″ (1970)
Eastnor Castle			88′ × 15′ 5″ (1970)
Eastnor Castle			115′ × 12′ 11″ (1970)
Eastnor Castle			107′ × 13′ 11″ (1969)
Broxwood Court	1859		99′ × 13′ 8″ (1957)
Tendring Hall			80′ × 13′ 4″ (1967)
Capenoch	1860		95′ × 9′ 3″ (1970)
Stourhead	1861	103′ × 9′ 8″ (1931)	80′ × 13′ 2″ (1965)
Stourhead			105′ × 14′ 5″ (1970)[1]
Bolderwood	1861		113′ × 10′ 3″ (1970)
Fulmodestone	1861	66′ × 7′ 4″ (1905)	73′ × 11′ 7″ (1969)
Ochtertyre	1863	64′ × 7′ 9″ (1931)	92′ × 12′ 7″ (1970)
Rossie Priory		80′ × 9′ (1931)	98′ × 10′ 9″ (1970)
Frogmore			95′ × 13′ 2″ (1967)
Errol			93′ × 11′ 5″ (1970)
Wyck Manor			100′ × 14′ 0″ (1965)
Pitt House			107′ × 13′ 10″ (1960)[1]
Pitt House		74′ × 8′ (1931)	91′ × 11′ 1″ (1960)
Mells Park			82′ × 13′ 6″ (1962)
Kilkerran			111′ × 8′ 8″ (1970)
Holme Lacey			91′ × 13′ 1″ (1962)
Mamhead			95′ × 13′ 4″ (1970)
Cricket St. Thomas			87′ × 13′ 3″ (1960)
Longleat			102′ × 12′ 5″ (1971)
Poltimore			88′ × 14′ 3″ (1964)

Locality	*Date Planted*	*Dimensions*	
Killerton (Chapel)			92′ × 13′ 0″ (1970)
Little Hall	1906	99′ × 3′ 9″ (1931)	65′ × 6′ 8″ (1961)
Bedgebury	1935		47′ × 5′ 9″ (1970)

1 (See text)
2 Main stem
3 Measured at 2 feet
4 Stout leaves in closed bunches

cv. Argentea. Possibly even more glaucous grey when young than the usual trees, and maintaining this colour. Batsford Park 35ft × 3ft 5in (1963). A tree at Wallington, 90ft × 8ft 3in in 1958 was remarkably glaucous.

cv. Pendula. A dense umbrella of rich green foliage, unable to grow appreciably in height so dependent for height upon the position of the graft. Hilliers Nurseries, Chandlers Ford, 30ft × 2ft 11in; "The Wellington Arms", Horsley, Surrey, 15ft × 3ft 0in (1968).

cv. Robusta. Open crowned, long branched; branches level, strongly decurved towards the tips. Leaves blue-green and very glaucous grey. Rare. In a few collections. Bedgebury, planted 1926, 44ft × 3ft 1in; 42ft × 3ft 7in (1970); Nymans, 74ft × 5ft 9in (1970); Castlewellan, 40ft × 4ft 9in (1970); Westonbirt, 52ft × 7ft 7in (1971). Many of the big trees listed in Table 21 have stout, long, deep olive-green leaves which remain in forward-pointing nearly-closed bunches rather than in opened-out whorls. They include the most vigorous trees, as at Blairquhan, Stourhead, Tortworth, Fairlawne, Redleaf and Pitt House. A similar tree at Sindlesham has a girth of 20ft 10in at 1 foot, and immense low branches. All these fit the description in Dallimore and Jackson—"leaves longer and stouter than is usual in the type"—but it is not 'Robusta'. One of the original trees at Dropmore is of this type, which, therefore, must occur in the natural population.

cv. Verticillata. A form with an untidy crown of level branches, upswept at the ends, bearing bunches of short shoots hanging from the branch-ends, very black and glaucous, mixed. The crowded short shoots bear whorled leaves 4–4·5 cm long, blackish blue-green banded blue-white. There are three big trees at the Frythe, Welwyn, the largest 60ft × 7ft 7in (1969). Others are: Wakehurst Place, 56ft × 4ft 2in (1970), Little Hall, planted 1906, 50ft × 4ft 3in (1963); Bedgebury 40ft × 2ft 11in and 39ft × 3ft 0in (1969).

GENERAL. The Deodar was tried as a forest tree by the Commissioners of Crown Lands in 1860. At Alice Holt, among oak, there were many losses and the best surviving trees are now 90ft × 9ft. At Bolderwood in the New Forest, it was planted mixed with Douglas fir and this outgrew it and suppressed many. Survivors stand in scattered groups and are shapely, to 105ft × 8ft, but have only a fraction of the volume of the Douglas firs.

The plot at Bedgebury has been very slow and difficult to establish.

As an ornamental tree the Deodar is valuable when young and growing vigorously, and when old and very big, but in the intermediate years it is not notable in any way and is often untidy with much dead twiggy wood in the crown. In a small garden there is thus a good case for growing several in rotation each to be cut when about 20 feet tall.

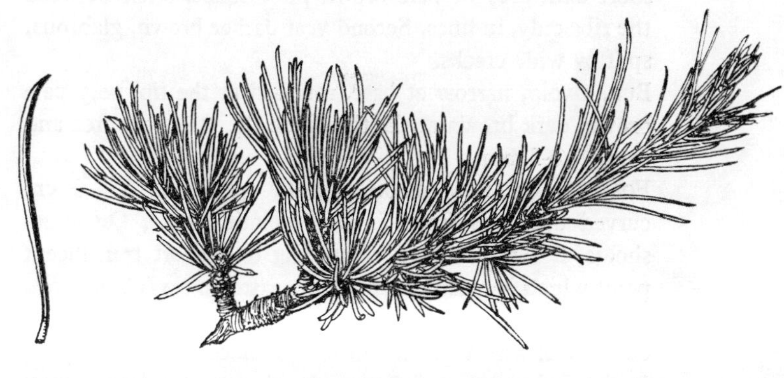

Cedrus libani

Fig. 46
Cedrus libani, Cedar of Lebanon, showing spirally set leaves on new shoot and whorl of leaves on spurs of older wood. The leaf (left ×1⅓) has a shorter spine than that of *C. atlantica*, but may be quite glaucous.

Cedrus libani A. Richard. Cedar of Lebanon

Mount Lebanon, Syria, and the Taurus Mountains in South-east Turkey. Introduced probably in 1638 and one original tree survives, at Childrey Rectory, near Wantage. The next oldest known dates only from 1707 and most of the biggest and finest date from 1800-1820. Common everywhere by mansions and castles and in town and city parks originating from these. Frequent in churchyards and graveyards. Sometimes scattered widely over deer-parks but otherwise not a countryside tree, and infrequent in West Scotland.

BARK. Dull browns, light and dark, or blackish: evenly and rather finely fissured into shallow, short flaking ridges.

CROWN. When young, until about 40 feet tall, rather narrowly conic with level branches slightly drooping or spreading at the tips. Broadens rapidly thereafter, and low branches become ascending and very strong. Trees in rather dense woods can be as slender and shapely as a larch (see list of specimens) and on the edges of woods or where somewhat crowded by other specimens, they can have long clear boles. Open grown trees usually develop, early in life, long ascending multiple boles and low branches which arch down, then level out. The top becomes broad and slightly domed or, as often seen in towns, low and as flat as a table. The foliage is held out to a great distance in dense flat plates with wide spaces between them.

SHOOT. Pale fawn or coffee-brown, slightly ribbed with short dark grey or pale brown pubescence, often between the ribs only, in lines. Second year darker brown, glabrous, split by wide cracks.

BUD. Ovoid, narrow at base, rounded at the tip, very pale brown, dark brown at the tip where the scales are free and papery; 2–3 mm.

FOLIAGE. On new shoots, spirally set leaves 2·5–3 cm curved outwards from forward pointing base. On spur-shoots, 2·5 cm slender, narrowing to a short translucent point which is green except at the extreme tip (*C. atlantica* under a lens is yellow or clear with a longer spine-tip); dark green with variable but few speckled lines of stomata, in the dark green-leafed trees. In blue or grey-leaved trees these lines are prominent, being very white and close together especially towards the leaf-tip.

FLOWERS AND CONE. Male flowers freely produced on old trees, pale grey-green, sugar-loaf shaped, to 1·5 cm, spread thickly over foliage and visible from mid-summer; expanding to 5 cm or more, and shedding pollen in early November, then turning brown, curving somewhat and falling off. Female flowers very small, green, globular, enlarging into grey-green cones, freely but not densely borne by most old trees. During the winter and following year they are ovoid barrel-shaped, tapering from one third of their length, and often made irregular by large lumps; 7–9×4·5–6 cm. By the next winter they are grey and pinkish-brown with purplish margins to the scales, and patches of white, dried resin. The apex may be domed all over or with a hollow in the centre.

GROWTH. Growth in height is fairly slow, seldom exceeding one foot per year over any period, so that the young, dated trees have a height in feet very close to their age in years, up to about 70 feet. Thereafter it is very slow, and most of the trees re-measured since 1906 and 1931 are now shorter than they were then claimed to be; many much shorter. None has grown as much as 20 feet in 30 years or 60 years, except one that was very young when first measured.

Growth in girth is exceptionally rapid in young trees. A good series of dated trees at Wilton gives the following: 61 years, 11ft 11in; 62 years, 11ft 8in; 63 years, 10ft 11in; 66 years, 11ft 0in (in 1970). At Land of Nod, Headley Down, Surrey, a tree on poor, sandy soil was 71ft×9ft 7in when 59 years old and at Bedgebury the best is, at 32 years, 56ft×9ft 0in. One of the above Wilton trees has added 7ft 8in to its girth in 39 years from 1931. With age this vigour decreases, but as with heights, some growth in girth since 1931 has been masked by gross over-estimation at that time, some healthy trees now measuring a foot or two less in girth, even in a few cases where a clear bole makes no difficulties in taking the girth. Omitting the obvious cases, increase in girth of old trees has been mainly 30 to 57 inches between 1904 and 1960–68 and since 1931 from 13 to 81 inches, usually 30–50. In general, many of the old trees are still increasing in girth at around the standard rate for almost all trees—one inch per year.

SPECIMENS.

1. *Old trees of known date.*

The oldest is the original tree at Childrey Rectory, planted 1646, 50ft×25ft 2in (1970). It has a fine bole. The next oldest known is at Biel, East Lothian, planted 1707, 75ft×23ft 8in at 2ft (1967). A short line of trees by the drive to Hinton House was planted in 1712, the best was 70ft×22ft 11in in 1959. Many cedars were planted at Peper Harrow in 1735 and Loudon remarks on the variety of form and colour among them. The best is a fine tree, 90ft×24ft 8in (1971).

The cedars at Belvedere, Windsor, planted in 1760 are remarkable for their length of clear bole. The best are 105ft×17ft 2in, 110ft×18ft 7in and 100ft×16ft 2in, the last with 41 feet of clear bole (1964). The cedars at Lockerley Hall were also planted in 1760. The best was 105ft×24ft 6in in 1957. The Bayfordbury cedars were planted in 1765 and their growth at various times between then and 1931 is recorded in the Report for 1931. The largest is 85ft×31ft 0in at 1 foot (1962); the best is 90ft×23ft 9in with 25 feet of good bole (1968). A cedar above Hagley Castle, planted in 1768 has a fine bole but is a short, broad tree 55ft×21ft 0in (1966). The Highclere cedars were raised from the Enfield cedars of 1680 planting but long gone. Those at Highclere date from 1792 and the best is 100ft×25ft 1in at 4 feet (1968).

2. *Other old trees of great size.*

Edenhall, Penrith, 92ft×30ft 1in at 3 feet (1966); Wilton, 85ft×28ft at 2ft (1971); Park Place, 95ft×23ft 5in, a fine tree (1969); Blenheim Palace, 115ft×23ft 3in; 118ft×19ft 8in (1965), Sherborne Castle 120ft×19ft 9in (1963);

Dogmersfield House, Hants., 126ft×16ft 6in (1961); Clavery House, Ascot 90ft×23ft 11in (1963); Lythe Hill, 115ft×19ft 8in at 1 foot (1960); Stanway, 100ft×25ft 4in (1965); Bowood, 125ft×19ft 6in (1968) Melbury 115ft×17ft 9in (1970); Woolbeding, Sussex, 80ft×22ft 10in (1967); Albury Park, planted 1780 110ft×18ft 3in (1966); Pains Hill, 115ft×20ft 7in (1969); Foxley Park 115ft×14ft 7in (1969); Wardour Castle 114ft×16ft 4in (1959); Jenkyn Place, Bentley, Hants., planted 1823, 80ft×19ft 6in (1965); Shrubland, Ipswich, 110ft×16ft 4in (1968); Dalkeith, planted 1770, 82ft×18ft 0in (1970); Eastnor Castle, 118ft×20ft 6in (1970).

3. *Outstanding trees with fine boles.*

The most remarkable is by the Cascade at Blenheim, 85ft×26ft 11in (1965) with about 20 feet clear bole. The most cylindrical big bole is at Claremont, 95ft×20ft 2in (1965) with a good bole for 50 feet. The finest for bole, crown and height together is perhaps that at Garnons, 120ft ×22ft 10in (1969). The tallest now, as in 1904, is at Petworth House, 132ft×18ft 0in (1971) with a fine bole but scarred badly on one side. Several of the cedars at Stratfield Saye have fine single boles; the best are 115ft×16ft 2in and 112ft×15ft 8in (1968). Other splendid boles are: Whitfield House (Hereford) 85ft×22ft 4in (1963); Poltimore, 102ft×20ft 5in, 8 feet clear (1964); Highclere 70ft×21ft 5in, bole 38 feet (1968); Eridge Castle 95ft×20ft 7in (1963); Walcot Park, 90ft×21ft 9in (1959); Exbury House, 70ft×19ft 1in (1968), Dupplin Castle Gardens, 121ft×12ft 7in (1970); Woburn (Evergreens) 98ft×22ft 1in (1970) clear bole 15ft; Albury, (Hill Garden) 105ft×15ft 7in (1966).

4. *Slender trees in woods.*

There are very few of these and they are very shapely trees. Leaton Knolls, 131ft×10ft 5in (103ft×4ft 4in, 1931) and 111ft×6ft 2in (1970); Mells Park, by the Temple, 105ft ×9ft 0in (1962) and Hallyburton, 111ft×9ft 2in (1970).

cv. Aurea. A rare and sometimes very slow-growing tree which is light gold in summer and paler in winter. The few old trees are very flat-topped and spreading. Rendcomb, 35ft×8ft 1in at 5ft 6in (1969); Frensham Hall, 40ft×5ft 10in and 40ft×5ft 2in (1967); Bedgebury, planted 1926, 27ft×1ft 7in (1969), Little Hall, planted 1906, 35ft×6ft 9in (1961); Wilton House, planted 1928, 45ft×4ft 6in (1961); Tittenhurst Park, 46ft×3ft 11in and 47ft×3ft 0in (1963).

cv. Glauca. Originated in 1855. A very distinct steely blue tree, quite different from the glaucous grey-blue commonly shown by the type. The leaves are short (2 cm) and dark blue-green with two relatively broad bright white bands on the upper surface. Known only from the tree at Pampisford, given in the Report of the 1931 Conifer Conference as var. *glauca* and then 81ft×12ft 2in. It is now 75ft×18ft 10in at 5ft 6in (1969). A similar tree by Powderham Castle is 70ft×16ft 5in (1970) at 4ft.

var. stenocoma (Schwarz) Davis. The form from South-west Anatolia is described as being always "pyramidal" (conic or columnar) and intermediate in features of cone and leaf between *C. atlantica* and *C. libani*. Unfortunately this apparently easy escape from some tricky naming problems cannot be used to separate large old trees since it has been in cultivation only this century.

Cephalotaxus Siebold and Zuccarini (Cephalotaxaceae)

Seven similar species from North-east India, China, Korea and Japan. Shoots bright green for three years, ribbed by decurrent leaf-bases. The leaves are fairly long and leathery, separated into two ranks on side-shoots. They are dioecious and male flowers are strung along the underside of young shoots while the females are stalked and arise in pairs near the nodes only. Fruit are acorn-shaped. Only two species have been introduced and these are hardy in all but the coldest regions.

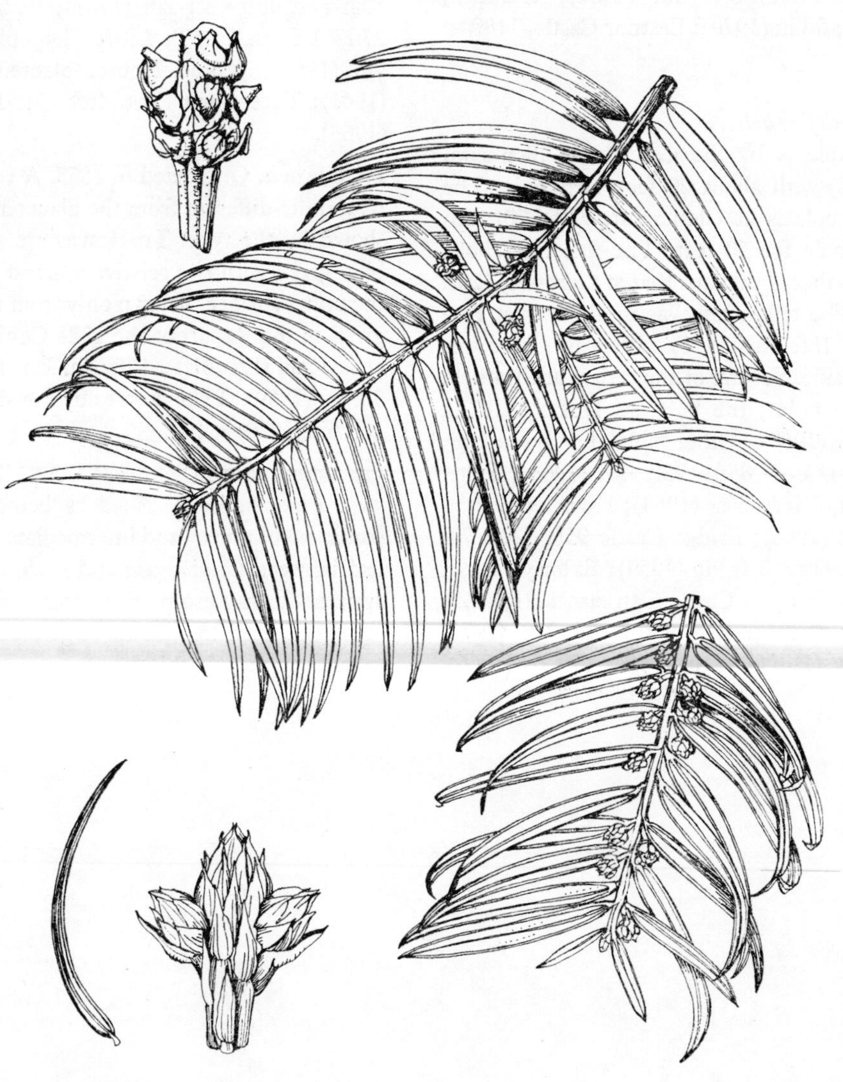

Cephalotaxus fortunei

Fig. 47
Cephalotaxus fortunei. Upper spray from female plant, with inflorescence inset (top left $\times 3\frac{1}{3}$). Lower spray from male plant, from beneath. Bottom left; leaf showing downward curve. Bottom, middle, vegetative buds ($\times 2\frac{2}{3}$).

Cephalotaxus fortunei Hooker. Chinese plum yew.

Central China. Introduced in 1848. In many large and a few small gardens mainly but not entirely in South and South-west England. Not seen in Wales or Scotland and rare in Ireland. More frequent than the next species—but more often measurable and less a small bush, so more noticed.

BARK. Red-brown with coarse, square scales, or long shreds.

CROWN. Varies from a gaunt, slender, small tree to a bushy tree with several main stems and frequently lying over on one side or with long branches resting on the ground.

LEAVES. 4–9·5 cm×5 mm in two flat pectinate ranks, slightly arched, very regular and parallel, rich, shiny rather yellow-green, ribbed, tapering gradually to a hard, fine point; underside with two broad, matt, bright grey bands, sometimes bright white.

BUD. Projects ahead of leaves, 5 mm across, globular, green.

FLOWERS AND FRUIT. Male flowers on short stalks below the shoot. Females on separate plants. Fruit 2 cm, ovoid, whitish green, striped vertically with green.

GROWTH. No specimen of known planting date has been found. But growth is evidently very slow for some of the plants must be quite old and none is big. A tall, slender tree at Pampisford, Cambridgeshire—an unexpected place for the species—has grown 4 feet in height and 6 inches in girth in the last 10 years, which is surprisingly vigorous growth. A tree in Cornwall at least as old as any, increased 7 inches in girth in 29 years.

SPECIMENS. Pampisford, 22ft×1ft 4in (1969); Dropmore, 13ft (1958); Walcot Hall, 8ft; Cambridge Botanic Garden, 15ft (1969); Chiltlee Place, 32ft×2ft 8in (1957); Tregrehan, 30ft×1ft 10in (1965); Coldrenick, 25ft×3ft 7in (1928); 31ft×4ft 2in (1957); Pencarrow, 34ft×5ft 4in (at 1ft) (1970).

Cephalotaxus harringtonia (Forbes) K. Koch.

Korean or Chinese originally, but unknown now in the wild. Introduced from Japan in 1848. Very rare; in a few collections only. Published descriptions are vague and incomplete, leaving only the inference that the distinctions between this and var. *drupacea* are in the longer stalked male flowers and longer leaves raised into a less narrow "V". The description here is from a female plant at Bedgebury and a plant at Borde Hill from Forrest's seed.

BARK. Purplish, smooth patches, flaking and peeling to leave cinnamon coloured areas.

BUD. 1–2 mm, green, globose, some basal scales with free tips.

LEAVES. To 5×0·4 cm roughly pectinate, mostly spreading perpendicular to the shoot and arched, but towards the base of the shoot many spread forwards, broad (0·4 cm), flattened, ridged on the upper surface, parallel sided tapering to a fine point; dark, shiny bluish-green; two broad pale green bands beneath.

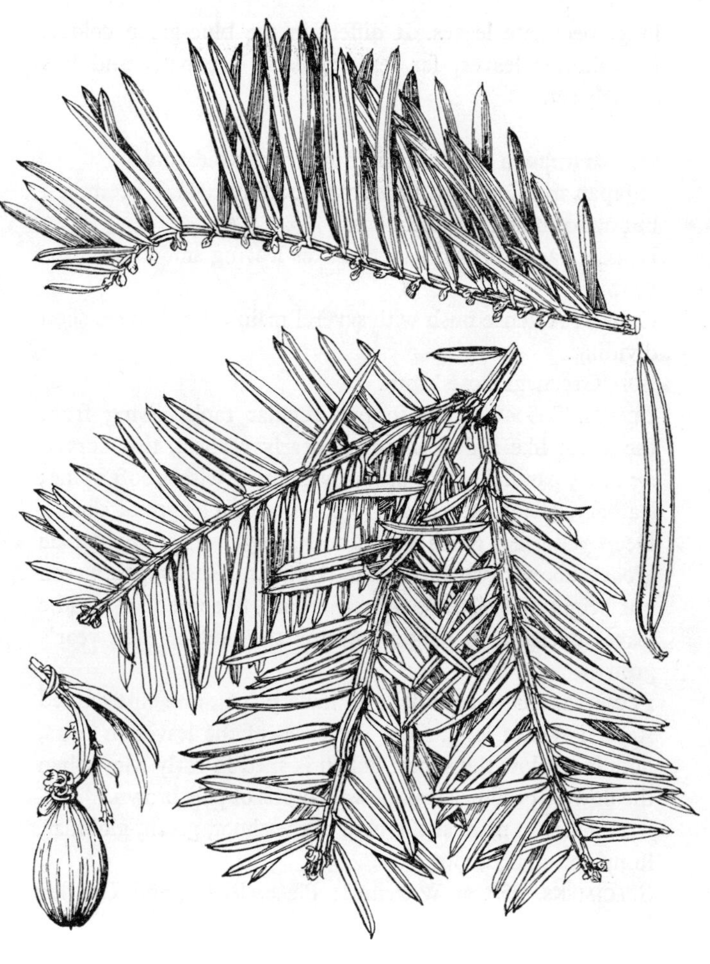

Cephalotaxus harringtonia v. drupacea
Cephalotaxus harringtonia

Fig. 48
Cephalotaxus harringtonia: Lower right, spray from male plant. Lower left, fruit from female plant. Centre right, single leaf (×2⅜). Top, spray of male plant of the variety *drupacea*.

Some shoots have the leaves raised in a wide "V" but the tips arch *outwards* and the leaf pairs are spread about 2 to a centimetre of shoot.

FEMALE FLOWERS. As buds, knobbly globular and pale green, 3 mm across in pairs on curved pedicels 2–2·5 mm long, from the node at the base of the new shoot. Fruit slightly obovoid, 2·5×1·5 cm to 3·0×2·0 cm smooth pale green striped darker green, ripening shiny brown;

MALE FLOWERS. In rows one beneath each leaf, 2 mm green globose, on stalks 1–5 mm long.

RECOGNITION. This resembles, in foliage, *C. fortunei* more than it does *C. harringtonia* variety *drupacea* owing to the long, pectinate leaves. It differs in the blue-green colour, and shorter leaves, far less regularly pectinate, and less densely set.

var. drupacea (Siebold and Zuccarini) Koidzumi.

Japan and Central China. Introduced in 1844. Uncommon but not confined to collections.

BARK. Coarse, brown papery flakes leaving smooth orange-brown.

CROWN. A dense bush with several main central stems soon dividing.

BUD. Green, globose 1 mm.

LEAVES. 2–5×0·3 cm in two regular ranks rising from the shoot like a dove's wings, nearly vertical, tips curved *inwards*; parallel sided, abruptly pointed with a soft spine; leathery, pliant, closely set. (3 pairs per cm length of shoot). Deep yellowish green above and shiny, with a slight pale groove above; two broad bands below, usually pale green but bright and silvery, almost joining, in some plants. The leaves decrease in length towards the end of each year's growth.

FLOWERS. Males abundant on male plants, on short curved stalks 1–4 mm long, from the bases of the leaves in pairs, nodding below the shoot. Pollen is shed in early May when the flowers become small powder-puffs of pale brown.

Females in pairs at the base of the shoot, green, globular, lumpy on stalks about 1 cm.

SPECIMENS. 25ft at Wakehurst Place, Bicton and Chiltley Place.

cv. Fastigiata. (Japan, Introduced 1861). In some collections and largest gardens but rarely elsewhere.

CROWN. Squat, barrel-shaped or broadest at the top where there are numerous vertical shoots; branches vertical, but slender shoots of normal foliage arch out and hang down.

BUD. Globular; deep shiny brown, pointed scales.

FOLIAGE. On vertical shoots, whorls of blackish green, long (3–8 cm) down-curved, ribbed leaves with 2 broad whitish-green bands below; narrowing suddenly to sharp, triangular tip; showing the annual extensions by graduated sizes. At the base of growth short (2–3 cm) progressively larger leaves upwards to the tips where the largest are, followed at once by the shortest of the subsequent year. Pendulous shoots arching out have pectinate foliage.

SPECIMENS. Stourhead, 17ft, Rendcomb 16ft.

RECOGNITION. Superficially resembles Irish yew, but long, unbranched shoots with graduated whorls of leaves to 8 cm are very different from the densely twigged yew with tufts of 2–3 cm leaves.

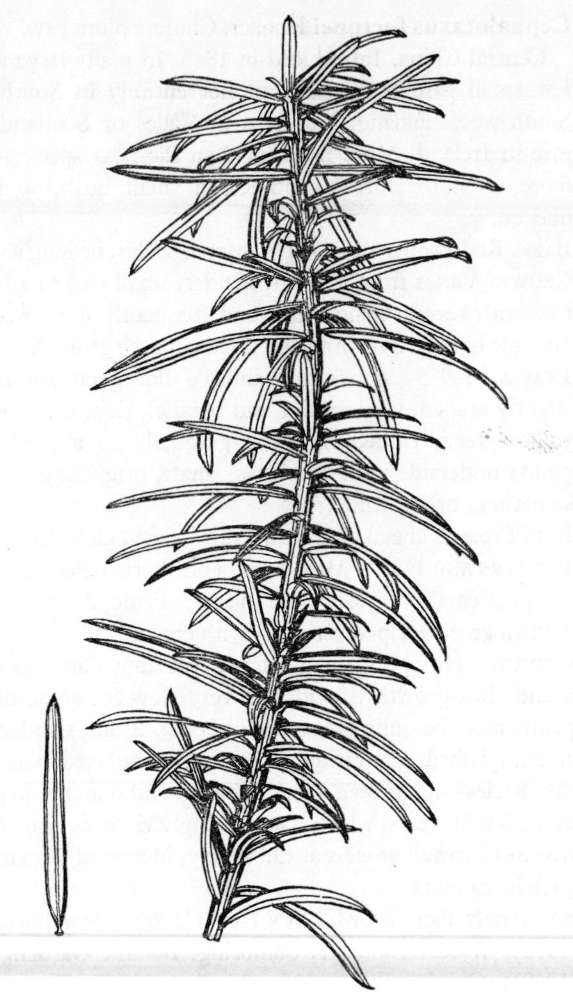

Cephalotaxus harringtonia v. fastigiata

Fig. 49
Erect shoot of *Cephalotaxus harringtonia* variety *fastigiata*, with a single leaf ($\times 1\frac{1}{3}$) showing the broad grey-green bands on the underside.

Chamaecyparis Spach (Cupressaceae)

Six species, from both sides of North America, from Japan and Formosa, varying in stature from a small tree in East America to trees of 200ft in West America and Formosa. Foliage scale-like and very small, overlapping and hard. Cones globular, small, five species ripening theirs within the year and one taking nearly two years. Three of the species are immensely variable in cultivation. All except that from Formosa are very hardy.

Chamaecyparis formosensis Matsumura. Formosan cypress

Mount Morrison, Formosa, at 7–10,000 feet. Introduced in 1910. Original seedlings planted in 1912 survive at Bayfordbury (2) Borde Hill, and planted 1913 at Tilgate. Fairly rare: in many collections and big gardens in South and West England and Ireland and a few in Eastern England.

BARK. Rich red-brown, occasionally pale grey-brown (algal

Chamaecyparis formosensis

Fig. 50
Foliage, and at base, female flowers and partly developed cone of *Chamaecyparis formosensis*, Formosan cypress. This resembles *Chamaecyparis pisifera* but has arched shoots, bronzed yellowish-green, lacking strong white markings beneath (left × 1⅓) and has a dank aroma when crushed.

TABLE 22. SPECIMENS OF CHAMAECYPARIS FORMOSENSIS

Locality	*Date Planted*	*Dimensions*	
Bayfordbury	1912	14′ (1931)	32′ × 2′ 8″ (1962)
Bayfordbury	1912	13′ (1931)	26′ × 2′ 4″ (1962)
Borde Hill	1912 (Seed)	15′ (1931)	44′ × 3′ 10″ (1968)
Borde Hill	1915 (Cutting)	15′ (1931)	37′ × 3′ ½″ (1968)
Tilgate	1913	19′ 4″ (1931)	38′ × 3′ 7″ (1961)
Tilgate	1913		35′ × 2′ 11″ (1961)[1]
Leonardslee		19′ 6″ × 1′ 6″ (1931)	38′ × 3′ 6½″ (1969)
Wakehurst Place	1915	14′ × 11′ (1931)	38′ × 2′ 4″ (1964)
Warnham Court		14′ (1931)	40′ × 4′ 2″ (1962)[2]
Bicton			42′ × 3′ 2″ (1968)
Castlewellan			29′ × 2′ 10″ (1970)
Nymans			45′ × 3′ 8″ (1970)
Fota	1916	14′ (1931)	41′ × 5′ 11″ (1966)
Tregrehan			48′ × 4′ 2″ (1971)
Hergest Croft	1919		37′ × 5′ 9″ (1969)[3]
Stourhead			43′ × 4′ 7″ (1970)
Stourhead			30′ × 2′ 9″ (1970)
Garinish I.			33′ × 5′ 7″ (1966)
Mount Usher			37′ × 4′ 8″ (1966)
Headfort	1921	13′ 6″ (1931)	33′ × 5′ 0″ (1966)
Headfort			36′ × 4′ 8″ (1966)
Birr Castle	1934		27′ × 2′ 8″ (1966)
Westonbirt	1936		38′ × 2′ 6″ (1971)

1 Main stem
2 Measured at 3 feet
3 Measured at 2 feet

covering) with regular shallow, vertical fissures, between which the ridges peel in vertical strips.

CROWN. Broadly conic to an obtuse point, the tip slightly nodding. Lower branches strong, level near the bole then upswept making the base of the crown a broad "U". Shoots at branch tips arch downwards.

FOLIAGE. General colour a distinct light, slightly yellowish, green, faintly bronzed. Shoots soon brown; leaves very small, overlapping, scale-like, acute, in four ranks, the laterals with a short mucronate incurved tip; marked slightly in white beneath or just a yellower green than the upper surface. Crushed foliage has the aroma of seaweed.

FLOWERS AND CONES. Male flowers minute, ovoid, terminal on ultimate branchlets; cones ovoid, very small, less than 1 cm long, green.

GROWTH. Slow but steady in height-growth, more rapid in increase in girth. The most rapid growth in height is 34 feet in 30 years but most dated trees have taken about 50 years to reach that height. In Ireland, growth in girth is far more rapid than in England.

Chamaecyparis lawsoniana (Murray) Parlatore. Lawson cypress

Siskiyou Mountains; above Galice in Oregon and in California from Crescent City to East of Basquet. Introduced from the latter area in 1854. Abundant everywhere. The type is almost universal in gardens of every size except the smallest, as trees or hedges; in churchyards, cemeteries and town parks. Some of the cultivars are indispensable in garden design and are planted in almost every new and old garden even in the inner suburbs of cities.

BARK. Young trees slightly shiny, smooth dark grey-green, later becoming fissured vertically. Old trees dark purplish brown or red-brown, fairly deeply fissured into thick plates and ridges which strip away after the ends curl outwards.

CROWN. Young trees narrowly conic, of an even density from the drooping leading shoot to the ground. Old trees very frequently many boled or forking repeatedly, making a columnar crown with a flat-top, made up of many nearly equal conic tops. Crown-density varies from dark and dense to thin and open in the middle. Breakage of one or more stems is frequent. Very big low branches often bend to the ground and may layer all round the tree. A few old trees are dense and narrowly columnar with a conic top.

SHOOT. Soon dull pinkish-brown, later purplish-brown.

LEAVES. Scale-like in fours which are two unequal pairs, the facial being shorter, but this is not at once apparent. The sprays and the scales are flattened, each scale with a translucent central oval spot visible when a spray is held in front of a light. Each scale is acute with a free but not spreading tip. The undersides are dusted white at the base of each scale, upper side dark green, variably bluish; crushed foliage has a parsley-like aroma mixed with a resinous one.

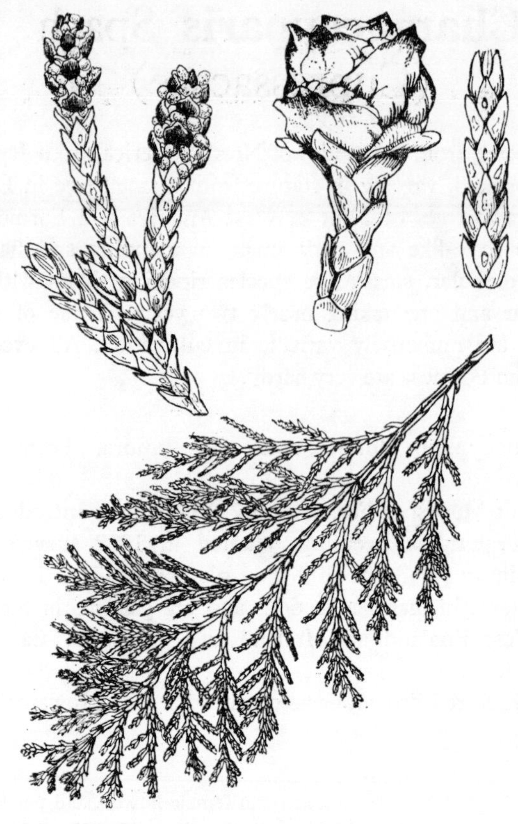

Chamaecyparis lawsoniana

Fig. 51
Chamaecyparis lawsoniana, Lawson cypress. Upper left, male flowers (×4) which are dark crimson-red before shedding pollen; upper centre, young cone (×4) upper right, shoot ($\times 3\frac{1}{3}$) showing translucent glands on leaves. Lower, spray of foliage.

FLOWERS AND CONES. Male flowers usually copious, terminal to a high proportion of ultimate shoots, slightly nodding, ovoid 1–2 mm; black scales broadly edged white; become crimson in late March and shed pollen in first half of April. Female buds on ultimate shoots near the axes of the sprays, point forwards or rise slightly, blue-black, each scale finely edged white, lower scales partially open during the winter. In March and April they all open and turn paler grey. Cones globular, wrinkled with small central spike or knobs, green, ripening purplish-brown and remaining on the tree after opening, purplish outer surfaces then widely separated showing pale brown inner surface; 7 mm.

GROWTH. Growth when young is usually moderate, although annual shoots of up to 3 feet can be grown. Over a long period height growth is slow, few of the oldest trees exceeding 100 feet in 100 years although they are still growing in height. Growth in girth is also very moderate, neither the 1931 measurements of dated trees, nor subsequent re-measurement showing annual increases of one inch except in rare cases. In southern Ireland growth in girth can be more rapid. Shoot growth starts very slowly in April but hardly significantly until June. 1–2 inches a week may be added until growth ceases in early September. Growth is hardly affected by lack of phosphate in the soil—this species gives less response than any other tested, when phosphate is added to very deficient soils.

SPECIMENS. Although an original tree survived at Abercairny until 1955 at least, losses in the older trees have been great. Less than one third of those recorded in 1931 has been found. The biggest losses have been in Scotland, and wind-throw would seem to be the factor, for standing old trees are remarkably healthy. The concentration of fine, big boles in south-central Ireland is noteworthy.

TABLE 23. SPECIMEN TREES OF CHAMAECYPARIS LAWSONIANA

Locality	*Date Planted*	*Dimensions*	
Abercairny	1854	56′ × 6′ 10″ (1931)	85′ × 10′ 0″ (1955)
Dawyck	1859	63′ × 5′ 7″ (1931)	94′ × 10′ 7″ (1966)
Adare Manor	1859		92′ × 9′ 11″ (1968)
Dupplin	1859		98′ × 8′ 6″ (1970)
Curraghmore	1861	73′ × 7′ 6″ (1931)	85′ × 11′ 7″ (1968)
Curraghmore	1861	67′	78′ × 11′ 7″ (1968)
Castle Kennedy	1861	53′ × 5′ 1″ (1926)	76′ × 6′ 11″ (1967)
Rhinefield Terrace	1861		108′ × 13′ 1″ (1970)
Rhinefield Terrace	1861	81′ × 5′ 0″ (1931)	105′ × 9′ 0″ (1970)
Cowdray Park	1870		83′ × 8′ 0″ (1967)
Stonefield		50′ × 7′ 10″ (1931)	83′ × 10′ 8″ (1969)
Stourhead	1871	61′ (1931)	79′ × 10′ 7″ (1957)
Stourhead			100′ × 8′ 10″ (1970)
Killerton		65′ × 6′ 0″ (1906)	103′ × 10′ 2″ (1970)
Kirkennan			105′ × 7′ 6″ (1970)
Inveraray (Frews Br.)			98′ × 11′ 11″ (1969)
Doune House			121′ × 11′ 3″ (1970)
Castle Forbes			75′ × 11′ 11″ (1968)
Birr Castle			82′ × 11′ 4″ (1966)
Gurteen le Poer			100′ × 13′ 3″ (1968)
Gurteen le Poer			105′ × 13′ 1″ (1968)
Gurteen le Poer			97′ × 12′ 9″ (1968)
Humewood Castle			100′ × 10′ 1″ (1968)
Longleat			95′ × 11′ 3″ (1971)
Abbeyleix			91′ × 10′ 5″ (1968)
Blandsfort			78′ × 10′ 0″ (1968)
Stradbally House			90′ × 10′ 4″ (1968)
Balmacaan			110′ × 12′ 7″ (1970)
Kinfauns			93′ × 10′ 7″ (1970)
Melbury Park			95′ × 10′ 8″ (1970)
Endsleigh			126′ × 9′ 10″ (1970)
Penjerrick			100′ × 11′ 1″ (1965)
Bodnant	1888	73′ × 7′ 0″ (1931)	80′ × 9′ 5″ (1959)
Westonbirt (Clay Island)		82′ × 8′ 5″ (1931)	95′ × 10′ 11″ (1971)
Westonbirt (Main)			100′ × 7′ 9″ (1969)
Fenagh House	1905		59′ × 7′ 8″ (1968)
Speech House	1921		59′ × 4′ 0″ (1963)
Bedgebury	1932		50′ × 4′ 3″ (1969)

CULTIVARS. Mention is restricted to those in which there are a number of tree-sized specimens or those forms which in the literature are lost among a host of others uninformatively described as "pyramidal, branches spreading, sprays fan-shaped, green". No tree is, or ever has been, pyramidal, while the rest applies equally to a score or so of other cultivars. Here there has been some attempt to describe the distinctive features. If none can be found between two named cultivars, they should, (vide the Code) be combined.

cv. Albospica: cv. Albomaculata. Many variegated cultivars have been united under these names. Such forms vary in the size of the patches of colour. Some have widely spaced large blotches and look diseased, others are rather finely variegated and attractive. It is difficult to find which belongs to which cultivar name since authors may not mention these differences. The distinctions between 'albo', 'argentea' and 'aurea' are often blurred, but should be quite positive.

A closely pale yellow-variegated form which looks from a small distance to be uniformly pale golden is a good narrowly conic plant. Fenagh House, planted 1910, 53ft × 5ft 10in (1968). Similar trees are at Strete Ralegh House, 62ft × 5ft 5in (1970), (N. Devon), 59ft × 5ft 1in (1970), and Escot, 56ft × 4ft 11in and 50ft × 5ft 0in (1965). A similar tree but quite distinctly white in the variegation, at Stonefield is 52ft × 5ft 10in (1969) and two grown at Bedgebury as 'albomaculata', planted 1939 are 38ft × 2ft 5in and 34ft × 2ft 6in (1969). The Devon trees are doubtless of the form raised by Veitch's in Exeter in 1886.

cv. Allumii. Unknown origin pre-1890. Erect plates of narrow sprays on pink-brown shoots, which turn orange-brown; scale-leaves closely appressed dusted white at base, mid or pale green, appearing dull blue-grey from distance. Inside surface yellow-green towards tip of each spray, otherwise as outer. For many years narrowly conic; base broadens until in oldest trees the long narrowly conic top arises from billowing incurved basal branches.

Oldest tree, Fenagh House, planted 1896, 54ft tall (1968); Bedgebury, planted 1925, two trees 46ft; Westonbirt, 72ft × 5ft 2in (1970); planted 1926, 50ft × 3ft 1in (1967), planted 1944, 54ft × 3ft 6in (1969), Endsleigh, 57ft × 5ft 2in (1963); Wakehurst Place, West Wood, 62ft × 4ft 7in (1965).

cv. Blue Jacket (Milford, pre-1932). Broadly conic with fine sprays bluish-green above, bluish-white beneath. Uncommon but now planted more. Bedgebury, planted 1925 47ft × 3ft 6in (1969).

cv. Columnaris. (Spek, Holland, 1940). Very narrowly columnar with short, nearly erect branches bearing sprays of pale grey-blue foliage.

The tallest trees tend to change at the top to a looser habit. Usually slow—shoots of 12–18 inches a year, but at Grayswood Hill, planted 1954, now 31 feet (1969) and at Bedgebury, planted 1955, now 24 feet.

cv. Grayswood Pillar is very similar, a little narrower, and remains narrow and dense at the top. The original tree has curious broad spirals of foliage in the top 8 feet. It was a sport from a cv. Blue Jacket, planted 1952 now 27 feet tall, at Grayswood Hill, Surrey.

cv. Ellwoodii (Swanmore Park, Bishop's Waltham, Hants. ±1920). Like 'Fletcheri' but greyer when young and, in older trees, remarkably tightly fastigiate at the base. Remains narrower, columnar, conic at the top, less liable to numerous tops. This is not a dwarf—to 27 feet so far at Westonbirt.

cv. Erecta (Knaphill, Surrey 1855). The first cultivar, arising from Californian seed, probably only the second lot imported. Distributed in 1870. Fastigiate with foliage in vertical plates on short appressed branches, forming a fusiform crown, i.e. broadest about the middle, tapering in a curve to the, usually multiple, tops. Often 2–6 stems from the base, and then crown broadest about 6 feet up. Foliage bright rather dark green both sides. Slower growing than the type; the few dated trees have grown fairly close to a mean of one foot per year planted. Few have a bole measurable at 5 feet. Bowood, 92ft × 13ft 7in at 2ft (1968); Westonbirt House, 73ft × 10ft 10in (1967); Scotney Castle, 86ft (1963); Abercairny 76ft × 10ft 6in, bole 10 feet (1962); Derreen 84ft × 11ft 10in, good bole (1966); Fota 78ft × 8ft 8in (1966); Headfort 82ft × 16ft 0in at 2 feet (1966); Cowdray Park 82 feet, Killerton (Chapel) 80ft × 9ft 3in, 79ft × 6ft 9in (1970); Keir House, 69ft × 9ft 2in (1970); Brahan, 79ft × 9ft 1in (1970).

Chamaecyparis lawsoniana cv. Filifera

Fig. 52
Spray of *Chamaecyparis lawsoniana* cv. Filifera with an open cone. The foliage is a rich pale green and has a lace-like appearance in the mass.

cv. Filifera. A name often used for cv. Filiformis. Here 'Filifera' is taken to be a narrow, conic tree of somewhat pendulous habit and rich pale green foliage with long, slender curved, distant branchlets, in lace-like open sprays. Each scale-leaf has a narrow white margin. Ultimate shoots sparse, to 3 cm long in somewhat flattened sprays. Leonardslee 37ft × 2ft 8in (1961); Endsleigh 46ft × 3ft 4in (1963); Wisley Royal Horticultural Society Gardens 39ft × 2ft 8in (1964); Bedgebury 35ft × 2ft 5in (1969); Holkham 37ft × 2ft 2in (1968).

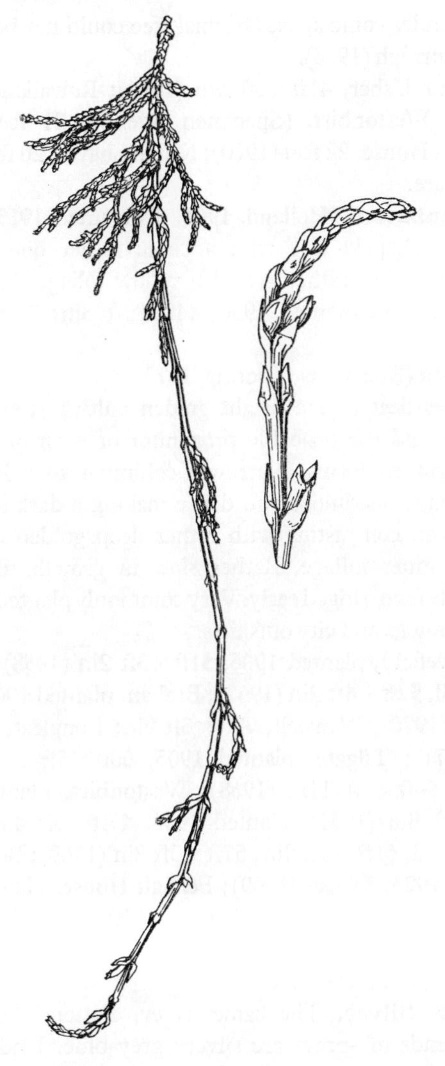

Chamaecyparis lawsoniana cv. Filiformis

Fig. 53
Foliage of *Chamaecyparis lawsoniana* cv. Filiformis, a pendulous tree with remote bunches of grey-green foliage at intervals on long, hanging, slender shoots. Shoot-tip on right (×2).

cv. Filiformis (Boskoop. pre-1878). A tree usually of several stems, broadly columnar or squat with arching branches from which hang long thread-like branchlets with occasional bunches of grey-green or yellowish-green dense branchlets. Rare.

Kew Royal Botanic Gardens, planted 1878, 44ft × 3ft 1in (1958); Bicton, 68ft × 6ft 8in (1968); Nymans, 66ft × 4ft 7in (1970); Sheffield Park, planted 1924, 44ft × 3ft 10in (1960); Exeter University, 47ft × 4ft 10in at 2ft (1967).

cv. Fletcheri (Fletchers of Chertsey, 1913, distributed 1923). Broad-topped, broad-columnar with many stems or narrowly columnar with one or two stems; pale bluish grey-green and feathery. Shoot soon dark pink-purple turning later purple-brown. Regular ascending sprays on the outer side of vertical shoots, slightly arched at the tips. Leaves in decussate pairs, slender, spreading perpendicular to shoot, 2 mm pale grey-green at tips, bluish mainly on outside; dark yellow-green on inner surface. Slow-growing but not dwarf. Very common.

Dropmore, 34ft × 1ft 4in (1965); East Bergholt Place, 32ft (1966); Carey, Wareham, 40ft × 2ft 1in (main stem) (1968); Holkham 36ft (1968); Gurteen le Poer 31ft × 2ft 0in at 3 feet (1968); Bedgebury, planted 1925, 33ft (1966); Westonbirt (Nursery) 29ft (1964); Welford Park, 30ft × 1ft 10in (main stem) (1966).

cv. Fraseri (About 1891). Similar in general appearance to 'Allumii' but darker grey-green, less spreading at the base. Rather thick leaves, grey-green bloomed whitish. Foliage sprays narrow forward-pointing; yellow-green beneath, lined with white. Fenagh House, planted 1901, 45ft × 3ft 3in (1968); Bedgebury 32ft × 2ft 3in (1969); Edinburgh Royal Botanic Garden, planted 1946, 21ft × 1ft 7in (1970). Fairly frequent.

cv. Glauca. Probably now a general term for tall-growing trees very like the type species but with foliage pale grey or grey-blue, but not one of the distinct, named glaucous cultivars. Such trees arise commonly from home-collected seed but the original form given the name arose at Lawson's Nursery in the very early batch of seed in 1855. Trees of this kind are: Inwood House, Sherborne, 77ft × 4ft 9in (1963) and Wakehurst Place, West Wood, 75ft × 5ft 1in (1965).

cv. Golden King (Seedling from cv. Triumph of Boskoop, distributed 1930). A fairly broad, conic tree with upright shoots fanning out a little (when young at least) and broadly splashed gold on yellowish green. Branchlets dense on the shoot, overlapping, laid forward, nodding; inside of foliage slightly grey-green. Vigorous.

Bedgebury, planted 1943, 45ft × 3ft 1in; 37ft × 2ft 6in (1969).

cv. Gracilis Pendula (Barrons, Derbyshire, pre-1881). Several trees in Western Ireland seem to be of this cultivar. Long, narrow sprays of hard, crisped, dense grey-green foliage; very elegant.

Dereen, 78ft × 9ft 10in (1966); Bicton 56ft × 4ft 2in (1968).

cv. Headfort. Broadly columnar with erect branching but spreading, light grey sprays of foliage. Original tree at Headfort, 41ft × 4ft 4in (1966); Dawyck 38ft × 2ft 3in (1960).

cv. Hillier. Rather slender, conic tree with level branching and spreading sprays of pale yellow foliage, greenish yellow interior foliage; pale in shade, brighter in the sun. Borde Hill, Gores Wood, 35 feet (1967); Westonbirt, Down Gate, planted 1952, 20ft × 1ft 3in (1967).

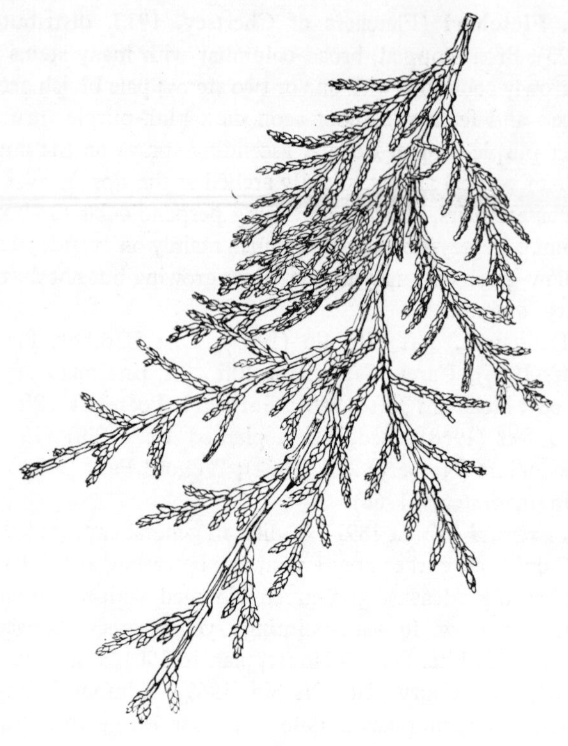

Chamaecyparis lawsoniana cv. Intertexta

Fig. 54
Hanging spray of *Chamaecyparis lawsoniana* cv. Intertexta, a curious cultivar with hard, dark grey-green, distant foliage.

cv. Intertexta (Lawson's, 1869). Bark dull, dark grey-brown with a few vertical fissures; crown narrowly conic but usually multiple stems open out to make a wider top, these stems are readily broken by snow. Foliage and leader very drooping. Shoots green, soon pink-brown in patches; branchlets regularly set 2 cm apart, minor branchlets 0·5 cm apart making very sparse, open, distant, foliage; ultimate branchlets hard, rounded, dark sea-green above, yellowish green below, faintly white at bases of leaves. Leaves have thick, incurved points. A rather vigorous tree growing about as fast as does the type tree. Largely confined to collections.

Walcot Hall, 76ft×5ft 10in (1963); Warnham Court 69ft×5ft 10in (1971); Dawyck, planted 1911, 66ft×4ft 11in single stem (1966); Batsford Park 72ft×4ft 3in (1964); Tubney Wood planted 1906, 64ft×3ft (1966); Bedgebury, planted 1927, 66ft×4ft 3in (1970); Carton 68ft×5ft 10in (1968); Honeyhanger, 67ft×6ft 2in (1971); Westonbirt, 70ft×6ft 2in (1970); Stourhead, 64ft×3ft 8in (1970).

cv. Kilmacurragh. An exceedingly slender, more tightly fastigiate form of 'Erecta', a little lighter green, columnar with slender conic apex. Original tree could not be found at Kilmacurragh (1966).

Mount Usher, 41ft×3ft 9in (1966); Rowallane, 37 feet (1966); Westonbirt, (Specimen Avenue) 21 feet (1969); Jermyns House, 22 feet (1970); Knightshayes, 20 feet (1970). Fairly rare.

cv. Lombartsii (Holland, 1904, distributed 1915). A rare, vigorous shapely tree with a conic rather dense crown; broad sprays of rather greenish yellow foliage. Noted only at Bedgebury; planted 1930, 44ft×3ft 3in; 39ft×3ft 2in (1970).

cv. Lutea (Rollissons, Tooting, 1873).

The earliest of the bright golden cultivars; still one of the best and the probable progenitor of most of the more recent golden forms. Narrowly columnar to a long-conic top; foliage pendulous and dense making a dark interior to the crown, contrasting with rather deep golden outer and whitish inner foliage. Rather slow in growth. Bark light orange-brown, ridged early. Very commonly planted, thriving even in towns and city outskirts.

Knowefield, planted 1906, 51ft×3ft 2in (1958); Trevarrick Hall, 52ft×4ft 2in (1962); Brahan, planted 1901, 66ft×6ft 5in (1970); Wansfell, 57ft×3ft 9in; Longleat, 57ft×6ft 4in (1971); Tilgate, planted 1905, 60ft×5ft 2in (1964); Bicton, 60ft×3ft 11in (1968); Westonbirt, planted 1896, 53ft×3ft 8in (1971), planted 1936, 45ft×3ft 4in (1969); Trawscoed, 61ft×3ft 9in; 57ft×3ft 8in (1969); Bedgebury, planted 1925, 58 feet (1969); Fenagh House, planted 1901, 52ft×4ft 0in (1968); Killerton, 60ft×4ft 4in (1970); Dupplin Castle Garden, 77ft×4ft 3in (1970); Scone (Pinetum) 66 feet (1970).

cv. New Silver. The same as cv. Pottenii but down-turned ends of sprays are silvery grey-blue. Under a lens the leaves are less acute, less spreading and are bloomed grey-blue. Very attractive dense, tight, narrow crown.

Bedgebury 43 feet (1966); Abbeyleix 42 feet (1968). Very rare, but may be being planted a little more now.

cv. Olbrichii (Zurich, pre-1904). A densely narrow-columnar tree, fastigiate, with conic top and drooping leading shoot. Sprays quite level from vertical shoots; bright green, fully adult, but otherwise like a large cv. Pottenii. Very rare; noted only at Bedgebury, planted 1932, 34 feet (1970).

cv. Patula (Before 1903.) Bushy and broadly conic with most distinct foliage, dark grey-green or sea-green, very long, slender ultimate shoots in narrow fan-like sprays curving outwards; leaves appressed, yellowish beneath with white bases.

Bedgebury, planted 1925, 40ft×3ft 1in (1970); Bicton 65ft×5ft 6½in (1968). May be "not rare" on the Continent but is extremely rare in Britain.

cv. Pendula. Dark green foliage as in the type, but shoots markedly pendulous. A tree of this form at Endsleigh is 102ft×8ft 1in (1963) but none other has been noted.

cv. Pottenii (Cranbrook, pre 1923). Narrow fusiform trees, bottle-shaped with long-conic top; pale green and feathery. Vertical shoots soon pale copper with regular, alternate branchlets ascending from the outer side, turning vertical then arching out at the tips. Leaves slender, acute, point 60° forward, yellow-green or grey-green above, very pale green below, lightly dusted grey; those on the outside of the crown darkish yellow-green. Not so slow-growing as it looks.

Westonbirt planted 1939, 41 feet (1970); Bedgebury planted 1925, 41ft; 37 ft; 35ft (1969); Bicton 45ft×2ft 4½in (1968); Nymans (Rough Ground), 45ft×3ft 2in; 43ft×3ft 5in (1968).

cv. Rosenthallii (Near Hamburg; pre-1884). A dense, narrow-topped conic tree rather like 'erecta' but with dense layers of level, cupped sprays, deep rich green above, strongly marked silvery below at the base of each leaf, on level branches. Branchlets close and regular on shoot making an attractive fern-like spray. A vigorous, rare tree, but possibly unrecognised in many localities.

Bedgebury planted 1929, 55ft×4ft 0in and 49ft×3ft 11in (1969).

cv. Silver Queen (England, 1883). Misleadingly named and, surely wrongly described as "a strikingly pale form of cv. Argentea". Narrowly conic and rather open-crowned in old trees, this has new leaves briefly silvery-grey but spends most of the year with a rather sad yellowish colour above and not very bright white bases to leaves below.

Kew Royal Botanic Gardens, 67ft×3ft 5in (1965); Batsford Park, 57ft×4ft 11in and 57ft×4ft 3in (1963); Westonbirt, (Morley Ride), planted 1935, 46ft×3ft 1in (1969); Bedgebury, planted 1925, 60ft×4ft 3in, 56ft×4ft 9in (1970). In many gardens as a young tree.

cv. Stewartii (Ferndown, pre 1920—said to be at Bodnant by 1888).

A decidedly conic tree with slightly ascending, long, fern-like sprays of golden foliage from a green interior. Very distinct when young, with these narrow, rising sprays; less so when older. Common in gardens, but slightly less so than cv. Lutea. Fairly vigorous.

Bedgebury, planted 1925, 44ft×3ft 8in (1969); Westonbirt, (Morley Ride), planted 1935, 34ft×2ft 7in (1969); Bicton, 51ft×4ft 0½in (1968); Leonardslee, 56ft×3ft 7in (1963).

cv. Triumph of Boskoop (Boskoop, ±1890). Broad-columnar, open crowned, level-branched and usually with a single bole to the tip, this cultivar is more vigorous and of much better form than is the type tree. Bark smooth until bole quite large. Large open sprays, outer leaves pale blue-grey or whitish grey; inner, dull blue-grey to grey-green. The open crown allows the bole to be visible nearly to the top. Widely planted; an excellent tree.

Tilgate, planted 1905, 57ft×4ft 3in (1961); Warnham Court, 67ft×4ft 7in (1971); Bicton, 81ft×6ft 7in (1968); Brahan, planted 1901, 62ft×8ft 6in (1970); Bedgebury, planted 1925, 56ft×4ft 9in (1970); Westonbirt, planted 1941, 52ft×3ft 7in (1967); Tongs Wood, 50ft×4ft 2in (1968); Fenagh House, planted 1911, 57ft×6ft 5in (1968); Nymans, 76ft×7ft 8in (1970); Fairburn, 62ft×7ft 4in (1970).

cv. Watereriana. A little-known tree of fair vigour. It is broadly conic and has elegant foliage with a yellow-green shoot, and greyish-blue green leaves which are whitish beneath. Bedgebury, planted 1925, 52ft×3ft 5in (1970).

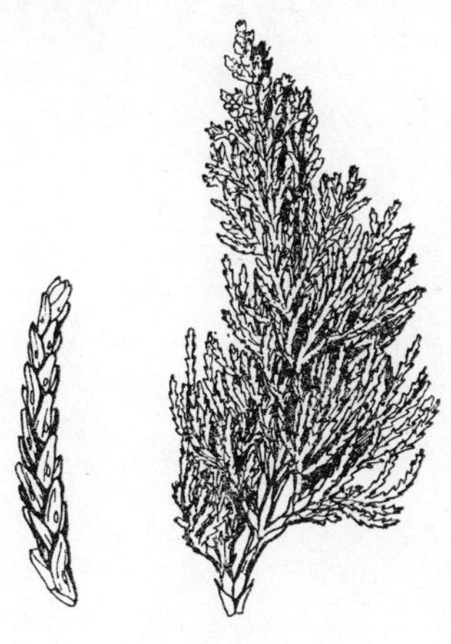

Chamaecyparis lawsoniana cv. Wisselii

Fig. 55
Tuft of foliage of *Chamaecyparis lawsoniana* cv. Wisselii, a deep blue-green foliaged cultivar with partial fasciation. Shoot on left enlarged ×2⅔.

cv. Wisselii (Epe, Holland, 1888). Columnar, very narrow to fairly broad, with pointed long spire or spires and level branches turning up to small turret-like spires all round the crown. Young trees often rather gaunt. From distance, deep blackish blue, turning crimson with dense masses of male flowers in April, and brown as these shed pollen but remain on the tree. Small branches wiry; shoots soon copper-brown becoming dark greenish-brown. Branchlets dense, spread at all angles round vertical shoots; congested, partly fasciated, with ultimate branchlets slender, ±alternately long and short, in flattened sprays; light grey-green dusted bluish-white outside, dark yellow-green inside. Fairly common. A deceptive tree, looking as if it would always be very slow-growing, as it is for some years, but then it becomes enormously vigorous, in height, and especially in girth.

Bicton, planted 1916, 80ft×11ft 4in (1968); Avondale, planted 1908, 52ft×9ft 1in and 57ft×10ft 6in (1968); Tongs Wood, 60ft×6ft 10in (1968); Lydhurst, 67ft×7ft 3in (1971); Nymans, 66ft×7ft 9in (1970); Abbeyleix, 52ft×5ft 7in (1968); Blackmoor, 60ft×5ft 10in (1968); Tilgate, planted 1905, 58ft×4ft 3in (1964); Sheffield Park, 66 feet (1968); Wayford Manor, planted about 1912, 53ft×6ft 5in (1961); Rossie Priory, 66ft×4ft 1in (1970).

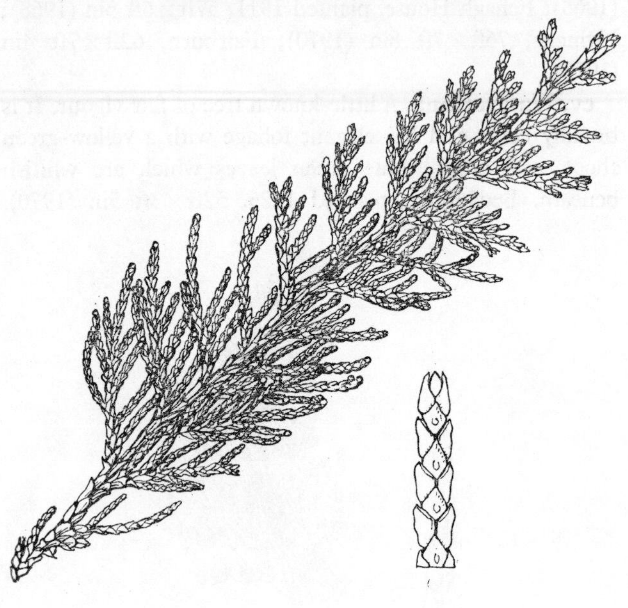

Chamaecyparis lawsoniana cv. Youngii

Fig. 56
Branchlet of *Chamaecyparis lawsoniana* cv. Youngii, a form with thick, rounded, dark grey-green foliage, slightly curled and of attractive form. Shoot ×2⅜.

cv. Youngii (Milford, pre 1874). A beautiful, slender, conic tree with short, small level branches on a single, smoothly tapered stem. Foliage in wide sprays of hard, rough, up-curled dark green rounded branchlets making a fern-like spray. The upturned branchlets are usually tipped with black male flower buds. A vigorous tree, much underestimated by other writers, and seemingly nearly confined to the neighbourhood of its birth-place—South West Surrey.

Wishanger, Churt, 58ft×6ft 7in (1963); Busbridge Lakes, Godalming, 61ft×3ft 8in and 59ft×4ft 4in (1963); Land of Nod, Headley Down, 61ft×3ft 11in (1964); Tittenhurst Park, Ascot, 56ft×3ft 9in (1963); Bicton, 62ft×4ft 10in (1968); Tongs Wood, 53ft×5ft 9in (1968).

Chamaecyparis nootkatensis. (D. Don) Spach. Nootka cypress

Alaska to Washington and Northern Oregon. Introduced in, or before, 1854. Reasonably common; although not frequent in small gardens, it is present in almost all large gardens and many parks and churchyards.

BARK. Brown to orange-brown, sometimes grey with algae, very shallowly fissured into narrow, vertical or spiral strips, which leave stringy, shallow ridges.

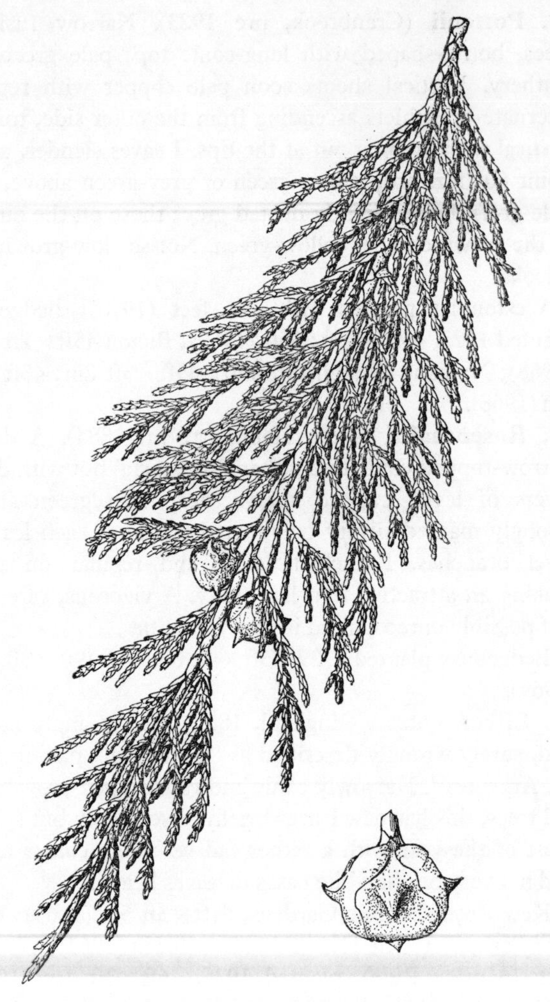

Chamaecyparis nootkatensis

Fig. 57
Foliage and cones of *Chamaecyparis nootkatensis.* The foliage is hard, thick and dark and the cones with spined scales (right ×1⅓) take two years to ripen.

CROWN. Always cleanly conic, whether broad or narrow, even in the rather rare forked trees. Open, especially in old trees, with little or no interior foliage, but often heavy, upturned low branches which may bear foliage of a different aspect from the rest of the crown. Branches ascending more towards tips; foliage variably pendulous, often hanging (but the crown is quite different from cv. Pendula.) The tip of the leading shoot nods to one side. In Western Ireland, crowns are hugely broad domes, short pointed.

FOLIAGE. Shoot soon orange-brown and purplish, bearing alternate branchlet systems in pectinate rows, each to 20×4 cm and flat. Scale-leaves in equal pairs, narrowly acute, the tips spreading forward and ridged in lateral leaves, with an abruptly mucronate incurved point. Dark grey-green above with pale green margins and sometimes a white line near the tip; pale grey-green below; yellowish towards the outer ends of the spray. Foliage in the hand is thick and rough (stroked inwards the points of scales on the main shoot catch the hand) and when crushed has a heavy odour like oxeye-daisies.

FLOWERS AND CONE. Male flowers abundant at shoot tips, yellow from summer until pollen is shed in early April. Female flowers, dark grey, some open much of the year. Cone on 5 mm stalk, two years ripening, oblate sphere 1 cm, each scale with raised sharply conic spike, yellow-green turning dark brown during first winter.

GROWTH. Slow but steady on almost any site. Even the oldest trees are still growing in height but few have a mean increment of as much as one foot per year. Young trees can grow fast—to 74 feet in 35 years at Westonbirt. In girth, growth is slow; on old trees a mean of 1 inch a year is a maximum, and young trees are not much faster, but at Bedgebury one is 5 feet and another 4ft 4in after 45 years. One older tree, at Rossdhu, has increased 16 inches in 14 years, but others are slower.

SPECIMENS. No tree planted before 1859 is known, although it is likely that several of the biggest date from the original seed of 1854 or before. The largest are in Table 24.

TABLE 24. LEADING TREES OF CHAMAECYPARIS NOOTKATENSIS

Locality	*Date Planted*	*Dimensions*	
Dawyck	1859	60′ × 3′ 6″ (1930)	85′ × 7′ 10″ (1966)
Leonardslee		50′ × 3′ 8″ (1906)	94′ × 7′ 7″ (1969)
Eastnor Castle		57′ × 4′ 6″ (1909)	80′ × 9′ 0″ (1970)
Eastnor Castle			93′ × 8′ 7″ (1970)
Boconnoc		63′ × 8′ 0″ (1927)	59′ × 10′ 4″ (1970)
Westonbirt		79′ × 10′ 5″ (1931)	88′ × 10′ 2″ (1969)
Eridge Castle			95′ × 9′ 10″ (1971)
Castle Leod			90′ × 9′ 7″ (1966)
Titness Park	1866		89′ × 7′ 5″ (1957)
Powerscourt	1867	43′ × 6′ 2″	86′ × 8′ 2″ (1966)
Curraghmore	1871	46′ × 6′ 6″ (1931)	58′ × 9′ 7″ (1968)
Gurteen le Poer			66′ × 9′ 7″ (1968)
Gurteen le Poer			74′ × 9′ 4″ (1968)
Broxwood Court			95′ × 8′ 9″ (1957)
Endsleigh			82′ × 8′ 10″ (1970)
Tittenhurst Park			88′ × 7′ 8″ (1963)
Moss's Wood			88′ × 7′ 0″ (1967)
Humewood Castle			88′ × 7′ 10″ (1968)
Linton Park		55′ (1931)	90′ × 7′ 6″ (1970)
Hewell Grange		60′ × 4′ 4″ (1908)	87′ × 7′ 0″ (1963)
Culzean Castle	1876	40′ × 5′ 6″ (1931)	69′ × 8′ 5″ (1970)
Penrhyn Castle	1881	63′ × 7′ 0″ (1931)	72′ × 9′ 0″ (1959)
Stourhead	1881	57′ × 5′ 11″ (1931)	79′ × 7′ 4″ (1970)
Fulmodestone		60′ × 4′ 0″ (1931)	80′ × 6′ 10″ (1969)
Glenlee Park			84′ × 9′ 3″ (1970)
Mells Park			83′ × 6′ 7″ (1962)
Bassett Wood			82′ × 6′ 8″ (1961)
Cragside			85′ × 6′ 0″ (1958)
Dupplin Castle			98′ × 8′ 1″ (1970)
Dupplin Castle			88′ × 9′ 3″ (1970)
Doune House			98′ × 8′ 10″ (1970)
Fota		52′ × 5′ 8″ (1931)	64′ × 8′ 9″ (1966)
Langholm	1885	59′ × 5′ 0″ (1931)	78′ × 6′ 7″ (1954)
Langholm	1885	64′ × 4′ 4″ (1931)	70′ × 6′ 4″ (1954)
Brahan	1901		66′ × 6′ 9″ (1970)
Wakehurst Place	1917	20′ × 1′ 6″ (1931)	60′ × 4′ 0″ (1964)
Bedgebury	1926	8′ 6″ (1931)	53′ × 5′ 0″ (1969)
Bedgebury	1926		51′ × 4′ 4″ (1969)
Westonbirt	1935		74′ × 3′ 5″ (1971)
Westonbirt (Loop)			90′ × 7′ 5″ (1971)

cv. Aurea. An uncommon, dull form, noticeably different only in early summer when the newest leaves are a dull yellowish green.

Brahan Castle, planted 1901, 66ft × 6ft 9in (1970); Little Hall, 49ft × 3ft 7in (1961); Embley Park, 45ft × 2ft 0in (1962); Wisley Royal Horticultural Society Gardens, 40ft × 2ft 1in (1964); Bedgebury, planted 1925, 40 feet (1967).

cv. Argenteo-variegata. A deservedly rare form with white blotches.

Bedgebury, planted 1925, 34ft × 2ft 1in (1969); Bayfordbury, 50ft × 3ft 6in (1968); Walcot Hall, 61ft × 4ft 2in (1959).

cv. Glauca. No plants of this have been found in 580 gardens, estates and parks visited.

cv. Pendula. A gaunt tree with few branches which curve sharply upwards and from which the foliage hangs in flat, plate-like masses. Young trees are very attractive, rather yellowish green and narrow, but older trees are very dark-leaved and lose their good shape.

Westonbirt, 60ft × 6ft 0in (1965); Bedgebury, planted 1925, 47ft × 3ft 5in (1969); Butleigh House, Glastonbury, 52ft × 6ft 7in (1959); Ardnagashel, 45ft × 6ft 1in (1966); Tongs Wood, 54ft × 3ft 6in (1968); Ashford Castle, 57ft × 5ft 3in (1968); Avondale, 68ft × 4ft 2in; very fine (1968).

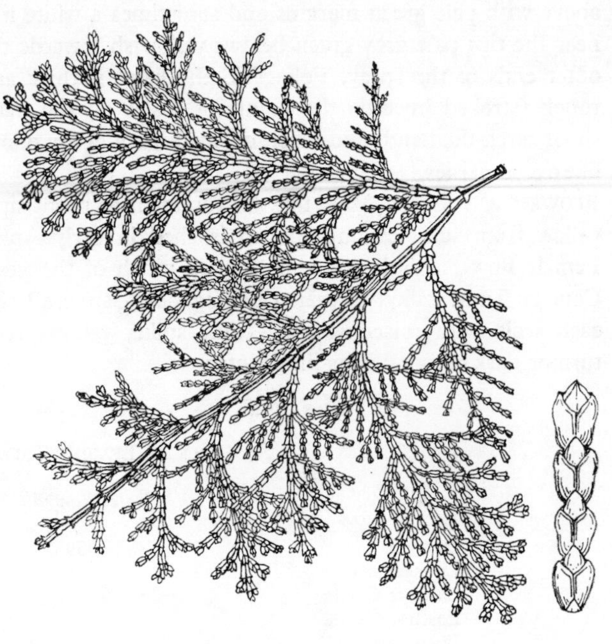

Chamaecyparis obtusa

Fig. 58
Foliage of *Chamaecyparis obtusa*, Hinoki cypress, showing the fan-like spray and (right $\times 2\frac{2}{3}$) distinctively blunt scale-leaves, strongly marked with white on the underside.

Chamaecyparis obtusa (Siebold and Zuccarini) Endlicher. Hinoki cypress

Southern Central Japan. Introduced in 1861. Frequent but mainly confined to the large gardens in the South and West except for some of the cultivars.

BARK. Rufous or grey-brown, well marked with parallel, long fissures and ridges, the ridges stripping away, coarsely in some trees.

CROWN. Broadly conic and obtuse at apex; oldest trees broad-columnar, more rounded at the top. Lower branches widely spread then upturned. New shoots project slightly arched and slender. The bole is smoothly circular in cross-section.

FOLIAGE. Shoots wiry, soon dull orange-brown with obovate branchlet systems each side; the smaller systems on these curves backwards. Scale-leaves in unequal pairs; laterals long with thick blunt incurved tips; facials short, obtuse; both shiny, bright green above; below strongly marked by thick white lines along leaf-margins (on the leaf below) and across the base of some lateral leaves. These very pretty sprays emit resinous scents when crushed, some like eucalyptus.

FLOWERS AND CONE. Male flowers terminal, minute, on smallest branchlets. Cones often densely borne, globular, 2 cm across, green ripening orange-brown, with few flat scales, each with a minute ridge in the centre.

GROWTH. Very slow in the east and slow in height also in the west, no dated tree having a mean increment of as much as one foot per year. In girth, growth can be relatively rapid in the west—87 inches in 78 years in County Carlow is the best recorded—and even, on a damp site, in the east, where 60 inches was grown on a heavy clay above chalk on the South Downs, in 47 years. A damp site is evidently important.

SPECIMENS. No tree is known to survive from the 1861 seed, but several of the largest in girth could be of this origin.

RECOGNITION. The bright green foliage contrasting with bright red-brown bark combined with the broad base of the crown and the scarcely branched new terminal shoots in the crown, distinguish this tree at a distance. The stubby, shiny, bright green leaves are also quite distinct from those of any other scale-leaved tree.

cv. Aurea. Brought from Japan in 1862, this somewhat dull golden form has been quite superseded by cv. Crippsii. Its growth is, however, probably more rapid than that of Crippsii, being very much like that of the type tree.

Bicton, 55ft × 5ft 10in and 42ft × 4ft 6in (1968); (Italian Garden) and 36ft × 3ft 0in (1968); Inistioge, 53ft × 7ft 11in at 4ft (1966); Haldon Grange, 42ft × 5ft 3in (1967); Keir House, 56ft × 4ft 7in (1970); Errol, 51ft × 5ft 0in (1970).

cv. Crippsii (Tunbridge Wells, 1900). A broadly conic, dense, slow-growing form with some of the brightest golden foliage of any conifer. This can vary, and needs full light for the best colour.

Tilgate, planted 1905, 50ft × 4ft 4in (1961); Little Hall, planted 1906, 41ft × 2ft 4in (1961); Kilmacurragh, 51ft × 6ft 3in; Headfort, planted 1916, 40ft × 4ft 10in (1966); Sindlesham, 49ft × 3ft 4in (1959); Nymans, 44ft × 3ft 9in (1970); Dropmore, 52ft × 4ft 6in (1970).

TABLE 25. SPECIMENS OF CHAMAECYPARIS OBTUSA

Locality	*Date Planted*	*Dimensions*	
Bedgebury House			83′ × 8′ 5″ (1966)[1]
Bedgebury House			75′ × 6′ 9″ (1966)
Bicton		36′ × 4′ 4″ (1906)	79′ × 7′ 2½″ (1968)
Bicton			70′ × 3′ 0″ (1968)
Killerton			69′ × 7′ 9″ (1970)
Coldrennick		30′ (1927)	57′ × 6′ 0″ (1970)
Scorrier House	1871	36′ × 3′ 9″ (1928)	48′ × 4′ 4″ (1965)
Cowdray Park	ca.1872		45′ × 7′ 2″ (1967)
Tregrehan		25′ × 3′ 0″ (1931)	53′ × 6′ 4″ (1971)
Westonbirt (Loop Walk)		50′ × 3′ 11″ (1931)	70′ × 4′ 7″ (1971)
Westonbirt (Willesley)			68′ × 3′ 11″ (1971)
Endsleigh			64′ × 5′ 7″ (1963)
Rossie Priory		41′ × 3′ 7″ (1931)	50′ × 4′ 3″ (1970)
Ardkinglas (Strone)			62′ × 7′ 0″ (1969)
Benenden House			74′ × 7′ 2″ (1970)
Benenden House			80′ × 6′ 2″ (1970)
Petworth House			80′ × 5′ 1″ (1971)
Fenagh House	1890		57′ × 7′ 3″ (1968)
Fenagh House	1890		60′ × 4′ 6″ (1968)
Powerscourt		30′ × 4′ (1931)	47′ × 5′ 4″ (1966)
Tubney Wood	1906		55′ × 3′ 1″ (1966)
Little Hall	1906	16′ × 10½″ (1931)	38′ × 3′ 4″ (1961)
St. Clere	1912		50′ × 5′ 6″ (1969)
Bedgebury	1926		41′ × 3′ 1″ (1969)

[1] Second stem × 5 feet 9 inches

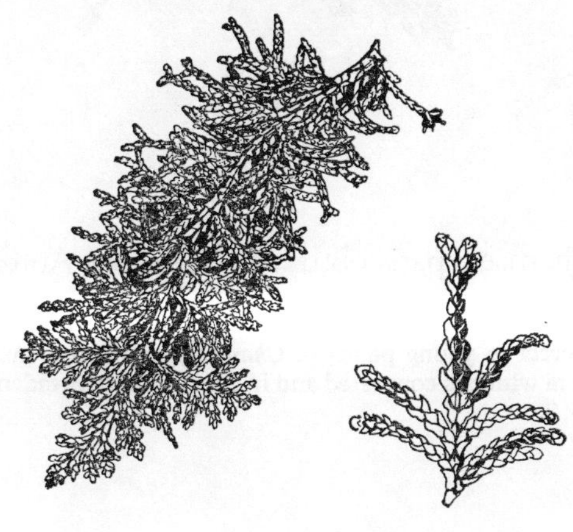

Chamaecyparis obtusa cv. Filicoides

Fig. 59
Hanging branchlet-system of *Chamaecyparis obtusa* cv. Filicoides. Branchlets are bright green on the "upper" side, margined white on the "under" side (right × 1⅓).

cv. Filicoides (Japan. Introduced 1861). A gaunt fairly narrow small tree with level branches. The foliage is short, dense, flat minor branchlets strung down long branchlets making a rectangular, narrow, arched, then hanging spray. Where the branchlet systems have been shed, the base of the shoot is very rough. A curious tree, unattractive as a whole but the bright green frond-like sprays are themselves highly decorative.

A tree at Scorrier is dated (Report 1932) as 1858. It is presumably an original plant from 1861 material and was 47ft × 4ft 9in in 1959. None other is nearly so big; Warnham Court, 33ft × 2ft 1in + 1ft 9in (1971); Hergest Croft, 30ft × 1ft 6in (main stem 1969); Wakehurst Place, 35ft × 2ft 6in (1964); Bedgebury planted 1925, 20ft × 1ft 5in (1966).

var. formosana (Hayata) Rehder. Formosa, 1910. A rare variety now seen in a few collections, and very distinct. The foliage resembles that of a *Thuja* but is rich shiny green on both sides and has broad scale-leaves with acuminate tips.
cv. Lycopodiodes (Japan. Introduced in 1861). A tree rather like 'Filicoides' in general aspect and, contrary to the literature, by no means a dwarf either. Few, level branches bear at their ends upturned, dense bunches of twisted, partly fasciated branchlets. From a distance a gaunt and dark grey-green tree; the foliage close to is bright green in places and strongly marked with grey-white on what would normally be the underside; especially on the fasciated parts. A poor, dull tree, but the foliage is interesting if not beautiful. It is found only in the larger gardens.

The oldest of known date is at Scorrier, planted in 1868, 44ft × 4ft 0in in 1965. A probable contemporary at Tregrehan is 52ft × 4ft 9in (1971) and another at Pencarrow is 44ft × 4ft 5in (1970). Other large plants are: Nymans, 49ft × 2ft 6in (1970); Linton Park, 37ft × 2ft 2in (1965); Coldrenick, 45ft × 3ft 8in (1957); Leonardslee, 35ft × 4ft 0in (1969); New Court, 38ft × 2ft 3in (1964); Bicton, 42ft × 2ft 1in (1968); Kilmacurragh, 38ft × 3ft 8in (1966); Haldon Grange, 45ft × 4ft 2in (1967); Westonbirt, 40ft × 2ft 3in (1969); Tregothnan 52ft × 5ft 2in (1971).

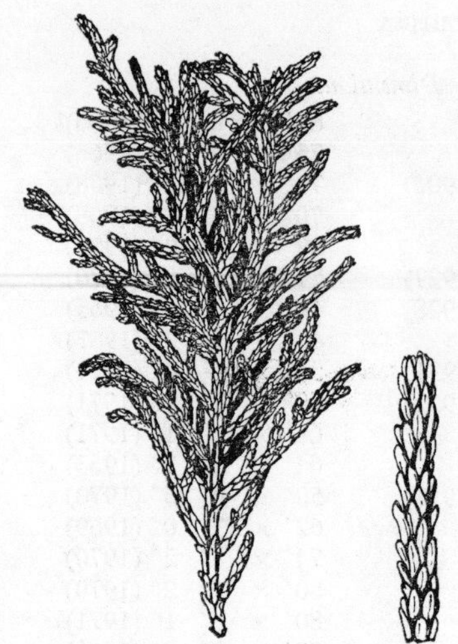

Chamaecyparis obtusa cv. Lycopodioides

Fig. 60
Spray from *Chamaecyparis obtusa* cv. Lycopodioides, a form with congested, partially fasciated foliage. The enlarged shoot (lower right ×2) shows the many rows of leaves with slightly projecting tips.

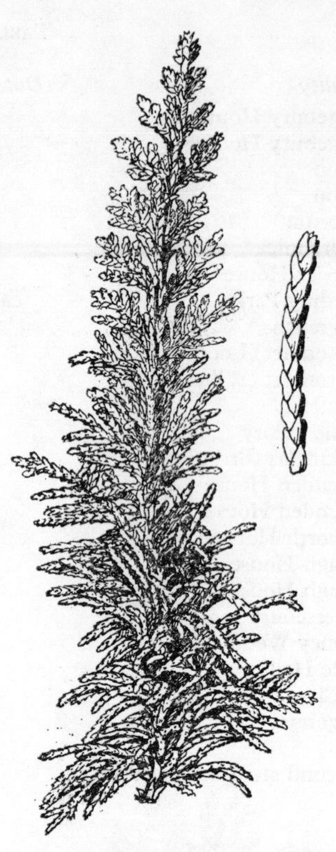

Chamaecyparis obtusa cv. Tetragona Aurea

Fig. 61
Foliage, erect in young plants of *Chamaecyparis obtusa* cv. Tetragona Aurea which is congested and in exposed parts, golden. Shoot on right ×2.

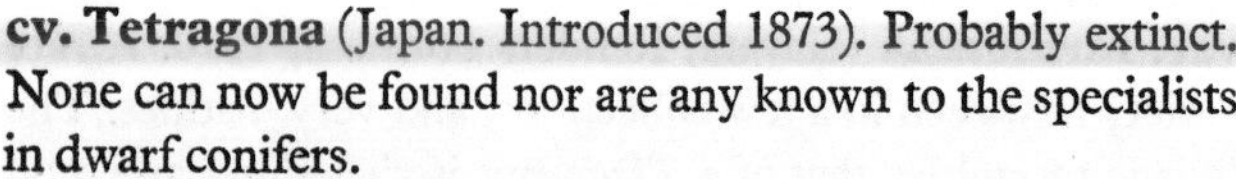

cv. Tetragona (Japan. Introduced 1873). Probably extinct. None can now be found nor are any known to the specialists in dwarf conifers.

cv. Tetragona Aurea (Japan. Introduced 1876). Another plant often noted as a dwarf but wrongly so. As a young tree, erect, narrow, with few branches, level then curving up to vertical at the tips, and densely clothed in bunched branchlets. Each is lanceolate, slender to 15 cm long. Toward the tip, the opposite-placed branchlets are flat, regular and light green, but with narrow, acute but very blunt round-tipped leaves; further back there is a tangle of square-sectioned unbranched shoots, curved and largely pale yellow. Old trees tall ovoid or broadly columnar. Quite frequently planted and one of the brightest golden conifers, but an awkward, spiky outline.

Tongs Wood, 38ft, and 32ft×2ft 3in main stem (1968); Bicton, 35ft×1ft 11in (1968); Grayswood Hill, 34ft×2ft 4in main stem (1968); Nymans, 30ft×3ft 2in (1970) main stem (1966); Wakehurst Place, 24ft (1970); Pencarrow, 23ft×3ft 9in (at 1ft 1970); Tregrehan 43ft×3ft 7in (1971).

Chamaecyparis pisifera (Siebold and Zuccarini) Endlicher. Sawara cypress

Central and Southern Japan. Introduced 1861. Abundant everywhere in the form of cultivars, but the type tree is uncommon and often unrecognised as such. It is, however, found in many large gardens and a few small ones in the south, west and north but is rare in East Anglia.

Bark. Rich rufous or dark red-brown, closely and finely fissured into long, straight flat ridges which shred a little. In old trees the ridges curl in groups and large pieces lift clear of the bole. Algae can discolour the bark grey-pink.
Crown. Broadly conic with pointed top. The straight, smooth very cylindrical bole frequently forks at 5–6 feet from the ground. Low branches sweep out level then curl upwards with little interior foliage making an open crown. Low branches may layer and make a ring of quite large boles.
Foliage. The branches end in fairly dense, slightly upturned, then spreading sprays with space between those from each branch and thus not a dense crown. The scale-leaves are narrowly acute with sharp, slightly spreading points; bright rather yellowish green, becoming dark; marked with bright white beneath. In the hand it is light, dry and rough and when crushed is acridly resin-scented.
Flowers and Cones. Male flowers abundant on the tips of smallest divisions; minute. Pollen is shed in late April. Cones often abundant, crowded across the sprays well back from the tips, pea-like, globular, 0·5 cm across, green bloomed white, ripening dark brown; few scales, flat with a minute spine in the centre.
Growth. Height growth is slow, just exceeding one foot per year at best. Growth in girth is moderate and sustained. There are few dated trees but several have grown more than one inch in girth per year, and older trees re-measured have in several cases increased at this rate, but more are considerably less vigorous.

Chamaecyparis pisifera

Fig. 62
Spray and fresh cones of *Chamaecyparis pisifera*, Sawara cypress, with mature cone above ($\times 2$). The leaves are marked with bright white on the underside of the spray. Shoot-tip $\times 2\frac{2}{3}$.

Table 26. Large Trees of Chamaecyparis pisifera

Locality	*Date Planted*	*Dimensions*	
Scorrier House	1868	45′ × 4′ 2″ (1928)	56′ × 6′ 7″ (1965)
Cowdray Park	1870		77′ × 7′ 3″ (1967)
Cowdray Park	1870		70′ × 6′ 1″ (1967)
Cowdray Park	1870		65′ × 6′ 3″ (1967)
Dropmore			70′ × 11′ 7″ (1970)[1]
Bicton			78′ × 5′ 1″ (1968)
Bicton			72′ × 5′ 9″ (1968)
Stourhead	1881	36′ × 4′ 10″ (1931)	69′ × 6′ 6″ (1970)
Endsleigh			65′ × 6′ 5″ (1970)
Longleat			77′ × 6′ 7″ (1971)
Killerton			75′ × 8′ 4″ (1970)
Wansfell			64′ × 4′ 6″ (1957)
Lythe Hill			62′ × 6′ 5″ (1969)
Linton Park			66′ × 5′ 10″ (1970)
Bedgebury House			63′ × 6′ 5″ (1969)
Wisley R.H.S.G.			67′ × 4′ 10″ (1969)
Inistioge			66′ × 5′ 6″ (1966)[2]
Gurteen le Poer			70′ × 5′ 3″ (1968)[3]
Warnham Court		35′ × 3′ 3″ (1931)	63′ × 4′ 5″ (1971)
Borde Hill		21′ 6″ (1931)	53′ × 3′ 11″ (1968)
Ardkinglas (Strone)			62′ × 6′ 1″ (1969)
Tubney Wood	1906		53′ × 3′ 7″ (1966)
Headfort	1914	17′ × 1′ 6″ (1931)	35′ × 4′ 10″ (1966)
Bedgebury	1926	8′ 2″ (1931)	39′ × 3′ 3″ (1966)
Bedgebury	1926		44′ × 3′ 5″ (1970)

1 Measured at 1 foot (×7ft 1in+6ft 0in at 5 feet)
2 Forty-seven branches layered
3 Layers to 70 feet tall

cv. Argentea (Japan, 1861.) Foliage of the type, coarsely variegated silver. One tree, Bear Wood (Sindlesham), 37ft × 2ft 0in (1970).

cv. Aurea (Japan. Introduced in 1861). A tree like the type, although much slower in growth, and with new shoots a good clear yellow during early summer, fading to greenish yellow. A bright, attractive and shapely tree, but very infrequently seen.

Bodvean, 32ft × 3ft 0in (1960); Busbridge Hall, 37ft × 2ft 10in (1963); Wisley Royal Horticultural Society Gardens, 39ft × 3ft 9in and (estimated), 40ft × 4ft (1964); Wishanger, 27ft × 2ft 8in (1963); Bedgebury, planted 1925, 21ft × 1ft 10in (1966); Kinnettles, 33ft × 3ft 4in (1970).

Chamaecyparis pisifera cv. Filifera

Fig. 63
Foliage of *Chamaecyparis pisifera* cv. Filifera, a form with slender, pendulous shoots, distantly branched. Shoot (×2⅜) shows acute scale-leaves.

cv. Filifera (Japan. Introduced 1861). A mound, domed bush, or slender, gaunt tree, of very dark green, thin foliage on twisted pale brown shoots; mainly threads hanging, with small tufts of branchlets at long intervals. A poor thing, in any form, except the golden one (see below), and very slow.

Tregothnan, 48ft × 5ft 6in (1971); Endsleigh, 66ft × 7ft 3in (reverting) (1970); Stourhead, planted 1891, 47ft × 4ft 0in (1957); Benenden, 49ft × 4ft 4in (1957); Bicton, 58ft × 3ft 4in (1968); Golden Grove, 54ft × 7ft 3in at 3 feet (1960); Kew Royal Botanic Gardens, 44ft × 3ft 3in (1965); Minterne, 55ft × 6ft 5in at 3 feet (1970); Trawscoed, 44ft × 4ft 7in (1969); Killerton, 52ft × 3ft 4in (1970, tree form.)

cv. Filifera Aurea. (Origin not recorded but pre 1889). Varying in shape from a beehive to a gaunt little tree, this is like 'Filifera' but a very good golden colour. It is quite frequent in all sizes of garden.

Little Hall, planted 1906, 28ft × 1ft 8in (1961); Stourhead, planted 1916, 27ft × 3ft 1in (1965); Tregrehan, 35ft × 3ft 8in (1957); Redleaf, 40ft × 3ft 10in at 4ft 1963);) Nymans, 36ft × 3ft 2in (1970); Bicton, 27ft 6in (1968).

Chamaecyparis pisifera cv. Plumosa

Fig. 64
Spray of foliage of *Chamaecyparis pisifera* cv. Plumosa, most frequently seen in the golden form. The dense foliage is made up of spreading leaves (inset ×2⅜).

cv. Plumosa (Japan. Introduced 1861). Broadly conic with a domed top, finally broad columnar, flat-topped, the crown is dense and usually the bole divides into two or three at around 5 feet up. The dense, fluffy foliage points upwards in tufts projecting at the edge of the crown and is yellowish, grey green. Very common especially as a suburban and town-outskirt tree, in parks and churchyards. Many were planted as 'Aurea' and reverted. An original tree, planted in about 1863 at Scorrier is 55ft × 8ft 8in at 4 feet (1959) and this shows the typical rates of growth—slow in height but quite rapid in girth. Another, planted in 1866 at Linton Park was 66ft × 9ft 2in in 1956 but has since died. Very few others are of known date. The biggest are: Longleat, 60ft × 7ft 4in (1971); Cowdray Park, 66ft × 7ft 6in (1967); Lydhurst, 72ft × 3ft 10in+ (1971;) Haldon Grange, 51ft × 7ft 5in (1967); Killerton, 66ft × 6ft 5in (1970); Heckfield Place, 63ft × 8ft 8in (1969); Strone, 63ft × 5ft 0in (1969); Stratfield Saye, 50ft × 7ft 1in (1968); Eggesford, 67ft × 5ft 5in (1970).

cv. Plumosa Aurea (Japan. Introduced 1861). Exactly as 'Plumosa' and at least as rapid in growth; new shoots bright gold on young trees, duller on old, and greenish on inner shoots. Many revert partially or wholly to 'Plumosa', but at Whiteways, Devon, one has partially reverted to the type.

Little Hall, planted 1906, 47ft × 3ft 7in (1961); Fenagh House, planted 1901, 53ft × 5ft 2in and 35ft × 4ft 3in (1968); Bowood, 59ft × 6ft 1in (1968); Westonbirt, Main Drive, 58ft × 5ft 3in (1967); Redleaf, 59ft × 6ft 6in (1963); Melbury, 66ft × 6ft 0in (1971); Wansfell, 60ft × 4ft 1in (1957); Stourhead, 58ft × 7ft 0in (1965); Golden Grove, 64ft × 8ft 3in (1960); Killerton, 59ft × 6ft 8in (1959); The Hendre, 66ft × 7ft 0in (1962); Wisley, 64ft × 6ft 4in (1964); Bicton, 87ft × 5ft 0½in (1968).

cv. Plumosa Albo-picta (Japan. Introduced 1861, probably). A fresh green 'Plumosa' with foliage splashed silvery white and even quite attractive. Seen only at Fota, where 55ft × 4ft 7in (1966).

cv. Squarrosa (Japan. Introduced via Java in 1843). A broad-crowned tree, obtusely pointed and wide-spreading; level low branches sweep upwards at their ends. The bark is red brown, sometimes bright, usually dull, and ridged evenly, as in the type. Frequently the bole divides at 5–6 feet but a few trees have a single stem to the tip. Foliage very dense on the outer crown; large, rounded, crowded bunches of blue-grey, soft, fluffy shoots, with brown, dead foliage internally. The leaves are linear, soft, flat 0·5 cm long, in pairs or fours.

Growth is slow in height but quite rapid in girth except in old trees. Scorrier, planted 1861, 56ft × 8ft 8in (1959); Linton Park, planted 1866, 68ft × 4ft 11in (main stem) (1965); Bodnant, planted 1890, 61ft × 6ft 9in (1966); Fenagh House, planted 1896, 44ft × 5ft 6in (1968); Bedgebury, planted 1926, 35ft × 3ft 8in (1966). Undated large trees: Endsleigh, 57ft × 7ft 1in (1970); Golden Grove, 52ft × 7ft 3in (1960); Redleaf, 63ft × 6ft 0in, single stem to the top (1963); Wisley Royal Horticultural Society Gardens, 63ft × 5ft 2in (1971); Lydhurst, 67ft × 5ft 2in, good long bole (1971); Dupplin Castle, 67ft × 7ft 1in (1970); Kitlands, 64ft × 6ft 8in, bole 34 feet (1965); Moss Wood, Leith Hill, 64ft × 8ft 3in, bole 14ft (1967); Westonbirt, Main Drive, 60ft × 4ft 8in (1967); Bicton, 70ft × 5ft 0in (1968); Capenoch, 62ft × 6ft 11in (1970); Killerton (Chapel), 60ft × 5ft 8in (1970).

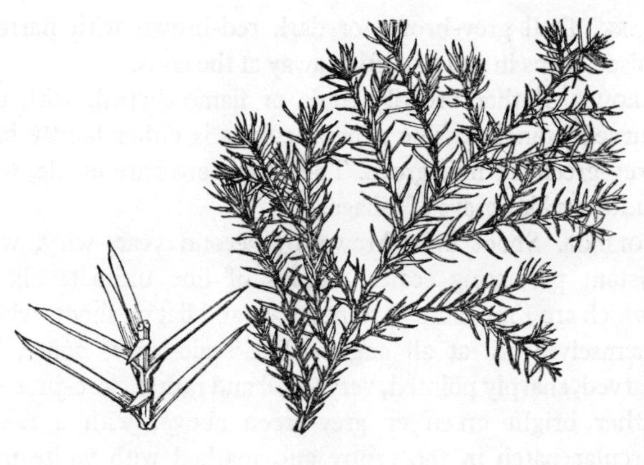

Chamaecyparis pisifera cv. Squarrosa

Fig. 65
Foliage of *Chamaecyparis pisifera* cv. Squarrosa. The spreading leaves (left × 2) are soft, and in the mass the foliage is pale blue-grey and fluffy.

Chamaecyparis thyoides (L) Britton, Sterns and Poggenberg. White cypress

Near the coast from Maine to Mississippi. Introduced 1736 or possibly 1680. A rather scarce tree, found in collections and a few large gardens, mainly in the South and West. Very rare in Scotland.

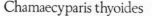

Chamaecyparis thyoides

Fig. 66
Foliage and cones of *Chamaecyparis thyoides*. The sprays are fine, dense and short, and the leaves (right × 6) have a prominent central gland.

Bark. Dull grey-brown or dark red-brown with narrow, raised strips in spirals, lifting away at the ends.
Crown. Rather broadly conic or flame-shaped, with up-curved branches. The general colour is either faintly blue grey-green, or mid-green. The shoots are bare inside, with sudden wide sprays of foliage.
Foliage. Shoot light brown by second year, wiry, with distant projecting scales. Sprays of fine ultimate shoots (which are 1 mm across) rather open and flat on shoots which themselves are at all angles. The scale-leaves acute, incurved, sharply pointed, very small and rather close-pressed, either bright green or grey-green above, with a raised circular patch in the centre and marked with white near their bases above and particularly on the underside; sometimes obscure. The slender foliage when crushed has a rather gingery, hot aroma.
Flowers and Cone. Male flowers tiny on the ends of smallest branchlets. Cones 0·6 cm across, roughly globular, slightly spined, few-scaled, bloomed blue-grey, ripening dark brown.
Recognition. The description is similar in many respects to *Ch. pisifera*, but the tree is very different and the fine branchlets in irregular, short angular sprays are quite distinct and are more like a species of *Cupressus*.

Growth and Specimens. Growth is slow, normally very slow, although one of the only two trees of known date is 36ft × 3ft 2in after only 40 years, at Bedgebury. It is a short-lived tree and none of the five given by Elwes and Henry in 1907–8, has been found. An old tree at Bedgebury, probably 90 years old, has lost one of its two stems; the other is 47ft × 4ft 4in (1970). The only other trees of comparable size are: Borde Hill, planted 1922, 41ft × 3ft 2in (1970); Kew Royal Botanic Gardens, 42ft × 2ft 5in (1956); Woburn, 45ft × 3ft 5in (1961); Eastnor Castle, 45ft × 5ft 0in (1969); Bicton, 50ft × 3ft 6½in; 48ft × 3ft 2in (1968); Nymans, 40ft × 3ft 4in (bluish form) and 43ft × 2ft 10in (green form) (1970); Tongs Wood, 38ft × 2ft 9in (1968). A tree at Endsleigh, 36ft × 2ft 2in main stem (1963) was labelled 'fastigiata' a cultivar now believed lost, and it seemed of normal habit. Another there labelled 'atrovirens glauca' (25ft × 2ft 8in) is a contradiction in terms as 'atrovirens' is described (Den Ouden and Boom) as grass-green lacking any trace of glaucous colouring, and probably no longer in cultivation. cv. Glauca is 20ft × 1ft 5in at Edinburgh Royal Botanic Garden (1970).

Cryptomeria Don (Taxodiaceae)

A genus of a single species found in China and Japan, and, in the latter country growing to a great size and long-lived. It most resembles, and is closely related to, *Sequoiadendron*, differing from it in having less closely appressed scale-leaves arranged in five ranks instead of three. In cultivation over a long period in Japan, it has produced numerous forms, mostly dwarfs.

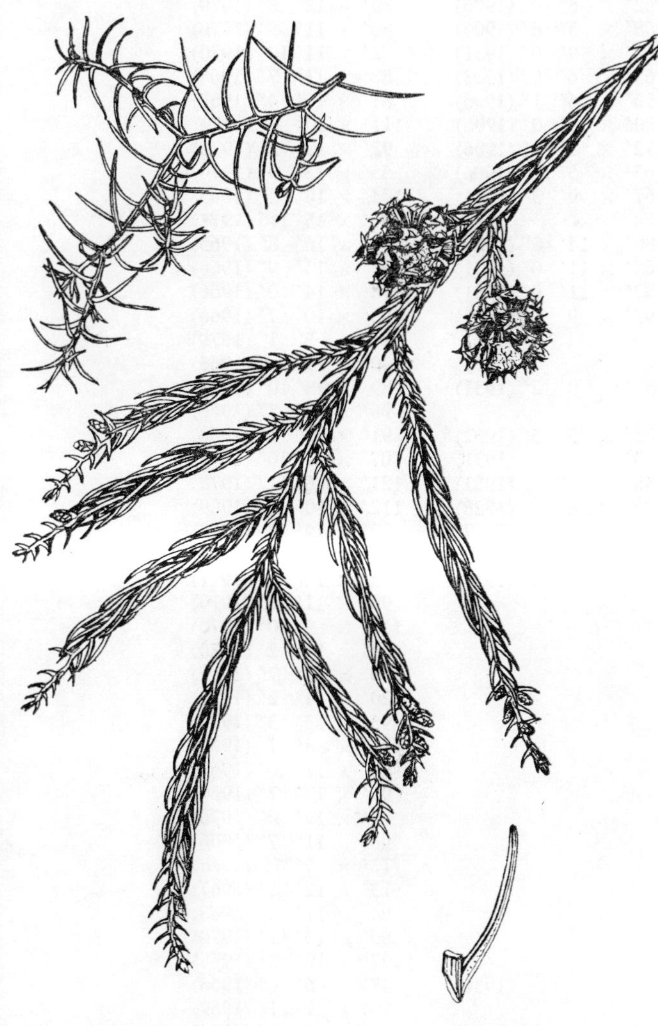

Cryptomeria japonica cv. Elegans
Cryptomeria japonica

Fig. 67
Foliage, male flowers (partly shed) and cones of *Cryptomeria japonica* retained for a second year. Bottom right a leaf ×1⅓. Upper left, foliage of cv. Elegans, a permanently juvenile form.

Cryptomeria japonica. (Linnaeus fil.) Don. Japanese cedar

China and Japan. Introduced from China in 1842; from Japan in 1861. Common in large gardens all over the country, though less in the eastern half than in the western. Occasional in small gardens, parks and churchyards, but not a tree generally seen away from large gardens.

BARK. Dark red-brown to bright orange-brown, deeply fissured in old trees into long thick, often spiralled, ridges which peel and fret away in long shallow strips or in thick, heavy ridges. Nearly black in some old trees or pink-grey with algae. Old trees in the west, may also have large pap-shaped protuberances pointing downwards in groups on the bole or underneath big low branches.

CROWN. Narrowly conic to a point and very open when young. Older trees may retain acute, pointed and rather thin crowns or become broader and domed, when they are usually very densely crowned. In the open, huge, low branches may develop, level for many feet then sharply upcurved. Amongst other trees, even in fairly open conditions, splendid clean cylindrical boles are found. Many old trees are extensively layered.

FOLIAGE. Stout shoots curving downwards and outwards, bear smaller but still quite stout shoots ascending and ending in open bunches of long cord-like branchlets. The Chinese form—which must include at least all trees planted before 1862—has open, lax foliage with long leaves; the Japanese forms vary but are more densely bunched and have shorter leaves.

LEAVES. Large, scale-like, with long, strongly forward-inclined then incurved, broad-ridged points, to 1·5 cm long (on assumed Chinese form). They are shiny deep green on the outside with two broad grey-green bands separated by a ridge, on the inside.

FLOWERS AND CONE. Male flowers grouped in nodding terminal clusters of about 20, on most or all side-shoots, each flower ovoid, 2 mm, pale green in autumn; pale yellow in winter and shedding pollen in February or, if delayed by long cold periods, in late March. Female flowers terminal on short side shoots, down-turned green rosettes, like daisy buds, with pointed scales. Cones, frequent on trees only 5–6 years planted and copious on some old trees but lacking entirely on others; globular, 2 cm across, green and rough with 5–6 curved hooks on the outer half of each of the ±20 scales; erect on curved 2 cm stalks, ripen dull dark brown and remain attached until spring.

GROWTH. This species can be very vigorous in the west but is less so in the east. Annual shoots of well over 3 feet are seen. Growth starts late in the year, about early June and may cease in August but if a leading shoot is damaged or killed a replacement may grow rapidly until late September. Growth in height falls off considerably with age and in many trees has ceased at about 80ft. Girth in growth can be rapid in early years but is very variable, some trees maintaining a rapid rate even when very big and others never achieving more than a very slow increase. Some representative rates of growth are shown in Table 27.

cv. Araucarioides (Japan. To Holland, 1859). A curious, rather strong-growing form with long, slender, distant and unbranched branchlets, pendulous.

TABLE 27. SPECIMENS OF CRYPTOMERIA JAPONICA

Locality	*Date Planted*	*Dimensions*	
Ardnagashel	ca.1845		55′ × 14′ 2″ (1966)
Dropmore	1847	62′ × 6′ 7″ (1906)	82′ × 11′ 2″ (1970)
Dropmore	1847	64′ × 5′ 6″ (1906)	75′ × 10′ 8″ (1970)
Bury Hill	1847	80′ × 7′ 2″ (1931)	75′ × 7′ 11″ (1971)
Pencarrow	1849	62′ × 8′ 0″ (1906)	85′ × 12′ 8″ (1970)
Pencarrow	1849	68′ × 5′ 6″ (1906)	80′ × 11′ 3″ (1970)
Keir House	1851	62′ × 9′ 6″ (1931)	72′ × 11′ 10″ (1970)
Coollattin	1853	63′ × 6′ 0″ (1903)	88′ × 11′ 7″ (1968)
Castle Kennedy	1856	56′ × 6′ 1″ (1906)	81′ × 10′ 4″ (1967)
Hemstead (Benenden)		80′ × 8′ 0″ (1906)	111′ × 10′ 8″ (1970)
Hemstead (Benenden)		72′ × 8′ 2″ (1906)	92′ × 12′ 3″ (1970)
Eastnor Castle		65′ × 5′ 10″ (1906)	55′ × 11′ 0″ (1970)[1]
Fonthill (1)		67′ × 9′ 3″ (1906)	104′ × 10′ 4″ (1963)
Monk Coniston			95′ × 15′ 11″ (1971)
Trevarrick Hall		70–80′ × 14′ 8″ (1929)	77′ × 16′ 8″ (1965)
Fota		68′ × 11′ 0″ (1931)	97′ × 13′ 9″ (1966)
Fota		82′ × 11′ 0″ (1931)	98′ × 14′ 0″ (1966)
Fota		92′ × 9′ 0″ (1931)	102′ × 10′ 7″ (1966)
Bolderwood	1860		91′ × 9′ 1″ (1970)
Powerscourt	1860		80′ × 11′ 8″ (1966)
Curraghmore	1861	57′ × 9′ 2″ (1931)	89′ × 13′ 10″ (1968)
Curraghmore			96′ × 12′ 7″ (1968)
Blackmoor	1869	83′ × 5′ 5″ (1931)	91′ × 9′ 1″ (1968)
Embley Park		83′ (1931)	107′ × 11′ 10″ (1971)
Woodhouse		88′ (1931)	121′ × 8′ 11″ (1970)
Bicton		95′ × 8′ 9″ (1928)	112′ × 10′ 7″ (1968)
Lamellan		70–80′ (1927)	87′ × 12′ 2″ (1963)
Lamellan			70′ × 13′ 5″ (1963)
Tregrehan		70′ × 11′ 0″ (1931)	85′ × 12′ 7″ (1971)
Leighton Hall			98′ × 11′ 8″ (1970)
Coldrennick			113′ × 9′ 0″ (1970)
Sindlesham (Bear Wood)			100′ × 14′ 2″ (1970)
Northerwood House			100′ × 12′ 7″ (1969)
Endsleigh			120′ × 14′ 2″ (1970)
Endsleigh			93′ × 13′ 3″ (1970)
Fonthill (2)			115′ × 8′ 7″ (1965)
Haffield House			88′ × 11′ 0″ (1966)
Derreen			95′ × 13′ 7″ (1966)
Taymouth Castle			97′ × 11′ 0″ (1970)
Inistioge			96′ × 11′ 7″ (1966)
Bodnant	1877		72′ × 9′ 10″ (1966)
Biel			73′ × 12′ 1″ (1967)
Post Green			94′ × 11′ 3″ (1968)
Munches			80′ × 10′ 11″ (1970)
Humewood Castle			97′ × 10′ 2″ (1968)
Fenagh House	1896	28′ (1931)	47′ × 6′ 6″ (1968)
Leonardslee	ca.1905		75′ × 7′ 11″ (1969)
Tubney Wood	1906		66′ × 4′ 5″ (1966)
Little Hall	1908	41′ × 2′ 11½″ (1931)	65′ × 5′ 8″ (1961)
Speech House (1)	1916		74′ × 5′ 3″ (1963)
Bedgebury	1926		65′ × 6′ 8″ (1969)
Bedgebury	1926		58′ × 7′ 1″ (1969)
Bedgebury (plot)	1933		53′ × 3′ 0″ (1965)
Westonbirt	1936		49′ × 4′ 7″ (1969)
Speech House (2)	1951		34′ × 2′ 4″ (1966)

[1] Stem broken

Borde Hill, planted 1927, 61ft × 4ft 4in (1960); Leonardslee, 70ft × 6ft 5in many stems from 20 feet (1962); Curraghmore, 34ft × 4ft 1in (1968).

cv. Compacta (Paris, 1877). Small round-topped tree, short branches. Foliage bright yellow-green, densely bunched like 'Cristata' but not fasciated. Wakehurst Place, 25ft × 2ft 1in (1970).

cv. Cristata (Japan. Introduced to Germany in 1900). Rather a narrow tree with few branches, short and upturned at the ends, but not gaunt because they carry much foliage. The leaves are partly normal on short shoots but amongst these shoots are congested and fasciated bunches with short, hard leaves. Despite appearance of the foliage, this is far from a dwarf form. It is decidedly rare.

Busbridge Hall, 48ft × 2ft 10in (1963); Tittenhurst Park, 49ft × 4ft 4in (1963); Bedgebury, 38ft × 2ft 2in (1971); Windsor Great Park, 33ft × 1ft 11in (1967).

cv. Dacrydioides. Branches spreading, upswept at ends; shoots long, unbranched, with distant, star-like whorls of unbranched minor shoots radiating in bunches of mixed lengths. Bedgebury, 25ft × 2ft 6in (1969).

cv. Elegans (Japan. Introduced in 1861). A broad, rounded-conic tree, apt to bend over in a hoop-shape or to have several main stems splayed out. Its grey-blue fuzzy foliage is in very dense bunches and turns pale purplish red at the tips in winter. The slender shoots are twisted and pale green with 1·5 cm-long leaves curved backwards and shiny, slightly bluish green both sides. Common, often seen in quite small gardens. Good trees are straight and unusual in texture and colour but the cultivar name is all too often quite inept. Growth is slow in the east but reasonably rapid, in girth at least, in the west and in Ireland. The largest trees noted are: two at Ashford Castle both 60ft × 10ft 0in (1968); Bicton, 60ft × 9ft 6in (1967); Derreen, 70ft × 9ft 7in (1966); Glendurgan, 62ft × 9ft 6in (1960); Pencarrow, 68ft × 9ft 8in at 3 feet (1970); Stonefield, 45ft × 9ft 2in (1969); Golden Grove, 56ft × 7ft 6in (1960); Luscombe Castle, 72ft × 9ft 5in (1970); Boconnoc, 63ft × 8ft 4in (1970).

cv. Lobbii. (Japan. Introduced via Java in 1853). A fair proportion of cryptomerias everywhere is of this form. The crown is narrowly conic even in the oldest trees, with short branches upturned at the ends and bearing dense bunches of foliage. This gives the crown a very uneven outline and varying density, allowing recognition from a distance. The top is a dense tuft like those lower down. One young tree of known date has grown as fast as those of the type beside it, and the largest Cryptomeria of any sort is a cv. Lobbii indicating that the rate of growth is similar to that of the type.

Two original trees survive at Dropmore—planted 1853, 85ft × 7ft 6in and 68ft × 7ft 0in (1970). The huge tree at Boconnoc, 92ft × 17ft 5in in 1970 has a most splendid bole; it was 80ft × 13ft in 1927. Other big trees are: Ashford Castle 94ft × 7ft 1in (1968); Lytchett Heath, 85ft × 10ft 5in (1966); Endsleigh, 118ft × 8ft 10in; 105ft × 9ft 6in (1970); (N. Devon), 90ft × 11ft 9in (1970); Killerton, 84ft × 7ft 2in (1970); Westonbirt, (largest) 89ft × 8ft 0in (1967) and a young tree planted 1936, 59ft × 4ft 6in (1969).

cv. Lycopodioides (Japan, 1875). Tall wide bush, many stemmed, wide spreading drooping scarcely branched shoots, lacking the bunched whorls of 'Dacrydioides'. Wakehurst Place, 25ft × 2ft 7in (1970).

cv. Pungens (China. Introduced in 1861). Extremely rare—known only from one tree at Abbeyleix; 45ft × 3ft in 1968. The leaves are very short, very dark green, spreading, stiff and sharp.

var. sinensis. (Siebold and Zuccarini.) Many of the biggest trees are of this form. (See opening paragraphs under this species).

Cunninghamia R. Brown ex Richard (Taxodiaceae)

Two closely related species from China and Formosa. Leaves long-tapered, hard and spiny, bright green, lying in two ranks.

Cunninghamia konishii Hayata.

Formosa. Introduced in 1918. Very rare; found only in a few collections. Young plants hardly differ from *C. lanceolata*. Leaves shorter, 2–4 cm×0·3 cm radiating more or less perpendicular to shoot or pectinate, arched downwards, a few vertical and swept backwards; many vertically spreading beneath; glossy yellowish-green above, slightly purple-bronzed in winter; two pale greenish white bands beneath.

Borde Hill, planted ca. 1928, 36ft×2ft 3in (1969); Sheffield Park, 20ft (1960); Woburn, 24ft (1961); Castlewellan, 23ft×3ft 0in (1970).

Cunninghamia lanceolata

Fig. 68
Foliage of *Cunninghamia lanceolata*. The leaves are spined but not rigid. Some have two narrow white lines on the upper surface, and all have broad bands on the underside, of varying whiteness. Leaf showing under-surface, right.

Cunninghamia lanceolata (Lambert) Hooker fil.

Central and Southern China. Introduced in 1804 and one tree probably of this origin is known, at Claremont, Surrey. Most of the other known trees of early date derive from a second import in 1844. A rather rare tree confined to collections and large gardens mainly across the south of England and in eastern Ireland; very rare in the Midlands, East Anglia and north west England; extremely rare in Scotland.

BARK. Rich chestnut-red, ridged vertically by shallow, narrow, parallel, long fissures; finely stringy; sometimes dull grey brown with wide vertical stringy fissures.

CROWN. Columnar, narrow or broad, with a domed top. There are few branches and the bole is untapered in its clear lengths, losing diameter abruptly at the insertion of the branches. Foliage shoots are long and somewhat hanging in thriving trees; short, leaving an open crown in trees not thriving.

SHOOT. Pale shiny green; second year orange-brown above, bright pale green below.

LEAVES. Broadest right at the base (to 5 mm); tapering evenly throughout their length to a fine point, 3–7 cm; pectinate below the shoot, roughly pectinate above but many leaves curve up over the shoot and bend backwards, others curve forwards and those at the side bend downwards at the tip. Dark glossy green above with a raised midrib and raised margins; two broad bands below silvery white in some; greenish white in others. Leaves at the base of shoots and all those in upper crown have two clear narrow white bands on the upper surface.

FLOWERS AND CONE. Male flowers 6 or more in a terminal bunch like a flower head.

Cones fusiform, long-pointed, to 4 cm long; scales stiff, forward-pointing with abrupt, incurved spine-tips.

GROWTH. Young trees can make quite rapid growth in height, once the plant is more than 3–4 feet tall; before this it is liable to be killed by frost. Shoots of two feet may be grown for several years. Growth in girth is fairly steady and moderately rapid as can be seen from the Table 28.

SPECIMENS. The tree at Claremont is thought to be an original plant, and the older tree at Dropmore could also be.

cv. Glauca. Not a strikingly different form but the upper side of the leaf is bloomed blue-grey on dark blue-green, which gives the tree a silvery sheen; leaf 4×0·4 cm.

Bedgebury, planted 1926, 37ft×2ft 9in (1969); Borde Hill, 49ft×3ft 5in (1970).

TABLE 28. SOME SPECIMENS OF CUNNINGHAMIA LANCEOLATA

Locality	*Date Planted*	*Dimensions*	
Claremont	1819		52′ × 6′ 2″ (1965)
Bicton		56′ × 4′ 10″ (1906)	105′ × 7′ 10″ (1968)
Killerton		62′ × 4′ 0″ (1904)	82′ × 7′ 8″ (1970)
Escot		45′	69′ × 7′ 5″ (1965)
Dropmore	prob.1822		56′ × 4′ 10″ (1970)
Dropmore	prob.1832		52′ × 4′ 4″ (1970)
Longleat			76′ × 6′ 2″ (1971)
Pencarrow	1850	40′ × 4′ 8″ (1905)	79′ × 8′ 8″ (1970)
Glendurgan		55′ × 6′ 5″ (1928)	61′ × 7′ 0″ (1959)
Trebah		50′ (1928)	80′ × 7′ 2″ (1959)
Tregrehan		40′ × 7′ 6″ (1931)	71′ × 8′ 4″ (1971)
Powerscourt		36′ × 4′ 0″ (1931)	44′ × 5′ 2″ (1966)
Mount Usher			62′ × 7′ 10″ (1966)
Mount Usher			62′ × 7′ 1″ (1966)
Lamellan		25′ (1930)	63′ × 5′ 5″ (1963)[1]
Oakley Park			59′ × 6′ 3″ (1971)
Benenden			62′ × 4′ 4″ (1970)
Sandling Park	1905		30′ × 2′ 10″ (1965)
Headfort	1914	13′ 6″ (1931)	35′ × 3′ 2″ (1966)
Stanage Park	1914		48′ × 3′ 4″ (1970)
Crarae	1917	7′ 2″ (1931)	43′ × 2′ 11″ (1969)
Bedgebury	1925		60′ × 2′ 11″ (1968)[1]
Bedgebury	1925		50′ × 4′ 4″ (1970)
Westonbirt	1932		35′ × 3′ 0″ (1966)

[1] Main stem

× Cupressocyparis Dallimore (Cupressaceae)

A hybrid genus which covers all crosses between species of the two genera *Cupressus* and *Chamaecyparis*. Whilst several are known or suspected, only one, the Leyland cypress has hitherto been described. The arrangement of the foliage is variable among the clones most commonly planted. The use of terms like "shoot", "branchlet", "branchlet systems" and "spray" is quite inadequate and each has been used in too many different meanings to be useful here. The conventional hierarchy of branching, 1st order, 2nd order, etc. can be used safely only in the presence of the whole tree, otherwise it is not evident at which order to start.

Therefore a reversed system is used here, starting from the ultimate, finest divisions. These are "A". They arise from "B shoots" which are pinnae on "C shoots" which may be pinnae on "D shoots". "D shoots" are usually of too diffuse and indefinite origin for a further category to be meaningful.

×**Cupressocyparis leylandii** (Jackson and Dallimore) Dallimore. Leyland cypress.

Chamaecyparis nootkatensis × *Cupressus macrocarpa*. Leighton Park, 1888 and 1911. Six seedlings from Nootka cypress cones picked in 1888 were sent to be planted at Haggerston Castle, Northumberland, in 1892. Cuttings from one, or possibly more, of these were taken and 3 resulting plants were put in Kyloe Wood in the same county, in 1897. One was evidently sent, unrecorded, at about this time to Inveraray, perhaps in 1906 when another cutting was planted in Kyloe Wood. Later in about 1916 more were sent out, 2 to Bicton and 4 to Headfort. Five of the six trees at Haggerston survive as do all the others mentioned.

In 1911 cones were picked from a Monterey cypress at Leighton Hall, and in 1912 two seedlings were planted, widely separated, on the hill behind. These are easily distinguishable in foliage from the earlier seedlings and from each other, and neither was propagated until 1926. In 1925 these trees were brought to the notice of W. Dallimore who acquired foliage from two at Haggerston and one at Leighton, and described and propagated them. The Leighton tree he had was the one still there, known as cv. 'Leighton Green'. The other or 'Naylor's Blue' was propagated only after it was overthrown by a small whirlwind in 1954. It was then 90ft×5ft 4in. After 1927 the Haggerston trees were extensively propagated and cuttings were planted around Leighton Hall and elsewhere. The only pre-1927 plantings known have been mentioned. The cv. 'Leighton Green' was also planted in a number of places, but being more difficult to root it has remained much less common, except in Ireland. Leyland cypress is now common as a young tree and hedge-plant, but the big trees are confined to collections and large gardens.

BARK. At first, smooth, dark brown-green. On older trees, dark brown shallowly ridged vertically, flaking somewhat, later stringy.

CROWN. All forms similar, columnar; in shade narrow; in the open flame-shaped with upswept branches, nearly always dense until a few feet below the tip where the leader emerges, slightly crooked at its base and leaning to one side, slender and thinly foliaged. This, and the darker foliage, distinguish this hybrid from *C. macrocarpa* at a distance, for the latter has a crown either evenly dense to the tip with a straight but hardly visible leading shoot, or a long straight, spikily feathered leader, with level shoots projecting. In West Ireland, and County Wicklow, crowns are hugely broad.

FOLIAGE

General. Main ("D") shoots yellow-green, then pink-brown, then dark purple-brown (orange-brown in one clone). "C" shoots bright yellow-green. Scale-leaves acute to a finely rounded, mucronate point, slightly incurved; ridged through a central gland. Shaded foliage has spreading points; foliage at shoot-tips is terete, and between the two it is intermediate.

The main clones differ in the arrangement and colours of the foliage, as follows:

cv. Haggerston Grey. Ultimate ("A") shoots slender, 1 mm across, widely spaced (about three times their own width), nearly pectinate on "B" shoots, making an open spray. "B" shoots pectinate on "C" shoots on vigorous sprays but at varying angles when less vigorous; "C" shoots, slender, lanceolate plumes or flat sprays at various angles on "D" shoots, the upper ones arching forwards and down. "D" shoots slightly sinuous. In the summer the axis of the "C" shoot becomes a livid yellow. Leaves dark yellow-green above, greyer in summer, brighter grey-green beneath.

cv. Leighton Green. "A" shoots, thick and broad (to 2 mm) closely and more evenly pectinate on "B" shoots, the spaces about equal to the breadth of the shoots. The "B" shoots are thus a regular series of flat diamond-shapes or triangles and are pectinate along "C" shoots. The "C" shoots are long, oblong-lanceolate, fern-like sprays and they also lie flat and pectinate each side of the "D" shoots. "D" shoots stouter than in 'Haggerston Grey' and straight. Leaves thick, ridged, and appear braided in the mass, very like *Ch. nootkatensis:* dark grey-green above, pale grey-green at base beneath. New shoots on young plants have young branchlet systems rather distant and each a thick, dense diamond-shape.

cv. Naylor's Blue. "A" shoots slender, long, angular in cross-section, finely roughened by slightly spreading points, making them serrated, except near shoot-tips. These shoots are mainly flat and pectinate on the "B" shoots, regularly

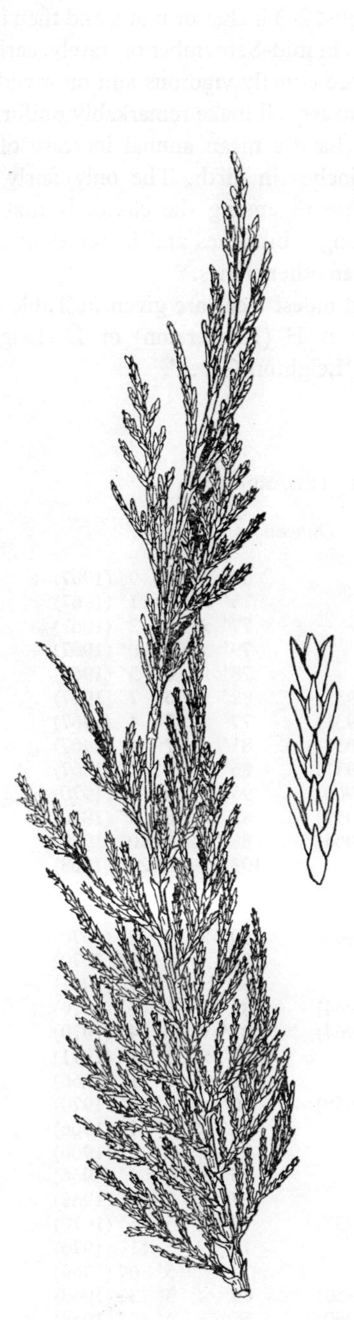

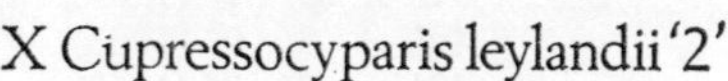

X Cupressocyparis leylandii '2'

Fig. 69
Branchlet of × *Cupressocyparis leylandii*, Leyland cypress, of Clone 2, Haggerston Grey, which has more slender, widely spaced ultimate branchlets and sprays more angular than Clone 11. Shoot on right ×2⅔.

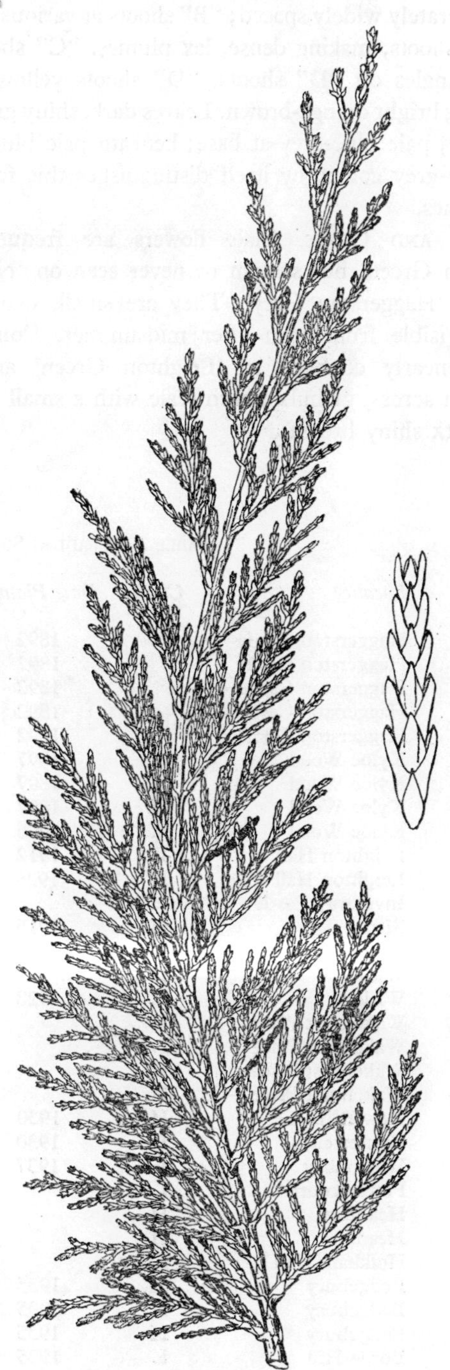

X Cupressocyparis leylandii '11'

Fig. 70
Branchlet of × *Cupressocyparis leylandii*, (Leyland cypress) Clone 11, Leighton Green, showing the broader, usually closely set, ultimate shoots and the regular, flattened branching, compared with Clone 2. The ultimate shoots (×2⅔) are flattened and scale-leaves bluntly tipped.

and moderately widely spaced; "B" shoots at various angles on "C" shoots, making dense, lax plumes. "C" shoots at various angles on "D" shoots. "D" shoots yellow-green becoming bright orange-brown. Leaves dark, shiny greenish blue-grey, pale blue-grey at base; beneath pale blue-grey. The blue-grey colour by itself distinguishes this from all other clones.

FLOWERS AND CONES. Male flowers are frequent on 'Leighton Green' but seldom or never seen on 'Naylor's Blue' or 'Haggerston Grey'. They are small, ovoid and yellow, visible from soon after midsummer. Cones are likewise nearly confined to 'Leighton Green' and are 1·5–2 cm across, globular; each scale with a small central spike, dark shiny brown.

GROWTH. Shoot growth starts very slowly in late April and is slow through May. In June 1–2 inches a week is normal; in July and August 2–3 inches or more, and then it decreases again and ceases in mid-September or, rarely, early October. All the clones are equally vigorous and on a wide range of sites and soils, nearly all make remarkably uniform growth; the older trees have a mean annual increase of 2 feet in height and 2 inches in girth. The only fairly consistent difference in growth among the clones is that 'Leighton Green' has stronger branches and increases in girth rather more rapidly than other clones.

The best and oldest trees are given in Table 29. Clones are given only as H (Haggerston) or L (Leighton), the latter all being 'Leighton Green'.

TABLE 29. LEADING SPECIMENS OF × CUPRESSOCYPARIS LEYLANDII

Locality	*Clone*	*Date Planted*	*Dimensions*	
Haggerston Castle		1892		80′ × 6′ 9″ (1967)
Haggerston Castle		1892		75′ × 5′ 11″ (1967)
Haggerston Castle		1892		77′ × 6′ 2″ (1967)
Haggerston Castle		1892		79′ × 6′ 0″ (1967)
Haggerston Castle		1892		78′ × 6′ 5″ (1967)
Kyloe Wood	H	1897	48′ × 4′ 10″ (1931)	82′ × 6′ 7″ (1967)
Kyloe Wood	H	1897	50′ × 5′ 10″ (1931)	79′ × 7′ 4″ (1967)
Kyloe Wood	H	1897	45′ × 4′ 10″ (1931)	81′ × 7′ 1″ (1967)
Kyloe Wood	H	1906	35′ × 3′ 2″ (1931)	86′ × 6′ 7″ (1967)
Leighton Hall	L	1912	81′ × 8′ 2″ (1960)	95′ × 9′ 8″ (1970)
Leighton Hall	H	1928	65′ × 4′ 9″ (1959)	82′ × 6′ 9″ (1970)
Inveraray Castle	H		64′ × 6′ 4″ (1954)	88′ × 8′ 10″ (1969)[1]
Bicton	H	1916		103′ × 8′ 2½″ (1968)
Bicton	H	ca.1916	81′ × 4′ 11″ (1957)	100′ × 6′ 6″ (1968)
Wisley	H	ca.1928	72′ × 5′ 5″ (1963)	84′ × 6′ 7″ (1970)
Wisley	L	ca.1928	62′ × 5′ 10″ (1963)	80′ × 7′ 2″ (1970)
Wakehurst Place	H			86′ × 4′ 7″ (1970)
Wakehurst Place	L			63′ × 7′ 7″ (1971)
Wakehurst Place	H		77′ × 5′ 9″ (1964)	81′ × 6′ 7″ (1970)
Wakehurst Place	H		77′ × 5′ 6″ (1964)	83′ × 6′ 4″ (1970)
Kew R. B. G.	H	1930		72′ × 3′ 11″ (1971)
Castlewellan	L	1930		66′ × 6′ 1″ (1966)
Westonbirt	L	1937	55′ × 3′ 8″ (1958)	60′ × 5′ 10″ (1970)
Powerscourt	L			54′ × 7′ 1″ (1966)
Headfort	H			73′ × 9′ 2″ (1966)
Headfort	H			75′ × 7′ 8″ (1966)
Holkham Hall	L			67′ × 5′ 4″ (1968)
Bedgebury	H	1935	50′ × 3′ 10″ (1957)	72′ × 5′ 6″ (1970)
Bedgebury	H	1935		75′ × 5′ 11″ (1970)
Bedgebury	H	1935		72′ × 5′ 0″ (1969)
Borde Hill	L	1935	57′ × 4′ 1″ (1960)	69′ × 5′ 3″ (1968)
Borde Hill	L	1935	49′ × 3′ 3″ (1960)	55′ × 4′ 9″ (1968)
Blairquhan				60′ × 5′ 6″ (1970)
Woburn	L	1936		66′ × 3′ 2″ (1970)
Powis Castle (Pinetum)	L			63′ × 5′ 1″ (1970)
Garinish I.	L			50′ × 5′ 10″ (1966)
Westonbirt	L	1937		57′ × 5′ 7″ (1969)
Savill Gardens	H	1947		49′ × 3′ 0″ (1963)
Trent College	H	1948		40′ × 2′ 3″ (1962)
Vivod Arboretum	L	1952		42′ × 2′ 11″ (1971)

[1] Measured at 4 feet

cv. 'Stapehill' Stapehill cypress.

Cones picked from a Monterey cypress (*Cupressus macrocarpa*) in about 1940, at Ferndown and sown at the nurseries of M. Barthélémy at Stapehill. Two aberrant seedlings were retained there and are now 39ft×2ft 9in and 34ft×2ft 10in (1966). One has been much propagated and distributed usually as 'The Stapehill Hybrid'. It is at least as vigorous and sometimes more so than any of the Leyland cypresses, and closely resembles 'Leighton Green' in the layout of its foliage. M. Barthélémy said that there were no Nootka cypress in the vicinity, and none was seen in 1963. L. Gough (in litt.) has analysed the resin and considers this hybrid to be of the same parentage as Leyland cypress, chemically distinct from the others analysed and closer to *C. macrocarpa*.

FOLIAGE. Rather thick and heavy like 'Leighton Green' but darker bluish green in one (tree "20") which is also well marked blue-grey beneath. Shoots bright yellow-green, soon orange-brown then purplish-brown. Both differ from 'Leighton Green' in the uneven outline of the branchlets. "A" shoots are few, rather irregular 1–2 mm broad. "B" shoots of very irregular length with a gap at the base of the "C" shoots with no "B" shoots. "C" shoots taper to end of one year's growth then widen again at the base of next year. These shoots are flat and arise in a vertical plane in the outer half of "D" shoots; flat and plane in inner half.

×**Cupressocyparis notabilis** Mitchell Hybr. nov. Alice Holt cypress

Cupressus glabra×*Chamaecyparis nootkatensis*. 1956 Leighton Hall.

In 1956, J. D. Matthews, decided that the Genetics Section of the Forestry Commission Research Division should collect seed at Leighton Park, to see if more seedling Leyland cypresses could be found. Mr. A. J. Waller and Mr. R. B. Collins, who did the collecting, also took cones from a *Cupressus glabra* some 20 yards from the Nootka cypress which had produced the first Leyland cypress. Two of the seedlings assumed abnormal adult foliage. They grow in the Genetics Nursery at Alice Holt. Cuttings have been sent to a few collections. Mr. L. Gough of the Borough Polytechnic, London has shown from analyses of the resin that this tree has *C. nootkatensis* as one parent and one of the American species of *Cupressus* as the other.

CROWN. Fairly narrow-conic, to a slightly wavy leader. Branches curled and upswept. Soft grey-blue-green foliage hanging in flat plates, with prominent yellow male flowers abundant from August to May.

FOLIAGE. Shoot yellow-green becoming dark purple-brown, bearing alternate, distant (1–1·5 cm apart), doubly pinnate flat branchlets at all angles. Leaves acute to pale mucronate spine, free and pointing forward; light grey-green bloomed blue-grey towards the base, on both sides. Very open and sparse sprays.

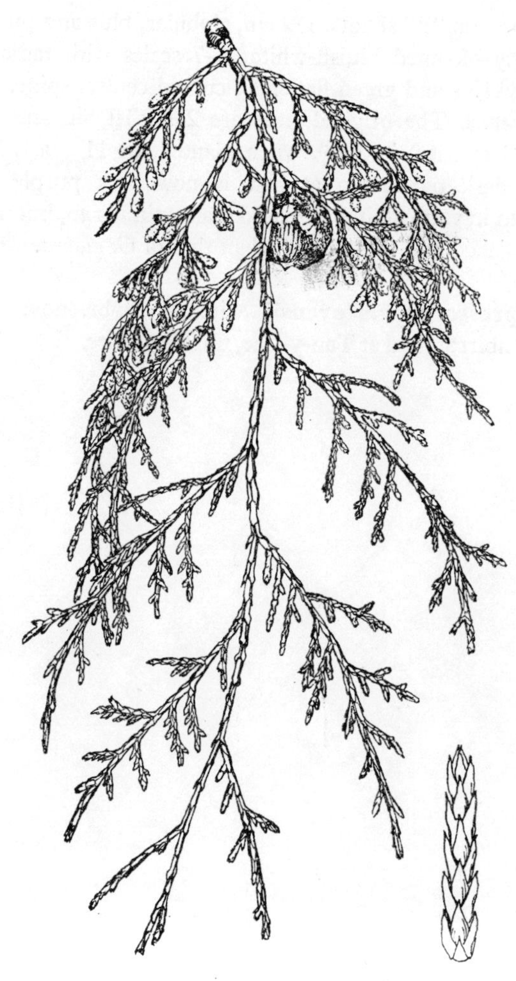

X Cupressocyparis notabilis

Fig. 71
Spray and cone of × *Cupressocyparis notabilis*, a hybrid between *Cupressus glabra* and *Chamaecyparis nootkatensis*. The male flowers (upper foliage) are abundant and pale yellow throughout the winter. The leaves (lower right ×2⅔) are acute.

"A" shoots—few, minute 2 mm×1 mm; pointed.

"B" shoots—few, flat on "C" shoot, regularly increasing in length from apex to base; vertical (at 90°) lower half.

"C" shoots—spaced 1–1·5 cm apart, lanceolate, spreading round "D" shoot or flat on outer half, hanging, except those upswept at tips of branches.

FLOWERS AND CONE. Male flowers terminal on "A" shoots and some "B" shoots on most sprays, ovoid, 3 mm long, pointing straight forwards, each a pattern of green scales and light yellow pollen.

Cones, on "B" shoots, 1·2 cm, globular, blue and purple, strongly bloomed bluish-white; 6–7 scales with radiating shallow ribs and green flattened, curved central spine.

SPECIMENS. The original trees are 23ft × 1ft 5in and 20ft (forked at base) in 1969, when planted for 11 years. The bark, dark red-brown at first, is now dark purple and covered in vertical lines of raised scales, similar to, but more finely flaked and more lined, than that of *C. glabra*.

× **Cupressocyparis ovensii** Mitchell. Hybr. nov. 1961 Westonbirt; raised at Tan-y-Cae, Cardiganshire.

Raised by Mr. Howard Ovens by collecting seeds from a *C. lusitanica* surrounded by *Ch. nootkatensis* trees at Westonbirt. (The mother tree has since died.) A very vigorous, upright, sturdy plant; with the habit of Nootka cypress; shoots green-brown, light pink towards the base, light red-brown second year. "B" and "C" shoots flattened, alternately pinnate; leaves deep bluish green, with long free, forward spreading, acute and spined tips. Crushed foliage has a sweet resinous lemony scent. Each scale above and below is finely lined with white stomata (under lens).

Cupressus Linnaeus (Cupressaceae)

About 20 species from South Western North America; the Mediterranean and North Africa; the Himalaya and China. All have small scale-leaves, mostly closely appressed, in pinnate shoots which may themselves be flattened but arise on the next shoot at various angles making plumose, not flattened sprays. Cones are globular, usually large, and woody and are often retained on the tree for years.

Key to the species of Cupressus

1. Branchlet systems flattened in the 2–3 smallest orders, (A shoots flat on B, B shoots $\pm$flat on C shoots) 2
   Branchlet systems entirely angular (on exterior shoots) 5

2. Leaves acute, with spreading or forward points; sprays very slender 3
   Leaves blunt, incurved tips; shoots terete; sprays broad 4

3. Leaves pale blue-grey or white, short; tips hard, acute, curved outwards; sprays pendulous, A and B shoots curved downwards *cashmiriana*
   Leaves shiny yellow-green, black towards tip, long; tip fine, forward-pointing; B shoots very distant, spray sparse (foliage like miniature Lawson cypress) *funebris*

4. Sprays held flat; ultimate shoots flat, shining rich green; shoot orange-brown, sinuous *lusitanica benthamii*
   Sprays pendulous; ultimate shoots distant, slender, long, curved, dull yellowish-green *torulosa corneyana*

5. Leaves grey, blue, grey-green or bloomed grey 6
   Leaves yellowish, bright, or deep green, not bloomed 14

6. Foliage spotted white with resin 7
   Foliage without white spots 10

7. Foliage bright blue-grey, shoots thick, spreading, upright, conspicuously spotted white on nearly every leaf *glabra pyramidalis; glabra conica*
   Foliage pale grey-green or dark green bloomed grey 8

8. Foliage pale grey or grey-green; shoot bright orange-brown; branchlets thick, distant; sprays spiky 9
   Foliage dark green bloomed grey, shoot dark red-brown; white spots large, oval, at base of branchlets; branchlets fine *bakeri ssp. matthewsii*

9. White spots numerous, small, on many leaves; shoots rising, foliage with scent of grapefruit *glabra*
   White spots few; large, some at base of branchlets; shoots nodding, foliage with sweet scent of verbena *stevensonii*

10. Foliage uniformly pale blue-grey 11
    Foliage mainly grey-green, patches of bluer, or entirely grey-green or dark green bloomed slightly grey 12

11. Leaves with fine, spreading points; shoot pink, violet and red-purple *lusitanica (juvenile)*
    Leaves incurved, shoots terete, open, sparsely branched at wide angles *lusitanica glauca*

12. Sprays very long, slender, upswept, sea-green, bluish and grey-green, leaves acute to blunt point; inner ultimate branchlets to 5cm (unbranched) *guadalupensis*
    Sprays short, bunched, broad; leaves with minute, incurved mucros 13

13. Foliage very dense, branchlets short, fine, sprays rising, grey-green, faintly scented of resin — *duclouxiana*
Foliage not dense, slender shoot-ends project from bunched sprays; aromatic, scented sweetly or like petrol — *forbesii*

14. Foliage spotted white; very dark green — 15
Foliage without white spots, long, dense sprays — 16

15. Branching perpendicular; foliage dark grey-green, B. shoots few, distant, short making sprays extremely narrow. Scent of lemons or oil of citrinella — *goveniana (juvenile)*
Branching wide-angled, foliage dark shining green, B shoots neither few nor distant. Scent of lantana or bergamot. — *macnabiana*

16. Ultimate branchlets rough with spreading tips of leaves — 17
Ultimate branchlets smooth and terete — 18

17. Foliage very fine, very dense, lemon-scented; shoot soon dark purple-red — *abramsiana*
Foliage not very fine; open, without marked scent; shoot soon pink, then red-brown — *lusitanica*

18. Branchlets slender, long, curved, partly pendulous; bright green. (cone 1–2 cm, bloomed) — *torulosa*
Branchlets thick, fleshy, short, mainly upright or spread, (cone 1·5–4 cm not bloomed) — 19

19. Foliage densely bunched, curved upwards, very dull dark green, without scent or faintly scented of india-rubber — *sempervirens*
Foliage less dense, more evenly spread, spreading, bright grass-green or rich deep green; sweetly aromatic — 20

20. Branchlets spreading perpendicular, short; blackish green; shoot chestnut-purple, strong scent of oil of citrinella (cone 1·5–2 cm). — *goveniana*
Branchlets spreading at varied angles less than 90°; shoot dull pink-brown; scent of lemon-verbena (cone 2·5–3 cm). — *macrocarpa*

Cupressus abramsiana Wolf. Abrams cypress

Santa Cruz Mountains, north of Monterey, California. Introduced in about 1950. Known only from Mr. Hillier's trees at Jermyn's House, and recent seedlings.

BARK. Purplish and orange-brown finely ridged grey.

CROWN. Dense and shapely ovoid-conic, with dark, fine foliage.

FOLIAGE. Shoot turning chocolate-purple on the tips of the scales first, then purple-red all over. "A" shoots jagged edged, lying at all angles on "B" shoots which themselves are largely in a vertical plane on the "C" shoots which arise stiffly forwards. Leaves deep green, pale grey-green at the tips which are forward-spreading, free, thick, rounded and incurved to a minute mucro. Crushed foliage has a soapy-lemon scent.

GROWTH. A remarkably vigorous tree. The specimen planted in 1954 is now 48ft×4ft 7in (1969).

RECOGNITION. The aspect of the tree is that of a dark green *C. macrocarpa*, but the foliage is finer and harder, like *C. goveniana*, but not so sparse, angular, nor in such narrow sprays.

Cupressus arizonica Greene. Rough-barked Arizona cypress

Arizona, New Mexico and Mexico. Introduced in 1880. Rare. Found only in a few collections. Most "Arizona cypresses", and probably all those planted recently, and all those called var. *bonita* are *Cupressus glabra.*

BARK. Greenish-brown, rather oak-like with shallow fine fissures, long and vertical or spiralled, slightly stringy. Oldest trees grey-barked.

CROWN. Rather broadly conic with a domed top; dense.

FOLIAGE. Rich green or greyish green, with or without a few white spots.

CONE. Globose, 2 cm, each scale with a prominent central process.

RECOGNITION. The stringy, finely and regularly fissured bark and greener foliage distinguish this easily from *C. glabra.*

SPECIMENS. Avondale, 76ft×7ft 4in (1968); Westonbirt (Rattrays), 75ft×5ft 3in (1970); Hergest Croft, planted 1921, 55ft×5ft 1in (1969); Headfort, planted 1914, 64ft×5ft 3in (1966); Exbury, 58ft×5ft 3in (1969); Linton Park, 67ft×2ft 11in (1970).

Cupressus bakeri Jepson. Baker cypress

Siskiyou and Shasta, California. Introduced soon after 1930. Very rare and only as young plants, since the Bedgebury tree was blown down in 1966. It had died back a long way, and in 1964 was 38ft × 3ft 4in. The dense, dark green foliage was prominently spotted white and when crushed had an aroma of sage. The cone-scales were prominently wrinkled. Bicton 6ft 5in (1968).

var. matthewsii Wolf. Siskiyou cypress. Siskiyou Mountains, Oregon and California. Introduced in about 1917. Very rare indeed. The crown is ovoid and upswept. Shoots are dark red-brown, becoming pale yellow-green between dark brown scales. Leaves dark green, paling at the points, terete on "A" shoots, spreading tips on larger shoots, very markedly on "C" and "D" shoots. Large white oval dots, especially in the axils; "A" shoots are bloomed white, some with resin glands exuding clear drops. Very fine foliage, dark and at all angles on the shoots. Crushed foliage has a faint scent of cigars.

Jermyn's House, 15 feet (1969).

Cupressus cashmeriana Royle ex Carriere. Kashmir cypress

Apparently not now known wild but described from Tibet. Introduced in 1862. Thought by some to be a juvenile form of *C. torulosa*, but the oldest trees, in Ireland, show no signs whatever of changing foliage. Very rare, but growing out of doors unharmed by severe winters in one Surrey garden. Here it is a slender, wand-like plant. In Ireland it is very broadly conic or bushy, and has stout low branches.

Bark. Brownish-red, shallowly and loosely stripping in long flakes.

Crown. Branches curve upwards; shoots spread level then arch downwards.

Foliage. Shoot slender, soon pink-brown, "A" shoots 1–2 mm, leaves in opposite pairs, bloomed blue-white all over, with a marked pale margin, wider on the underside, which is greyer and bluer than the soft grey-green blue of the upper side; sharply acute, free tips, hard. "B" shoots lie curving forwards, opposite or alternate, flat on "C" shoots. "C" shoots are very narrow and long to 11 × 2 cms, lying forward, then arching over hanging below the "D" shoot.

Specimens. Headfort, planted 1918, 28ft × 4ft 10in (1966); Castlewellan, planted 1946, 24ft × 2ft 2in (1970); Kilmacurragh, a stem over 20 feet long but recumbent (1966); Mount Usher, 16ft × 2ft 0in (1966); Garinish Island, 8ft and 5ft (1966); Casa di Sole, 12ft (1970).

Recognition. The pendulous blue-grey shoots are unmistakable.

Cupressus duclouxiana Hickel. Yunnan cypress

Yunnan, China. Introduced in about 1910. Very rare, and then only in Ireland and near the south coast of England. The bark is pinkish-grey, stripping vertically between fine fissures. The crown is irregular but narrowly conic in general, with branches upswept and branchlets rising from them.

Foliage. Shoot deep burnt sienna. "A" shoots very slender, blue-grey-green, some to 2 cm long, spreading widely and curving (like *C. torulosa*), mainly flat on "B" shoots. "B" shoots at all angles on "C" shoots.

Leaves. Terete on shoots, with minute incurved points; mottled colouring from a dark green centre, grey-green surround and grey margin; same on both sides; crushed foliage has a faintly resinous scent.

Cone. Irregular globose but very smooth, bloomed at first, ripening dull brownish purple, 3·5 × 3 cm, shallowly networked with fine cracks. The sutures are finely waved, not coarsely wandering as in *C. sempervirens*.

Headfort, planted 1919, 32ft × 2ft 6in (1966); Mount Usher, 37ft × 3ft 1in (1966); Kilmacurragh, 40ft × 4ft, 30ft × 3ft 8in (1966); Dunloe Castle, 33ft × 2ft 6in (1968); Wakehurst Place, 15ft × 8in (1966); Westhill, Budleigh Salterton, 20ft × 2ft 4in main stem (1967); Avondale, 27ft × 2ft 0in (1968).

Recognition. Most like *C. sempervirens*, especially if large cones are visible, but the foliage is much more slender and greyer.

Cupressus forbesii Jepson. Tecate cypress

South West California, from south of Los Angeles to Lower California. Introduced after 1927. Very rare indeed.

Bark. Dark purple-red-brown, scaling to leave lemon and pink.

Foliage. Shoot soon dark chestnut-red. New shoots slender; other shoots in short, bunched sprays. Leaves acute, terete or with an appressed abrupt short mucro; dark green centre, white-bloomed margins. All shoots arise at varying angles. Sprays as a whole not dense; bruised foliage has a sweet scent or that of petrol.

Jermyn's House, 25ft; 9ft (1969).

Cupressus funebris Endlicher. Chinese Weeping cypress

Central China; cultivated in the Himalaya. Introduced in 1846. Very rare. In a few collections in Ireland and in South and South West England and West Scotland. Apparently short-lived as only one small one of 12 previously recorded, some then large, has been found surviving.

Bark. Dark grey-brown, shallowly fissured but deeply fluted.

Crown. Ovoid; slender strongly ascending branches; pale yellow-green rather pendulous foliage, yellow in winter with abundant male flowers.

Foliage. Very slender. Shoot dull pink-brown, pale green toward tip. "A" shoots numerous, flat on "B" shoots, "B"

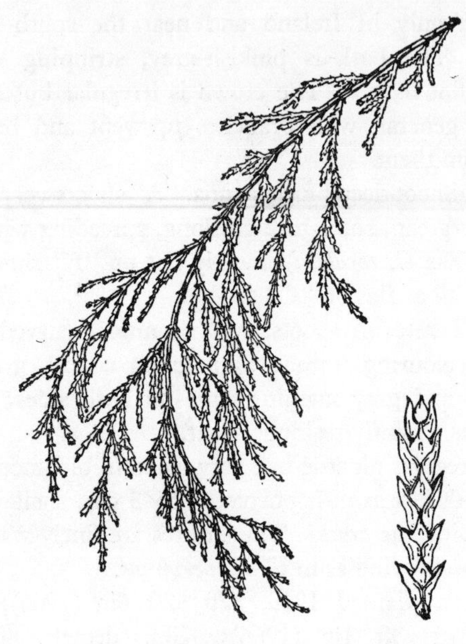

Cupressus funebris

Fig. 72
Adult shoot of *Cupressus funebris* which resembles in miniature the foliage of *Chamaecyparis lawsoniana,* and like it, has translucent glands (seen on shoot, right ×3⅓).

shoots distant, slender, mainly set flat on "C" shoots. Ultimate shoots less than 1 mm broad.
LEAVES. Like miniature Lawson cypress leaves; laterals with long, slightly spreading spine tip, and shining yellow-green, with a black patch near the clear yellow spine. Some leaves have a white or translucent central gland. The foliage is hard and fine; when crushed it has a scent of grass. Juvenile foliage may occur from 5 to 10 feet into the crown of trees up to 15 feet tall. This foliage is densely fluffy, pale bluish-green with spreading leaves 10×1 mm, soft and acuminate with two pale green-grey bands beneath.
CONE. Like a large, knobbly pea; 1–2 cm across each scale with a small central spine; blue-green.
SPECIMENS. Borde Hill, 13ft (1958); Killerton, 41ft×1ft 3in, 36ft×1ft 8in (1970); Bath Botanic Garden, 18ft (1962); Powerscourt, 25ft×3ft 10in at 1ft (1966); Mount Usher, 32ft×1ft 9in (1966); Kilmacurragh, 36ft×4ft 3in at 3ft (1966); Crarae, planted 1933, 18ft (1956); Casa di Sole, planted 1958, 10ft; planted 1955, 15ft (1970).

Cupressus glabra Sudworth. Smooth Arizona cypress. (*C. arizonica bonita* Lemmon)

Central Arizona. Introduced either undistinguished with *C. arizonica* in 1880, or a few years after, being distinguished and discovered in 1907.

BARK. Deep purple or reddish-purple, heavily blistered from the fourth or fifth year, and soon flaking away in circular scales leaving pale cream patches.
CROWN. Conic or ovoid-conic, curving to a blunt point. A most distinct and shapely fuzz of pale blue-grey, tinged yellow with abundant male flowers in autumn and winter.
FOLIAGE. Sprays rather open and branched at wide angles, bent, shoot bright orange-brown; leaves bright blue-grey or pale grey, terete, occasional white resin spots. When crushed it has an aroma of grapefruit.
FLOWERS AND CONE. Male flowers abundant, on smallest shoots, pale yellow. Cones shiny green-brown, somewhat bloomed grey, with pink sutures, globular, 1·5 cm, each scale with a central small, curved spine.
GROWTH. This is a very hardy cypress, undamaged, anywhere, so far as has been seen, even by the winter of 1962–3. It is also tolerant of limestone soils and of drought. Growth is slow but steady. It starts in late May and may continue until mid-September, and shoots of 2 feet or more can be grown on young trees. Some early growth rates are shown by the trees in Table 30.

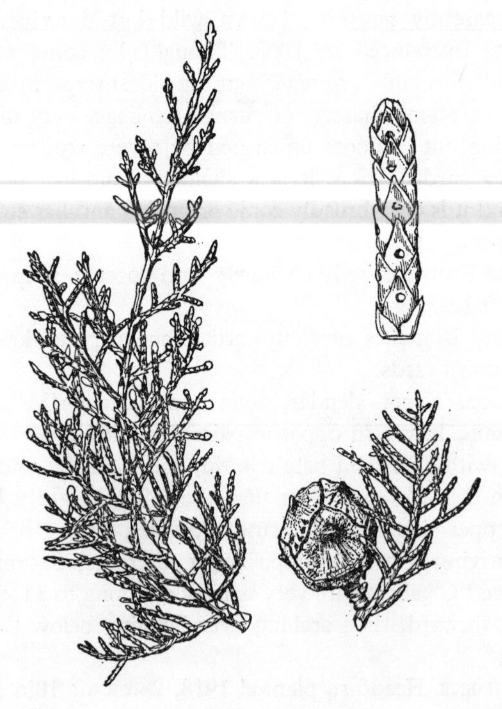

Cupressus glabra

Fig. 73
Spray with male flowers (left) and with cone (right) of *Cupressus glabra*, a blue-grey tree often grown as "*C. arizonica*" but with a purple, blistering bark. Shoot (top right ×4⅔) shows white glands on the leaves; some forms have fewer than this.

TABLE 30. GROWTH OF SOME YOUNG TREES OF CUPRESSUS GLABRA

Planted	1926	Bedgebury	37′ × 2′ 4″	43 years
	1927	Birr Castle	39′ × 3′ 10″	39 years
	1927	Bodnant	43′ × 2′ 8″	32 years
	1934	Ryston	40′ × 3′ 7″	35 years
	1939	Monk Hopton	36′ × 1′ 11″	23 years
	1939	Highnam	39′ × 3′ 9″	30 years
	1949	Kildangan	32′ × 3′ 6″	19 years

SPECIMENS. Sheffield Park, 70ft (1960); Westonbirt House, 64ft×5ft 0in (1967); Borde Hill Garden, 62ft×4ft 6in and Gores Wood, 53ft×3ft 2in (1968); Wisley Royal Horticultural Society Gardens, 60ft×4ft 2in (1969); Edinburgh Royal Botanic Garden, 42ft×3ft 1in (1970); Leighton Hall, 54ft×4ft 8in (1970); Lamellan, 60ft×3ft 9in (1962); Powerscourt, 53ft×6ft 2in, 57ft×4ft 11in (1966); Mount Usher, 60ft (1960); Holkham, 52ft×3ft 8in (1968).

cv. Pyramidalis. The most attractive form; conic crown, thick branchlets upswept, intense blue-white, well covered with bright yellow male flowers, and each scale-leaf with a prominent white dot.

cv. Conica This has more slender, less bright shoots.

Cupressus goveniana Gordon. Californian cypress

Monterey, California. Introduced in 1847. Very rare; in a few collections northwards to the Southern Midlands only, and one in Ireland. Of the 30 specimens seen, 19 of the best were at Wakehurst Place, Sussex, in 1964.

BARK. Pale grey-brown, peeling in shallow strips.

CROWN. Columnar but very variable. Of adjacent trees one may be a slender column to a pointed top and the other a broad, irregular, spreading tree with a domed top. Branches dense and strongly ascending; in broad trees the outer parts spreading level.

FOLIAGE. Shoot soon bright chestnut-purple then scaly and dull purple-brown.

LEAVES. Dark grey-green on old trees; dark blackish-green on young; smoothly terete; when crushed give off strong scents of oil of citrinella or, in some, more like petrol. "A" shoots short, thick ovoid, widely spreading at all angles from "B" shoots which are short, distant, and nearly at right angles in various planes on the "C" shoots which are very long and slender. Shaded foliage is square in cross-section. Foliage of young trees distant and spindly; but the shoots are packed densely in old trees. Leaves obtuse, incurved pointed; pale margins, faint white bloom, and some spots of white resin, few and obscure on old trees.

MALE FLOWERS. Usually numerous terminally on minor shoots at base of spray, cylindric, 3 mm, bright yellow and green.

CONE. Clustered at the base of the outer, long "C" shoots; dark grey-brown, still partly dark green in December; slightly shiny, ovoid-globose, 1·5–2 cm, large wide green ridge pointing upwards and with a hook in the centre.

GROWTH. Apparently short-lived, for none of the trees mentioned by Elwes and Henry survives 60 years later, and only one young one of the four more trees given in 1931 survives. This one is, however, at Bedgebury where very few *Cupressus* survived 40° of frost in 1940. Growth would seem to be quite rapid in height and girth, for the trees at Wakehurst Place have a mean height increment of up to one and a half feet a year and girth increment, as at Bedgebury, averages above one inch a year. In cooler areas, as in Ireland, growth is evidently much less rapid.

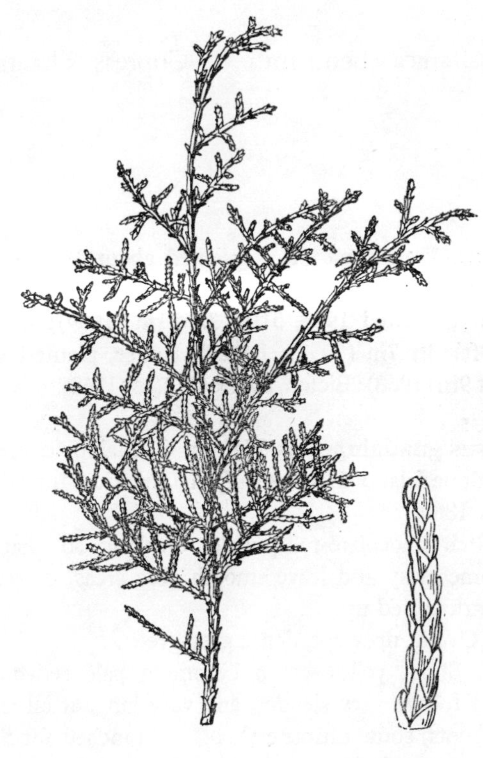

Cupressus goveniana

Fig. 74
Foliage of *Cupressus goveniana*, (shoot on right × 4) showing similar features to *C. macrocarpa* but a wider angle in the branching. It also has a very different scent when crushed.

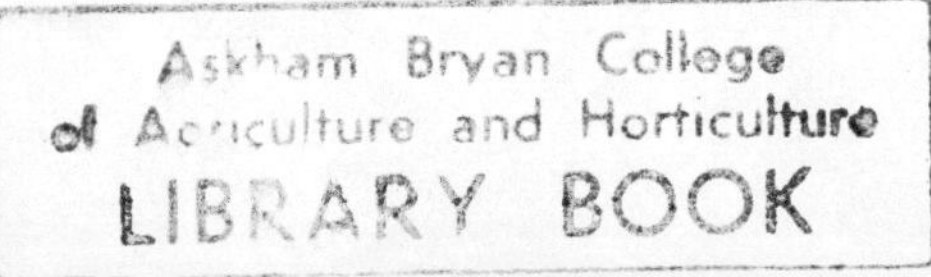

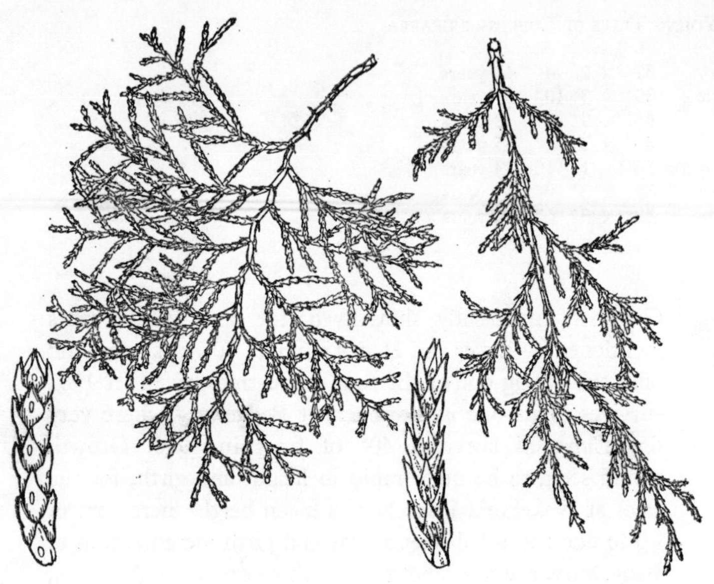

Fig. 75
Foliage of (left) *Cupressus lusitanica* var. *benthamii* showing the flattened spray, sinuous shoot and (left ×4) appressed leaf-tips of the bright, shiny green foliage. The type, *C. lusitanica* (right) differs in all these features, and the shoot (×1⅓) shows the spreading, more acute leaf-tips.

SPECIMENS. Wakehurst Place, planted about 1911, 72ft × 5ft 4in, 71ft × 5ft 8in (1964); 70ft × 8ft 3in at 6in (1970); Bedgebury, planted 1925, 51ft × 3ft 11in (1969); Bagshot Park, 60ft × 3ft 7in (1957); Fenagh House, planted 1910, 35ft × 2ft 9in (1968); Bicton, 69ft × 6ft 0½in (1968).

Cupressus guadalupensis Watson. Guadalupe cypress

Guadalupe Island, Lower California, Mexico. Introduced in about 1880.

BARK. Rich chocolate-red-purple, cracking so that big flakes come away and leave smooth grey areas, or remain on the bark curled up.

CROWN. Ovoid, upswept, dense grey-green.

FOLIAGE. Shoot yellow-green becoming pale red-brown. Sprays of foliage very slender, and very long, at all angles on the shoots, some ultimate shoots unbranched for 5 cm. A sea-green, tangled but open mass of foliage. Leaves long, slender, acute to blunt tip, more or less terete on outer shoots; acutely forward spreading free tips on inner shoots; grey-green and blue-green in different parts of the spray; pale margins; crushed foliage has a very faint resinous scent.

CONE. Large, irregularly globular, about 5 cm across, purplish-brown, each scale with a raised centre.

SPECIMENS. Borde Hill, 63ft × 2ft 11in + 2ft 9in (1970); Jermyn's House, 25ft (1969); Casa di Sole, 15ft (1970).

RECOGNITION. The bark and grey-blue foliage resemble *C. glabra*, but the long, slender shoots and the big cones are unlike that species. It is similar to, and sometimes united with, *C. forbesii* but the foliage is in longer sprays, on paler shoots and is greyer.

Cupressus lindleyi Klotsch. (*C. lusitanica ?*)

Small plants raised from Mexican seed sent in 1962 are very vigorous, growing 3 feet or more in a year, with nodding, very glaucous grey foliage on shoots which are bloomed violet-purple and by the second year are orange-purple-brown.

Cupressus lusitanica Miller. Mexican cypress; Cedar of Goa. See Fig. 75, right.

Mexico and Guatemala. Introduced in about 1680. Uncommon; in some collections and a few large gardens mainly in South England and Ireland; very rare in Scotland.

BARK. Rich dark brown; bole smoothly circular in cross-section in the better trees; finely and regularly fissured into parallel strips, vertical or slightly spiralled; thin strips close, bent away at the ends in a few places.

CROWN. Columnar with long narrow conic apex when young and may retain the narrow spire when older and the crown has spread; it may then be slightly bent. Some trees broaden out with big, low spreading branches. Crowns are fairly open in young trees, dark and dense in old.

FOLIAGE. Young plants have fine dark green, grey-green or glaucous foliage on pink to dark red shoots; older trees dark grey-green with shoots turning orange-brown then dark purplish brown. "A" shoots are few, spreading forwards, "B" shoots are distant, pointing only slightly forwards and radiating all round the "C" shoots. "C" shoots are about 7×3 cm, straight or curving over and below the "D" shoot. Leaves narrowly acute to a short spine, free for most of their length and pointing forwards. In old trees the sprays are short and broad; leaf-tips less spreading. Almost without scent when crushed.

FLOWERS AND CONE. Male flowers very small, ovoid on the ends of the smallest shoots. Cones, small, globular, 1·5 cm across, with a hooked spine in the centre of each scale, bright glaucous green for the first year, ripening dark, shiny purple-brown.

GROWTH. Young plants can grow rapidly. An annual shoot of 33 inches, which began at the beginning of May, grew its last inch in the last two weeks of October, with a maximum of 3 inches in a week in mid-July. In girth, dated trees in England mostly have exceeded 1 inch per year of growth but in Ireland 2 inches a year is probably more usual. A small group of trees was killed at Westonbirt by the winter of 1962–3 after the best had grown 60ft× 4ft 2in in 36 years, but this winter did not harm older trees half a mile away, nor has it damaged the few trees seen north and east of Westonbirt. Few of the trees measured earlier survive and this may be caused by deaths in the hardest winters.

SPECIMENS. A remarkable tree at Bicton with a bole like a ship's mast, blew down in 1969. It was 102ft×6ft 11in. The very old tree at Birr Castle is dying back.

TABLE 31. LARGE TREES OF CUPRESSUS LUSITANICA

Locality	*Date Planted*	*Dimensions*	
Birr Castle			75′ × 8′ 10″ (1966)
Birr Castle			68′ × 6′ 0″ (1966)
Inistioge			76′ × 10′ 5″ (1966)
Clonmannon			60′ × 8′ 3″ (1968)
Castlewellan			65′ × 7′ 8″ (1966)
Blackmoor	1901	40′ × 3′ 6″ (1931)	69′ × 4′ 6″ (1968)
Tregrehan		40′ × 4′ 6″ (1931)	68′ × 6′ 10″ (1971)
Brooklands House			55′ × 6′ 6″ (1969)
Borde Hill	1911	32′ × 3′ 1″ (1930)	67′ × 6′ 3″ (1968)
The Hendre			71′ × 5′ 5″ (1962)
Mount Usher			65′ × 6′ 7″ (1966)
Fota (ex Cintra)	1915		69′ × 10′ 7″ (1966)
Fota (ex Cintra)			70′ × 10′ 1″ (1966)
Wootton House			47′ × 5′ 2″ (1957)
Bodnant			44′ × 5′ 3″ (1957)
Leonardslee		32′ × 2′ 5″ (1931)	50′ × 5′ 6″ (1969)
Trebah			65′ × 5′ 7″ (1959)
Wisley			57′ × 4′ 5″ (1964)
Stonefield			45′ × 4′ 10″ (1969)
Holkham Hall			58′ × 4′ 4″ (1968)
Wakehurst Place			76′ × 6′ 5″ (1970)
Wakehurst Place			70′ × 6′ 10″ (1971)
Chandler's Ford	1927		57′ × 5′ 3″ (1961)
Endsleigh			64′ × 7′ 10″ (1963)[1]

[1] Measured at 4 feet

var. benthamii (Endlicher) Carriere. (See Fig. 75). Mexico. Introduced 1839. Very rare. A few collections in the extreme South and South West of England; equally rare in Ireland. See Fig. 75, left.

In Cornwall, a tree of remarkable form having a markedly conic crown and long, clear, cylindrical bole. Elsewhere tending to be broad or even bushy, and seldom happy. One was killed in Herefordshire by the winter of 1962-3.

FOLIAGE. Differs in the flattened pinnate arrangement and in shining leaves with scarcely spreading tips. All shoots slightly sinuous, most obvious in small order ("B" and "C") shoots. "A" shoots widely spaced, widely spreading 1 mm across; "B" shoots, which are flat, slightly arched, spreading at right-angles flat in one plane from "C" shoots which are mostly flat on "D" shoots, but some rise above.

Leaves shiny dark rich green with a whitish or dark central pit and greyer green at the base; yellow-green with grey centres on the under-surfaces; blunt, abruptly and minutely mucronate on free, incurved or slightly spreading tips. Handsome, rich green, rather lace-like sprays, which when crushed smell only faintly of resin.

TABLE 32. SPECIMENS OF CUPRESSUS LUSITANICA VAR. BENTHAMII

Locality		*Dimensions*	
Bicton			92′ × 7′ 10″ (1968)
Bicton			91′ × 8′ 5″ (1968)
Bicton			88′ × 9′ 3″ (1968)
Tregrehan			85′ × 7′ 7″ (1971)
Tregrehan			85′ × 6′ 7″ (1971)
Borde Hill	26′	(1931)	55′ × 3′ 6″ (1958)
Glasnevin B.G.			43′ × 4′ 5″ (1966)

cv. Fastigiata (cv. Stricta). A narrowly fastigiate form seemingly confined to Westonbirt. The original tree, 50 feet tall in 1909, is 85ft×9ft 8in at 6 feet and is now a fairly broad, tall column but the branches are very erect. A cutting from this, planted in 1942, is very slender, 54ft×2ft 9in (1971). This cultivar has escaped notice since Elwes and Henry (1909).

cv. Flagellifera. A pendulous form with upswept branches, and foliage in hanging sparsely branched threads. The crown is bushy and round-topped—a dense tangle of branches. Very rare. Castle Leod, 62ft×6ft 5in (1966).

cv. Glauca. A columnar, pointed tree of neat form and pale blue-grey foliage. The shoots are sparse in open, angular sprays, the ultimate shoots being round and terete. Rare. Two of the specimens below have grown rapidly in the intervals between measurements: Crarae, 43ft×4ft 11in (1956) but 62ft×6ft 4in in 1969. Bicton, 57ft×5ft 6in (1959) but 66ft×6ft 6in in 1968 and 64ft×5ft 6in (1968). Stourhead, 62ft×4ft 10in (1957); Leonardslee, 52ft×3ft 5in (1969); Sidbury Manor, 50ft×6ft 8in and 50ft×5ft 8in (1959); Chiltley Place, 67ft×4ft 3in (1961); Glasnevin Botanic Garden, 43ft×4ft 5in (1966); Wisley Royal Horticultural Society Gardens, 62ft×2ft 8in (1969).

cv. Glauca Pendula. The foliage of this beautiful tree is of the type of 'Glauca', hard, terete, in widely angled sprays, hanging in long plumes densely set at the ends of wide level branches. The crown is broad and low but obtusely pointed. Rare. Confined to extreme South and South West England and to Ireland. Glendurgan, 45ft×4ft 4in; 37ft×4ft 8in (1959); Highdown, 30ft×2ft 5in (1965); Headfort, planted 1914, 45ft×4ft 7in (1966); Kilmacurragh, 64ft×10ft 4in; 47ft×7ft 1in (1966); Castlewellan, 49ft×3ft 8in (1970); Haldon Grange, 50ft×3ft 3in (1967); Carton, 50ft×11ft 3in at 2 feet (1968).

RECOGNITION. The regularly ridged bark and dark narrowly conic, rather open crown distinguish the tree from *C. macrocarpa*. The foliage differs from other cypresses in the length of free acute tips of leaves.

Cupressus macnabiana Murray. Macnab cypress.

Northern California. Introduced in 1854. Now apparently confined to the extreme South of England and to Ireland.

BARK. Rich brown and smooth, with fine, vertical flaking or finely criss-crossed with orange cracks. At Powerscourt smooth, grey with dark red patches.

CROWN. Broad, rather bushy; level branches, domed or obtuse top.

FOLIAGE. On old trees, hard, very small, shiny, dark leaves on bright brown shoots; branchlets spreading at wide angles.

LEAVES. Closely pressed with enlarged blunt ends, many with a bright white spot. Crushed foliage smells of lantana or bergamot.

CONES. Globular with very regularly pointed raised centres to the scales; 2 cm diameter, grey-green, ripening to dark somewhat shiny brown.

SPECIMENS. None of the trees measured earlier has been found surviving. Wakehurst Place, 38ft×2ft 1in, 33ft×4ft 5in at 1ft 6in (1968); Birr Castle, planted 1933, 37ft×3ft 5in (1966); Avondale, planted 1954, 31ft× 1ft 11in (1968); Mount Usher, 25ft×1ft 8in (1966); Powerscourt, 28ft×3ft 4in (1966).

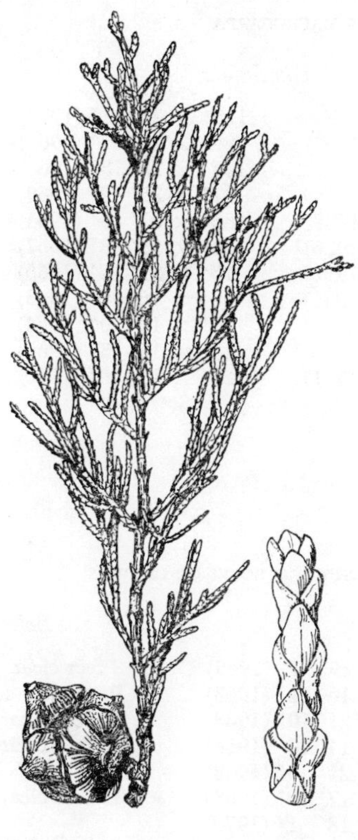

Cupressus macrocarpa

Fig. 76
Foliage and cone of *Cupressus macrocarpa*, Monterey cypress. The side leaves have swollen tips (right ×5½) and when crushed have a lemon scent.

Cupressus macrocarpa Hartweg. Monterey cypress

Cypress Point and Point Lobos, Monterey, California. Introduced in 1838. Abundant throughout Great Britain and Ireland, but particularly in the South West of England. Frequent in small gardens on the outskirts of towns, and near coasts.

BARK. Young trees; soon pale brown finely and shallowly ridged. Old trees pinkish brown, cigar-brown or pale grey with algae, with flat, shallow ridges either vertical or at a slight angle and criss-crossed, stripping.

CROWN. Extremely variable after a youthful columnar period. Middle-aged trees variably broad-columnar with rounded top or tops, or slender with very level branching; spiky shoots projecting, and a long spire feathered with level shoots of varying length. Old trees either hugely ace-of-spades-shaped with upswept branches, or Cedar-of-Lebanon shaped with wide level branching and a flat-top, sometimes on 40 or so main stems from the ground. In Ireland, immensely broad.

FOLIAGE. Young trees have strong plumes, narrow and ascending, projecting from the crown, especially in Ireland where they are very long and vigorous.

SHOOT. Dull pink-brown becoming dark grey-brown. Smaller shoots at all angles around larger and all forward at 45–60°.

LEAVES. More or less terete, completely so on ultimate shoots with thick rather broad points dark in the centre, pale on the margins, dark green, faintly bloomed white all over some leaves. The foliage is dense, but becomes more dense on old trees or on trees exposed to sea-winds, and thicker, the ultimate shoots then being blob-ended. When crushed the foliage has a strong scent of lemon-verbena.

FLOWERS AND CONES. Male flowers in patches on some old trees but by no means regular in many areas; pale yellow in spring, at the tips of the smallest branchlets, shedding pollen in mid-May (late April in Devon) and sometimes again, or mainly, in early June. Female flowers pale yellow in dense patches, visible in June. Ripen into globose, shining purple-brown cones 3 cm across; 7-8 scales with central obscure hooked process; rough and lumpy with waved margins.

GROWTH. Shoot growth lasts from early May until early September in South-east England, probably two weeks or more each end in the far south-west. A very vigorous tree in the west but much less so in the east. Few dated young trees have been found but at Wakehurst Place, where growth is much less rapid than further west, one 51 years old is 83ft×12ft 0in and has added 9ft 7in to its girth in the last 38 years. At Sidbury Manor a girth of 20ft 9in at 3 feet was attained in 79 years. Even when 20 feet in girth a few, especially in Ireland, have added the last 7 to 9 feet in 37 years. The fine, pruned tree at Montacute has increased in girth by 42 inches in 21 years, although it is probably the oldest in the country. Among those trees with multiple boles, none can equal that at Powerscourt for sheer vigour. When only 68 years old it was 90 feet tall with 47 stems emerging from a base which was 37ft 5in round.

SPECIMENS. The earliest trees were from seed of unknown origin acquired by Lambert in 1838 and were grown as "*C. lambertiana*". These thus were raised before Hartweg's seed of 1846.

TABLE 33. OLD TREES OF KNOWN DATE OF CUPRESSUS MACROCARPA

Locality	*Date Planted*		*Dimensions*
Montacute House	ca.1840		115′ × 23′ 11″ (1970)
Hamwood House	1844	85′ × 10′ 6″ (1903)	85′ × 21′ 7″ (1968)[1]
Bicton	pre 1846		105′ × 22′ 8″ (1968)[1]
Bicton	pre 1846		97′ × 25′ 2″ (1968)[3]
Osborne House	1846	78′ × 16′ 0″ (1909)	85′ × 23′ 0″ (1964)[2]
Castle Kennedy	1850	64′ × 12′ 0″ (1926)[3]	84′ × 16′ 8″ (1967)[3]
Derreen	1856	70′ × 16′ 0″ (1931)	75′ × 21′ 10″ (1966)
Hewell Grange	1860	58′ × 5′ 6″ (1931)	88′ × 6′ 10″ (1963)
Osborne House	1862		85′ × 16′ 0″ (1964)
Powerscourt	1867		118′ × 15′ 5″ (1966)
Culzean Castle	1886	42′ × 10′ 0″ (1931)	80′ × 13′ 0″ (1970)

[1] Measured at 2 feet
[2] Measured at 0 feet
[3] Measured at 3 feet

TABLE 34. BIG CUPRESSUS MACROCARPA OF UNKNOWN DATE, WITH GOOD BOLES OR CROWNS

Locality		*Dimensions*	*Boles*
Tregothnan		120′ × 19′ 7″ (1965)	8 feet clear
Adare Manor	72′ × 8′ 0″ (1931)	108′ × 16′ 11″ (1968)	Pruned to 42 feet
Adare Manor	88′ × 11′ 7″ (1931)	70′ × 21′ 10″ (1968)	15 feet clear
Adare Manor		100′ × 14′ 10″ (1968)	30 feet clear
Adare Manor		85′ × 21′ 9″ (1968)	
Clonmannon		75′ × 17′ 10″ (1968)	15 feet clear
Castlewellan	90′ (1931)	101′ × 18′ 1″ (1970)	
Osborne House (Norris Castle)		102′ × 13′ 2″ (1964)	44 feet clear
Melbury House		108′ × 19′ 1″ (1971)	
Strete Ralegh (House)		105′ × 22′ 2″ (1970)	
Trevince	× 17′ 7″ (1928)	85′ × 19′ 11″ (1959)	
Thomas Hall		98′ × 17′ 7″ (1967)	
Trebah		92′ × 19′ 7″ (1959)	
Chyverton		100′ × 16′ 11″ (1959)	
Hinton House		80′ × 18′ 2″ (1959)	
Birr Castle	76′ × 13′ 2″ (1931)	90′ × 17′ 3″ (1966)	
Biel		94′ × 12′ 10″ (1967)	
Leighton Hall		110′ × 10′ 6″ (1967)	
Titness Park		108′ × 10′ 9″ (1957)	
Smeaton House	60′ × 11′ 4″ (1931)	73′ × 14′ 6″ (1966)	
Bicton		112′ × 13′ 2″ (1968)	
Bicton		111′ × 13′ 6″ (1968)	
Beauport	65′ × 14′ 0″ (1905)	103′ × 16′ 8″ (1965)	

TABLE 35. BIG CUPRESSUS MACROCARPA NOT MEASURABLE AT 5 FEET

Locality	*Date Planted*		*Dimensions*
Bodorgan		80′ × 11′ 4″ (1906)	100′ × 19′ 3″ (1966) at 6 feet
Pitt House		87′ × 20′ 0″ (1931)	90′ × 23′ 0″ (1960) at 3 feet
Embley Park			112′ × 18′ 1″ (1971) at 4 feet
Tregrehan		75′ × 22′ 6″ (1931)	95′ × 25′ 4″ (1971) at 3 feet
Boconnoc			90′ × 24′ 8″ (1970) at 3 feet
Northerwood House			112′ × 21′ 2″ (1969) at 2 feet
Cuffnells			118′ (1970) Forked from 0ft
Inistioge			80′ × 23′ 0″ (1966) at 2 feet
Watcombe			115′ × 27′ 10″ (1970) at 1 foot
Watcombe			100′ × 24′ 8″ (1962) at 1 foot
Strete Ralegh (House)			105′ × 29′ 10″ (1970) at 1 foot
Beauport		64′ × 17′ 0″ (1905) at 3 feet	85′ × 27′ 1″ (1965) at 1 foot
Emo Park			95′ × 30′ 0″ (1968) at 1 foot
Fenagh House			86′ × 22′ 7″ (1968) at 1 foot
Fota			75′ × 21′ 0″ (1966) at 1 foot
Powerscourt	1898		90′ × 37′ 5″ (1966) at 0 feet
Kilmacurragh			90′ × 24′ 10″ (1966) at 0 feet

TABLE 36. YOUNG DATED TREES OF CUPRESSUS MACROCARPA

Locality	*Date Planted*	*Dimensions*	
Nymans	1898	63′ × 6′ 9″ (1931)	80′ × 11′ 8″ (1970)
Glendoick	1901	49′ × 3′ 6″ (1931)	92′ × 9′ 0″ (1970)
Wakehurst Place	1918	30′ × 2′ 6″ (1931)	85′ × 12′ 0″ (1970)

cv. Fastigiata (Possibly introduced with the type in 1838). Extremely narrow as a young tree, with erect branching. Erect, fan-shaped and narrow when old. Rare. Tower Court, 60ft×4ft 3in (1965); Bear Wood, 75ft×9ft 0in (at 2 feet) 1970; Warnham Ct. 102ft×9ft 7in (1971); Tregothnan 105ft×19ft 11in (1971) at 2 feet.

cv. Lutea (Chester, 1890). Usually a good golden form but some are of a very dull yellow and a few of these were planted as cv. Aurea. This name is now, however, applied to a recent, prostrate form. The foliage of 'Lutea' is slightly thicker and more fleshy than that of the type at the same age. It is less vigorous than the type, but seems to be marginally more hardy and better against salt-laden winds.

SPECIMENS. Two original trees at Westonbirt (Mitchell Drive), planted in 1896 are of a good colour. The larger was 75ft×7ft 4in in 1971; Smeaton House, 64ft×7ft 9in at 3ft (1967); Westonbirt House, 70ft×7ft 4in (1967); Dropmore, planted 1902, 75ft×8ft 8in (1970); Eastnor Castle, 69ft×8ft 7in (1970); Haldon Grange, 84ft (ungirthable), 1967; Tyninghame, 64ft×8ft 5in at 3ft (1967); Holkham, 67ft×6ft 6in (1968); Gurteen le Poer, 82ft×11ft 8in (1968); Westonbirt (Holford Ride), planted 1933, 70ft×4ft 10in and 58ft×6ft 8in (1967); Little Hall, planted 1906, 55ft×7ft 2in (1961); Castlewellan ("aurea"), 93ft×15ft 1in (1970); Kilmacurragh, 70ft×10ft (1966).

cv. Pendula (Glencormac, County Wicklow, 1880). One tree only, now 50ft×11ft 4in and spreading wide, with long drooping branches and hanging foliage. A fine and curious sight, spreading over the ruins of burnt-out out-houses, at Glencormac.

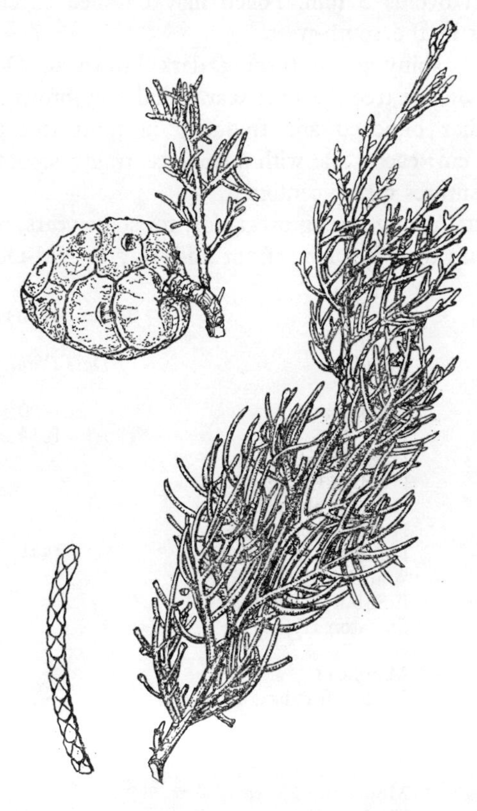

Cupressus sempervirens

Fig. 77
Spray and cone of mature *Cupressus sempervirens*, Mediterranean cypress. Young trees have more open, slender foliage. Shoot (×2) showing closely appressed scale-leaves without enlarged tips, contrasting with those of *C. macrocarpa*.

Cupressus sempervirens L. Italian cypress; Mediterranean cypress

Mediterranean, north to Switzerland; through Persia to the Himalaya. Introduced very early, probably before 1500. Uncommon but far from confined to large gardens in the south; seen in churchyards and small gardens, particularly from Surrey to Somerset; but rare north from the Midlands to Perthshire.

BARK. Pinkish brown, usually grey with algae; broad shallow fissures and flaky shallow, often spiralled, ridges.

CROWN. In this country there are two main categories, but both are of columnar form, the Italian cypress described by Linnaeus. The broad, spreading form is not seen. They are thus, strictly variations of the type which has been called "cv. Stricta". They are so different, however, that it seems desirable to separate them and resurrect a cv. Stricta. The normal crown is columnar and square-topped, sometimes very narrow; more often approaching the shape of an Irish yew, or irregular and with many tops.

FOLIAGE. Shoot soon coppery brown then brownish-purple. Shoots are wiry and open, tapering to fine points and terete.

LEAVES. Dark green, shiny under a lens, acute, with blunt, incurved tips. "A" shoots are slender, short and often curved. "B" shoots are nearly flat with 3–4 "A" shoots mostly on one side (outer or upper). "B" shoots arise at all angles from the "C" shoot which is thus angular and these are similarly arranged on the "D" shoots. Crushed foliage has a faint smell like india-rubber or none. Foliage on old trees is thick, dense, curved forwards and dull grey-green.

FLOWERS AND CONE. Males terminal on "A" or "B" shoots, greenish ovoids 3 mm. Pollen may be shed as early as January in the south-west.

Cones, shiny green turning dark brown in October, remain on the tree the next year a dull grey-brown. They are rather bunched and frequent on most trees; 2·5–3·5×3 cm; each scale with a spike centrally; smooth and shiny; sutures highly contorted.

GROWTH. Young trees grow rapidly for some years, making shoots up to 2 feet long, from mid-May to mid-October. Later in life, growth is very slow and old trees scarcely add a few inches in girth in 30 years. This species must be much more hardy than is usually believed. There are good trees, one very old, east of Edinburgh, which were unharmed by the winter of 1962–3. A tall tree, somewhat exposed at 400 feet in Gloucestershire remained deep green in that winter and no trees have been reported as lost. Some winters earlier in this century, although apparently of no greater intensity of cold, may have caused the large gaps in the list of surviving trees recorded around 1905 and in 1931, for few have been found, but such missing trees are far more prevalent in some species regarded as being quite hardy, like *Juniperus virginiana* and many pines. It may often be a short-lived species, although some are known to be old.

TABLE 37. SPECIMENS OF CUPRESSUS SEMPERVIRENS

Locality	*Date Planted*	*Dimensions*	
Dropmore	ca.1800	42′ × 5′ 9″ (1906)	48′ × 6′ 1″ (1957)[2]
Fota	1814	38′ (1931)	71′ × 8′ 5″ (1955)[1]
Hurn Court		60′ × 5′ 0″ (1906)	52′ × 4′ 3″ (1968)[3]
Penrhyn Castle		65′ × 2′ 10″ (1906)	67′ × 3′ 5″ (1959)
Nettlecombe Court			67′ × 12′ 7″ (1971)
Nettlecombe Court			60′ × 8′ 3″ (1971)
Killerton	1841	50–60′ × 4–5′ (1906)	62′ × 6′ 5″ (1970)
Whittingehame		42′ × 3′ 0″ (1931)	46′ × 3′ 7″ (1956)[5]
Edinburgh R.B.G.			66′ × 4′ 11″ (1955)
Smeaton House			40′ × 1′ 0″ (1966)
Biel			52′ × 9′ 0″ (1966)[2]
Mamhead			59′ × 6′ 2″ (1970)
Blenheim Palace			43′ × 7′ 10″ (1964)[4]
Blenheim Palace			60′ × 7′ 7″ (1964)
Glasnevin B.G.			51′ × 6′ 2″ (1966)[1]
Crowthorn Church			46′ × 2′ 6″ (1959)
Montacute House			40′ × 7′ 2″ (1962)[4]
Henham Hall			65′ × 5′ 0″ (1956)
Exbury House			67′ × 4′ 10″ (1955)
Exbury House			66′ × 5′ 0″ (1955)
Hewell Grange			49′ (1963)
Hergest Croft			38′ × 3′ 1″ (1961)
Wayford Manor	1902		48′ × 4′ 10″ (1961)
Maesllwch Castle	1910		38′ × 3′ 2″ (1963)
Headfort	1918	22′ × 2′ 0″ (1931)	58′ × 3′ 4″ (1966)
Lytchett Heath	1930		37′ × 2′ 0″ (1966)

[1] Measured at 3 feet
[2] Measured at 1 foot
[3] Measured at 4 feet
[4] Measured at 6 inches
[5] Measured at 2 feet

cv. Stricta. Those separated under this head are, as young trees extremely slender and erect, and even those of 60 feet are still slender, fine columns on a single stem to a pointed conic top (when the "type" are flat-topped and broader well below this height). Others included are of the Italian type with dense narrow crowns, conic from half-way up, with a bent top, like a tall dunce's hat falling off. The finest of the first type are: Dropmore, 60ft, thinly crowned, a pole straight to the tip; Bodvean, 61ft×2ft 8in (1960) and Powerscourt, 60ft×3ft 3in (1966); and about 55ft×3ft next to it. Of the second type, the best is at Nymans, 66ft×3ft 4in (1970).

RECOGNITION. The only tree likely to be confused with this is Monterey cypress. The crowns differ markedly and the retained cones of *C. sempervirens*, being dull grey and the foliage darker, distinguish it. With foliage in the hand only, the lack of lemon-verbena scent when crushed is the easiest distinction, followed by the more slender ultimate shoots which are pointed and not "blob-ended" and similarly the individual leaves have much finer points.

Cupressus stephensonii Wolf.

Cuyamaca Mountains, San Diego County, California. Introduced probably since 1950. One vigorous tree, at Jermyn's House, 14 feet tall with 3 feet of growth in 1969.
BARK. Rich chocolate-purple, scaling away to leave dark brown.
CROWN. Fastigiate, narrow, with shoots nodding, open and glaucous grey.
FOLIAGE. Shoot pale yellow-green then bright chestnut red. Sprays distant and spiky. "A" shoots sparse, to 1·5 cm long, all round "B" shoots which are strongly forward-pointing. Leaves terete on "A" shoots, but with short sharp appressed spines on "B" shoots; pale grey-green, dark centred with a gland exuding clear drops of resin later turning white. Many white spots at the base of "B" shoots. Crushed foliage gives a scent of lemon-verbena.

Cupressus torulosa D.Don. Bhutan cypress; Himalayan cypress

Western Himalaya and Szechwan, South West China. Introduced in 1824. Infrequent; mainly in collections and large gardens in South and South West England and in Ireland, but also, if rarely, in similar gardens in the Midlands; West, Central and North-east Scotland.
BARK. Dull-brown with shallow ridges curling away; may be dark grey and spiralled with age.
CROWN. Rounded-conic, moderately narrow and dense; branches level at first then curving upwards; foliage pendulous dull mid-green from distance.
FOLIAGE. Dense, hanging irregular bunches of rather sparsely branched shoots which are long, slender and curved. When crushed the foliage smells of lawn-mowings. "A" shoots few, 2 mm long, forward, on outer foliage. "B" shoots long, slender, at all angles on "C", scarcely branched; "C" shoots to 12×4 cm broadest in the middle pointing forwards and pendulous. Leaves bright rather yellowish-green with pale margins; nearly terete with incurved narrow, blunt tips, slightly bloomed white. Shoot becomes dull orange then dark purplish-grey.
CONE. Globose, 1 cm, whitish-green slowly turning dark red-brown, with minute, down-curved spines, or knobbly processes. Often numerous.
GROWTH. Only three trees are of known date and nine have been remeasured after reasonable periods, but these show on the whole a slow growth, except in Somerset, Cornwall and Ireland. In the Midlands, one tree had a girth of 3ft 11in in 1909; 4ft 8in in 1931 and 5ft 4in in 1963. Another, at Woburn added only 3 inches in girth in 39 years, but at Scorrier, in Cornwall a tree 100 years old by 1958 had added 38 inches in the previous 31 years.
SPECIMENS. Heanton Satcheville, 64ft×6ft 1in (1960); Hewell Grange, planted 1866, 76ft×5ft 4in (1963); Woburn, 68ft×6ft 8in (1970); Lyndon Hall, Rutland, 51ft×2ft 11in (1964); East Bergholt, 45ft×2ft 7in (1966); Keir House, planted 1845, 60ft×6ft 11in (1970); Rossie Priory, 66ft×6ft 8in (1970); Castle Leod, 52ft×3ft 8in (1966); Stonefield, 42ft×2ft 5in (1969); Scorrier, planted 1858, 60ft×8ft 1in (1965); Nettlecombe, 90ft×9ft 4in (1971); 86ft×14ft 3in (1971); 77ft×9ft 10in (1971); Headfort, planted 1914, 45ft ×4ft 4in (1966); Gurteen le Poer, 56ft×4ft 10in (1968); Abbeyleix, 60ft×5ft 9in; 58ft×8ft 11in at 2 feet (1968); Inistioge, 45ft×3ft 0in (1966). A tree at Woodhouse, was 87ft×4ft 7in in 1957 but had recently died.
var. corneyana (Knight and Perry) Carriere. Himalaya. Introduced in 1847. Even less common than the type except perhaps in Ireland. Broadly conic in the crown with level branches; the foliage differs from the type in being duller, more yellowish green, more distantly branched and spreading, on branches which do not curve upwards. The ultimate shoots are 3-4 mm across; branchlets not flattened; curled at shoot-ends.
SPECIMENS. Kew Royal Botanic Gardens, planted 1931, 51ft ×2ft 8in (1965); Leonardslee, 38ft×2ft 0in (1969); Batsford Park, 51ft×4ft 0in (1964); Fota 73ft×10ft 5in; 66ft×8ft 4in; 58ft×6ft 9in (1966); Powerscourt 85ft×6ft 7in; 74ft× 6ft 10in (1966). (The last three, at least, are more likely to be the type.)

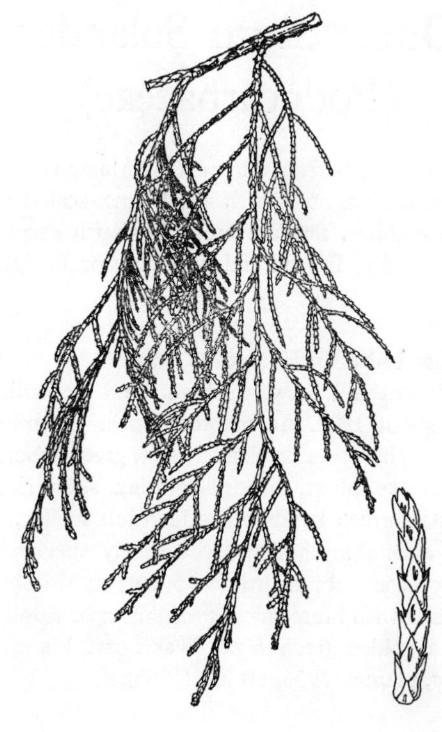

Cupressus torulosa

Fig. 78
Foliage of *Cupressus torulosa*, Himalayan cypress, which is a bright fresh green and is held in dense, finely branched bunches. Shoot (×3½) showing acute scale-leaves with free tips.

Dacrydium Solander (Podocarpaceae)

Twenty-one species from Australasia, Malaysia and Chile mostly monoecious and with hard, fine scale-leaves on hanging branchlets. Two are doubtfully hardy except in the South-west and in Ireland and two more probably reliable only in Ireland.

Dacrydium bidwillii Hooker fil. Tarwood.

South Island and Stewart Island, New Zealand. Introduced in about 1920. An upswept bush. Juvenile leaves 1×0·1 cm, spirally set on slender, soft, green shoots 10–12 cm long; sparse, blunt, forward-pointing, shiny rich green above, 2 pale green bands beneath. Adult foliage, upright shoots of dark shiny yellow-green, finely speckled white, some near base unbranched for 5 cm; at tip short and thicker scales with blunt thick spreading tips. Adult bushes resemble a golden-green *Hebe*. Wakehurst Place, 7 feet; Bedgebury, planted 1926, 6ft 3in (1965).

Dacrydium colensoi Hooker.

New Zealand. Two plants seen, one at Castlewellan, 3 feet high, had juvenile foliage mixed with the adult. The other is 7 feet tall at Borde Hill.

Dacrydium cupressinum Solander. Rimu.

New Zealand. Very rare—Far south-west and in southern Ireland. Bark smooth, dark brown; crown weeping, foliage hanging in strings from short branches mainly on one side of the tree. Dense shoots, sea-green or yellowish green, surrounded by tiny hard scale-leaves with tips protruding all round. Very attractive. Scale-leaves 2–3 mm long, pointing 30° forward of perpendicular, sharply acute, flattened laterally and decurrent with a broad pale stomatal band. Strings of unbranched foliage hang for 25–30 cm or more.

Garinish Island, 25ft×1ft 6in; 20ft×8in (1966); Annesgrove, 20ft×10in (1968); Mount Usher, 7 feet (1966); Tresco Abbey, 30ft×8in (1970); Casa di Sole, 9 feet (1970).

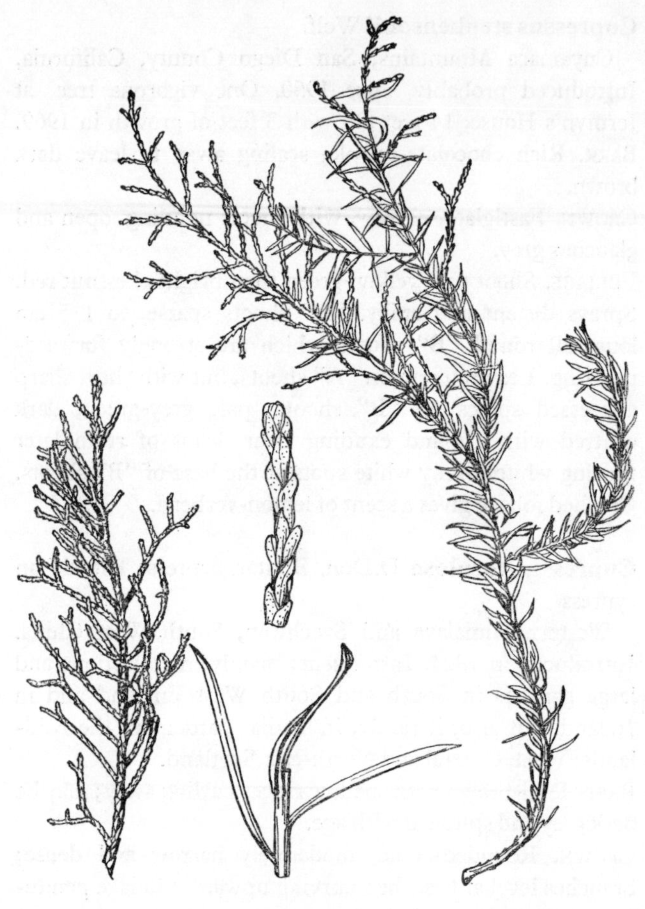

Dacrydium bidwillii

Fig. 79
Adult foliage (far left and ×3⅓, upper middle) and juvenile foliage (lower middle ×3⅓) of *Dacrydium bidwillii* with shoot on right turning from juvenile to adult.

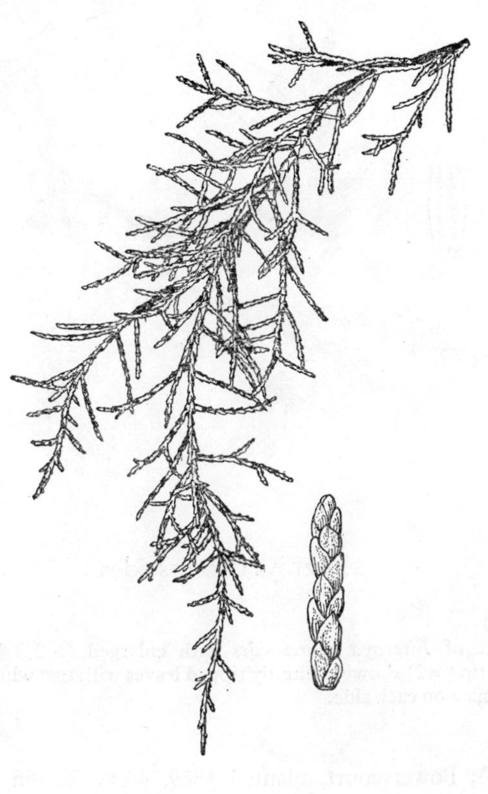

Dacrydium franklinii

Fig. 80
Hanging spray of *Dacrydium franklinii*, which has very slender, dark green shoots clad in closely appressed scale-leaves (lower right $\times 5\frac{1}{3}$).

Dacrydium franklinii Hooker fil. Huon pine

South and West Tasmania. Introduced in about 1840. Very rare. Occasionally found in collections in South and South-west England, the borders and Wales, South-west Scotland and in Ireland.

BARK. Smooth and silvery, striped horizontally grey-brown.

CROWN. One gaunt stem, or several, splaying outwards, with long strings of foliage arching out and hanging from short branches. The oldest tree seen, at Fota, has a sturdy main stem and regular branching—it is not at all gaunt.

FOLIAGE. Minor shoots arch out distantly all round each long, hanging shoot, and curve downwards; each bearing a few lesser shoots at right angles. Each is very slender and terete, clothed in tiny scale-leaves which are pale or bright green, shiny, with a convex point, speckled white with stomata each side. Older shoots become orange-brown.

SPECIMENS. The oldest known surviving tree is at Fota. Planted in 1854, it was 28ft × 3ft 4in in 1966. One planted in 1857 at Coldrennick was 22ft × 2ft 11in in 1957, but dead. Other trees are: Bedgebury, 15ft × 8in (1969); Leonardslee, 20ft × 1ft 2in; 20ft × 1ft 0in and others (1969). Sheffield Park, 20ft × 1ft 2in (1960); Borde Hill, 12ft × 1ft 0in (1958); Grayswood Hill, 10ft (1969); Hergest Croft, 8 feet (1961); Castle Kennedy, 18ft × 1ft 6in; 10ft × 1ft 5in (1967); Garinish Island, 16 feet (1966); Headfort, 10 feet (1966); Fenagh House, 14ft × 2ft 0in at 2 feet (1968); Bodnant, planted 1890, 20ft × 1ft 8+1ft 8in; planted 1892, 16ft × 1ft 10in+1ft 6in (1959).

Fitzroya Hooker f. (Cupressaceae)

A single species reaching to 160ft × 30ft in Chile.

Fitzroya cupressoides (Molina) Johnston

The southern Andes, in Chile and Northern Argentina. Introduced in 1849. Rather rare; confined to collections and large gardens in Ireland, across southern England and along the west coast to Scotland. In the east, only at Bedgebury and Edinburgh Royal Botanic Garden.

BARK. Usually dark brown, deeply fissured into rough, stripping and shredding ridges. Old trees with clear boles have grey-brown bark in shallow strips, not lifting.

CROWN. Asymmetrical; the top often leaning and each main branch with a projecting conic crown. Pendulous; dense in patches, open between. Branches upswept, small branches twisted. New shoots sparse and slender.

FOLIAGE. Scale-like leaves in threes; hard, thick blunt ends curling out from shoot 2–4 mm, but tips incurved; deep blue-green with two bright white bands on each face, often on the outer half only.

FLOWERS AND CONE. Male and females on the same or on different trees. Males among the leaves near the ends of shoots. Cones terminal, 9 woody scales, opening far apart like radiating wedges and remaining on the tree for some time, 6–7 mm, sometimes very abundant.

GROWTH. In general a very slow-growing tree but young plants may grow more than one foot and growth can continue until October. Increase in girth is very slow on older trees—6 inches in 31 years in one case—but younger trees have added 6 inches in 8 years.

SPECIMENS. Ardkinglas, (Strone), 58ft × 6ft 6in (1969); Inistioge, 57ft × 3ft 0in (1966); Kilmacurragh, 42ft × 7ft 2in (1966); Powerscourt, planted 1869, 44ft × 5ft 9in (1966); Castlewellan, 35ft × 5ft 3in (1970); Mount Usher, 41ft × 7ft 6in; 40ft × 4ft 11in (1966); Killerton, 60ft × 6ft 3in at 4 feet and 49ft × 4ft 5in (1970); Bicton, 48ft × 4ft 8in (1968); Borde Hill, 33ft × 2ft 4in (1968); Exbury, 27ft × 2ft 11in (1968); Scorrier, planted 1868, 50ft × 5ft 2in (1959); Woodhouse, 39ft × 4ft 3in (1970); Strete Ralegh Pinetum, 40ft × 4ft 8in (twin stem) (1964); Tregothnan, 35ft × 3ft 9in (1961); Garinish Island, 40ft × 3ft 8in (1966); Bedgebury, planted 1925, 28ft × 2ft 7in (1970); Edinburgh Royal Botanic Garden, 17 feet (1958); Pencarrow, planted, 1905, 35ft × 4ft 3in at 4 feet (1970); Tregrehan 51ft × 6ft 9in (1971) forked.

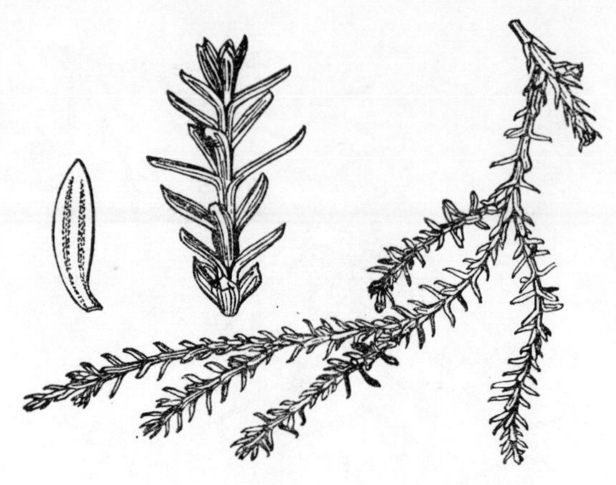

Fitzroya cupressoides

Fig. 81
Foliage of *Fitzroya cupressoides* with enlarged (×3⅓) leaf and shoot-tip (×2) showing bluntly tipped leaves with two white bands of stomata on each side.

Fokienia Henry and Thomas (Cupressaceae)

Two very similar species, perhaps the same one, from China. Only *F. hodginsii* is considered here.

Fokienia hodginsii Henry and Thomas.

Eastern China. Introduced in 1909. Extremely rare and scarcely hardy except in the extreme south and west, but, surviving where it does, under some high shade in Sussex and Hampshire, it ought to be hardy further west and in Ireland. Juvenile plants only have been seen, without boles or crown or adult foliage. Juvenile foliage is fanned sprays of broad, flat, bright yellow-green leaves. The smallest shoots are the same breadth as the larger and end abruptly, 3–4 mm across. Each leaf is 4 mm long, with an obtuse swollen, minutely mucronate tip. The underside of the shoot is marked boldly in bright white, two smaller inner, oblong bands and two larger, inclined or curved outer bands.

Borde Hill 7 feet (1968); Leonardslee, 3 feet 6 inches (1962); Jermyn's House, 3 feet (1969); Garinish Island a procumbent mat to 5 feet (1966); Exbury, 6ft 6in (1970).

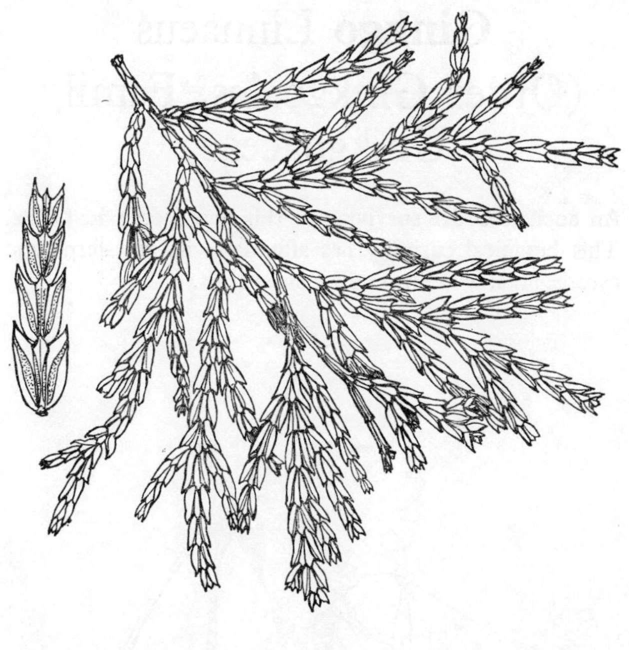

Fokienia hodginsii

Fig. 82
Juvenile foliage of *Fokienia hodginsii* as seen on the few small plants grown in the British Isles. The underside of the leaf (left × 1⅛) has bright white bands.

Ginkgo Linnaeus (Order Ginkgoales; Family Ginkgoaceae)

An ancient Order surviving in this one species in China. This botanical curiosity has affinities with tree-ferns and cycads, notably in the motile male sperms.

Ginkgo biloba

Fig. 83
Foliage of *Ginkgo biloba*, Chinese maidenhair tree. These leaves are on two-year wood and are broader and less deeply lobed than leaves on new shoots.

Ginkgo biloba L. Maidenhair tree.

China, surviving genuinely wild in Chekiang Province. Introduced in 1758 and at least one original tree survives in full health (at Kew). Frequent in Southern England in parks, large gardens and many small roadside gardens and as a street tree in a few places; common in some areas, notably Bath–Bristol–Yeovil; less frequent in South Wales (street tree in Cardiff), the Borders and Midlands and East Anglia and in Ireland; rare in Southern Scotland; one against a wall in Central Scotland.

BARK. Dull grey, with wandering and crossing ridges, their edges shredding, and broad fissures between them, deep and pale buff, or pale orange in vigorous trees.

CROWN. Varying greatly from gaunt, straight poles with few level or ascending branches to broad, much forked, many-stemmed irregularly spreading and vase-shaped trees.

BUD. Broad, flat, conic, brown.

FOLIAGE. Shoot bright green at first, then dull, turning brown by autumn. Second year shoot woody pale pink-grey or dull grey.

LEAVES. 1) on new shoots, set spirally, long cuneate on 2 cm petiole, to 12×11 cm cleft narrowly down the middle to within 2 cm of the base, each lobe shallowly cleft again. Basal margins entire; outer margins irregular. Rich green above, yellower beneath. 2) on old spur-shoots. Short cuneate on petioles to 4·5 cm; to 6×8 cm, very broad, shallowly cleft less than half way to base, each lobe irregularly toothed. Dark green both sides; veins radiating from base, numerous, many thick, others fine.

FLOWERS AND FRUIT. Male flowers: thick pale yellow catkins emerging before the leaves are fully spread; rarely seen although nearly all trees are probably male. Females seen on (or as fruit beneath) a few trees, (which are usually slender and have good, straight stems), after good summers only. They are borne in pairs or singly on long (4–5 cm) stalks and are ovoid, about 3 cm long. Before they fall they are pale yellow and turn pale orange before the outer parts rot with a putrid smell.

GROWTH. Growth in height is quite unpredictable in small plants. They may make a shoot, between late May and the end of August, nearly 3 feet long or they may make none at all. The terminal bud in that case, produces just a rosette of small leaves. Whether new growth occurs or not seems to be independent of water or nutrients. From the very few young dated trees, and from remeasurements, height increases by an average of rather under one foot per year. The best is 53 feet in 59 years, and over short periods 11 feet in 10 years and 12 feet in 11 years. Girth also increases slowly but attains the usual one inch per year in Cornwall at least (36 inches in 35 years Carclew). Trees given by Elwes and Henry have increased (apart from two large, inexplicable decreases) by between 5 inches and 60 inches in 55–60 years, with three reliable increases between 20 and 26 inches in that time.

Many of the largest and best trees seem to be on soils over chalk or limestone flanking the North and South Downs and the Cotswolds. Ginkgos will scarcely grow, however, at Westonbirt over limestone, nor will they on acid silts at Bedgebury.

SPECIMENS. A few of the largest trees are: Kew Royal Botanic Gardens, planted 1762, 72ft×13ft 5in at 3 feet

(×9ft 6in+6ft 8in at 5 feet) (1970); Blaize Castle, 68ft×12ft 4in (1969); Maesllwch Castle, planted 1820, 73ft×13ft 7in (3 stems coalesced; 1963); Peckover, 76ft×11ft 7in (1962); Panshanger, 78ft×12ft 3in (1969); The Lodge, Wateringbury, 70ft×10ft 9in (1962); Carclew, 80ft×10ft 5in (1962); Longleat, 70ft×10ft 0in (1971); Cobham Park, 67ft×11ft 4in; 62ft×9ft 9in (1963); Whitfield, planted 1780, 68ft×12ft 5in (1963); Bitton Vicarage, 74ft×9ft 8in (1959); Engelfield House, 80ft×11ft 0in (1968); Melbury, planted 1807, 79ft×6ft 9in and 72ft×9ft 1in (1970); Linton Park, planted 1844, 93ft×8ft 8in (1970); Tregrehan, 86ft×5ft 11in (1971); Penshurst House, 80ft×6ft 9in (1954); Farnham Castle, 75ft×8ft 8in (1961); Bath Botanic Garden, 80ft×4ft 5in very slender (1963); Walcombe, Wells, 80ft×6ft 8in (1963); Avington House, 81ft×6ft 10in (1965); Ashford Castle, County Mayo, 69ft×6ft 8in (1968); Dalkeith, planted 1851, 52ft×5ft 10in (1970); Oxford Botanic Garden, 83ft×8ft 3in (1970); Badminton House, 68ft×10ft 1in (1966).

Known female trees are:—Glanfield Road, Bath, 50ft×5ft 3in (1962); The Rookeries, Dorking, 77ft×5ft 2in (1959); West Dean, 57ft×4ft 6in (1967); Snowdenham House, Bramley, 40ft×2ft 9in (1964) and near Kew Green Station, about 50ft.

Glyptostrobus Endlicher (Taxodiaceae)

Closely similar to Taxodium; 1 species in China.

Glyptostrobus lineatus (Poiret) Druce. (*G. heterophyllus* Endlicher; *G. pensilis* (Staunton) Koch).

Canton, China, possibly extinct. Introduced probably early this century. A few older trees grown as this species are *Taxodium ascendens nutans*. The Chinese swamp cypress differs mainly in the 2 cm stalked obovoid cone but only juvenile plants are known here—Tregrehan, 6 feet 9 inches (1957); Leonardslee, on a wall, 9 feet; Nymans, 14ft × 1ft 1in (1970). The fresh, pale green leaves are in three ranks, very slender, 1·5–2·5 cm, soft, on slender, bright green shoots 10 cm long which arch down from the branches. The leaves are the same colour on each surface.

Juniperus Linnaeus (Cupressaceae)

About 64 species, the majority in North America, China and Japan, but widely distributed as far south as the Equator in Africa. Foliage of two kinds is found, in many cases on the same tree. The juvenile kind, persistent in many species is of hard sharp, acute spreading leaves in pairs or in threes. Adult foliage in some other species is small scale-leaves, overlapping and appressed as in Cupressus. The fruit are made up of fleshy scales closely joined, looking like a berry.

Key to the species of Juniperus

Foliage of Junipers is of two kinds. (1) Free, long-pointed, usually hard, spiny, lanceolate, usually spreading and revealing shoot. (2) Close, minute and scale-like, free only at spined tip if at all, covering shoot.
(1) is juvenile but retained in adult life by many species exclusively, or in a few, together with adult, scale-leaves. A few species, and more cultivars soon lack all juvenile leaves.

In a few species, the transition from (1) to (2) is gradual or incomplete, (*J. excelsa*) or not completed in specimens known here (*J. deppeana pachyphloea*).

1.	Leaves on all shoots juvenile; free, spine-pointed	2
	Leaves on some or all shoots, scale-like, adpressed to shoot	12
2.	Shoots lax and long-pendulous	3
	Shoots not lax; spreading, or upright with side-shoots nodding or spreading	8
3.	Shoot angled and winged	4
	Shoot round, not winged	6
4.	Shoot white, leaves deep blue-grey, bloomed; not spined	*cedrus*
	Shoot yellow, pink and red-brown; leaves not bloomed, spined	5
5.	Leaf 1 mm broad; outer surface dull dark green, inner with broad white bands and narrow margin	*formosana*
	Leaf to 2 mm broad, outer surface glossy grey-green; inner with white bands ± equal to margins	*oxycedrus*
6.	Leaves spreading, 2 cm long, uniformly bright shiny green outer surface, inner with central blue-white band	*rigida*
	Leaves strongly forwards, to 1·5 cm long	7
7.	Leaves 1–1·5 cm, uniform dark green outer surface; hard	*communis oblonga pendula*
	Leaves 8–10 mm, bright pale green with white margin and spine; inner surface with 2 pale green-white bands, soft	*recurva* v. *coxii*
8.	Main shoot rising, nodding at tip; side shoots level then arched; foliage soft, dry, rustling; leaves 5–8 mm, crowded closely forward hiding shoot; pale margins	*recurva*
	Shoots all rising or spreading; foliage hard, spiny; leaves spreading to reveal shoot	9
9.	Leaves big, broad, 1·2–2·5 cm × 1·5–3 mm rigid, bright pale green; two broad white bands on inner surface joining near tip, tree narrowly columnar	*drupacea*
	Leaves small, slender, 0·5–1 cm × 0·5–1 mm, tree irregularly conic, or ovoid	10
10.	Inner surface with one grey-green stomatal band; outer bright green dusted with white stomata; leaf 8 mm	*flaccida* (juvenile)
	Inner surface with bright blue-white band or bands, leaf 5 or 10 mm	11

11.	Leaf 5 mm foliage dense, bright green and blue; upper surface with 2 thickly blue-white bands merging across midrib	*morrisonicola*
	Leaf 10 mm, foliage more open; grey-green and white; upper surface with central broad white stomatal band	*communis*
12.	Juvenile and adult foliage both present on most shoots or inter-grading on the same shoot	13
	Adult foliage only; no juvenile foliage present	18
13.	Gradual and partial transition; foliage blue-green or blue-grey, fine; leaves with projecting, hard points	14
	Juvenile and adult on separate shoots or on different parts of the same shoot; foliage not blue or white	15
14.	Shoots very fine, blue-green, pale; without white spots (bark shredding into fine strips)	*excelsa*
	Shoots thick, ascending, foliage blue-white, with white spots; (bark deeply fissured into square, scaling plates)	*deppeana pachyphloea*
15.	Juvenile foliage terminal on adult shoots as well as on separate shoots, adult foliage very slender	16
	Juvenile foliage on separate shoots or basal to adult; adult foliage not slender	17
16.	Foliage bright green; juvenile often scarce among adult foliage	*flaccida*
	Foliage dark green; juvenile foliage plentiful	*virginiana*
17.	Foliage thick; silvery-blue; juvenile drooping; adult patterned dark grey; fruit black, 10 mm	*wallichiana*
	Foliage relatively open; scale-leaves dark green with pale margins; fruit glaucous 6–7 mm	*chinensis*
18.	Leaves with spreading, acute tips; very dark grey-green; strong musty scent	*thurifera*
	Leaves with incurved tips or shoots quite terete; bright green or grey-green or glaucous, need crushing to release scent	19
19.	Fruit 7–9 mm pale grey-green or glaucous	20
	Fruit 3–5 mm bright deep blue or blue bloomed white	21
20.	Foliage bright green, bloomed grey; very dense, stiff	*chinensis* 'Kaizuka'
	Foliage shiny dark grey-green; (crown very conic)	*chinensis* 'Keteleerii'
21.	Foliage brilliant yellowish-green (crown densely columnar, spire-topped)	*virginiana* 'Canaertii'
	Foliage pale blue-grey, upswept, dense bunches but open crown	*virginiana* 'Glauca'

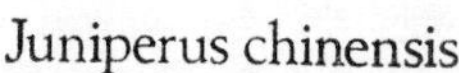

Juniperus chinensis

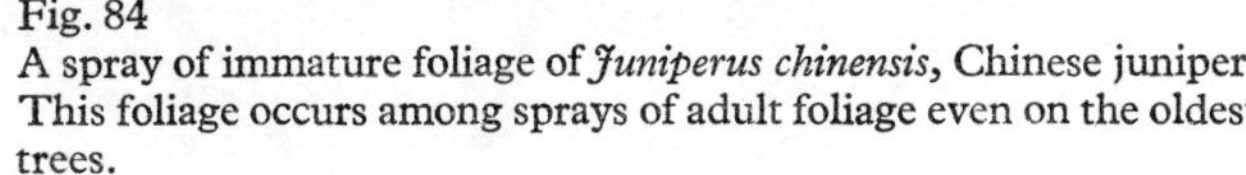

Fig. 84
A spray of immature foliage of *Juniperus chinensis*, Chinese juniper. This foliage occurs among sprays of adult foliage even on the oldest trees.

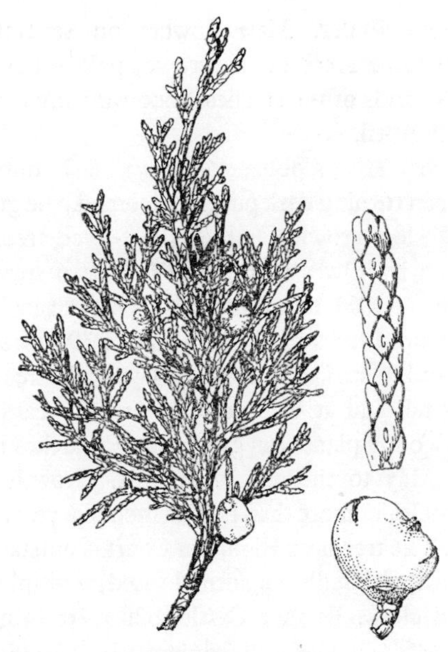

Juniperus chinensis

Fig. 85
Spray of adult foliage with fruit of *Juniperus chinensis* with shoot ($\times 5\frac{1}{3}$) and fruit enlarged ($\times 1\frac{1}{3}$). Adult trees also bear sprays of juvenile foliage. The fruit are bloomed greenish blue-grey.

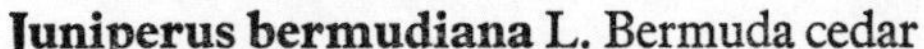

Juniperus bermudiana L. Bermuda cedar

Bermuda. Introduced by 1684. Said not to be hardy but the distribution of the only three outdoor specimens known did not really confirm this, until two of them died.

BARK. Very smooth and grey, like a beech. Said to be red with age.

FOLIAGE. Dark brown shoots bearing very small hard scale-leaves, in threes, 3 mm long, ovate, blunt, incurved, bloomed greyish on the outside.

SPECIMENS. Fota, planted 1916, 45ft×2ft 7in (1966); Woburn, 9 feet and 8 feet (1961), dead before 1970.

Juniperus cedrus Canary Island juniper. Webb and Berthelot.

Canary Islands. Introduction not recorded. An island form of *J. oxycedrus* differing in being, in this country, a wide-branched, bushy tree, with a low open crown and strikingly white, pendulous shoots with blue-grey foliage.

Highdown 15 feet (1965); Castlewellan, 33ft×2ft 2in+2ft 0in (1966).

Juniperus chinensis L. Chinese juniper

China, Mongolia and Japan. Introduced from Canton in 1804. Common; in town gardens more as cultivars, but the type is quite frequent in small gardens, parks and churchyards; less common in Scotland.

BARK. Dark cigar-brown, stringy, with long, narrow, twisted strips peeling away. Bole irregular, often two fused.

CROWN. The best trees are ovoid-conic, with rounded base and long narrow acute apex, slightly curved towards the top. Very variable in density but may be open enough to see short, slightly ascending upper branches; more strongly ascending lower branches. Very dark green.

FOLIAGE. Shoot soon pale yellowish brown, then shiny, dull purple. Juvenile leaves very prickly, in pairs or in threes, 2–5 mm spreading, convex, dark green outside; inner surface with two broad, curved white bands separated by a broad midrib.

These leaves are on branchlets at the base of each spray of adult foliage; on sprays of their own, and, less often at the tips of adult sprays, which are of small scale-leaves.

Crushed foliage has a rather sour resinous scent.

Flowers and Fruit. Male flowers on separate trees, crowded on some areas of the crown, pale yellow ovoids, visible on the ends of the smallest shoots during the winter; pollinating in April.

Fruit, irregularly globular (lumpy), 6–7 mm across, glaucous green turning dark purple, bloomed pale grey.

Growth. A slow-growing, rather short-lived tree. Of five visited, given by Elwes and Henry only two survive, and several given in 1931 no longer exist. Growth in height in three remeasured trees has been 3 feet in 39 years, 22 feet in 38 years and 9 feet in 11 years. A 94-year old tree at Mells was 57 feet tall and at Whiteknights one 66 years old was 36 feet tall. Young plants can grow quite 20 inches in a year, from early May to the end of August. Growth in girth seems to be seldom more than half an inch in a year.

Specimens. The tree near Highnam Court is outstanding for its bole which, although the normal fused, multiple stem, is straight and clean. Eastnor Castle, 52ft × 7ft 11in (1969); Bicton, 67ft × 5ft 8in (1968); Highnam, 61ft × 7ft 9in (1970); (N. Devon), 59ft × 5ft 6in (1970); Kinfauns, 52ft × 4ft 1in (1970); Pampisford, 56ft × 3ft 10in; 51ft × 2ft 7in (1969); Fairlawne, 56ft × 5ft 1in (1965); Bowood, 56ft × 4ft 6in at 6 feet (1968); Westonbirt House, 58ft × 6ft 5in at 3 feet; 48ft × 7ft 11in (1967); Westonbirt Arboretum, 59ft × 5ft 0in (1970); Poles, 53ft × 4ft 9in (1969); Maesllwch Castle, 53ft × 5ft 11in (1963); Mells Park, planted 1868, 57ft × 7ft 1in at 1 foot 6 inches (1962); Wallington Hall, 52ft × 3ft 6in (1958); Moor Park, Ludlow, 53ft × 4ft 8in; Mamhead, 53ft × 8ft 0in; 50ft × 9ft 10in at 2 feet (1962).

cv. Aurea. (1855, Milford), Distributed 1872. Golden Chinese juniper. Frequent in gardens, parks and churchyards, and seems to be well suited to towns. A compact, male-flowering, narrowly columnar form with narrow conic top or, often, several narrow tops, flattened with age, and bright gold. Slow growing.

Golden Grove, 43ft × 3ft 4in (1960); Adhurst St. Mary, 43ft × 3ft 2in (1964); Lythe Hill, 42ft × 3ft 0in (1969); Tregrehan, 40ft × 3ft 5in (1957); Stourhead, 38 feet (1970); Sheffield Park, 33 feet (1968); Nymans, 36 feet (1970).

cv. Columnaris (China, to California, 1905). A specimen, probably of this form is dark and very narrowly conic, at Lytchett Heath, 44 feet (1967).

cv. Femina (J. c. *reevesiana*) Japan, 1861). An upright bush with adult foliage only; yellow-green with whitish margins and bases to the scales, rather thick and twisted. Fruit abundant, clustered, 1 cm irregularly ovoid yellow-green bloomed, blue-white. Bedgebury, 12 feet.

var. fortunei. At Kew, a bluish grey-green plant covered in pink-brown male flowers, with some bluish juvenile foliage, 14 feet (1969).

cv. Glauca. At Bedgebury, has papery flakes of red-brown bark; pale grey-blue adult type foliage only, covered in profuse male flowers which are yellow-pink.

cv. Kaizuka (Japan to United States, ca. 1920). A densely narrow-conic tree, liable to lean to one side; conic branch systems project on the upper side as secondary leaders. Foliage adult, dense, stiff; ultimate shoots terete and to 4·5 cm long, bright green. Fruit 9 mm lumpy, green bloomed grey.

Bedgebury, 26ft × 1ft 5in (1969).

cv. Keteleerii (Belgium, pre-1910.) A dense, regular, narrowly conic, desirable cultivar, dark grey-green. All the foliage is adult, scale-leaved with unbranched, terete, ultimate shoots to 2 cm long, and shiny. Fruit frequent, 7 mm bloomed blue-green. [This and cv. 'Aurea' are the only forms worth planting.]

Bedgebury, planted 1925 to 29ft × 1ft 6in (1969); Dawyck, planted 1913, 28ft × 1ft 6in (1961).

cv. Leeana (Lee of Hammersmith, pre-1865.) Conic dense, usually leaning, with new conic leading shoots vertical from the upper side; foliage mixed slender green scale-leaved shoots and blue juvenile shoots. A male form.

Bedgebury, planted 1925, 23ft × 1ft 6in (1969).

cv. Pendula. Fastigiate in branching but with pendulous outer shoots, partly adult foliage, partly distant, spreading juvenile.

Kew Royal Botanic Gardens, 30ft × 1ft 1in (1969).

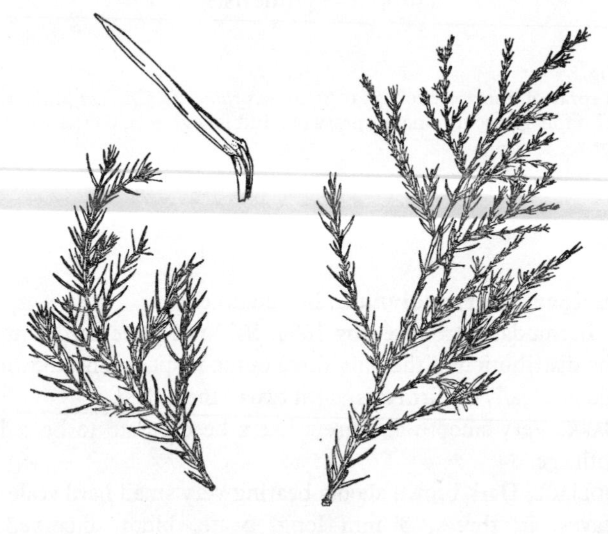

Juniperus communis

Fig. 86
Two sprays of foliage *Juniperus communis*, Common juniper, on the left with juvenile leaves, on the right with adult and juvenile. Single leaf × $1\frac{1}{3}$.

Juniperus communis L. Common juniper

Northern Hemisphere, in both America and Eurasia south to Asia Minor. Native, growing on the open downs of chalk and limestone in England, but where there is least sunshine and most rain, in North Scotland, it grows in shady woodlands on acid boggy peats. Having got things thus reversed, it is understandable that it is seldom other than a narrow, spiky bush. Rare. Almost unknown in gardens except as cultivars. Pale brown shoots bear finely pointed leaves 1 cm long spreading, showing one broad white band on the inner surface; light grey-green outer surface. Trees of some 20 feet tall in a natural stand near Penpont, Dumfries, have narrowly conic tops.

cv. Oblonga pendula. Very rare. Distant, long-acuminate leaves to 2 cm, in threes, hanging from short, upturned branches. Very like *J. oxycedrus* but leaves grey-green on inner surface, and shoot not winged.

cv. Stricta (Ireland, 1836.) Slim, regular column of dense foliage, very blue from short branches pointing outwards showing the upper surface of the leaves.

Riccarton, 25ft (1967); Westonbirt, planted 1939, 16 feet (1967); Wayford Manor, planted 1902, 30 feet (1961); Dunloe Castle, 30 feet; 28 feet (1968); Fenagh House, 22 feet; 19 feet (1968).

cv. Suecica. Flame-shaped narrow bush with upright branches and short horizontal shoots nodding at the tips. Shoot whitish green turning orange-brown. Leaves 1–1·4 cm in whorls 0·5 cm apart on main shoot; tapering to a long spine, prominently ridged outer surface, two broad blue-white bands on inner surface. Differs from 'stricta' mainly in the nodding shoots.

Juniperus deppeana var. pachyphloea (Torrey) Martinez. Alligator juniper

Texas, Arizona and New Mexico. Introduced in 1873. Very rare indeed.

BARK. Dull red-brown, deeply cracked into square plates from the surface of which thin scales flake away. Resembles some trees of *Crataegus* or *Malus*.

CROWN. A slender, domed tree, or upswept to a broadly conic top, the branches and shoots curving upwards.

FOLIAGE. Shoot curled at the tip, covered in thick, green acute scales with white dots and spreading tips, then pink-brown. Leaves on outermost shoots spread strongly forwards, hard, prickly, fine blue-white bloomed and dotted with white.

Three trees at Bedgebury, planted 1926, the best two 21ft × 1ft and 20ft × 10in (1969); Jermyn's House, 8 feet.

RECOGNITION. The bark is unique among Junipers. The foliage resembles that of *J. excelsa stricta* in being very fine, prickly and blue, but has white resin-dots.

Juniperus distans Florin. Szechuan juniper. N.W. China 1926.

Three trees of about 15 feet dating from 1931, at Bedgebury. Bark pale brown, papery. Crown ovoid upswept; branches tortuous. Foliage strongly scented of soap, mainly juvenile, in threes. 7 mm, sharply pointed, light green, pale at tip, two bright blue-white bands on inner surface. Adult foliage very slender, pale green, terete; incurved tips with whitish margins.

Juniperus drupacea Labillardiere. Syrian juniper

Greece, Asia Minor and Syria. Introduced in 1853, perhaps in 1820. Rare. Confined to a few collections. This is most surprising, for the species is perfectly hardy, it tolerates drought and limestone and is of good shape, a fresh light green colour unique among the Junipers. It is the best of a large and predominantly dull genus.

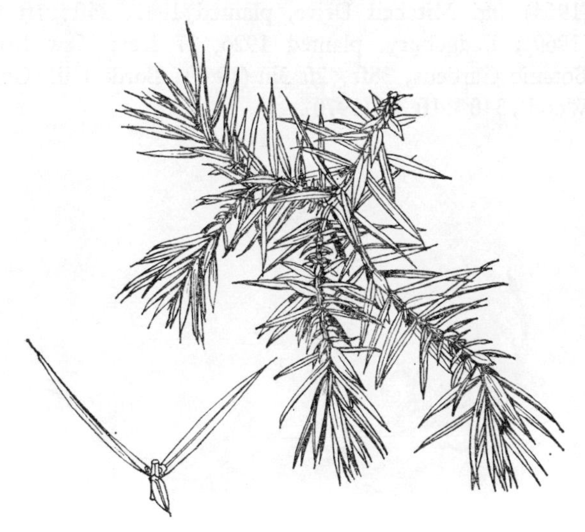

Juniperus drupacea

Fig. 87
The Syrian juniper, *Juniperus drupacea*, with a single whorl of leaves (× 1⅓). The foliage is a fresh bright green with two bands of white on the upper surface, uniting toward the tip.

BARK. Orange-brown, apt to be grey with algae in old plants; stripping vertically leaving bright rufous strips.

CROWN. Narrowly columnar, curving to sharply conic apex or apices. In the open, old trees are broader and domed and branched to the ground, but in light shade they have long bare stems. Branching upright.

FOLIAGE. Young shoot green, furrowed below each leaf, becoming grey-brown.

LEAVES. Hard, spiny, spreading in whorls of three, narrowly lanceolate 1·0×0·15 cm to 2·5×0·3 cm; outer surface rich, shiny green, inner surface with two broad white bands joining near the tip. These are easily the largest leaves in the genus.

FLOWERS. Male trees only are known in cultivation. The small ovoid pale yellow flowers cluster in 1 to 3's among the leaves towards the tips of small hanging shoots; bright green like the leaves, until they open.

SPECIMENS AND GROWTH. One of the only two known dated trees has grown about 23 feet in 23 years but this is probably about the maximum rate.

Leonardslee, 49ft × 1ft 10in (1969); Batsford Park, 47ft × 5ft 6in at 1 foot (1963); Stanway, 45ft × 4ft 10in at 3 feet (1964); Haffield House, 32ft × 5ft 1in at 3 feet, procumbent (1966); Carton, 44ft × 2ft 3in (1968. 17 feet in 1931); Wakehurst Place, 43ft × 2ft 3in (1969); Tortworth, 45ft × 5ft 7in at 2 feet (1964); Westonbirt, Willesley, 32ft × 1ft 11in (1963) and Mitchell Drive, planted 1946, 25ft × 1ft 0in (1969); Bedgebury, planted 1926, 27 feet; Kew Royal Botanic Gardens, 38ft × 2ft 3in (1969); Borde Hill (Gores Wood), 34ft × 1ft 3in (1970).

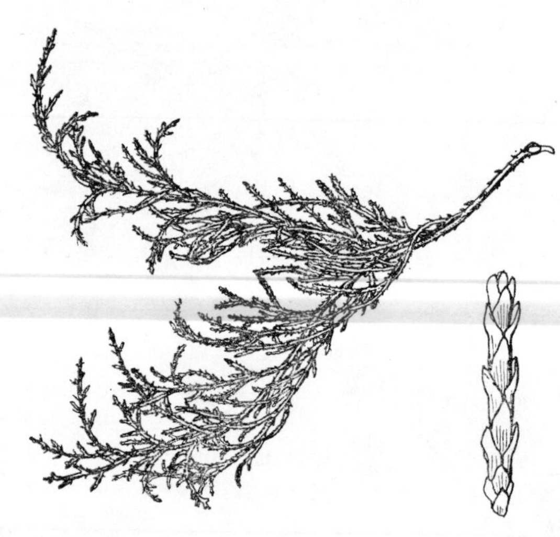

Juniperus excelsa

Fig. 88
The slender, grey-green foliage of *Juniperus excelsa* with a shoot enlarged (×4). The foliage is intermediate between juvenile and adult forms on all trees of this species.

Juniperus excelsa Bieberstein. Grecian juniper

Balkan Mountains; Asia Minor, the Caucasus Mountains and Persia. Introduced in 1806. Very rare; found in only a few collections.

BARK. Purple-brown, scaling away irregularly.

CROWN. Slender, thin at the base, diffuse and shapeless at the top.

FOLIAGE. Neither fully adult nor properly juvenile, but varying around an intermediate condition. Shoot slender, curved, light pink-brown, bearing curved sprays of light grey-green very fine foliage.

LEAVES. Along shoots paired, acute with spreading tips. Ultimate shoots less than 1 mm across, with long-acute leaves, tips pointing forwards, dark; margins and base pale. These shoots at all angles on short shoots which are also at all angles. Crushed foliage emits a warm resinous scent.

SPECIMENS. Westonbirt, Wigmore, 56ft × 4ft 1in (1970); Tortworth, 30ft × 5ft 4in, top lost (1965); Adhurst St. Mary, 47ft × 5ft 0in (1964); Glasnevin Botanic Garden, 38ft × 5ft 7in at 3 feet, (1966); Bodnant, 26ft × 1ft 7in (1959); Borde Hill (Warren), 29ft × 1ft 1in (1970).

cv. Stricta. A narrowly conic form with glaucous foliage; more juvenile than in the type, leaves to 3 mm, and a tangle of upswept branches.

Wisley Royal Horticultural Society Gardens, 24ft × 1ft 4in (1964); Kew Royal Botanic Gardens, 20ft × 1ft 9in; 18ft × 1ft 1in (1969).

Juniperus flaccida Schlechtendal. Mexican juniper

Mexico and Texas. Introduced in 1838. Very rare; in a few collections only.

BARK. Reddish grey-brown, stringy, long strips coming away leave orange-brown stripes.

CROWN. As a young tree fairly narrow, rounded-conic. The old tree at Bicton was broad, with an open crown of spreading branches.

FOLIAGE. Shoot pale pink-brown. Juvenile foliage is a soft, fresh green; leaves in opposite pairs, widely spreading, 8 mm long, acute and spined; outer surface bright, rather grey-green, dusted with white stomata; inner surface with two broad grey-green bands. Adult foliage not yet attained by some trees 20 feet tall, but plentiful on another 22 feet tall, mixed with juvenile shoots. It is the same colour, the small scale-leaves are long-acute to an abrupt, free but closely forward-pointed spine tip, dark in the centre with pale margins.

Outer parts of sprays are terete, but inner parts on all shoots have spreading tips. The ultimate ("A") shoots lie nearly flat each side of the "B" shoots but these arise all round the "C" shoots. Crushed foliage has a soapy, resinous scent.

FRUIT. Slightly long-globose, glaucous green. 7 × 5 mm, with a minute flat, green spine in the centre of each scale.

SPECIMENS. The old, possibly original tree at Bicton was blown down in 1967. In 1906 it was 40ft × 3ft 10in and by 1959 it was only the same height and 4ft × 2in in girth. Several young trees have been planted at Westonbirt: Circular Drive, planted 1936, 20ft × 1ft; 18ft × 10in; Broad Drive, planted 1949, 20ft; 12 feet (1967); Jermyn's House,

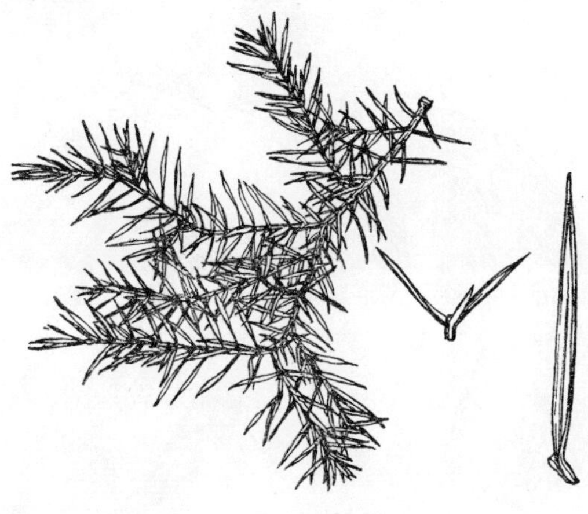

Fig. 89
Juvenile foliage of *Juniperus flaccida*, a rare Mexican tree, with a single whorl of leaves, and (×3⅓) a single leaf. This foliage is soft and a bright green.

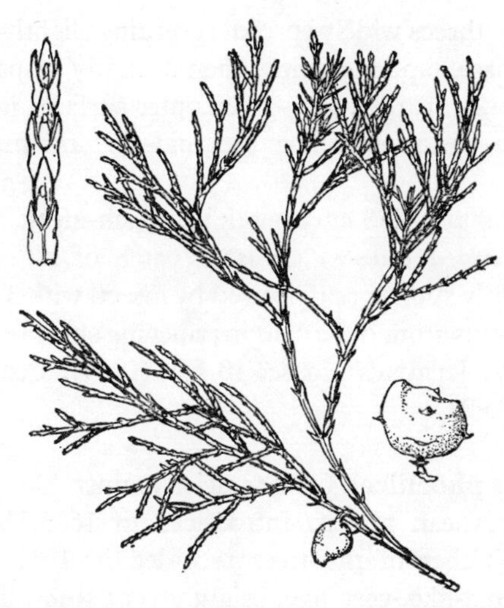

Fig. 90
The rare Mexican *Juniperus flaccida* with bright green, slender adult foliage (also top left ×3⅓) and some juvenile, which is also bright green and soft and is dominant on small trees. Fruit (right) ×1⅓.

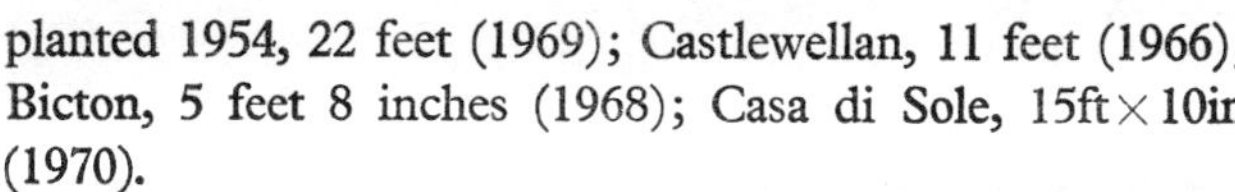

planted 1954, 22 feet (1969); Castlewellan, 11 feet (1966); Bicton, 5 feet 8 inches (1968); Casa di Sole, 15ft×10in (1970).

Juniperus foetidissima Willdenow. Stinking juniper

Balkans and Crimea. Introduced in 1910. Rather like *J. excelsa* with sage-green, fine foliage, but thicker shoots, leaves on terete inner shoots, scale-like, short, glossy and blunt; on outer, spreading and acute, convex, spined, to 4 mm; inner surface solid pale blue. Shoots sparse and curved, retaining dull pale brown old leaves. Crushed foliage gives a soapy scent. Known only from one tree, at Bedgebury, 7 feet.

Juniperus formosana Hayata. Prickly cypress, Formosan juniper.

China and Formosa. Introduced probably in 1844. At Bedgebury, a 15 foot tree has a thin, open crown and sparsely set, very large, spiny forward-pointing leaves 1 cm ×0·2 cm. It has an angled yellow shoot turning pink then purple. The leaves have two broad grey bands and wide green margins beneath. This plant seems almost the same as *J. oxycedrus*. Young plants at Westonbirt have longer, more slender leaves, 1·4×0·1 cm, more spreading and darker blue-green than those of *J. oxycedrus*. The inner surfaces are whiter, obscuring part of the midrib.

Juniperus morrisonicola Hayata. Mount Morrison juniper.

Formosa. Introduced before 1930. Very rare. A close, dense, conic or ovoid bush with branches level, then upswept. Old leaves are retained, bright rufous, inside the crown. Leaves 5 mm acute to a spine tip; outer surface convex, grass-green bloomed grey or white with a pale midrib; inner surface thickly white often obscuring the midrib.

Bedgebury, planted 1930, 11 feet; 9 feet 0 inches (1971); Glasnevin Botanic Garden, 7 feet (1966); Mount Usher, 6 feet (1966); Borde Hill (Warren), 11 feet (1970).

Juniperus oxycedrus L. Prickly juniper, sharp cedar.

Mediterranean and Caucasus, to Persia. Introduced in 1739. Very rare.

Bark. Pale red-brown, bloomed grey-pink, smooth but cracking (young tree) shredding vertically (older).

Crown. Slender, few branches, hung with slender strings of distant long leaves; yellow, pink and bluish green in general (cf. *J. cedrus*).

Foliage. Shoot red-brown at tip, then pale pink-brown, with longitudinal narrow grooves on ridges; winged and nearly triangular.

Leaves. In threes widely spaced, spreading slightly forward, broad at base, tapering gently then abruptly to pale spine, to 1·5×0·2 cm; dark grey-green outer surface; inner with two white bands equalling the mid-rib and margins in width.
Fruit. Globular, 1·3 cm smooth yellowish-green where not thinly bloomed blue-white; large patch of blue-white at apex, slightly sunken as if chewed by insect, with 3 minutely spined humps around the margin; ripening shiny red-brown.
Specimens. Jermyn's House, 10 feet (1969); Leonardslee, 11 feet (1958).

Juniperus phoenicea L. Phoenician juniper

Mediterranean region. Introduced in 1683. Very rare indeed. Neither of the trees recorded in 1931 survives. Foliage scale-like, very fine, bright green; scent, if bruised, like paint; terete; incurved tips; a few resin-spots. Monoecious; male flowers pale brown all winter; fruit ovoid, bright green, 1 cm, both on very young plants.

Borde Hill, 15 feet (1958). Bedgebury 4 feet (1970).

var. turbinata Parlatore. Found within the range of the type. Very rare—in a few recent collections. Foliage as the type—very slender, terete, widely angled shiny green branchlets and acute scale-leaves. Differs in the fruit being obovoid, or lumpy ovoid, 1×0·7 cm, bright yellow-green.

Juniperus procera Hochstetter. East African juniper

Kenya, Ruwenzori etc. and Abyssinia. Introduced in 1914. Two plants in Ireland; none known to survive in England. A rather gaunt tree with bunches of soft yellowish grass-green foliage (still juvenile) like *Ch. pisifera squarrosa* but larger, and in threes.

Fota, planted 1918, 42ft×3ft 11in+1ft 9in (1966); Kilmacurragh, 25ft×1ft 5in+1ft 0in (1966).

Juniperus recurva Buchanan-Hamilton. Drooping juniper.

Eastern Himalaya, Burma and China. Introduced in 1830. Uncommon, but in many collections and large gardens throughout these Islands.
Bark. Dull grey-brown, coarsely stripping in long vertical shreds.
Crown. Broadly conic to a narrow spire; lower branches upswept; foliage nodding from upswept branch-ends.
Foliage. Shoot dull pale red-brown or purplish orange. Smaller shoots in dense bunches, dry and rustling to the touch. Leaves long, acuminate to a sharp point, 5–8 mm, bright dark grey-green with pale margins, the inner surface with two bands of blue-white; forward pointing, densely overlapping. Old leaves retained, orange-brown.
Flowers and Fruit. Male flowers frequent; 4 mm ovoid pale yellow and green, terminal on short shoots 2–3 cm back from the tips of the spray. Fruit purplish-brown or black, ovoid to 1 cm.
Growth. Slow growing in all parts of the country. Two large plants have not grown appreciably in height over a period of fifty years, in Devon and Denbighshire; a young one in Hampshire grew 24 feet in 28 years and in Cornwall 10 feet in 37 years and 13 feet in 30 years have been recorded. At Curraghmore, two trees symmetrically and prominently placed on the lawn show no sign of breakages but one is now scarcely half as tall and substantially less in girth than either of the two reported in 1931.
Specimens. Cortachy Castle, 50ft×5ft 4in (1962); Kilmacurragh, 51ft×4ft 6in (1966); Castlewellan, 49ft×3ft 6in main stem (1966); Mamhead, 49ft×4ft 0in 15 stems (1970); Hafodunas, 46ft×4ft 8in+3ft 11in+3ft 3in (1960); Bicton, 43ft×2ft 5in (1968); Scorrier, 46ft×5ft 0in at 3 feet (1965); Keir House, planted 1866, 52ft×4ft 7in (1970); Abercairny, 44ft×2ft 11in leans but fine spire-top (1962); Birr Castle, 40ft×5ft 1in (1966); Fenagh House, planted 1881, 34ft×4ft 0in+3ft 9in (1968); Highnam, 46ft×3ft 0in (1970); Pencarrow, 39ft×4ft 1in (1970).

cv. Castlewellan (Castlewellan, County Down.) In England, a thin plant with many pale brown slender stems diverging and arching over like fishing-rods, from which hang long slender bunches of close, dark grey-green foliage. The original tree, however, is impressive.

Castlewellan, 36ft×5ft 9in at 1 foot (1966); Grayswood Hill, 12 feet (1969); Jermyn's House, 15 feet (1969).

Juniperus recurva

Fig. 91
Juniperus recurva. Shoot from male tree (left) and female tree with fruit (right) and leaf (×3½) showing two white bands on the inner surface.

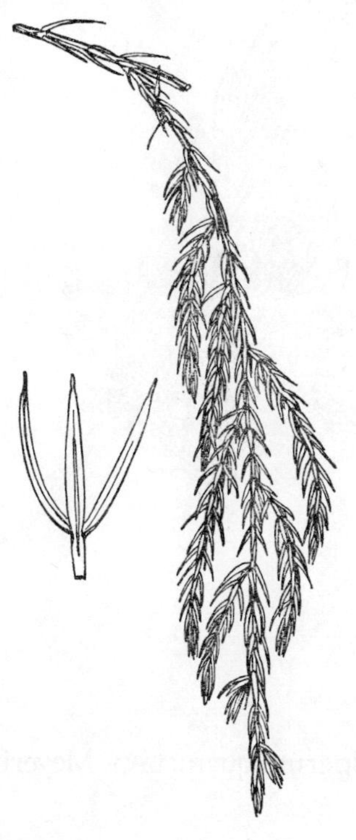

Fig. 92
The pendent foliage of *Juniperus recurva* var. *coxii* showing how it differs from the type *J. recurva* in being more open and the leaves more slender. (Inset whorl ×3½).

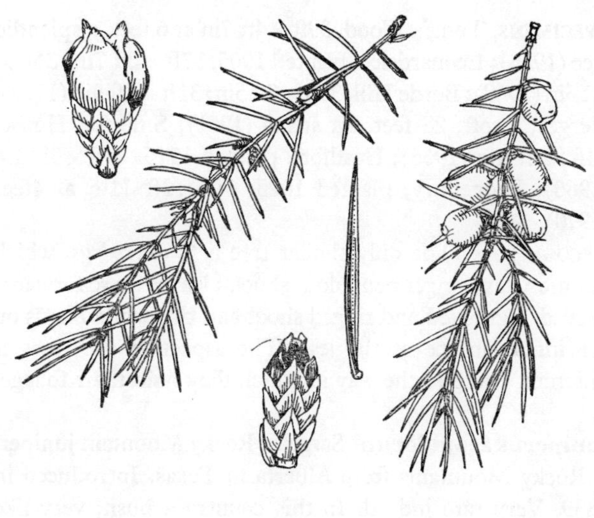

Fig. 93
Shoot from male tree (left) and female tree (right) of *Juniperus rigida*. Inset (middle) male flower (×4) and a leaf (×1⅜); (top right) young fruit (×4).

var. coxii (Jackson) Melville. Coffin juniper.

Upper Burma. Introduced in 1930. A tree of very different foliage, possibly better regarded as a full species. Rare, but has been planted lately in many large gardens and some smaller. A much more vigorous tree than the type. The bark is more orange; strips even more freely, and the boles are draped in hanging strips. The foliage is in long, pendulous, brighter sprays of much more widely spaced leaves, with the shoot clearly visible between them; 8–10 mm long; narrowly margined white and with a white spine-tip; inner surface with two broad whitish green bands. The widely spaced leaves especially, distinguish this variety from cv. 'Castlewellan'.

Glendoick, 20ft×10in (1970); Hergest Croft, 34ft×2ft 0in; 32ft×2ft 4in (1969); Fenagh House, 28ft×2ft 2in (1968); Exbury, 41ft×2ft 6in+1ft 9in (1970); Westonbirt, planted 1942, 19ft×8in (1967).

Juniperus rigida Siebold and Zuccarini. Temple juniper.

Japan, Korea and Manchuria. Introduced in 1861. Rare; confined largely to collections, but in all parts of these Islands.

Bark. Dull brown or grey, stripping away in long pieces.
Crown. Slender at first then opening out at the top; upswept branches and pendulous or nodding shoots; thin. Some straight single boles. Foliage in dense, twisted bunches, from which hang short shoots.
Foliage. Despite the name, soft and lax unless the spine-points are deliberately grasped; yellowish in the mass. Shoot light green, or pinkish, turning orange-brown. Leaves slender, linear, sharply pointed, sparsely set in threes (about 3 whorls per cm) convex and bright, glossy green outer surface, yellow and white at the tip; 2 cm long; inner surface concave with a sunken central bluish-white band.
Flowers and Fruit. Male flowers abundant, clustering among the leaves for the length of the smaller shoots on male trees. Female trees bear globose irregular, bluish-white bloomed pale green fruit nearly 1 cm across, almost sessile in a close line along small shoots. A few large white dots of resin are often present. The fruit ripen to dark purple, slightly bloomed grey-blue.
Growth. Slow growing in height and girth. In 37 years, three trees in Sussex have increased in height by 18, 18 and 19 feet. The most rapid growth is that of a tree planted 30 years at Westonbirt and 30 feet tall, but only 1 foot 7 inches in girth.

SPECIMENS. Tong's Wood, 39ft × 4ft 7in at 6 feet, a splendid tree (1968); Leonardslee, planted 1905, 37ft × 2ft 7in; 36ft × 2ft 5in (1969); Borde Hill, 33ft × 2ft 5in; 31ft × 1ft 9in (1968); Hergest Croft, 28 feet, six stems (1961); Smeaton House, 34ft × 2ft 4in (1966); Headfort, planted 1915, 30ft × 3ft 4in (1966); Bedgebury, planted 1925, 31ft × 2ft 11in at 4feet (1970).

RECOGNITION. The only similar tree is *J. oxycedrus*, which has more lax, longer pendulous shoots; leaves more forward-curved, a grooved and ridged shoot and two white bands on the inner surface of the leaf. The aspect of the trees is different owing to the way in which they hold their foliage.

Juniperus scopulorum Sargent. Rocky Mountain juniper.

Rocky Mountains from Alberta to Texas. Introduced in 1839. Very rare indeed. In this country a bush, very like *J. virginiana* in foliage.

Dawyck, planted 1909, 28ft × 1ft 8in + 1ft 2in (1961).

cv. Argentea. Narrowly conic; silvery foliage. Bicton, 22ft × 1ft 6in (1967).

Juniperus squamata Buchanan-Hamilton. Himalayan juniper.

Afghanistan, through the Himalaya to China and Formosa. Introduced about 1824. Very rare indeed as the type, and scarcely growing. The foliage is dense, with acute leaves in whorls of three, slightly spreading and sharply pointed; upper surface white; old leaves remaining in position brown and dead.

Westonbirt, Mitchell Drive, 11 feet (1967); Specimen Avenue, 14ft × 5in (1966).

var. fargesii Rehder and Wilson.

Untidy columnar bush or neat conic tree, to 20 feet at Bedgebury. Leaves all juvenile, hard, long-spined, 5 mm, rich glossy green outer surface, 2 whitish bands on interior; spread 60°–90° from shoot. Soapy smell when crushed. Male flowers ovoid, 3 mm 1–2 near base of short, nodding shoots.

cv. Meyeri (China, 1914). Common now in gardens of all sizes. Young plants, bright steely blue; either spreading or fairly narrowly conic with a bent apex. Larger plants occasionally remain roughly conic and become more bent, or they splay out into strange shapes, and may resemble an armchair. The branches are deep red; smaller shoots are pale brown and the leaves densely lying forwards on short, bunched shoots are 8 mm long, acute and spined; deep green, bloomed white on the outer surface, and with two bands of brilliant blue-white on the inner surface. Occasional shoots are yellow and white at the tip.

Wayford Manor, 20 feet (1961); Curraghmore, 16 feet (1968); Bodnant, 15 feet (1966); Headfort, 15 feet, spreading 25 feet, (1966); Knightshayes, 27 feet (1970); Westonbirt, 14 feet (1959); Colesbourne, 27 feet (1971).

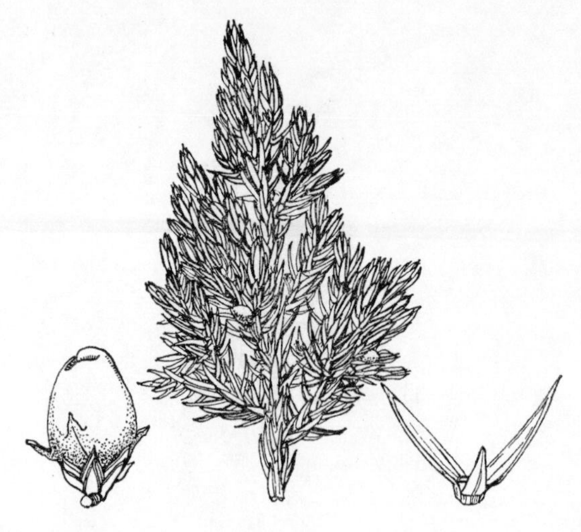

Juniperus squamata cv. Meyeri

Fig. 94
Foliage of the bright blue-green *Juniperus squamata* cv. Meyeri with fruit (×2⅔) and a single whorl of leaves (×2).

Juniperus thurifera L. Spanish juniper

France, Spain and North West Africa. Introduced in 1752. Very rare. Of the six trees recorded previously in 1911 or 1931 none has been found.

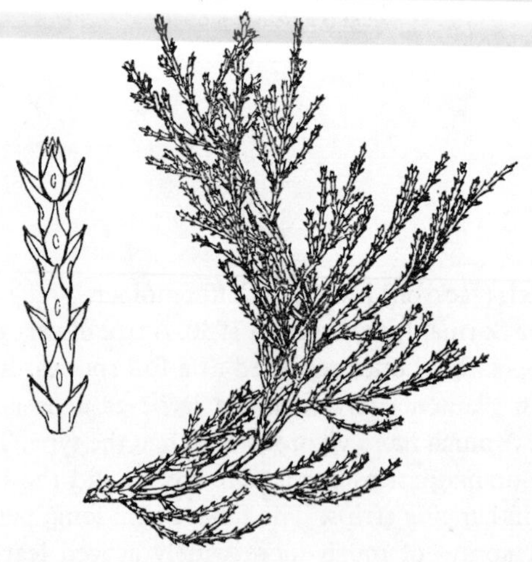

Juniperus thurifera

Fig. 95
A spray of foliage of *Juniperus thurifera*, a highly fragrant tree with dark green leaves with spreading tips. Shoot (left ×4) showing leaves with central glands.

Bark. Dark brown, scaly and lifting away in vertical strips.
Crown. Densely and regularly narrow-conic slightly rounded; dark green, may be gaunt, branches upswept, foliage bunched, hanging, main shoots curved upwards.
Foliage. Strongly musty-fragrant, detectable some feet from the tree. Dull, dark grey-green on pink shoots, rather distant, very slender, rather flat-pinnate. "A" shoots very small and few. "B" shoots long and slender in one plane on "C" shoots. Leaves with hard, spreading, finely spined tips.
Specimens. Sheffield Park, 45ft×3ft 1in (1960); Powerscourt, 46ft×5ft 3in (1960); Westonbirt, planted 1942, 20ft ×8in (1969); Jermyn's House, planted 1954, 12 feet (1969).
Recognition. The strong musty scent combined with hard dark grey-green foliage with fine, spreading pointed leaves identify this species.

Juniperus virginiana L. Pencil cedar

Eastern North America from Quebec to Texas. Introduced in about 1660. Frequent, in large gardens, but much less so than *J. chinensis,* which is also true of the cultivars.
Bark. Dull grey-brown or pale red-brown with very shallow narrow strips adhering, often spiralled. Often green with algae.
Crown. Conical when young but soon irregular. Old trees with heavy low branches and wide tops; wide, open crowns of bent, upswept branches thinly foliaged; often forked or stems coalesced.
Foliage. Juvenile leaves mixed with adult at the base of most sprays and in little whorls at the tip of many adult shoots. The dull dark grey-green foliage gives an aroma of soap or paint if crushed.
Shoot. Soon pale brown, then dark grey. Adult foliage very slender, spread at all angles on the shoots.
Leaves. Sharply acute, tips slightly spreading, dark shiny green, a pale narrow margin visible under a lens.
Growth. Very slow-growing and, apparently short-lived. None of the trees mentioned by Elwes and Henry has been found, and of 27 given in 1931 only two trees then young, and three others, one now dead, have been re-found. The only dated plant measured is one at Bedgebury, 41ft×2ft 2in when 41 years old, but this would seem unusually rapid in growth in height, for no tree is much taller, yet many must be about three times as old as this.
Specimens. Ham Manor, Arundel, 43ft×10ft 4in; forks at 6 feet, and measured over the scar from loss of a large limb (1965); Holkham, 57ft×8ft 5in at 4 feet; unusually bright and dense columnar tree, (possibly cv. 'Canaertii') and 54ft ×6ft 3in (1968); Killerton, 59ft×9ft 5in at 1 foot (1970); Albury Park, 53ft×5ft 4in (1961); Bagshot Park, 53ft×5ft 2in main stem (1969); Bodnant, 47ft×5ft 4in (1959); Dropmore, 49ft×4ft 11in (1961); Yewden Manor, Hambleden, 45ft×6ft 9in (1963); Hatherop Castle, 45ft×6ft a fine column (1964); Adhurst St. Mary, 51ft×4ft 3in+2ft 4in (1964); Althorp, 55ft×4ft 10in main stem (1964); Arley Castle, 45ft×4ft 11in (1964); Highnam Court (Pinetum), 50ft×6ft 10in (1970); Kew, 52ft×4ft 0in (1970).

cv. Canaertii (Belgium, pre-1868.) A form worth growing. It has a dense, upswept columnar or conical crown of brilliant dark green, short, dense, adult foliage. The acute leaves have dark, incurved tips with a pale pit well below the centre. The fruit, usually plentiful, are dark purple bloomed grey-blue, ovoid, 5×4 mm very attractive among the bright leaves. The big tree at Holkham may be of this cultivar. (see list above).

Bedgebury, planted 1925, 30ft×1ft 9in; 28ft×1ft 7in (1967); Jermyn's House, planted 1954, 15 feet.

cv. Elegantissma. (pre-1882). Very rare. Sparse gaunt straight tree with few level branches, or bushy plant, with wide, open, hanging sprays of both juvenile and adult foliage, the new shoots banded lemon-yellow.

Bedgebury, 26ft×1ft 3in (1969).

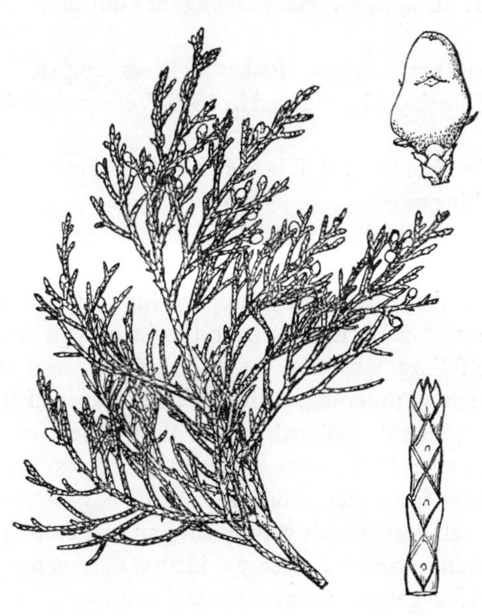

Juniperus virginiana v. glauca

Fig. 96
Foliage of *Juniperus virginiana* variety *glauca* with male flowers. Inset, fruit and shoot (×3½). The foliage is pale grey-blue and is more bunched and erect than in the type.

cv. Glauca (1855). Uncommon but quite desirable, this form makes a more shapely rather upswept tree. Bark rich cigar-brown, or grey with algae; lifting away in strips, usually spiralled. Foliage in upswept sprays rather thinly spread but themselves dense, and a soft pale grey. Smallest shoots mainly terete. Fruit 3 mm ovoid, white or deep blue.

Endsleigh, 50ft × 6ft 6in (1963); Westonbirt, 41ft × 3ft 0in (1966); Leonardslee 45ft × 1ft 11in (1969); Wakehurst Place, 42ft × 1ft 11in (1964); Hergest Croft, 33ft × 3ft 1in (1969); St. Clere, 31ft × 2ft 11in (1969); Bedgebury, 31ft × 1ft 10in (1969); Nymans, 36ft × 1ft 10in (1970).

cv. Pseudocupressus (U.S.A. pre-1932). A very narrow, flame-shaped, bright grey-green form, with mainly adult, slender foliage, each leaf white at the base; and some grey juvenile sprays. Westonbirt, 31 feet; Bedgebury, 29 feet; 28 feet (1969).

cv. Schottii (Britain before 1855). An attractive form similar to cv. Canaertii; columnar with a more rounded apex, and more dense, yellow-green foliage.

Bedgebury, 25 feet.

RECOGNITION. *J. virginiana* is very like *J. chinensis*, but the markedly finer (in the sense of smaller) foliage is apparent when the two are seen together, and the soapy smell contrasts with the sour smell of *J. chinensis*. The tufts on the ends of fine shoots are more characteristic of *J. virginiana* and the patterned, dark-centred adult leaves are typical of *J. chinensis*. The much smaller fruit of *J. virginiana* is a valuable indicator, especially among the cultivars.

Juniperus wallichiana Hooker fil. Black juniper.

The Himalaya. Introduced in 1849. Very rare; collections only.

BARK. Red brown or dull brown with very loose scales, and strips falling away.

CROWN. A narrowly conic small tree or ovoid bush; branches strongly ascending; often with a narrowly conic, spire-top.

FOLIAGE. Very attractively mixed blue and green when juvenile and patterned dark and pale grey when adult. Juvenile foliage, which on young plants is about four fifths of each spray, drooping, with spreading leaves in threes, 5 mm long, sharply pointed, bright deep green, convex on the outer side; 2 blue-white bands uniting near the tip on the concave inner side. Adult foliage, thick upswept shoots clad in scale-leaves with grey centres and pale margins and bases, shiny, convex, strongly incurved, mucronate tip. Crushed foliage gives a scent of musty soap.

FRUIT. Ovoid 1 × 0·6 cm, pendulous, 1–3 together sessile, dark green in autumn blackish blue during the second year.

SPECIMENS. Hergest Croft, 34ft × 1ft 9in main stem (1969); East Bergholt Place, 34ft × 1ft 11in; 28ft × 1ft 7in (1966); Westonbirt, planted 1934, 25ft × 11in (1968); Wakehurst Place, 29ft × 1ft 4in; 29ft × 1ft 4in (1970); Borde Hill, Stonepit Wood, 23ft × 10in (1958); Castlewellan, 27ft × 1ft 7in (1970); Bedgebury, planted 1927, 26ft × 1ft 3in (1969).

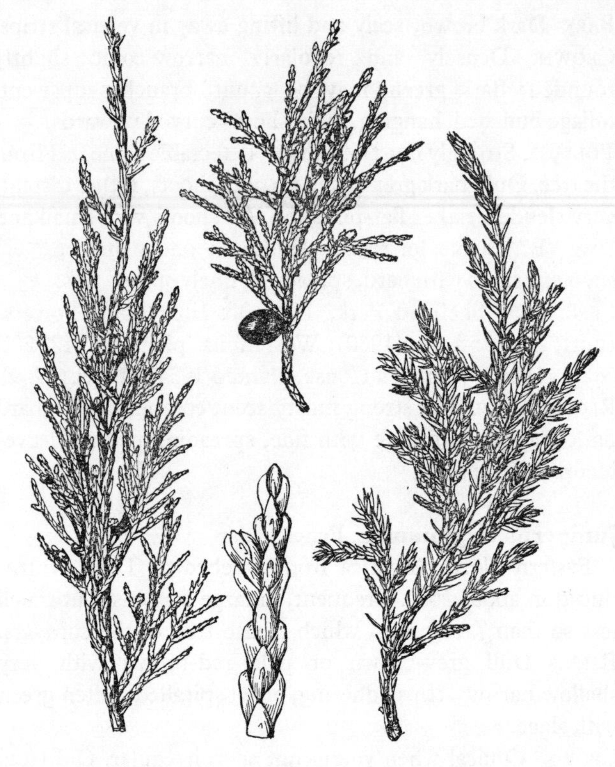

Juniperus wallichiana

Fig. 97
The Himalayan *Juniperus wallichiana* usually bears both juvenile foliage (right) and adult (left and above). It also flowers and fruits freely. Inset is adult foliage ($\times 5\frac{1}{3}$).

Keteleeria Carriere (Pinaceae)

Trees from China and Formosa, related to *Abies*. Six species described but possibly only variants of the two main species. These trees are monoecious, and bear erect cones which do not disintegrate as do those of *Abies*.

Keteleeria davidiana (Bertrand) Beissner.

Widespread in the drier parts of China and Formosa. Introduced in 1888. Very rare; confined to a few collections in South England and in Ireland.

BARK. Grey-pink, finely cracked vertically.

CROWN. A slender slightly sinuous bole, apt to lean and, in fact, recumbent in two cases; bearing slender, long, level branches, arching down somewhat at the ends and bearing a mass of dense, straight, but mainly bare twigs.

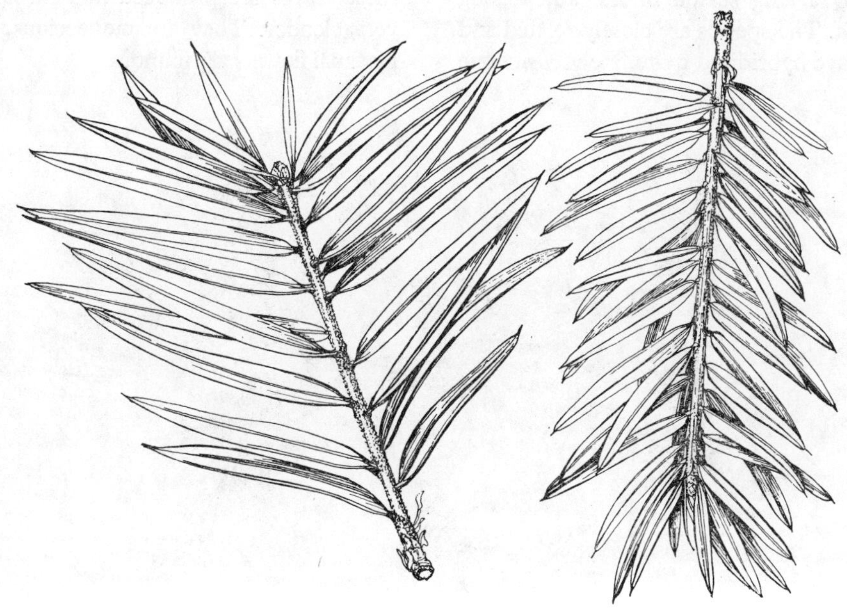

Keteleeria davidiana

Fig. 98
Juvenile foliage (left) and adult foliage (right) of *Keteleeria davidiana*, a relative of the silver firs. Juvenile foliage is grown for about 30 years.

FOLIAGE. Shoot dull or light brown, slightly ridged, densely set with stiff, dark hairs but sometimes main shoots are nearly glabrous. Second year shoot grey-brown.

BUD. Ovoid, dark brown, 2–3 mm.

LEAVES. Pectinate, slightly raised and a few straight below the shoot; spreading perpendicular to shoot, straight or slightly curved from a small petiole, broadest near the base; on young trees 5–6 cm × 0·5 cm tapering gradually to a fine stiff point; hard, rigid. On older trees, leaves are 3·5 × 0·4 cm and on oldest trees only, round-tipped. Shiny yellowish-green with a midrib above, pale green beneath, with a shiny midrib, occasionally the two broad bands are grey or bluish-white.

CONE. Seen (by the author) only in California. Erect, cylindric, domed, about 8 × 3 cm, bright pale green.

SPECIMENS AND GROWTH. An original tree is recumbent at Dropmore. Its stem is 31 feet long and its girth 4 feet (1970). As this was then 70 years old from seed this represents about 1 foot in height and 1½ inches in girth for every two years, which seems about the same rates as the fastest growing of other dated trees. At Bayfordbury one has added only 8 feet to its height in 31 years, but at Leonardslee a good tree has grown 24 feet in height and 17 inches in girth in 38 years. It is now 40ft × 2ft 1in. Other specimens are: Wakehurst Place, 39ft × 2ft 8in; 30ft × 1ft 8in (1971); Borde Hill, 15ft × 8in (1969); Headfort, 13ft (1966); Westonbirt, planted 1934, 18ft × 1ft 1in (1966), died back to 5 feet.

Keteleeria fortunei (A. Murray) Carriere.

East China. Introduced in 1844 but died out. Re-introduced in about 1935 but again, it would seem, it has died out. None has been found. It differs from *K. davidiana* mainly in its slender, orange-red, less hairy shoots.

Larix Miller (Pinaceae)

A genus of 10–12 deciduous trees distributed across the northern temperate regions. Three species together cover almost the entire circumpolar plains whilst seven are relicts on mountain ranges further south. They are pioneer species, unable to grow in shade, but with an exceptionally vigorous early growth aided by a long season in leaf and a long season of shoot-growth. The species are closely related and with one exception, have hybridised quite freely. Only one of these hybrids is known in this country. Foliage is of two kinds; new shoots, produced from May onwards, have spirally set leaves, sometimes quite broad and very large on vigorous leading-shoots. On second year and older wood, the leaves arise in rosettes from short, spur-like shoots and these leaves are produced in February or March and are very slender. They are monoecious, and occasional freak bisexual flowers are found.

Larix decidua·

Fig. 99
Foliage, male flowers, fertilised female flower and cone of *Larix decidua*, European larch. Single leaf × 1⅓.

Larix decidua Miller. European larch

Alps, from Savoy to the Tyrol and the Wienerwald, and in isolated patches (vars. *sudetica*, *tatrensis* and *polonica*) from the Sudeten Mountains and Tatra to the Carpathians and down the Vistula valley in Poland. Introduced a few years before 1629. Abundant in wooded areas, especially in hilly country, as plantations and shelter-belts, but elsewhere common as parkland trees. Unsuitable near towns, but occasional in town parks and gardens. This is a first class tree for medium-sized gardens, for beauty, good growth and its great attraction for birds, but it is seldom planted in such places.

BARK. Young trees smooth at first, fissuring vertically early in Eastern provenances, later in others. Plantation trees varying from pale grey, coarsely but shallowly fissured and scaling, to reddish brown. Very big old trees have dark pink bark, very flaky and heavily ridged with wide fissures, flaking at the sides between big scaling ridges.

CROWN. Young trees should have symmetrical open, narrowly conic crowns formed of annual whorls of strong, upswept or ascending branches three to four feet apart and internodal lesser, level branches. Trees still growing in height remain pointed and fairly narrow, regularly conic, the middle branches level and the lower descending; shoots with foliage often long and pendulous. Really old trees often have huge, low buttressed branches, level for 8 or 10 feet then abruptly turning to nearly vertical. Others have innumerable heavy, densely set, descending branches. Shoots on these trees are still very stout and vigorous, upward-pointing at branch-ends; hanging inside the crown.

FOLIAGE. Main shoots vary in stoutness and colour fairly consistently with provenance, ranging from stout and pink-buff in the Western Alps to very slender, and white in Poland. The lowland Alpine and Austrian are intermediate and straw-yellow, and the Sudeten larch are pale cream. Leading shoots vary in branching from tree to tree and from year to year within individual trees. Some vigorous leading shoots are quite un-branched and almost or quite straight. The majority have a straight lower quarter, grown slowly from the expanding bud from May until mid June, then a sinuous mid-section with several short ascending shoots each arising from the outside of a bend, then a long straight, unbranched terminal section.

A few trees, of eastern origins, have graduated branches, long at the base of the leading shoot and decreasing to mere rosettes a little way below a clear terminal length. The sinuous mid-section is then absent. Where present it represents rapid midsummer growth, and the straight terminal section is of equally, or even more rapid growth continuing into early October. Such shoots will grow five inches in a week and can be over 4 feet 6 inches long. The leaves on slow-grown leading shoots and on the lower portions of all, are appressed strongly to the stem and are 2–4 cm long. On the fast-grown sections, broad spreading and reflexed leaves may be 6–7 cm long. The last leaves before growth stops are small, narrow, and thrown into a spiral around the developing terminal bud. Second-growth may occur when a vigorous tree stops growth in early August and hot, wet weather re-starts growth, often from a partially formed bud. Such growth has a thick, bright green shoot and long leaves. Trees in shade or in ill-health grow only the first sector, the shoot elongated from the resting-bud, and make no more. They thus cease growth by July or before.

Leaves on the short shoots open bright fresh green, darkening in summer. They are strap-shaped, rounded at the tips and parallel-sided, 3–3·5 cm long, slender, very thin and soft. Larches colour well in autumn, starting late, in early November and reach their golden best in mid-November. Some often still have leaves in early December. Seedlings are partially evergreen, the leaves near the tip of the leading shoot at least remaining green and on the plant throughout the winter, often bronzed.

FLOWERS. Male flowers are borne normally only on weak, pendulous shoots. They are therefore not found on young trees whose branching still is in the vigorous spreading or upright stage. The flower buds are ovoid-conic, dark red-brown, at the sides or underneath the shoots. They expand in late March and in April, opening to nearly flat discs, often crimson-edged, pale yellow as the centre expands and pushes through the coloured scales. Each male flower sheds most of its pollen within one day and the flowers of a single tree may span two weeks.

The female flowers are on strong two-year-old wood and, more scattered, on older wood. The buds are at the sides of the shoot or sometimes the top or bottom, but from every position the conelet stands exactly vertical when out of the bud. The conelets are then about 1 cm tall, pink-purple or dark red, sometimes light green, rarely white, with the bracts pointing straight outwards showing gaps between the scales. After a week the bracts bend down closing the gaps and are pressed tightly to the cone, which then turns green. During the early summer the cone enlarges to full-size, pale green with purplish fringes to the scales, then it ripens dark brown.

CONES. In general these grade from big, tall conic cones in the western Alps to very small ovoids in Poland but only the extremes are constant; between them the gradient is only general and some large-coned trees occur throughout the Alps. Large cones can be 4·5 cm long, either narrowly conic or cylindric, tapering to a domed top; and 2 cm across at the broadest point. Medium ovoid cones are 3 cm × 2–3 cm, and the smallest are 1·5 cm × 1·0 cm. The scales have their outer margins slightly waved, curved slightly out in some of the larger cones, while the smaller cones have convex scales with turned-in margins. Proliferous cones, with the shoot extending through and beyond them, are not rare.

GROWTH. Seedlings of one year are usually 8–10in, but can be 15 inches. Transplanted for one year they frequently grow a further 3 feet. At this stage they are planted out and check variously so that the growth in the next year may be 8 inches or over 2 feet. The year after that, they are established and shoots of over 4 feet may be made. A two-year old Sudeten larch 4 feet 4 inches tall, when planted, was six years later 24ft × 1ft 1in and sixteen years from planting it is 46ft × 3ft 0in. The fastest growth between 30 and 75 years found so far is shown in Table 38.

TABLE 38. FAST GROWTH IN YOUNG EUROPEAN LARCHES, LARIX DECIDUA

Location	*Date Planted*	*Dimensions*	*Age*
Bedgebury, (Gordon Castle plot)	1931	69′ × 3′ 3″	34
Novar, Ross	1906	101′ × 5′ 4″	49
Yester, E. Lothian	1918	94′ × 7′ 4″	49
Camusvrachan, Perth	1887	102′ × 5′ 2″	68
Dunalastair, Perth	1889	110′ × 5′ 3″	72
Dunkeld, Perth	1887	111′ × 9′ 0″	82

The entries in the 1932 *Report* are poor in larches and few of them have been found since. Among those that have four of the five old trees in Hercules Walk, Blair Castle, in 1955 (largely gone by 1970) were not then as big as their reported size in 1931, which shakes the confidence. Those that have grown since 1931 have added between 3 and 42 inches in girth in periods of from 23 to 36 years. Old trees rarely maintain one inch increase in girth in a year. The 1738 tree by Dunkeld Cathedral has added 35 inches in 87 years, 24 of them in the last 39 years and one of the same age at Monzie Castle has increased in girth by 14 inches in 58 years, which is less than trees of similar age at Ombersley Court, (26 inches in 60 years) and Inveraray Castle, (26 inches in 65 years).

SPECIMENS. There are several references in literature to larch trees planted in the seventeenth century but the only survivors among them are the trees at Lee Park, Lanark. A traditional story about larch in Scotland, which occurs in scores of accounts and books is that the first two larches in Scotland were planted by Dunkeld Cathedral in 1737 and that John Menzies of Culdars had brought them from Switzerland and had given several away on his journey home from London to Meggernie Castle. The Dunkeld trees were put in a glasshouse but not thriving were thrown out as dead, only to spring up and become the "Mother Larches", producers of all the oldest larch in Scotland. This story is an amalgam of several different tales, first appearing in this form in 1819, and widely quoted thereafter. What really happened can be reconstructed from the references to these trees written from 1770, and a summary by the Duke of Atholl in 1832. No later story does anything but quote and confuse these earlier accounts. Two larches were sent in 1727 with orange-trees for the glasshouse at Dunkeld. After a while under glass they were planted outside and grew rather slowly. Menzies brought his larch from London in 1737 and five were planted straight out by the Cathedral. These grew very rapidly, in 1765 they were bigger than the earlier trees. Before 1770, one of the 1727 trees was felled to obtain timber to make a summerhouse. By 1809 three of Menzies trees had been felled and the remaining 1727 tree was lost. From that time onwards the glasshouse history of the 1727 trees was transferred to the two surviving 1737 trees. One of these remains by the Cathedral and of the eleven from the same parcel sent to Blair Castle, nine remain, and two of the five sent to Monzie Castle. Many estates were planting larch in the policies at this time and all the trees of about this date, 1738, have been credited sometime or another, to Menzies's parcel.

The first progeny of the Cathedral trees, were raised in about 1750 and have been taken to be the magnificent trees 200 yards away on Kennel Bank. One of them 131ft × 10ft 8in has a clear bole for 90 feet. A remarkable tree at The Whittern, Herefordshire, stands on a pedestal of twisted roots (a planting trick also done at Dunkeld, shown by a tree near the present House). The pedestal has a girth of 26 feet 5 inches at five feet but the true bole girths 16 feet, six feet from the ground. Another extraordinary tree, at Kelburn, Ayrshire, now 40ft × 13ft 2in has huge, spreading layers, to 6ft 5in in girth arising from slender old branches rooting 10 yards from the bole.

Some younger trees of rapid growth have been given in the preceding section. The Table 39 gives the oldest and largest trees on each estate, some of them growing in plantations.

TABLE 39. OLDEST AND LARGEST TREES OF LARIX DECIDUA

Locality	*Date Planted*	*Dimensions*	
Lee Park	ca.1675		80′ × 12′ 11″ (1971)
Lee Park	ca.1675		70′ × 10′ 5″ (1971)
Lee Park	ca.1675		82′ × 10′ 6″ (1954)
Dawyck	1725	82′ × 11′ 6″ (1931)	82′ × 12′ 0″ (1961)
Dawyck	1725		70′ × 13′ 6″ (1966)
Kailzie	1725		93′ × 12′ 10″ (1954)
Kailzie	1725		82′ × 10′ 1″ (1954)
Kelburn	1730	50′ × 11′ 8″ (1931)	40′ × 13′ 2″ (1970)
Blair Drummond	1734		110′ × 10′ 11″ (1954)
Blair Drummond	1736		100′ × 16′ 3″ (1955)
Dunkeld Cathedral	1738	100′ × 13′ 9″ (1883)	105′ × 16′ 8″ (1970)
Blair Castle	1738	112′ × 13′ 1″ (1931)	98′ × 14′ 3″ (1970)

Locality	*Date Planted*	*Dimensions*	
Blair Castle	1738	113′ × 12′ 6″ (1931)	130′ × 13′ 8″ (1970)
Blair Castle	1738	× 14′ 1″ (1931)	111′ × 14′ 6″ (1970)
Monzie Castle	1738	109′ × 17′ 4″ (1904)	111′ × 18′ 6″ (1962)
Gordon Castle	1738		98′ × 17′ 2″ (1970)
Keir House	1738	70′ × 13′ 2″ (1931)	82′ × 14′ 6″ (1970)
Kippendavie	1738		78′ × 13′ 9″ (1955)
Dungarthill	1738		117′ × 13′ 8″ (1954)
Monymusk (1)	1738		87′ × 8′ 5″ (1961)
Birkhill	1738		105′ × 13′ 8″ (1963)
Dalguise House	1738		100′ × 13′ 1″ (1955)
Kinloch House	1738		102′ × 15′ 5″ (1970)
Lude House	1738		108′ × 13′ 2″ (1961)
Gask House	1738		108′ × 12′ 8″ (1962)
Fasnacloich Village	1738		92′ × 10′ 4″ (1962)
Wallington Hall	1738		105′ × 13′ 9″ (1958)
Minto House	1739 (seed 1715)		141′ × 10′ 3″ (1955)
Minto House	1739 (seed 1715)		97′ × 14′ 8″ (1955)
Craigdarroch	1740		105′ × 12′ 8″ (1954)
Eliock House	1740		75′ × 13′ 0″ (1954)
Monymusk (2)	1741		98′ × 14′ 8″ (1961)
Inveraray Castle	1746	110′ × 11′ 0″ (1904)	80′ × 13′ 3″ (1969)
Dunkeld (2)	1750	120′ × 11′ 10″ (1904)	132′ × 13′ 7″ (1970)
Dunkeld	1750		131′ × 10′ 8″ (1970)
Dunkeld	1750		141′ × 7′ 4″ (1961)
Glamis Castle	1810	91′ × 11′ 3″ (1931)	75′ × 13′ 4″ (1970)
Ombersley Court		80′ × 15′ 7″ (1904)	72′ × 17′ 9″ (1964)
Tottenham House		× 12′ 0″ (1904)	84′ × 14′ 11″ (1967)
Abercairny		90′ × 14′ 2″ (1931)	111′ × 14′ 3″ (1962)
Rossie Priory			98′ × 13′ 10″ (1970)
Penpont			80′ × 14′ 0″ (1962)
Aldourie Castle			70′ × 15′ 1″ (1956)
Yester House			70′ × 16′ 2″ (1967)
Hewshott House			75′ × 14′ 8″ (1965)
Sheffield Park			80′ × 14′ 2″ (1960)
Preston Hall			92′ × 14′ 6″ (1954)
Sprivers	1761		72′ × 11′ 0″ (1956)
Cardross	1763		95′ × 12′ 4″ (1954)
Linley Hall	1769		135′ × 7′ 10″ (1961)
Linley Hall	1769		125′ × 11′ 4″ (1961)
Dunans	ca.1775		130′ × 10′ 11″ (1969)
Ardvorlich	1780		139′ × 8′ 8″ (1961)
Ardvorlich	1780		118′ × 14′ 7″ (1961)
Langholm	1795		96′ × 11′ 2″ (1969)
Dunira	1805		124′ × 9′ 5″ (1954)
Bonskeid			135′ × 9′ 1″ (1955)
Stonefield			130′ × 8′ 9″ (1969)
Whitfield Hall (Northumb.)	1809		124′ × 9′ 11″ (1958)
Glendoick	1810	84′ × 5′ 2″ (1931)	106′ × 9′ 8″ (1970)
Bolton Hall (Quarry)			126′ × 10′ 0″ (1954)
Cowdray Park		100′ × 7′ 9″ (1931)	90′ × 11′ 3″ (1967)
Welford Park		80′ × 10′ 2″ (1931)	78′ × 11′ 8″ (1966)
Cawdor Castle	1822		121′ × 8′ 7″ (1955)
Glamis (Woods)	1830		138′ × 7′ 11″ (1970)
Glenlee Park			132′ × 9′ 5″ (1970)
Raehills	1790		112′ × 13′ 7″ (1970)
Trebartha Hall			95′ × 13′ 4″ (1957)
Walcot Park			90′ × 12′ 8″ (1962)
Heanton Satcheville			90′ × 13′ 0″ (1960)
Drumlanrig Castle			121′ × 14′ 1″ (1970)
Alltcailleach	1835		116′ × 6′ 3″ (1955)
Powis Castle	1847		134′ × 8′ 3″ (1970)
Glackour	1862		121′ × 5′ 7″ (1956)
Castle Forbes			70′ × 12′ 1″ (1968)
Park Hatch	1855		142′ × 9′ 7″ (1970)
Park Hatch	1855		130′ × 7′ 3″ (1970)
Oakley Park			115′ × 12′ 4″ (1971)

cv. Pendula. "An erect tree with very hanging branchlets" —a description which seems to fit the type tree equally well —but grafts of this cultivar are irregularly umbrella-shaped with a tangle of twisting branches above the graft union. Very rare indeed.

Cambridge Botanic Garden, 15ft × 4ft 2in (1969).

var. polonica (Raciborski) Ostenfeld and Larsen. Poland; Tatra Mountains and scattered relict forests down the Vistula river. Introduced in 1912. A few small trial plantations and a few specimens.

BARK. Early in life, widely fissured brown between broad grey ridges.

CROWN. Narrowly conic, often a long thin spire, but always a sinuous bole; sometimes in young trees wildly so.

FOLIAGE. Shoots very slender, white and pendulous except for main ones.

CONE. Few scales, incurved; very small; 1·5–2 cm.

GROWTH. Young trees have grown very fast. At Savernake, trees from three of the isolated forests on the plains were planted in 1954. By 1969 the best plots had mean heights of 24 feet, with individual trees to 40 feet tall.

SPECIMENS. Bedgebury, planted 1925, 65ft × 4ft 5in (1968); planted 1926, 79ft × 4ft 8in (1970); Blairquhan, planted 1955, 52ft × 2ft 11in (1970).

GENERAL. Formerly European larch was a major forest species, the standard tree for bracken-covered land and thin soils on steep valley-slopes. It was particularly planted by private estates because of its rapid early growth and the manifold uses on the estate for small sizes of timber, whilst the best large trees commanded a good price for boat-skins. From about 1930 it was largely replaced on all but the best sites by the Japanese larch because this species grows slightly faster on the poorer soils and is resistant to the disease-complex known as die-back which almost destroys young plantations of European larch in certain conditions. More recently planting of both species has been much curtailed in state forestry by two further factors. These are the relatively low final volume of timber per acre and the lack of a pulp-wood market for larch thinnings. For maximum vigour with resistance to die-back and a reasonable proportion of straight stems, larch from the natural stands in the Sudeten is nowadays preferred.

Larix × eurolepis Henry. Dunkeld Hybrid larch

In 1885 the Duke of Atholl planted eleven Japanese larch below Kennel Bank, Dunkeld House, intending to use them as a source of seed, in the Atholl tradition. He also planted one with two European larches in an isolated hollow nearby. That appears to have been a deliberate attempt to produce a hybrid. Seed was duly collected from the eleven trees and plantations of their progenies were made. Possibly the first few were planted along Bishops' Walk near the Cathedral in 1897. In 1904 some young plants were noticed which were exceptionally vigorous and had paler shoots. They were planted at the sawmill at Inver and at Blair Castle.

TABLE 40. SPECIMENS OF LARIX × EUROLEPIS

Locality	*Date Planted*	*Dimensions*	
Blair Atholl	1897		97′ × 3′ 7″ (1955)
Dunkeld Cathedral	ca.1900		97′ × 7′ 2″ (1970)
Murthly (Rohallion)	1904		93′ × 6′ 4″ (1956)
Murthly (The Gelly)	1904		98′ × 6′ 5″ (1970)
Blair Castle	1905	60′ × 4′ 4″ (1931)	84′ × 8′ 9″ (1970)
Blair Castle	1905		88′ × 6′ 4″ (1970)
Dawyck	1910	32′ × 2′ 10″ (1931)	65′ × 7′ 6″ (1966)
Glasnevin B.G.	1911	44′ × 2′ 8″ (1931)	65′ × 5′ 11″ (1966)
Edinburgh R.B.G.	1912		66′ × 6′ 1″ (1970)
Edinburgh R.B.G.	1912		50′ × 6′ 11″ (1970)
Keir House	1912		100′ × 6′ 6″ (1970)
Borde Hill	1916		67′ × 5′ 4″ (1968)
Crarae (ex Glamis Cas.)	1918	24′ × 1′ 2″ (1931)	74′ × 6′ 1″ (1969)
Drumlanrig Castle	1920		72′ × 3′ 3″ (1954)
Killerton			79′ × 6′ 1″ (1970)
St. Clere			55′ × 5′ 0″ (1969)
Pencarrow			79′ × 7′ 5″ (1970)
Highclere			60′ × 6′ 1″ (1968)
Westonbirt			60′ × 5′ 11″ (1968)
Leonardslee			68′ × 4′ 1″ (1969)
Abercairny			95′ × 5′ 8″ (1962)
Bedgebury	1925	14′ 3″ ′ (1931)	70′ × 4′ 11″ (1968)
Kew	1926		66′ × 4′ 11″ (1971)
Ae Forest	1930		70′ × 3′ 1″ (1954)
Speymouth Forest	1930		63′ × 3′ 11″ (1955)

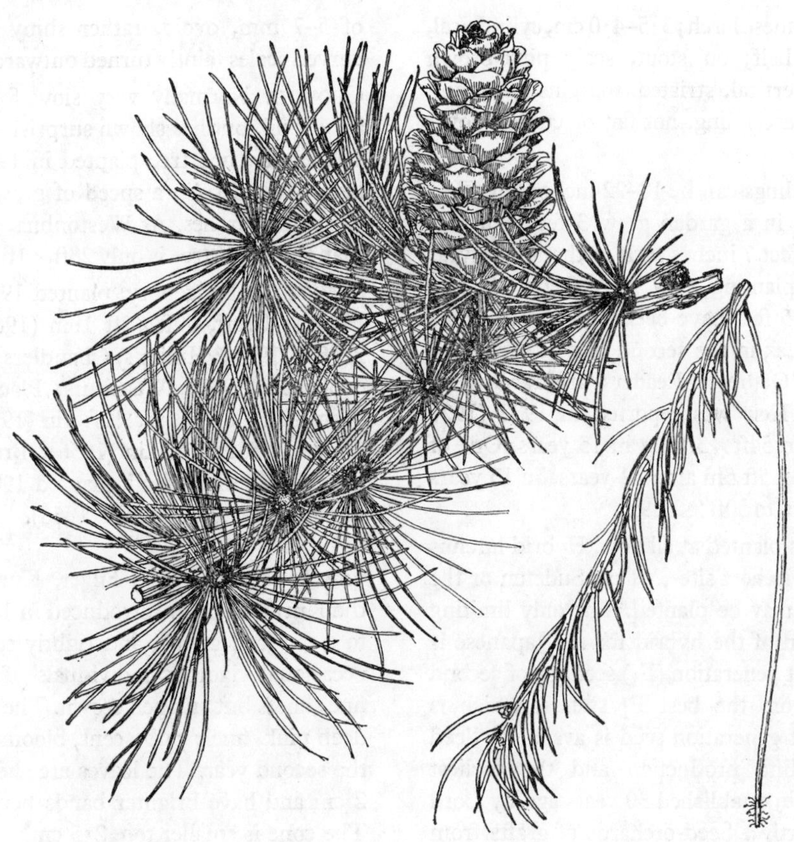

Larix x eurolepis

Fig. 100
New shoot (right) and two-year shoot with foliage and cone of *Larix × eurolepis*, Hybrid larch (*L. decidua × L. kaempferi*), showing the cone with partially reflexed scales but much taller than the cone of *L. kaempferi*. Single leaf × 1⅓.

These were the first recognised hybrids, but more recently a plantation a few miles up the road from Blair Atholl, made in 1897, and the line along the Bishops' Walk, have been found to contain hybrid trees. They are variable, but always quite intermediate between the parents in all characteristics except for vigour, in which they usually excel both. There are nearly Japanese types and European-tending types, the range of colour of the shoots being from orange-brown to pale pinkish-buff. Female flowers range from pink-purple through red and cream, pink and cream to pure cream or green.

BARK. Young trees purplish-black and red-brown with dark grey-green scaly surface. Older trees dark red-brown, widely fissured and scaly.

FOLIAGE. Shoot variably coloured (see above) but usually a shade of yellow-brown, shining, or pink-buff slightly bloomed.

LEAVES. On vigorous leading shoots (see European larch) to 5 cm × 0·2 cm, falcate; on normal new wood 2·5 cm. Leaves on spur-shoots in whorls of up to 100 or more, but usually nearer 50, 3·5–4·5 cm, the long ones on strong main shoots; dark grey-green matt above, (shiny on vigorous leading-shoots) with two grey bands beneath. The contrast between the two surfaces is very marked, and this is a distinction from European larch where the two surfaces are almost the same colour.

CONE. This is the most stable distinguishing feature, combining the large size and tall shape of the European with the reflexed scales of the Japanese larch; 3·5–4·0 cm, cylindrical, tapering in the upper half; on stout, scaly pink-brown stalks of 1 cm; scales vertical, striated, margins wavy and bent outwards but still ascending, not flat or curved down as in the Japanese larch.

GROWTH. One year seedlings can be 18–22 inches tall. Two such seedlings; planted in a garden grew 3 feet 6 inches each in the first year, 4 feet 7 inches each in the fourth year and by 7 years after planting they were 27ft × 1ft 5in. Leading shoots of over 5 feet have been grown; and these grow 7–8 inches in a week in the second half of their long season—May to early October. Leaders are rarely unbranched. One tree at Keir was reported in 1932 (1927 figures) to have grown to 54ft × 3ft 7in in 15 years. One of the same group was 90ft × 5ft 5in after 41 years. In 15 years a tree in Surrey has grown to 50ft × 2ft 9in.

GENERAL. Where larch is planted at all now, Hybrid larch is preferred on all but the richest sites, where Sudeten or the best Scottish European may be planted. The only limiting factor in the substitution of the hybrid for the Japanese is the shortage of good first generation (F_1) seed, or of second generation (F_2) seed from the best F_1 stands, which is acceptable until the first generation seed is available. Seed orchards are coming into production and the earliest orchards, at Birkhill, Fife, established 30 years ago by Lord Dundee are now productive. Seed-orchards of grafts from selected 'Plus' trees only, established between 1952 and 1960 by the Forestry Commission are slow in coming into production, but the controlled-parentage hybrids raised experimentally to test the first orchard have grown with immense vigour.

Larix gmelinii (Ruprecht) Kuzeneva. Dahurian larch

Siberia, eastwards from the Yenisei River to the Pacific Coast and, as varieties on some of the islands there. Introduced in 1827. Rare; not even in very many collections.

BARK. Dark red brown, finely scaly.

CROWN. The few good trees are rather broadly conic with level branching and dense, fine shoots. The more numerous others are low, broad, and bent badly to one side, or umbrella-shaped; long branches descending nearly to the ground; occasionally a straight stem with tangles of constantly damaged shoots unable to form real branches. Foliage very bright green or yellowish.

FOLIAGE. Shoot pink-brown, slightly ribbed; buds very dark brown with some white resin.

LEAVES. Usually out in February, very slender and thin, to 4 × 0·05 cm; 2 cm on struggling trees when yellowish also. Healthy leaves bright, shiny grass-green above; two narrow pale grey-green bands beneath.

FLOWERS. Females bright yellow-green, 1 cm, becoming rich rose-purple conelets.

CONE. Usually abundant, small, to 2·5 × 1·8 cm on a stalk of 5–7 mm, ovoid, rather shiny pale brown, the broad, curved scales faintly turned outward at the margin.

GROWTH. Normally very slow for many years and then almost nil, but has shown surprising vigour occasionally. At Bedgebury, one tree planted in 1949 is now, twenty years later 48ft × 3ft 4in a speed of growth that rivals the better European larches. At Westonbirt, a tree eleven years older than the above tree is only 28ft × 1ft 9in.

SPECIMENS. Bedgebury, planted 1930, 62ft × 2ft 7in (1969); Hergest Croft, 60ft × 2ft 10in (1961); Leonardslee, 60ft × 2ft 8in (1969); Hillier's, Chandlers Ford, planted 1927, 45ft × 3ft 8in (1961); Wakehurst Place, 49ft × 4ft 6in (1966); Warnham Court, 59ft × 2ft 0in (1971); Kew Royal Botanic Gardens, 53ft × 2ft 2in (1956); Brocklesby Park, 41ft × 2ft 1in (1956); Little Hall, planted 1906, 45ft × 3ft 0in (1961); Castle Milk, 32ft × 2ft 1in (1966).

var. japonica (Rege) Pilger. Kurile larch. Sakhalien and the Kurile Islands. Introduced in 1888. Very rare. Confined to a few collections, and rightly so. This variety lacks the occasional vigorous individuals of the type. It has dense, fine shoots but an open crown. The shoots are pale purple or deep pink, finely pubescent, bloomed grey, purplish-brown the second year. The leaves are shorter than in the type, to 2 cm and have brighter bands beneath, narrow but white. The cone is smaller too, 2·5 cm.

Brocklesby Park, 41ft × 2ft 2in (1956); Borde Hill, planted 1927, 48ft × 1ft 10in (1957); Bedgebury, planted 1937, 27ft × 2ft 1in; 26ft × 1ft 10in (1963); Edinburgh Royal Botanic Garden, W7328, planted 1915, 21ft × 1ft 3in (1970).

var. olgensis (Henry) Ostenfeld and Larsen. Olga Bay larch. East Siberia around Olga Bay. Introduced in 1911. This variety has even smaller leaves and cones than var. *japonica* but is most easily recognised by the dense red-brown pubescence on the shoot. The only specimen seen alive is at Warnham Court, 47ft × 2ft 2in (1971).

var. principis-rupprechtii (Mayr) Pilger. Prince Rupprecht's larch. Korea, Manchuria and just into China. Introduced in 1903. A sturdy variety capable of considerable vigour, with level branching and a rather open crown; stout orange-brown shoots and large cones, to 4 cm, (usually 3 × 2·5 cm) like those of some European larch; slightly shiny, dark purple-brown, the scales with waved, slightly out-turned margins.

Borde Hill, planted 1927, 55ft × 3ft 10in (1967); Hergest Croft, 42ft × 2ft 5in (1961); Bedgebury, planted 1926, 34ft × 1ft 5in, planted 1928, 36ft × 1ft 7in (1970); Kew Royal Botanic Gardens, 36ft × 1ft 10in (1956); Edinburgh Royal Botanic Garden, 9 feet (1955); Glendoick, 30ft × 2ft 0in (1970).

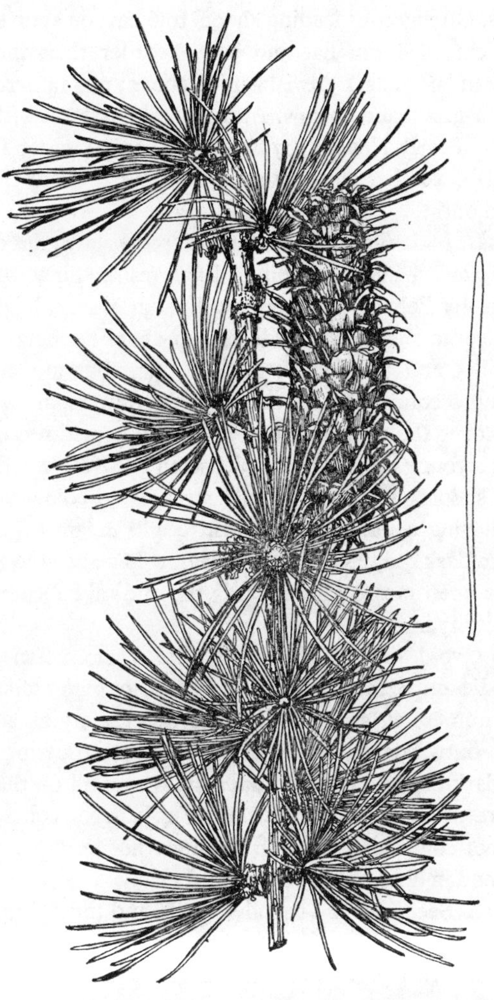

Fig. 101
Typical pendent shoot of *Larix griffithii*, Sikkim larch, showing the large cone with exserted and reflexed bracts. The shoot is a rich orange in the first year. Single leaf × 1⅓.

Larix griffithii Hooker fil. Sikkim larch

Eastern Nepal, Sikkim, Bhutan and Tibet. Introduced in 1848 and one original tree survives. Very rare. A few small trees survive in collections in Sussex, despite some recent deaths, and in Ireland, and Hereford, but the only old trees are in Devon and Cornwall. Closely related to *L. potanini* (q.v.).

BARK. Like a Corsican pine, dull purple-grey broadly and shallowly fissured into coarse, thick, scaly ridges.

CROWN. Small trees gaunt; a few flat branches, upturned at the ends, and foliage hanging from them in long strings. Old trees broad, ovoid with wide-spreading, low branches.

FOLIAGE. Shoots rich orange with a fine white pubescence; slightly corrugated. Second year dark orange-brown.

BUD. Ovoid, bright red-brown, smooth and resinous.

LEAVES. On new shoots, appressed but curved out slightly at the tips, 3 cm, showing their pale-banded underside. Leaves on the long spur-shoots 30–40 per whorl, to 3·5 cm, flat above and deep, shiny green; two narrow greenish-white bands beneath.

CONE. Usually abundant even on the smaller trees, because they remain many years on the tree; when newly ripe, dark purple-brown, 6–8·5×2 cm slightly tapered cylinders, crusted with white resin near the apex. The bracts are exserted 0·5–1 cm; broad at the base, pale brown with dark purple-brown centre and spine, those in the upper parts arched and the middle and lower ones curved strongly downwards. The female buds are big, conic and chestnut brown.

SPECIMENS AND GROWTH. Evidently only doubtfully hardy along the South coast of England east of Devon and hardy to the west, in sheltered sites in Herefordshire and in Ireland. All the trees previously measured, by Elwes & Henry from 1903 to 1905 and in the 1932 Report have been found, although one has died since—but these total only six specimens. Growth rates are shown to be slow. (Table 41).

[The Coldrennick tree is likely to be an original tree contemporary with the known original at Strete Ralegh.]

TABLE 41. TREES OF LARIX GRIFFITHII

Locality	*Date Planted*	*Dimensions*	
Strete Ralegh	1848	40′ × 4′ 0″ (1905)	62′ × 7′ 3″ (1964)
Coldrennick	?1848	51′ × 4′ 6″ (1905)	70′ × 6′ 3″ (1970)
Pencarrow		12′ × 1′ 3″ (1905)	35′ × 3′ 0″ (1957)
Strete Ralegh (2)			51′ × 3′ 1″ (1964)
Borde Hill		6′ (1931)	39′ × 1′ 5″ (1960)
Hergest Croft	1920		62′ × 3′ 2″ (1963)
Wakehurst Place Valley			35′ × 2′ 4″ (1965)
Headfort			35′ × 2′ 10″ (1966)
Avondale			57′ × 3′ 0″ (1968)
Leonardslee			37′ × 2′ 8″ (1969)
Glasnevin B.G.			35′ × 1′ 2″ (1966)

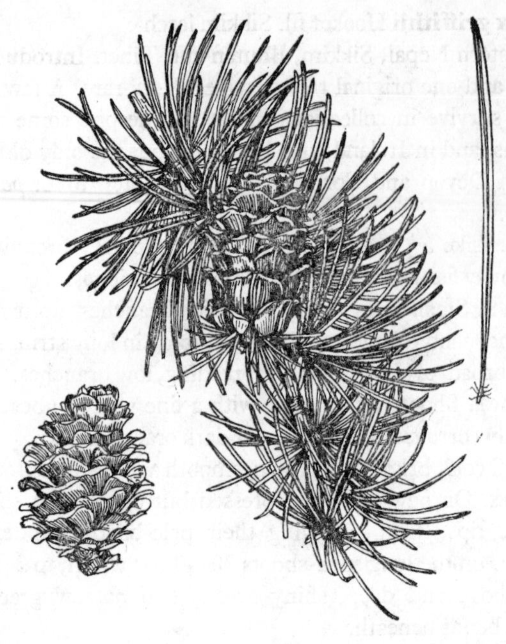

Larix kaempferi

Fig. 102
Cones, foliage and leaf ($\times 1\frac{1}{3}$) of *Larix kaempferi*, Japanese larch, with immature cone on the shoot and ripe cone separately, showing the decurved margins of the scales.

Larix kaempferi (Lambert) Carriere. Japanese larch. (*L. leptolepis*, Siebold and Zuccarini)

Central Honshiu, Japan. Introduced in 1861. A plantation tree over large areas of the west, particularly in Wales but in smaller areas in most forests; unusual as a park tree, sometimes in smaller gardens.

BARK. Dark red-brown or purple-brown, scaly, or fissured and smooth.

CROWN. Usually somewhat broadly conic and when young upswept, but some are as narrow as a good European larch whilst others are very broad, having level slightly descending lower branches to 30 feet long. Tends to be more stocky than the European with a stouter bole in a tree of the same height, and stouter branches. The method of branching on the leading shoot and the branch leaders gives a noticeably more dense crown. The leading-shoot of a healthy tree is never unbranched but bears numerous shoots usually from the base to near the apex and these branch again. Thus although the whorls of annual branching are plainly visible owing to the large size of the branches, the bole between the whorls carries many strong and much branched shoots

FOLIAGE. Shoot varies in colour from orange-brown to deep purple and the dark red and purple shoots are often much bloomed grey.

LEAVES. On vigorous leading shoots to 6 cm; on spur-shoots 3·5–4 cm×0·1 cm flat and soft, broader than those of European larch, dark greyish-green above; two rather broad greenish-grey bands below. Autumn colour starts with pale yellows in early November, becoming orange in good years by mid-November and russet until falling at about the end of the month.

FLOWERS. Male flower-buds are dark red-brown, flat domes 3 mm across, slightly whitened by resin. They become globular by February and open yellow in March, lengthening to conic shape. They cluster on short hanging shoots especially, and terminate many of them but are also on stronger second year shoots. Female flowers are widely spread over the crown on old wood and sometimes on the bole of a young tree, but most dense on two-year wood from strong shoots. They are usually strongly bi-coloured each bract having a purplish-pink centre and cream edges but uniform dark red, bright pink or yellow have been found. A few are open most years towards the end of February and the majority in mid-March.

CONE. Ovoid or bun-shaped 3 cm×3 cm when open, subsessile on 3 mm stout, scaly, dark orange stalks, the scales numerous, striated with the outer margins sharply turned outwards flat and curled under at the tip. They ripen dark brown but when open and dry, still on the tree, they are pale brown. Proliferous or ex-current cones, with the shoot continuing through them are not infrequent, and may stand in lines of five or six together.

GROWTH. Seedlings are usually sturdy and much branched rather than tall. Planted out when 6in tall a seedling grew slowly for two years but then made shoots of 3–4 feet, growing 4 feet 8 inches in the sixth year planted, which brought it to 19 feet tall. This species is immensely vigorous, even if slightly less so than the hybrid larch and the best European larches. The reputation it has for culminating early and being slower than the European after, say, fifty years, is false. The older trees are still growing very rapidly. In increase in girth, the Japanese larch is, as would be expected from its dense crown and stout branches, more rapid than all but a few exceptional European and hybrid larches. Nearly all the specimens are of known date, the majority dating back only to 1885, 1901 or 1906. Most of those measured in 1931 have been found and although there are some which have grown very slowly since, the majority have increases in girth representing one inch or more per year in the 25–35 years since then. Rates of growth in height and girth of a wide sample of trees can be seen in Table 42.

SPECIMENS. An original tree is at Kew, and another probable, planted soon after 1861, is at Tortworth Court. The very poor growth of this tree in this century has been a possible source of the reputation this species has for failing in its later years. In 1904 it was 45ft×4ft 7in; in 1931, 48ft×5ft 0in and in 1964, 58ft×5ft 7in. That this is untypical, to say the least, is shown by the figures in Table 42 following.

TABLE 42. THE GROWTH OF JAPANESE LARCHES, LARIX KAEMPFERI, OF KNOWN AGE

Location	*Date of Planting*	*Dimensions*	
Kew	1868		63′ × 4′ 4″ (1971)
Inveraray	1876 (Graft)	74′ × 7′ 0″ (1931)	90′ × 8′ 4″ (1969)
Dunkeld	1885	68′ × 6′ 0″ (1931)	98′ × 8′ 1″ (1970)
Dunkeld	1885	54′ × 5′ 5″ (1931)	88′ × 8′ 8″ (1970)
Dunkeld	1885		102′ × 9′ 8″ (1970)
Munches	1885 (seed)	69′ × 5′ 8″ (1931)	79′ × 7′ 4″ (1970)
Munches	1885 (seed)	63′ × 6′ 3″ (1931)	88′ × 9′ 3″ (1970)
Kirkennan	1885 (seed)	41′ × 2′ 0″ (1904)	79′ × 7′ 9″ (1970)
Blair Atholl	1886		121′ × 8′ 11″ (1970)
Glamis	1894	66′ × 4′ 7″ (1931)	105′ × 7′ 10″ (1970)
Castle Kennedy	1898	58′ × 3′ 5″ (1931)	85′ × 7′ 6″ (1967)
Brocklesby Park	1900	68′ × 4′ 4″ (1931)	92′ × 6′ 6″ (1956)
Blairquhan	1900	70′ × 4′ 11″ (1931)	105′ × 6′ 6″ (1970)
Brahan Castle	1901	60′ × 4′ 0″ (1931)	90′ × 6′ 8″ (1970)
Culzean Castle	1901	45′ × 3′ 4″ (1931)	73′ × 5′ 10″ (1970)
Langholm (Deans Bank)	1903	49′ × 2′ 3″ (1931)	106′ × 6′ 9″ (1969)
Langholm (Deans Bank)	1903	47′ × 2′ 3″ (1931)	108′ × 5′ 11″ (1969)
Dunkeld (Bishops Walk)	1905		111′ × 8′ 4″ (1970)
Glenapp	1906		98′ × 5′ 4″ (1970)
Glen House	1906		90′ × 8′ 9″ (1966)
Fonthill	1906		120′ × 4′ 7″ (1965)
Fonthill	1906		110′ × 6′ 0″ (1965)
Drumlanrig Castle	1906		93′ × 8′ 2″ (1953)
Achnacloich	1923		79′ × 4′ 0″ (1953)
Bedgebury	1925		64′ × 4′ 2″ (1968)

GENERAL. The remarks under *Larix decidua* apply here also. Wherever possible, the Japanese larch is replaced by the hybrid larch. Japanese larch produces a singularly heavy leaf-fall which has recommended it for three specialist uses in which it should maintain its place. It can grow well, and rapidly build up a soil rich in humus, on some spoil heaps and degraded ground. Together with the dense crown, the heavy leaf-fall rapidly suppresses all other vegetation, a valuable feature in the reclamation of Rhododendron areas, and used beside rides in forests to act as additional fire-breaks in some pine areas.

cv. Pendula. Trees with remarkably pendulous shoots are found rarely in plantations. A few have been propagated by grafting and weep in an umbrella shape. 'Pendula' has fresh green leaves, another cultivar 'Dervaes' has glaucous leaves.

Larix laricina (du Roi) Koch. Tamarack.

Alaska and Canada, south to the Lake States and North Alleghanies. Introduced in 1737, 1739 or 1760, the earlier dates no doubt referring to P. Collinson's plant. (See *L. pendula*). Rare; found in a very few large gardens and a few collections in all parts of these islands.

BARK. Pinkish-orange to dark red, flaking finely into small circular scales.

CROWN. Narrow and thin, usually slender-pointed but often bent at the top. Bole straight and nearly cylindric. The short, level branches characteristically diffuse rapidly into slender, curly shoots, usually curling upwards and inwards on the outside of the crown but at random inside. In young plants the sinuous leader is surrounded by an upswept basal whorl of shoots.

FOLIAGE. The slender shoot is pink-buff bloomed grey-pink. Second year shoot pale brown. Side-buds dark red-brown and resinous.

LEAVES. On new shoots are appressed and have two broad pale bands on each side. Leaves on spur-shoots very slender and thin, to 2·5 cm, dark green above, 2 broad grey bands beneath.

FLOWERS. Male flowers very numerous and very small compared with the European larch. Female flowers numerous, scarcely 1 cm tall, a good red, appearing over a long period in March and April.

CONE. Small but variable, tall ovoid usually only 1·5 cm sometimes 2 cm, pale brown, with very few scales, erect and slightly incurved, the tips slightly spreading. Proliferous cones are sometimes numerous, the slender continuation of the shoot through the cone being 5–6 cm long.

GROWTH. Young plants, put experimentally on ill-drained land in South West Scotland have made leading-shoots of 3 feet but older trees elsewhere have been very slow, particularly in increase of girth. Since the tree is evidently short-lived (none of the four mentioned in 1905 is known to survive, although four of the five much smaller ones given in 1931 have been re-found) there are no boles of any large size. A tree planted in 1909 increased in girth in the 35 years since 1931 by only 5 inches. At Bedgebury there is a big contrast in the growth of two adjacent trees planted in 1925. At the age of 43 one was 40ft × 1ft 9in and the other 54ft × 4ft 3in. This tree has a short-term, decorative value in planting boggy land that cannot be drained. Some specimens have very fine, if small, boles with imperceptible taper.

Fig. 103
Shoot and shoot with cone of *Larix laricina*, tamarack, showing the slender shoot and very small cone. The cone is purple-red in early summer.

TABLE 43. NOTABLE TREES OF LARIX LARICINA

Locality	*Date Planted*	*Dimensions*	
Borde Hill		38′ × 1′ 8″ (1931)	65′ × 3′ 8″ (1957)
Warnham Court		63′ × 2′ 7″ (1931)	62′ × 2′ 11″ (1971)[1]
Dawyck	1909	43′ × 1′ 6″ (1931)	55′ × 1′ 11″ (1966)
Chiltley Place			54′ × 5′ 1″ (1960)
Sutton Place			53′ × 5′ 11″ (1966)
Wakehurst Place			67′ × 4′ 3″ (1970)
Cambridge B.G.			68′ × 4′ 3″ (1969)
Leighton Hall			66′ × 3′ 4″ (1968)
Nymans			75′ × 3′ 2″ (1970)
Hergest Croft			51′ × 2′ 9″ (1961)
Sunninghill Nurseries			25′ × 4′ 7″ (1958)
Blairquhan			58′ × 2′ 9″ (1954)
St. Clere			37′ × 2′ 10″ (1969)
Edinburgh R.B.G.			27′ × 2′ 7″ (1967)
Glasnevin B.G.			47′ × 3′ 5″ (1966)
Bedgebury	1925	9′ 6″ (1931)	54′ × 4′ 3″ (1968)

[1] Top blown out many years before

Larix lyallii Parlatore.

Cascade Mountains locally, and nearby ridges in British Columbia and Washington. Introduced possibly in 1883. One moribund tree known.

Known by the densely pubescent buff shoots and quadrangular leaves, this tree has been tried several times and always fails.

At Hillier's Nursery, Chandlers Ford, a gaunt 15-feet tree suffers bad damage from frost every year.

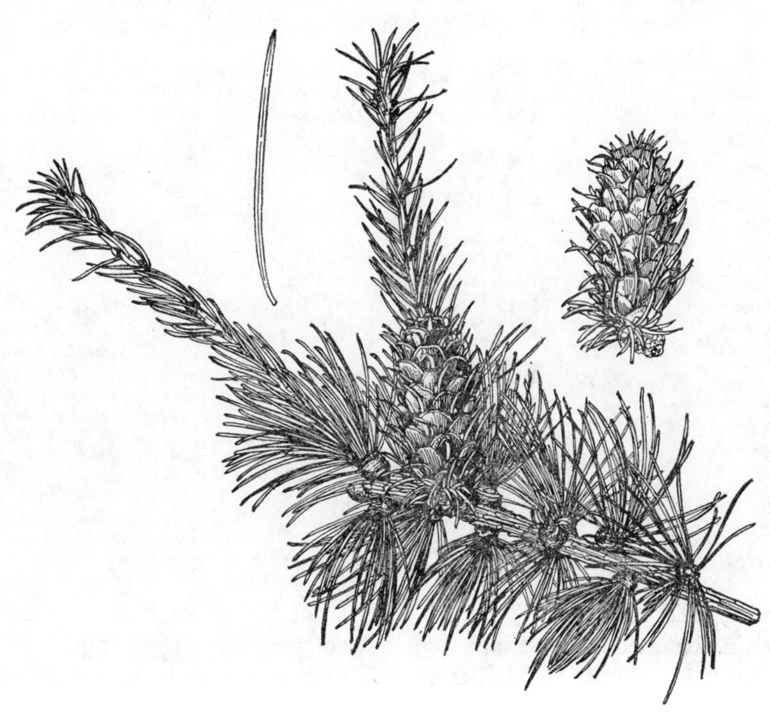

Larix occidentalis

Fig. 104
Shoots, cones and a single leaf ($\times 1\frac{1}{3}$) of *Larix occidentalis*, Western larch, showing the exserted, straight bracts on the cone.

Larix occidentalis Nuttall. Western larch

Southern British Columbia, Washington, Montana, Idaho and Northern Oregon.

Introduced as seedlings to Kew in 1881. These were planted out in 1889 at Kew and Warnham Court, Sussex. Four are still at Kew and one at Warnham Court. One of these was also planted at Grayswood Hill in 1882 but has not been seen since 1906. This seed came from Oregon. The next seed came in 1903 from Idaho and grew into bigger and better trees on the whole than the Oregon seed. More seed came in 1906 and 1908, but the tree remains rare, being found only in collections and in a few small plantations.

BARK. Purplish grey, deeply and widely fissured into vertical ridges with flaking edges.

CROWN. Good trees are narrowly conic with very whorled branches; short, level, upturned at the ends.

FOLIAGE. Shoot pale orange-brown, slightly shiny; second year dusky dark brown. Leaves on spur-shoots, in whorls of about 50; very slender, to 3·5 cm, bright and shiny grass green on both sides or with whitish bands beneath.

CONE. Cylindric, purple-brown, 3·5–4 cm; scales reflexed at tips; bracts protruding as spreading or down-curved spines.

GROWTH. This, the finest of all the larches in its native lands, has been disappointing here. Some trees suffer damage from frost and from canker and die-back. However, good trees are very good, with fine boles and narrow crowns and have grown with moderate vigour. Many of the earliest trees have a recorded origin and history but the finest tree found is unrecorded previously despite being at Bayfordbury. Its size accords well with a 1903 Idaho origin.

SPECIMENS. The original seed from Oregon is represented by the trees planted in 1889. The trees planted from 1904 to 1908 are known to have come from the Idaho seed of 1903 in the cases of Kew, Tortworth and Borde Hill and it is highly probable that this is true of the trees at Edinburgh, Bayfordbury and Dawyck.

TABLE 44. LARGE SPECIMENS OF LARIX OCCIDENTALIS

Locality	*Date Planted*	*Dimensions*	
Kew R.B.G.	1889	29′ × 1′ 5″ (1906)	75′ × 4′ 7″ (1970)
Kew R.B.G.	1889		72′ × 4′ 4″ (1971)
Kew R.B.G.	1889		75′ × 4′ 1″ (1971)
Warnham Court	1889	48′ × 2′ 9″ (1921)	65′ × 3′ 2″ (1971)
Kew R.B.G.	1904	49′ × 1′ 9″ (1921)	75′ × 4′ 11″ (1970)
Tortworth Court		30′ × 1′ 7″ (1919)	73′ × 4′ 10″ (1964)
Borde Hill	1908	17′ (1920)	61′ × 2′ 9″ (1967)
Borde Hill	1908	7′ (1920)	54′ × 2′ 1″ (1957)
Dawyck	1908	13′ (1920)	64′ × 3′ 8″ (1966)
Bayfordbury			85′ × 4′ 9″ (1968)
Edinburgh R.B.G.	1909		60′ × 5′ 8″ (1970)
Edinburgh R.B.G.	1909		66′ × 4′ 1″ (1970)
Brocklesby Park	1912	30′ × 3″ (1931)	62′ × 1′ 6″ (1956)
Culzean Castle	1914	40′ (1931)	76′ × 3′ 0″ (1970)
Arley Castle			63′ × 3′ 3″ (1961)
Hopetoun	1924		60′ × 3′ 7″ (1955)[1]
Kyloe Wood	1925		53′ × 2′ 5″ (1958)[1]
Bedgebury	1925	9′ 6″ (1931)	57′ × 2′ 11″ (1968)
Woburn	1929		75′ × 3′ 9″ (1970)
Blackmoor			53′ × 2′ 7″ (1968)
Blackmoor (road)			62′ × 3′ 2″ (1969)
Windsor Great Park	1934		49′ × 2′ 7″ (1956)[1]

[1]Plantation Trees

Larix × pendula (Solander) Salisbury.

A tree of mysterious origin. Reported and described from Newfoundland and New Jersey in 1789 and 1814, it has not been seen wild since. Peter Collinson's tree of 1739, moved to Mill Hill, seems likely to have been *L. laricina*. The old trees at Woburn and Bayfordbury were long referred to as *L. dahurica* (=*L. gmelinii*). Neither now exists, but seedlings from the second are growing at Bedgebury and are typical of × *pendula*. This appears to be a hybrid between *L. decidua* and *L. laricina*. The date of introduction of *L. laricina* into Britain is often given as 1739 which may refer to Collinson's tree which could have been one parent of the hybrid cultivated here, and has been assumed to be the origin of the old trees mentioned above. The European larch was not known to be introduced to America until later in that century, so the 1739 tree is unlikely to have been *L* × *pendula*.

BARK. Strikingly coloured grey-purple and orange-brown, cracking finely into rough, flaking squares, but vertical fissures larger than horizontal cracks.

CROWN. Very conical; lower branches level with pendulous shoots—not markedly more pendulous than many old European larches—but noticeable even in young trees.

FOLIAGE. Shoot pink-buff faintly bloomed purple; second year dusky-brown.

LEAVES. On new shoots appressed, with 2 broad grey bands each side. Those on spur-shoots very slender, 3·5 cm long, green above and two very narro w white bands below.

CONE. Long-ovoid with tapered apex, plum-purple in the summer, turning green in shiny patches near the centre of each scale, dark purple at the base, ripening greyish brown; 2·5–3 cm long with smoothly appressed scales. Proliferous cones common, sometimes graduated through small cones with strong shoots through them, to shoots with just a few cone-scales around their base.

GROWTH. None of the nine specimens given by Elwes and Henry has been found, but three of the smaller trees given in the 1932 Report still exist. Two of these were then of medium size and have grown little, but the third was very young and small in 1931 and has grown vigorously. Other young, dated trees have grown rapidly, and early fast growth but slow later growth seems to be the usual pattern.

SPECIMENS. Hergest Croft, planted 1859, 60ft×5ft 11in (1969) main stem broken at 50 feet; Kew Royal Botanic Gardens, 62ft×5ft 1in (1970); Borde Hill, 60ft×2ft 7in (1957); Warnham Court, 84ft×4ft 8in (1971); Bedgebury, planted 1925, 72ft×4ft 10in (1970); 65ft×3ft 10in; 52ft×4ft 0in (1965).

RECOGNITION. A larch with the shoot resembling *L. laricina* and similar bark, but quite different crown, the minor shoots hanging straight down instead of curling upwards as in *L. laricina*. Seen with the cones purple, there is no difficulty.

cv. Repens. Known only from the original at Henham Hall and some small grafts at St. Clere and Wakehurst Place

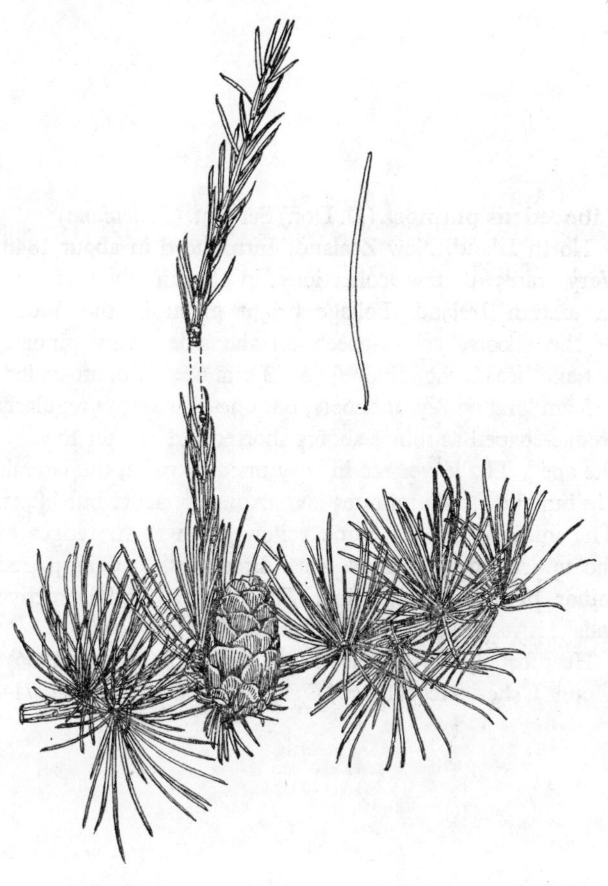

Fig. 105
Larix × pendula, a larch of obscure origin, has small cones which are rich plum-purple in summer. Leaf × 1⅓.

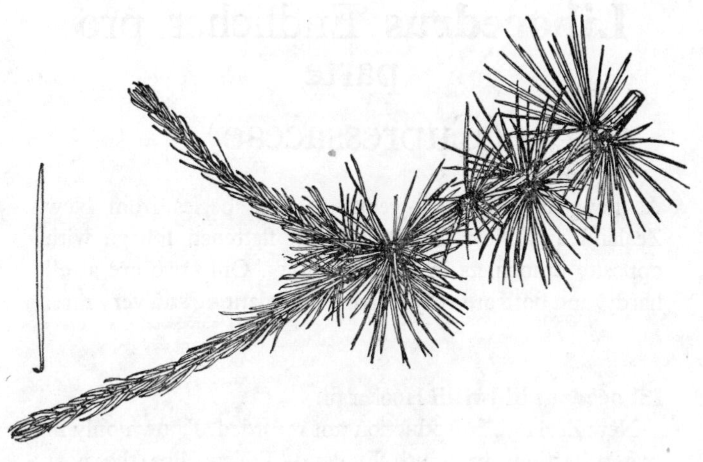

Fig. 106
The rare Chinese *Larix potaninii* has orange-brown shoots and yellowish-green leaves which are closely appressed to the new shoot. Single leaf × 1⅓.

obviously derived from it. The tree at Henham Hall, planted in 1810, has a bole 9 feet in girth (1956) from which at 7 feet up, heavy branches have been trained along 60 feet of pergola then flow over the ends and arise from the grass around. The shoots are very strong and ascend slightly at first, bending down as each year a long new shoot is added. This was grafted at ground level but the others were grafted 2–4 feet up and have been left to form mats.

Larix potaninii Batalin.

South West China and East Tibet. Introduced in 1904. Very rare; known in a very few collections only. A rather stocky tree but less so in woodland, known by its stout bright orange-brown shoots surrounded by closely pressed slender yellowish leaves. Second year shoots are dark, shining brown. The bark is purple-grey with deep, wide, scaly-edged fissures. The crown is usually dense, but some trees are sparsely branched; low branches upswept, higher ones level with tips curved up. Dense shoots spread at wide angles. The leaves are 2 cm long, 4-angled and with two bright white narrow bands beneath. The cone is a slightly tapered domed cylinder, like that of *L. griffithii* but smaller, 2·5 cm × 2·5 cm with exserted bracts, spines pointing upwards or decurved, 5 mm long, black against shiny orange brown of the scale, or dull purple and brown.

St. Clere, 40ft × 4ft 7in (1969); Borde Hill (The Tolls), 57ft × 2ft 9in (1970); (Stone-pit), 36ft × 1ft 3in (1957); (Warren Wood), 40 feet; 28ft × 1ft 4in (1958); Bedgebury, (Thornhill), 25ft × 1ft 6in (1970); Wakehurst Place, 50ft × 2ft 7in (1971).

Larix russica (Endlicher) Sabine ex Trautvetter. Siberian larch. (*Larix sibirica* Lédébour).

Northern Russia, east to the Yenisei River in Siberia. Introduced in 1806. Very rare; if present at all. This tree comes into leaf in January or February and suffers from the foliage being damaged by frosts more than does *L. gmelinii*. A tree 56 years old was 11 feet tall and dying, at Kew, in 1957. The shoot is slender and very pale buff; leaves slender, to 4 cm light grassy green above, two widely separated pale grey lines beneath. The cone is similar to the ovoid-conic type of European larch cone, 3 cm long with pubescent scales. Kew, planted 1946, 13 feet (1971).

Trees previously thought to be *L. sibirica* at Kew, Cambridge and Brocklesby Park have been found not to be of this species.

Libocedrus Endlicher pro parte (Cupressaceae)

As now constituted, a genus of five species from New Zealand and New Caledonia with flattened foliage with opposite branchlets in fan like sprays. Only two are at all hardy, and both are very restricted in planting and very rare.

Libocedrus bidwillii Hooker fil.

New Zealand. Introduction not recorded. Known only in two collections in South England. Foliage like the next species but narrower and ultimate shoots four-sided.

BARK. Dull brown, shaggy, with long thick flakes. Overlapping fans of regularly pinnate deep green branchlets, paler and uniform beneath, tetragonal. Lateral leaves project slightly with incurved tips. Faint sweet resinous scent when crushed. Nymans, 27ft × 1ft 11in (1970); Blackmoor, 30ft × 1 ft 5in (1968).

Libocedrus plumosa (D. Don) Sargent. (*L. doniana*)

North Island, New Zealand. Introduced in about 1848. Very rare; a few collections in South England and in eastern Ireland. Foliage bright green in the middle of the shoots, yellow-green on the sides, very pinnate, flat and broad, the minor shoots 3 mm across, blunt-ended, 1·5 cm long on 2-year shoots, but one-year sprays regularly wedge-shaped as minor shoots shorter and shorter towards the apex. The leaves are in very unequal pairs, the laterals big but the facials minute; laterals fleshy, acute but blunt. The underside is the same yellow-green as the edges of the upper side but dead matt. Branchlets end in paired minor branchlets diverging. This curious and attractive foliage is very like that of a *Selaginella* in a hot-house.

Headfort, 22ft × 2ft 2in; 17ft × 2ft 6in at 3 feet (1966); Mount Usher, 9 feet (1966); Wakehurst Place, 16 feet (1971).

Metasequoia S. Miki (Taxodiaceae)

A genus long known from fossil species over much of the world but regarded as *Sequoia* and *Taxodium* species until 1941 when the opposite arrangement of leaves and shoots was pointed out (*Sequoia* and *Taxodium* have alternate or spiral arrangement of foliage). One species, found surviving in Central China in 1941 by T. Kan.

Metasequoia glyptostroboides Hu et Cheng.

The Shui-sha valley, in the North West part of Hupeh Province and just crossing into Szechwan; China. Introduced in 1948, (January). It had been seen, but not collected in 1941; a specimen was collected and described by T. Wang in 1944 and the discovery was published in 1946. The

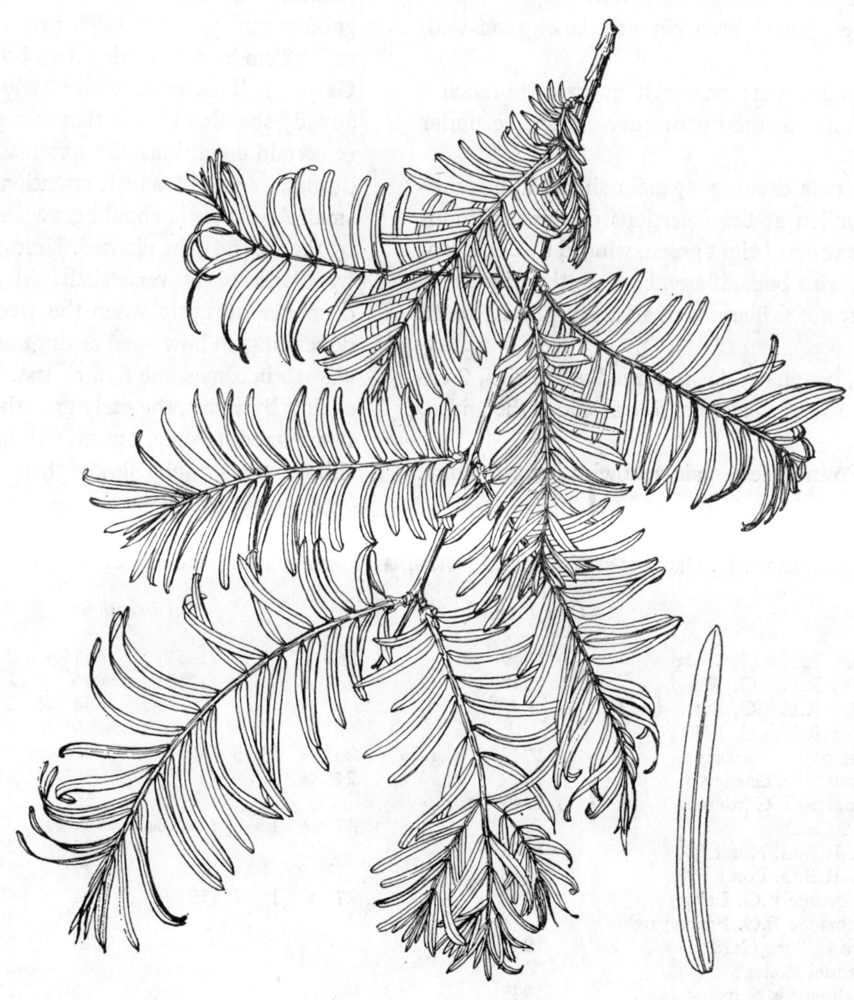

Metasequoia glyptostroboides

Fig. 107
Foliage of *Metasequoia glyptostroboides,* the Dawn redwood or Chinese water-fir. The side-shoots are deciduous with their leaves. The single leaf ($\times 1\frac{1}{3}$) shows the pale underside.

description was published by H. Hu and W. Cheng in 1948. Dr. Merrill of the Arnold Arboretum realised its importance in 1946 and obtained a grant for an expedition to collect seed, which was widely distributed in January 1948. Becoming quite common, with the large original trees in numerous collections and many larger and a few small gardens, and cuttings from these now widely planted in parks and gardens in England, Wales and Ireland. Rare in Scotland where the lack of warmth in summer limits growth considerably.

BARK. Bright orange-brown or red-brown, flaking away at first in large, dark brown scales even on small branches; soon, on the main stem, stringy and often deeply fissured into curving ridges. Small branches are dark green with orange flakes.

CROWN. Conical so far, some narrow, a few broad; branches often upswept. Dense in the open, but very sparse under shade.

FOLIAGE. Small shoots deciduous; main shoots light pink-brown slightly swollen at the insertions of the deciduous shoots. Deciduous shoots bright green, winged by decurrent petioles, opposite, with buds, if any, beneath their insertion on the main shoot, not axillary as in all other plants; to 12 cm hanging, lax.

LEAVES. Opposite, pectinate, down-curved at the tips, 2 cm long, bright green above, a paler band each side of the midrib below.

BUD. Globular, 1 mm or less, pale yellowish brown, shiny. Buds sprout beneath shoot junctions and produce deciduous shoots far back along branches. The leaves emerge in March and are often curled by frosts, sometimes being killed, but this does not seem to affect the new long shoots which grow in May and soon hide the damage. Autumn colour starts late in October as yellowish pink in some trees, dull brownish pink in others. In good years many go on to turn bright salmon-pink and then deep red in November and may not be bare until early December.

FLOWERS AND CONE. Male flowers have not yet been seen in Europe except in plants treated indoors with short day lengths. They are ovoid, set opposite on few—branched panicles which are some 25 cm long. Cones, occasional in good summers since 1955, green globose, 2 cm across on stalks 2 cm long, maturing dark brown.

GROWTH. This tree, whose early growth is very rapid, is already showing clearly that fast growth is maintained only in certain conditions. On any reasonable site not subject to drought, and with a little attention to weeds and fertilisers, a small *Metasequoia* should grow shoots of three feet or more by the second year planted. Unless, however, it is in a damp woodland or is very sheltered and near water, growth decreases abruptly when the tree is some 25–30 feet tall, depending on how open or dry the site is. From 3 feet a year growth becomes one foot or less. In woodland and in some shelter by water, the early growth rate is being more or less maintained, to date, but growth in girth is, on the sheltered thinner trees, much slower than those grown in more open

TABLE 45. GROWTH OF SOME OF THE ORIGINAL TREES OF METASEQUOIA GLYPTOSTROBOIDES

Location	*Date Planted*	*Dimensions*	
Wisley R.H.S.G. Wood	1949	26′ 6″ (1957)	51′ × 2′ 8″ (1970)
Wisley R.H.S.G. Wood	1949	23′ 6″ (1957)	56′ × 2′ 7″ (1970)
Wisley R.H.S.G. Battleston Hill			54′ × 2′ 0″ (1970)
Wisley R.H.S.G. Lake			39′ × 2′ 4″ (1970)
Leonardslee Rockery	1949	26′ × 1′ 5″ (1958)	40′ × 3′ 11″ (1968)
Leonardslee Garden	1949	24′ × 9″ (1958)	55′ × 2′ 6″ (1969)
Leonardslee Garden	1949		55′ × 3′ 0″ (1969)
Savill Gardens		37′ × 1′ 8″ (1960)	57′ × 3′ 1″ (1969)
Kew R.B.G. Nursery	1948		45′ × 2′ 8″ (1970)
Kew R.B.G. Pond	1948		47′ × 3′ 8″ (1970)
Cambridge B.G. Lake		27′ × 1′ 7″ (1959)	51′ × 4′ 5″ (1970)
Cambridge B.G. Frameyard			41′ × 3′ 5″ (1970)
Clare College Garden	1948		46′ × 3′ 8″ (1969)
Emanuel College			43′ × 3′ 9″ (1969)
Engelmann's Nursery	1949		26′ × 1′ 4″ (1962)
Oxford B.G.	1949		49′ × 3′ 3″ (1970)
Westonbirt, Specimen Avenue	1949		34′ × 1′ 6″ (1969)
Bedgebury. Best in plot	1950		29′ × 1′ 5″ (1969)
Ladham House	1950		46′ × 3′ 9″ (1967)
Alice Holt Lodge	1950	26′ × 1′ 6″ (1960)	38′ × 3′ 7″ (1971)
Chiddingly			39′ × 2′ 0″ (1967)
Mamhead			23′ × 1′ 4″ (1963)
Snowdenham House	1949		54′ × 3′ 11″ (1970)
Birr Castle	1949		23′ × 1′ 0″ (1966)
Headfort			26′ × 1′ 11″ (1966)
Castlewellan			28′ × 1′ 10″ (1970)
Glasnevin B.G.	1949		23′ × 1′ 2″ (1966)
Edinburgh R.B.G.	1948		19′ × 1′ 1″ (1967)

places by water. Growth starts at the beginning of May. 1957 had a very early spring and a *Metasequoia* being observed then had a shoot one inch long by April 1st. Elongation is most rapid in the latter half of July and the first week in August when 3 inches growth in a week should be expected, but ceases usually at the end of August.

A rooted cutting 3 feet 8 inches tall, planted in sandy soil but on a few cubic feet of leaf-mould, was, after 6 years growth 23ft × 1ft 1in in 1968. In 1969, a dry year, despite some watering, its shoot was 1 foot. A cutting planted beside a small but permanent stream near Guildford was, when 18 years old, 50ft × 4ft 2in with a steady growth. Examples of the biggest trees in damp, light woodland or by standing water, among those in the Table 45 opposite are: Wisley; Savill Gardens; Leonardslee; Emanuel College, Snowdenham House, Ladham House and the largest at Cambridge Botanic Garden.

Other quite large trees, mostly of more recent planting but probably including a few of the original trees are: Nymans, 41ft × 2ft 4in (1968); Bedgebury (Lake), planted 1955, 34ft × 1ft 11in (1969); Stourhead, 44ft × 3ft 0in (1970); Hungerdown House, Seagry, 35ft × 1ft 9in (1968); Kennington Nursery, 34ft × 2ft 4in (1967); Stratfield Saye, 32ft × 2ft 2in (1968); Wayford Manor, 33ft × 1ft 3in (1967); The Vine, Henbury, Bristol, planted 1955, 40ft × 1ft 11in (1969); Killerton, planted 1951, 50ft × 3ft 2in (1970); Knightshayes, 46ft × 2ft 4in (1970); Bodnant, 32ft × 1ft 9in (1966); Springkell, 27ft × 1ft 11in (1966); Annesgrove, 25ft × 1ft 1in (1968); Bicton, 47ft × 2ft 5in (1970); Keir House, 31ft × 2ft 1in (1970); Talbot Manor, planted 1950, 37ft × 3ft 0in (1970).

General. A most attractive tree, from the fresh green of early spring to the reds, pinks and russets of late autumn, but unless the bark is bright orange, rather dull and twiggy in winter. The opposite branching and pointed crown distinguish it easily from *Taxodium* and the buds below the branch-insertions are unique. The early idea that, being like *Taxodium*, this species would benefit from a site near water is being shown to be more true, for continued fast growth, than it is for the slower but more steady *Taxodium*, but it will stand more high shade than will *Taxodium*. Many trees develop an enlarged base to the bole with flutes. Several cultivars, differing in habit, have been distinguished in the U.S.A. and in Europe.

Phyllocladus L. C. and A. Richard (Podocarpaceae)

Six species from the Philippines, Borneo, New Zealand and Tasmania. They have flattened, hard, leaf-like branchlets. Three of them are marginally hardy in the extreme south and west.

Phyllocladus alpinus Hooker fil.

New Zealand. Introduction unrecorded. Straight, slender little trees. Shoot dull yellowish grey-green with a narrow rib below each leaf. Base of petiole dark purple. Bud well clear of leaves, ovoid, 3 mm, dark purple. Leaf long-cuneate from broad petiole, 2×0·8 cm, oval, truncate broad tip; coarse irregular jagged teeth with minute incurved spines at tip of each; shiny grey-green above, rough, with faint radiating ribs; the same beneath. Hard, leathery.

The "leaves" are really phylloclades, modified shoots. The female flowers are minute, bright red, ovoid and terminal on the phylloclades. Bedgebury, 11 feet; Rock-garden at Wakehurst Place, 6 feet.

Phyllocladus glaucus Carriere.

New Zealand around Auckland. Introduction unrecorded. One at Ilnacullin, 19 feet (1966).

Phyllocladus trichomanoides D. Don. Celery-topped pine

New Zealand. Introduction unrecorded. A slender little tree with grey bark and the shoots emerging reddish-brown, changing to dark grey-green. The phylloclades lie alternately on whorled shoots, some 6 cm long and are bluntly triangular, variously lobed.

Leonardslee, 12 feet, 4 stems (1962); Fota, 22ft×1ft 0in (1966); Mt. Usher, 22ft×1ft 4in (1966).

Phyllocladus alpinus

Fig. 108
Sprig of *Phyllocladus alpinus*, Alpine Celery-Top pine, a rare plant from New Zealand. The projecting buds are dark purple, and the minute flowers deep red.

Picea A. Dietrich (Pinaceae)

There are about 37 species of spruce, spread across the northern temperate world and including some of the tallest trees in North West America, Europe and the Himalaya. Their shoots are very rough with the bases left by shed leaves and their foliage is hard and usually spiny, unlike the leathery, pliant foliage of all but a few species of *Abies* and the soft, blunt foliage of all but one Douglas fir. The buds are broad and conic, usually resinous. The trees are monoecious and have pendulous woody or leathery cones. Their bark is usually scaly and never deeply fissured nor stringy. Many are of the greatest value for timber, especially for pulp, within their native areas and a few are widely planted elsewhere for the same purpose. They all grow best on damp soils and in a cool, damp atmosphere, and they are with few exceptions, poor and thin, generally failing, in polluted air.

Key to the species of Picea

1. Leaves similarly coloured on all surfaces — 2
   Leaves much whiter or bluer on under-surfaces — 23

2. Leaves green with minute stomatal lines on all surfaces — 3
   Leaves grey or bluish with prominent stomatal lines on all surfaces — 15

3. Leaves spreading all round shoot — 4
   Leaves pectinate, or well parted, beneath the shoot — 8

4. Leaves <1 cm long; shoot very pubescent, and smooth, pale brown — *orientalis*
   Leaves 1·5–4 cm long, shoot glabrous, strongly grooved or ribbed — 5

5. Shoot orange; side-shoots wanting — *abies virgata*
   Shoot shining white or cream; side shoots present — 6

6. Leaves thick, rigid, sharply spined, 1·5–2 cm; bud shining chestnut — *polita*
   Leaves slender, flexible 3–4 cm long — 7

7. Shoot stout (4–5 mm); bud whitish not resinous, leaves densely set, 1·5 mm broad; shoots spreading — *schrenkiana*
   Shoot not stout (2–3 mm); bud red-brown, resinous; leaves sparsely set 1 mm broad; side shoots long-pendulous — *smithiana*

8. Leaves spreading or depressed — 9
   Leaves curved strongly upwards from below, erect above shoot, bright yellow-green — *rubens*

9. Leaves depressed below shoot — 10
   Leaves spreading perpendicular at side of shoot; forward on top — 12

10. No long, keeled scales at base of bud; leaves needle-slender, 0·5 mm broad; shoot white for two years; glabrous — *morrisonicola*
    Long keeled scales at base of bud; leaves less slender 0·8–1 mm broad, shoot buff or pale brown, pubescent — 11

11. 1–2 leaves spread widely from beneath each side-bud; leaves 1·2–1·5 cm slender, rather sparse — *obovata*
    No spreading leaves from side-buds; leaves 0·8–1 cm relatively thick and dense — *rubens*

12. Shoot shining cream-white; pulvini pale orange; bud shining chestnut-orange — *wilsonii*
    Shoot dark orange-brown or pubescent and brown, buff or orange — 13

13. Shoot plainly pubescent, buff to brown; leaf 0·5–0·8 cm — *orientalis*
    Shoot glabrous or minutely pubescent, leaf 1–2·5 cm — 14

14. Leaves glossy, to 1·5 cm; shoot pale orange — *maximowiczii*
Leaves sub-shiny, to 2·5 cm, shoot dark orange-brown — *abies*

15. Leaves fully pectinate beneath shoot, flat each side of it — 16
Leaves more or less all round shoot — 17

16. Leaves soft, upper ones forward along shoot, scent of camphor, upper side bloomed blue-white — *engelmannii glauca*
Leaves stiff, spined, upper ones rising from shoot, scent of sweet resin; upper side dark blue-green with 2 narrow lines blue-white — *koyamai*

17. Leaves slender, not rigid or stiff, pointing forwards — 18
Leaves not slender; stiff ± perpendicular to shoot — 20

18. Leaves very short, usually 1 cm, crowded all round shoot, shoot densely pubescent; bud basal scales with long points equal to bud — *mariana*
Leaves 2–2·5 cm, more above than below shoot, bud without long basal scales; shoot glabrous or nearly so — 19

19. Shoot golden-buff to white, leaves 2·0 cm, upper ones well forward — *engelmannii*
Shoot pale red-brown; leaves to 2·5 cm, rising from above shoot — *hurstii*

20. Leaves upswept from beneath shoot; upper ones usually erect; bud scale-tips straight or close — 21
Leaves spread below shoot; perpendicular or forward; bud scales often rolled outwards at tips — 22

21. Shoot white to pink-buff; all shoots glabrous; leaves 1·2–1·3 cm — *glauca*
Shoot pale orange to dark orange; side-shoots pubescent; leaves 1·5–2 cm — *koyamai*

22. Bud with long, pointed scales around base; shoot always glabrous, leaves beneath shoots forward; upper surface of leaves lined blue-white or bloomed white, blue-white etc. — *pungens* (and varieties)
Bud without long, basal scales; pulvini and ribs often finely pubescent; leaves beneath shoot partly backwards; leaves dull grey banded — *asperata*

23. Leaves spread all round shoot — 24
Leaves parted or pectinate beneath shoot — 29

24. Shoot densely pubescent — 25
Shoot glabrous or with fine, scattered pubescence — 26

25. Leaf 2–3·5 cm, slender, flat, curved away from shoot; side-shoots long-pendulous — *breweriana*
Leaf 1–1·5 cm not very slender, quadrangular, straight; side-shoots spreading, short — *mariana*

26. Leaves flat, spread evenly around shoot, all forward; shoot arched, side shoots pendulous — *spinulosa*
Leaves quadrangular, crowded above or curving to above shoot, few below, shoots not pendulous — 27

27. Leaf dark green above, without stomatal lines — *bicolor*
Leaf grey-green or bluish above from stomatal lines — 28

28. Shoot pale red-brown; leaf 2–2·5 cm — *hurstii*
Shoot buff or pale orange; leaf 1·5 cm — *glauca albertiana*

29. Leaves narrowly parted beneath shoot pressed down on and below shoot — 30
Leaves below shoot fully pectinate or swept up — 32

30. Pulvini forward or perpendicular; leaves bright green above, without stomata; brilliant white beneath; bud orange — *brachytyla*
Pulvini spread backwards; leaves dull green or lined grey above; white or grey beneath; bud purple-brown — 31

31. Leaves lined grey or blue above, white banded beneath, shoot sparsely pubescent (crown open; bark grey with few dark fissures) — *likiangensis*
Leaves dark green above; greyish banded beneath; shoot ± densely pubescent; (crown dense, branch ends vertical; bark orange-brown, flaking) — *likiangensis purpurea*

32. Leaves quadrangular in cross-section — 33
Leaves very flat in cross-section — 35

33. Bud with long-pointed, keeled basal scales; shoot bright orange, densely pubescent; lower leaves spreading; upper very forwards — *glehnii*
Bud without long-pointed free basal scales; shoot with minute or scattered pubescence; lower leaves often strongly upswept, upper ± vertical — 34

34. Leaves short (1 cm) thick, very blunt; shoot pale orange-brown — *montigena*
Leaves 1·5–2 cm, short-spined; shoot white or buff — *bicolor*

35. Leaves hard, stiff, sharply spined; upper leaves flat along shoot — *sitchensis*
Leaves pliant, round-ended — 36

36. Shoot shining white or buff; glabrous, leaf strongly keeled, straight — *jezoensis*
Shoot dull pinkish; pubescent; leaf flat upper surface, curved outwards or upwards — *omorika*

Picea abies (L.) Karsten. Norway spruce

The Alps, Balkan Mountains and Carpathians, north to Northern Scandinavia and merging into *Picea obovata* in Northern Russia. Introduced probably around 1500. Common everywhere, as a forest tree, shelter-belt and garden tree. Many grow in small gardens in the most unsuitable places, having done their time as Christmas trees, and some of these thrive surprisingly in city suburbs.

Bark. Young trees and trees in plantations until about 50 years old, deep copper-brown or rich red-brown, with pale, fine shreds rubbing off. Old trees, especially where exposed, dark purple, grey with algae in places, with shallow, rounded scales lifting away.

Crown. Narrowly conic, only the oldest trees deviating from this shape and becoming broadly columnar or, if bearing some massive limbs, irregular. Variations in aspect and density arise from the well-marked and quite common "comb" form with level branches ascending at the tips and hung with dense short curtains of shoots but far enough apart for daylight to show between the branches. The normal tree is more of the "brush" type with a plume of spreading shoots giving a crown of even density. Old trees become very thin in the crown, usually with straggling long pendulous shoots. A few trees have layered branches around them.

Foliage. Shoot, dull orange-brown above, golden-brown beneath, finely grooved and usually glabrous; the uncommon variably pale-brown-pubescent trees are probably from the eastern end of the range.

Terminal Buds. Surrounded by short, vertical leaves; dark red-brown; basal scales strongly keeled but not long-pointed; bud ovoid, shiny or purplish with resin.

Leaves. Pectinate beneath, or slightly radiating on strong shoots, laterals slightly forward, upper leaves dense and forward strongly, all hard, rigid, sub-shiny dark green, quadrangular, all surfaces the same colour with faint stomatal lines, 1–1·5–2 cm long, short-spined.

Flowers and Cone. Male flowers not very frequent and confined to old trees, globular, beneath and terminally on minor shoots, shedding pollen in the second week of May. Female flowers spread over the crowns of older trees but confined to the topmost shoots of young vigorous trees; open pinkish-red in early May, one week to ten days before the same tree sheds pollen. Cones cylindrical, tapering towards the tip, slightly curved, 15–20 cm long, with leathery scales; pendulous at shoot-tips.

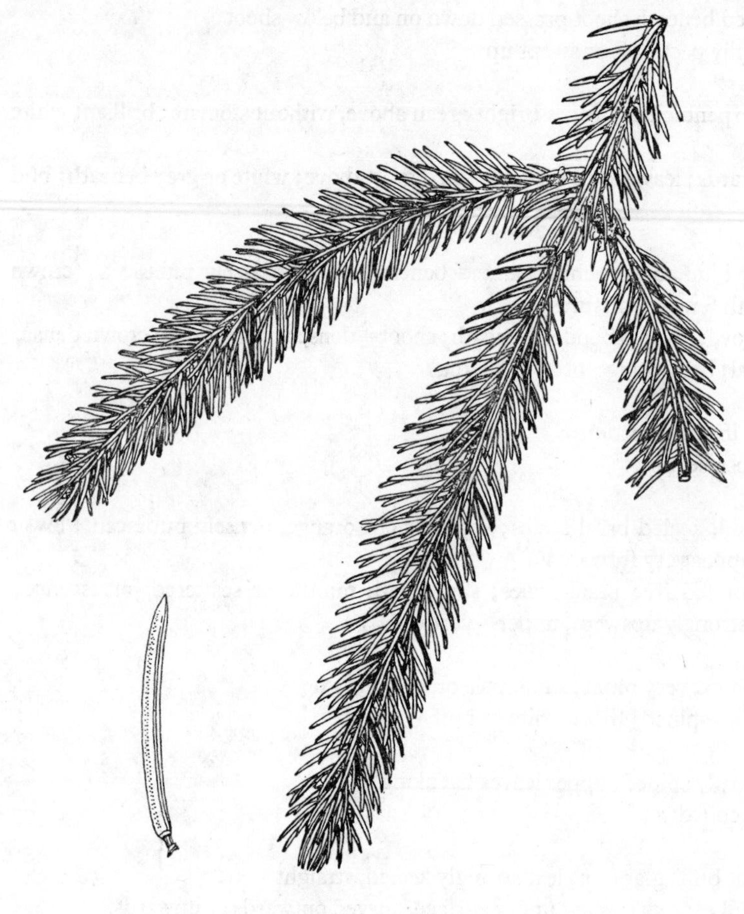

Picea abies

Fig. 109
Foliage of *Picea abies*, Norway spruce. The leaf (×2) is sub-shiny deep green on all four faces.

GROWTH. Although growth is rapid at first with 3-feet shoots common on young trees, and is sustained well through middle age, in girth as well as in height, it falls off rapidly after some 60 years. Old trees have small boles—anything over 10 feet in girth is quite unusual—and are growing extremely slowly. No very old trees are known and the extreme age would seem to be below 200 years. None of the eleven trees given by Elwes ahd Henry is now known, although two had survived until 1956. The oldest known dated trees were planted in 1820 (Arley Castle) and 1829 (Westonbirt) but no tree at either place is of any great size. Even more remarkable is the failure of the trees recorded as recently as 1931 to survive. Only five can be found, and two of these are doubtfully the same trees, among the 40 trees then given, although every estate except one has been visited. Good, sustained growth has been shown by trees at Invertrossachs, where the best at 60 years of age was 121ft × 6ft 0in in 1953, and at High Force, Durham, also 60 years old, in 1958, when the best was 123ft × 7ft 8in.

SPECIMENS. The huge tree at Studley Royal was found by the Hon. Maynard Greville, to measure 156ft × 14ft 2in in 1956 but it was gone before 1966. It was 140ft × 12ft 10in in 1905 and 150ft × 14ft 1in in 1931, so it had virtually ceased to grow for 26 years at least. Some fine trees, to 142ft × 14ft were at Inveraray in 1954 but have been blown down many years now.

The largest trees now are: Dunkeld, above the River Tay, 131ft × 9ft 10in (1970); and Kennel Bank, 115ft × 12ft 8in (1962); Strathallan, 138ft × 10ft 4in (1962); Petworth House, 135ft × 8ft 9in (1961); Glenlee, 134ft × 8ft 9in and 121ft × 11ft 7in (1970); Fonthill, 138ft × 7ft 6in (1965); Dupplin Castle, 111ft × 12ft 7in (1970); Eridge Park, 130ft × 10ft 9in

(1957); Durris Ho., 138ft×9ft 6in (1970); Abercairny, 128ft×11ft 5in (1962); Raehills, 128ft×11ft 7in (1970); Fairburn, 111ft×12ft 9in (1970); Moncrieffe House, 98ft× 13ft 1in (layered) (1956); Castle Leod, 94ft×12ft 2in (1966); Curraghmore, 103ft×12ft 3in (1968); Springkell, 106ft× 13ft 9in; 116ft×11ft 7in (1966); Crwys Morchard, 113ft× 11ft 7in (1959); Blairquhan, planted 1830, 108ft×11ft 2in (1970); Bicton, 123ft×9ft 6in (1968); Rossie Priory, very narrow, rather pendulous, 131ft×7ft 7in (1970).

Among the smaller trees the finest specimens are: a fine tree by Dunkeld Cathedral, 113ft×9ft 0in (1970); one of a group in a deep valley at Trebartha, 125ft×9ft 2in (1959); a splendid tree at Lowther Castle, 105ft×10ft 0in (1967); and a densely crowned vigorous tree at Dropmore, 87ft×6ft 11in (1961); 95ft×7ft 11in (1970).

cv. Aurea (England, 1838). The trees seen lose the yellow colour at about midsummer and become a dull green. The yellow new growth is almost white in some trees which might be cv. Argenteospica but the whitest, at Vernon Holme, was planted as 'Aurea'. The leaves are short and the shoots slender but the tree is otherwise like the type.

Vernon Holme, planted 1908, 61ft×4ft 10in (1961); Little Hall, 45ft×2ft 2in (1961); Busbridge Hall, 43ft×3ft 0in (1963); Chiltley Place, 45ft×3ft 6in (1961); Nymans, 72ft×4ft 11in (1957); Hergest Croft, 60ft×4ft 6in (1961); Ballimore, 60ft×4ft 4in (1969); Westonbirt, 90ft×5ft 5in (1969). This last tree has grown very fast. It was 27 feet tall in 1921, 53ft×2ft 10in in 1931 and 85ft×4ft 10in in 1958.

cv. Laxa. Leaves very fine and short, bright green, pressed down on and below the shoot as in *P. obovata* and a single leaf at each bud projecting widely and curved forwards. Since the buds are numerous and regularly spaced, these leaves give the foliage a curious aspect but it is a dull, thin tree.

Kew Royal Botanic Gardens, 38ft×2ft 4in; 37ft×1ft 11in (1969).

cv. Pendula Narrow crown of rather pendulous, slender branches. Rossie Priory, 131ft×7ft 7in (1970); West Dean, 118ft×9ft 4in (1971).

cv. Tuberculata (Kerkrade, Holland, ca. 1860.) A young, very vigorous tree at Bedgebury is of this form, perhaps of spontaneous origin. Planted in 1926, it is 64ft×8ft 7in (1969). Heavy, upcurved lower branches arise from disproportionately large swellings almost covering the bole. It is not recorded that it was planted as of this form, but Mr. Dallimore collected widely for Bedgebury. None other has been seen.

cv. Virgata (pre-1854.) A vigorous form with a strong straight stem and sparse branches themselves carrying very few shoots. The shoots are stout, long, unbranched, light orange, turning orange-brown, and bear leaves all round, spreading radially, curved slightly forward, stiff 2–2·5 cm, long, bright shiny green. The crown is thus very open and gaunt and the few minor shoots are pendulous.

Leonardslee, 70ft×4ft 0in and ca. 65ft×4ft (1969); Borde Hill, 68ft×4ft 2in (1968); Hergest Croft, 50ft×2ft 8in (1961); Abbeyleix, 55ft×3ft 5in (1968).

General. The Norway spruce has always been, since the eighteenth century, a popular forest tree on private estates. It had been of rather minor importance in Commission forests until recently, but now with early returns of good pulping timber a powerful economic factor, the steady growth and high yield make this species attractive. Sitka spruce is preferred for its greater yield, but there are many inland districts and frost-susceptible areas where Norway spruce will establish itself rapidly and Sitka will hardly do so at all. Many sites which might earlier have been planted with Japanese larch or Douglas fir are now planted with Norway spruce. The Christmas tree trade handles vast numbers of small plants and some thinning and felling-tops annually. Young trees grown for this purpose are commonly seen, sometimes as a cash-crop in fire-rides or elsewhere where large trees are not wanted, as under transmission lines.

Picea asperata Masters. Chinese spruce; Dragon spruce.

West China. Several varieties occur in different parts of the wide range and were introduced under specific names between 1908 and 1911. (*P. aurantiaca*, *P. heterolepis*, *P. meyeri*, *P. notabilis*, *P. ponderosa*, *P. retroflexa*.) There are very minor and inconsistent differences, and these are usually treated as varieties. In var. *ponderosa* the distinction given amounts to one quarter of an inch in the upper limit of the length of cone! In others the descriptions given are the same but in different words, or the feature distinguished tends not to be described in the other forms. Little importance is attached here to any of this. Commonly found in collections everywhere except in Scotland where rare. Hardly ever seen in ordinary gardens but a few noted.

Bark. Purplish at base, elsewhere dark chocolate brown loosely hung with long papery dark reddish-brown flakes; which may be pale grey in early stages.

Crown. Rather broadly conic but relatively more narrow with age as growth in height becomes more rapid. Branches level, from quite large protuberances on the bole in lower crown, then upturned. Rather dense, with narrow, dense systems projecting from the upper crown.

Foliage. Shoot stout, grooved into distinct plates, pink-brown or orange-brown above, yellowish below often finely pubescent, especially on the pulvini.

Bud. Yellow-brown, pink-purple tinged, and white resin at base, 1 cm, conic; pale scales at tip may open out in a rosette. Leaves radiating all round the shoot but rather more densely above it, where they lean slightly forward, than below where they bend backwards; stout, slightly curved in some trees, rigid and abruptly short, yellow-spined; quadrangular; dark bluish-green with some 1–3 stomatal lines on each surface; 1·5 cm–2 cm.

Flowers and Cone. Male flowers densely borne on most

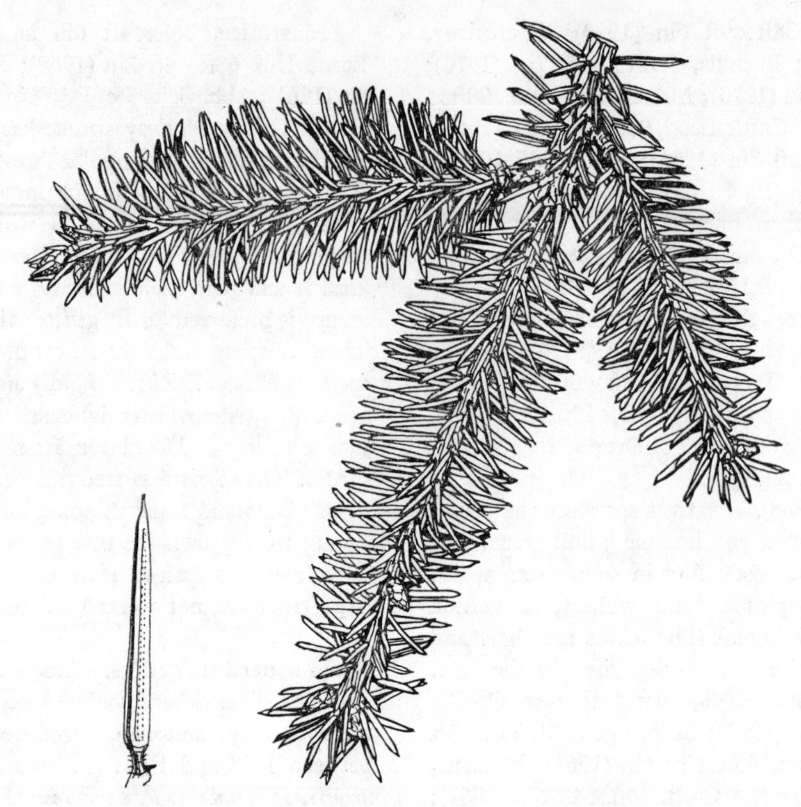

Picea asperata

Fig. 110
Foliage of *Picea asperata*, Dragon spruce, a tree with a wide range on the mountains in China and thus variable in foliage. The spined, hard leaves radiate from a grooved pink, orange or brown shoot, and have short hairs on the pulvinus. (Below ×2).

trees above 30 feet tall, globular, beneath new shoots, shedding pollen during the latter half of April. Female flowers on strong shoots near the ends of branches down to quite low in the crown, bright red. Cones cylindric, shortly tapered to a rounded end, 9–13 cm long, to 6 cm across when dry, dull brown.

GROWTH. For many years many trees, as at Bedgebury, have been bushy and very slow, due to damage by late spring frosts. Once, however, above 5 or 6 feet, growth is usually steady and sometimes rapid. The tallest trees are still growing quite rapidly and most would seem to be all set to make big trees.

SPECIMENS. The many specimens dating from between 1914 and 1919 and many others at Wakehurst Place and Bicton for example, are probably all original trees from Wilson's seed of 1910. Certainly those at Abbotswood are. Some of those given in the 1932 report have made very little growth as can be seen from Table 46.

TABLE 46. SPECIMEN TREES OF PICEA ASPERATA

Locality	*Date Planted*	*Dimensions*	
Vernon Holme	1914	21′ × 5″ (1931)	39′ × 2′ 7″ (1961)
Hergest Croft	1916	23′ (1931)	59′ × 3′ 9″ (1961)
Abbotswood	1916		46′ × 2′ 2″ (1966)
Crarae	1914	9′ (1931)	40′ × 2′ 7″ (1969)
Speech House	1916		36′ × 2′ 5″ (1959)
Birr Castle	1914		49′ × 4′ 0″ (1966)
Borde Hill		13′ (1931)	49′ × 2′ 6″ (1958)

Locality	*Date Planted*			*Dimensions*
Powerscourt				61′ × 4′ 2″ (1966)
Bicton				58′ × 3′ 6″ (1968)
Bicton				50′ × 4′ 2″ (1968)
Stourhead	1919	5′	(1931)	35′ × 2′ 1″ (1957)
Wakehurst Place	1919	8′	(1931)	45′ × 4′ 1″ (1969)
Wakehurst Place	1921	10′	(1931)	45′ × 3′ 8″ (1964)
Stanage Park				60′ × 3′ 3″ (1970)
Fenagh House	1921	13′	(1931)	50′ × 3′ 6″ (1968)
Westonbirt	1923	13′ × 6″	(1931)	52′ × 2′ 6″ (1967)
Westonbirt	1929			44′ × 4′ 2″ (1968)
Westonbirt (Rock 15042)	1932			28′ × 2′ 3″ (1968)
Westonbirt	1936			51′ × 4′ 0″ (1968)
Bedgebury	1925			51′ × 3′ 9″ (1970)
Avondale				42′ × 3′ 6″ (1968)
Blairquhan				44′ × 3′ 8″ (1970)
Eastnor Castle				64′ × 4′ 10″ (1970)
Curraghmore				40′ × 3′ 11″ (1968)

var. heterolepis (Rehder and Wilson) Cheng ex Rehder. Introduced in 1910. The differences are given as shoot reddish or yellow-brown (as in many trees) leaves bluish green (as in most trees of this species) and lower cone scales deeply emarginate. One has been identified at Wakehurst Place, 58ft × 4ft 0in (1964).

var. notabilis (Rehder and Wilson.) Distinguished by the cone-scales "narrowed towards the apex" or "gradually narrowed towards the apex or abruptly contracted at the top". These descriptions might be applied to the cones of many of the trees at Westonbirt at least, and many trees in the above list may be of this variety. Trees labelled thus are at: Dawyck, planted 1918, 52ft × 2ft 9in; 43ft × 2ft 2in (1961); Borde Hill, specimen W4068, 60ft × 3ft 5in (1968); Abbotswood, planted 1916, 45ft × 3ft 2in (1966).

var. retroflexa (Masters). Introduced in 1911. Distinguished by yellow shoots, grey flaking bark and "leaves acuminate and pungent" as opposed to "stiff and prickly". Trees so labelled are at Fenagh House, planted 1921, 29ft × 2ft 2in (1966); Dawyck, 24ft × 2ft 3in (1961); Borde Hill, 44ft × 3ft 0in (1968); and Stanage Park, 30ft × 2ft 4in (1970).

RECOGNITION. The whole tree can be distinguished by the branching and the coarsely flaking, dark bark, papery flakes often hanging under the branches. The foliage, being radial and stiffly pungent is like that of *P. polita*, but differs in the blue-green colour and the papery pale buds, and like *P. pungens*, in which buds on the main shoots have long free scales around the base, and the shoots are glabrous.

(No specimens purporting to be var. *aurantiaca* have been found.)

Picea bicolor (Maximowicz) Mayr. Alcock's spruce

Central Japan. Introduced in 1861. Infrequent. In some collections and very few other large gardens in all parts of the British Isles, but rare in East Anglia and North and West Scotland.

BARK. Dark pinkish-brown, finely cracked into square plates between small vertical fissures, roughened by the plates curling away.

CROWN. Characteristic in its broadly conic crown, obtusely topped at times, composed of strong branches from ground level where possible, straight and gently ascending all the way. They are numerous but far enough apart for the dense plumes of foliage at their ends to be separated as bushy spikes. In the upper crown the branches curve upwards. The whole crown is usually fairly dense from the outside and open inside.

FOLIAGE. Shoot white, sometimes buff or pale orange-brown, grooved into smooth plates, occasionally pubescent. Second year orange-brown, third year purple-grey. Leaves pectinate below curved forwards; those above lying slightly forward of erect so that all are somewhat forward-pointing; 1·5 cm quadrangular, blue-green with faint stomatal lines on the upper surfaces, two broad white bands beneath.

CONES. Large, cylindric, slightly tapered, 10-11 cm long, 5 cm across when dry; pink-brown.

GROWTH. In the 1932 report, three of the six young specimens had grown less than one foot a year and the other three only a little more than this. The subsequent growth of four of these six, which includes all three of the faster, trees has put them well below an average of one foot per year in height. Only one has an average increase in girth exceeding one inch per year. Of the three older trees remeasured one has grown 10 feet in 40 years and another 11 feet in 36 years, but the third has added 37 feet in 27 years. It can be said that this tree starts slowly and continues slowly, with an occasional tree achieving a moderate growth.

RECOGNITION. This species resembles closely *P. jezoensis.* It is distinguished mainly by the quadrangular leaves (flat in *P. jezoensis*), the long, ascending branches and projecting branch-ends and also by the brown more scaly bark. *P. glehnii* is also similar, but has orange, densely pubescent shoots.

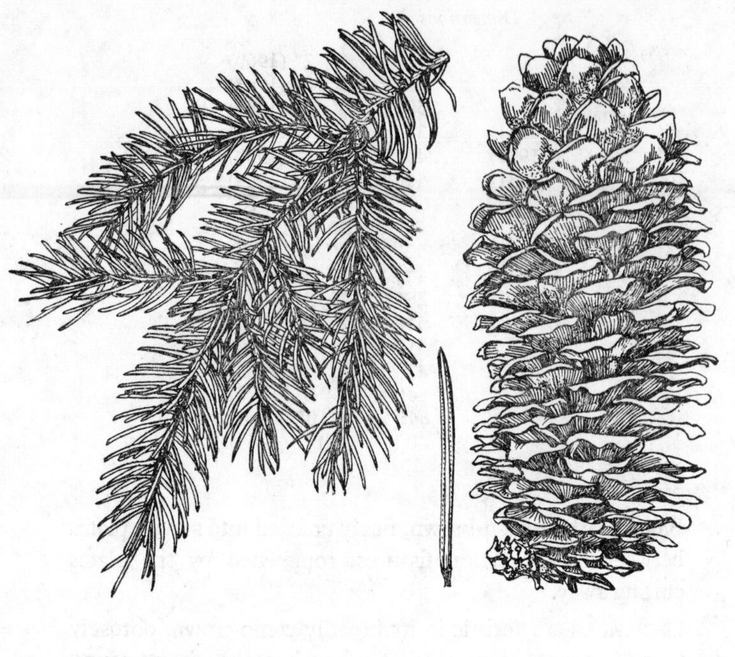

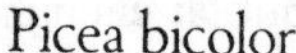

Fig. 111
Foliage, cone and ($\times 2\frac{2}{3}$) single leaf of *Picea bicolor* from Japan. The foliage resembles that of *P. jezoensis* but the leaves are rhombic in cross-section, although the two under surfaces have a blue-white band.

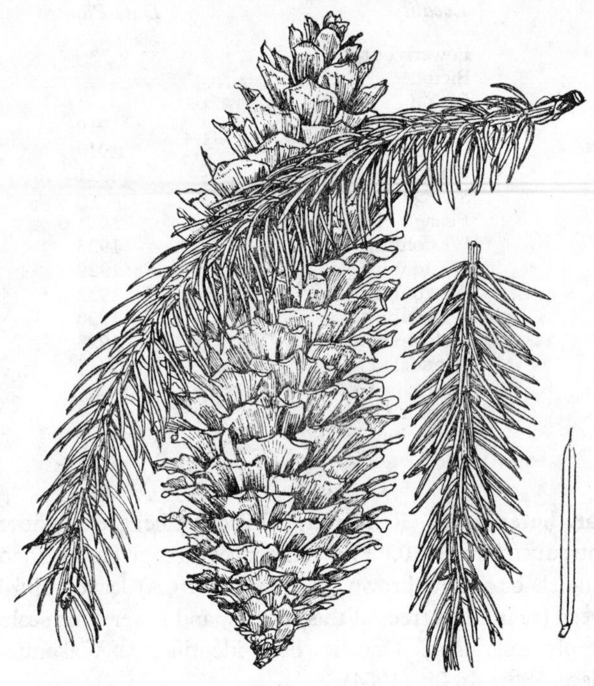

Fig. 112
Cone, strong, arched shoot and weak hanging shoot of *Picea brachytyla*. The bright, blue-white stomatal bands on the underside of the leaf (right $\times 1\frac{1}{3}$) often unite to obscure the midrib.

SPECIMENS. Bicton, 74ft×7ft 6in (1968); Warnham Court, 72ft×5ft 2in (1957); Tilgate, 58ft×4ft 0in (1961); Dunkeld Cathedral, 50ft×4ft 0in (1970); Moncrieffe House, 58ft×5ft 10in (1956); Westonbirt, (Specimen Avenue), 55ft×4ft 3in (1968); (Willesley Drive), 50ft×4ft 10in (1968); Borde Hill (Warren), 50ft×4ft 0in (1957); (Pinetum) 47ft×3ft 11in (1970); Avondale, 45ft×5ft 5in (1968); Crarae, 45ft ×4ft 6in (1969); Scone Palace, 52ft×6ft 0in (1970).

var. acicularis Shirasawa and Koyama. Mount Shirane, Central Japan. Longer, bluer, more incurved leaves and entire, smooth cone-scales distinguish this very rare variety. The tree at Borde Hill (Gore's Wood), has a flaking papery bark like *P. asperata*. It is 33ft×2ft 4in (1968).

var. reflexa Shirasawa and Koyama. Mount Shirane, Central Japan. Distinguished by the reflexed tips to the cone-scales. The only trees seen, planted as this variety are at Borde Hill (Gore's Wood). These have a smooth bark and the best is 44ft×3ft 0in (1968). Similar cones with sharply recurved scales (when dry) are borne by several normal-barked trees of this species.

Picea brachytyla (Franchet) Pritzel. Sargent spruce.

Western Hupeh and Western Szechuan, China. Introduced in 1901. Infrequent but in most collections and occasionally in large gardens. One in a churchyard in Shropshire.

BARK. Young trees smooth pinkish-grey, heavily stippled with white resinous spots. Older trees nearly all clean pale grey with some reddish-brown, cracked into small shallow squares or rounded scales 5–8 cm across. Some are purplish-grey and one at Borde Hill is orange-pink, and shredding finely, very like that of *P. abies*.

CROWN. Rather broadly conic, open inside, pendulous shoots on the outside.

FOLIAGE. Shoot pure white, sometimes pale buff, often arched, rather stout, grooved; second year pale orange-brown.

BUD. Ovoid, light chestnut, shiny with resin.

LEAVES. Most distinctive in arrangement and colour beneath; short 1·2–1·6 cm; broad at base. They are crowded stiffly forward flat on the shoot and bent below it to either side, pectinate and perpendicular beneath but with a "V" between the ranks, not flat-pectinate; flat in cross-section but ridged above or convex; shortly pointed; fresh bright green above at first, then dark very matt green; brilliantly white or bluish white beneath often quite obscuring the midrib and right to the edge. (Only *P. spinulosa* among the spruces shares this feature.)

CONE. Cylindric, tapered at each end, slightly oblique at base, on a short slender stalk; sometimes slightly curved, 10–15 cm long, 5 cm across when dry, 3 cm closed, dark purplish brown with a purple band across each scale; margins rounded, variably waved and slightly toothed, slightly reflexed as it matures, fully reflexed when dry.

GROWTH. A remarkably vigorous tree, often after a rather slow start. The biggest trees are still growing very fast. Since the 1931 measurements, the smallest increment in height is 31 feet in 27 years and the largest 65 feet in 40 years. In girth, increments can be found only for the four whose girth was given in the 1932 Report and these vary from 20in in 26 years to 75in in 37 years. At Westonbirt one tree has added in the 13 years from 1956 to 1969, 26 feet in height, despite the loss of its leader in 1967, and 19 inches in girth; at Stourhead in the same period 28 feet and 19 inches were added.

SPECIMENS. Although introduced in 1901, all the earliest known planting dates, in collections which received Wilson's seed, range from 1912 to 1920 and show that they belong to the second or third seed lots sent in 1908 and 1910. The trees at Werrington Park are known to be from Wilson's seed but the year of planting is not known. The best trees are given in Table 47.

RECOGNITION. This species is normally very distinctive with its white shoot and the leaves heavily silvered beneath and bent down each side of the shoot. The nearest resemblance is to *P. spinulosa*, in which the slender-pointed leaves are much narrower and arise all round the shoot. There may be some resemblance to *P. jezoensis*, and there are young trees at Vivod Forest Plots which are almost intermediate, but in general the leaves of *P. jezoensis* rise from the shoot, are longer, less tapered and the white beneath is confined to two bands. The crowns of the two species are widely different.

TABLE 47. THE BEST TREES OF PICEA BRACHYTYLA

Location	*Date*	*Dimensions*
Westonbirt (Morley Ride)	1933	84′ × 5′ 7″ (1969)
Westonbirt (Sand Earth)	1933	66′ × 4′ 5″ (1969)
Hergest Croft	1912	79′ × 6′ 2″ (1969)
Bicton	1920	73′ × 5′ 4″ (1968)
Bicton	1920	72′ × 5′ 4″ (1968)
Bicton	1918	66′ × 6′ 0″ (1968)
Wakehurst Place	1914	67′ × 7′ 8″ (1971)
Wakehurst (Valley)		65′ × 3′ 10″ (1968)
Wakehurst Place	1915	59′ × 5′ 6″ (1964)
Stourhead		84′ × 5′ 5″ (1970)
Borde Hill (Gores Wood)		60′ × 3′ 7″ (1968)
Albury Park		63′ × 4′ 9″ (1968)
Stanage Park		66′ × 6′ 1″ (1970)
Stanage Park	1923	62′ × 6′ 10″ (1970)
Werrington Park		62′ × 5′ 7″ (1969)
Linton Park	1931	62′ × 4′ 3″ (1970)
Tregrehan		64′ × 7′ 1″ (1971)
Warnham Court		63′ × 5′ 7″ (1971)

Picea breweriana Watson. Brewer's weeping spruce

North West California and South West Oregon, in isolated areas grouped around the Siskiyou Mountains. Introduced in 1897 when a single plant was sent to Kew and grows there still, near the Pagoda. In 1904 and 1908 Mr. Balfour of Dawyck brought many plants and these are the first in gardens other than Kew. Uncommon but increasingly planted in gardens of all sizes.

BARK. Young trees, dull dark grey-pink, stippled by leaf-traces, with cracks appearing each side of the prominent branch scars. Older trees, dark purple-grey; chocolate brown curved cracks marking out small circular plates which are hard and curl away at the edges.

CROWN. In the open, rather squat, conic, becoming taller and proportionately less broad. In the shade fairly slender and conic. Shoots at the top curve up sharply around the leading shoot and compete strongly with it. Branches in upper crown of old trees curve upwards; those in the middle level and curve upwards at their tips only; those in the lower crown of the biggest trees descend. Foliage on long hanging shoots strung out below the branches, progressively longer towards the crown interior. Very dense in the open; thin in shade. Young seedling trees have thin open crowns of ascending, slender branches. These are very different from the tree in later life, and many who purchase young trees, but know only older trees, think that they have been sold another species. This may account for the number of young grafted trees seen. These are adult and pendulous in habit, but there are difficulties in having long pendulous shoots on a plant only 2 feet tall. They not only look ridiculous, but they are one sided and very slow growing and it is by no means certain that they will make good trees.

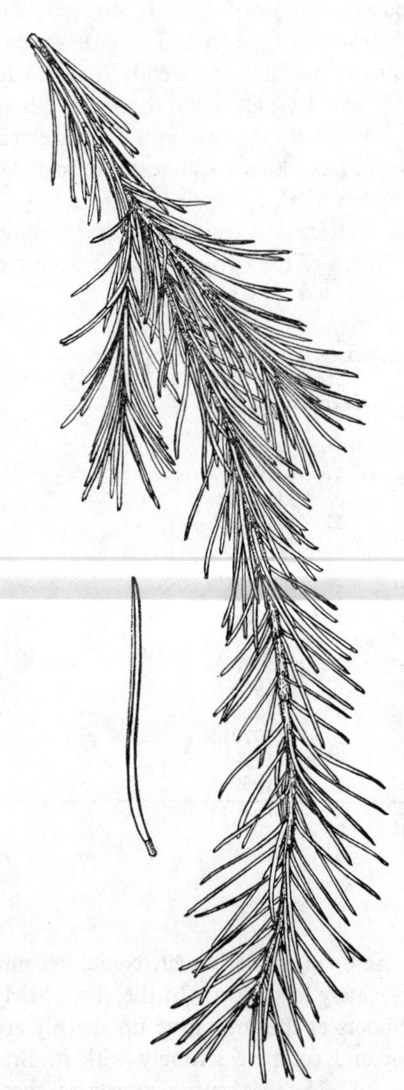

Fig. 113
Hanging shoot of *Picea breweriana*, Brewer's spruce, a spectacularly pendulous-foliaged tree. The flattened leaf (right ×1½) is slender and has narrow white bands on the lower surface.

FOLIAGE. Shoots slender, flexible, pink-brown, finely pubescent. Bud pale brown, very blunt with papery scales. Leaves all round the shoot, pointing forwards, slightly curved outwards; very slender to 3·5 cm long, subacute, flattened; upper surface shiny dark green at first, matt later. Lower surface with the narrow but bright white bands. From a distance the foliage looks nearly black.

FLOWERS AND CONE. Male flowers large, 1 cm, globular on ends of hanging shoots, shed pollen early in May. Female flowers cylindric, dark red, confined to topmost shoots. Cone 10–12×2·5 cm; slightly curved cylindric, long-tapered to base, abruptly to apex; scales light red-brown, flexible, incurved, rounded; some encrustations by resin.

GROWTH. This is a remarkably consistent tree in its growth, which is slow in height, but, in trees in the open, fairly rapid in girth. Of the 19 given in the 1932 Report, one has been cut and 16 sought and found. Of these, the original at Kew has grown very slowly in both dimensions. Of 9 of the others remeasured between 34 and 38 years after 1931, one has grown 22 feet, and 8 have all grown between 26 and 32 feet. Only four can be compared for increase in girth, and these added from 29 to 48 inches in from 33 to 37 years. There is a long period of very slow growth both as seedlings, which may take four years to exceed one foot in height, and when these are planted out. After another four years, the annual shoot may be only 5–6 inches and then not always straight upwards. Older trees are mostly now adding rather more than one foot a year, but the leading shoot may either be broken or lose dominance and takes a few years to recover.

SPECIMENS. The oldest and largest specimens are given in Table 48.

RECOGNITION. No extra notes should be necessary, but every so often a Brewer's spruce is reported 100 feet tall. These are all *Picea smithiana*, and, apart from the size difference, which is decreasing, and of no help in small trees, the flattened leaf with white bands beneath is distinct from the rounded (quadrangular) leaf of *P. smithiana* which is green on all sides, and is on a stout shiny cream-white shoot.

TABLE 48. THE OLDEST AND LARGEST PICEA BREWERIANA

Locality	*Date*	*Dimensions*	
Kew R.B.G.	1897	18′ 6″ × 1′ 5½″(1931)	36′ × 2′ 1″ (1963)
St. Clere	1907		37′ × 4′ 1″ (1969)
Dawyck	1908	14′ 3″ × 1′ 5″ (1931)	43′ × 3′ 10″ (1966)
Dawyck	1908		42′ × 3′ 5″ (1961)
Dawyck	1908		39′ × 2′ 10″ (1961)
Vernon Holme	1908	20′ × 1′ 9″ (1931)	48′ × 4′ 7″ (1965)
Edinburgh R.B.G.	1910		24′ × 2′ 2″ (1970)
Sheffield Park	1910		42′ × 3′ 9″ (1968)
Sheffield Park	1910		40′ × 3′ 9″ (1968)
Hergest Croft	1913		35′ × 4′ 7″ (1961)
Wakehurst Place	1915		46′ × 4′ 1″ (1970)
Woburn Abbey			39′ × 4′ 7″ (1970)
Woburn Abbey			36′ × 4′ 8″ (1970)
Leonardslee			44′ × 3′ 10″ (1969)
Exbury		9′ (1931)	39′ × 4′ 6″ (1968)
Wakehurst Place (Valley)			48′ × 3′ 6″ (1968)
Stanage Park			43′ × 3′ 7″ (1970)
Hergest Croft	1916		42′ × 3′ 8″ (1963)
Biel (ex Dawyck)			39′ × 2′ 9″ (1967)
Kilmacurragh			38′ × 6′ 0″ (1966)
Tongs Wood			44′ × 4′ 9″ (1968)
Blandsfort	1919	8′ (1931)	37′ × 3′ 5″ (1968)
Dropmore			37′ × 3′ 9″ (1970)
Castlewellan	1924	8′ (1931)	35′ × 5′ 2″ (1970)
Bedgebury	1926	3′ 3″ (1931)	37′ × 4′ 0″ (1970)
Headfort	1927	9′ 7½″ (1931)	31′ × 3′ 10″ (1966)
Headfort	1927		27′ × 3′ 0″ (1966)
Mount Usher	1928		28′ × 3′ 11″ (1966)
Powis Castle			32′ × 3′ 5″ (1970)
Westonbirt (Acer glade)	1935		39′ × 3′ 7″ (1969)
Blairquhan			41′ × 3′ 11″ (1970)

Picea engelmannii (Parry) Engelmann. Engelmann spruce

Rocky Mountains from Alberta and British Columbia, Washington and Oregon to Arizona and New Mexico. Introduced in 1864. Rare; in some collections in all four countries, frequently only as cv. 'Glauca'.

BARK. Red-brown with a pattern of curving raised strips, paler and peeling away vertically. Older trees cracked into hard square flakes, pinkish grey-fawn, smooth, with grey lenticels and pale vertical striae.

CROWN. Narrowly conical with densely set level branches.

FOLIAGE. Shoot whitish or pale golden-brown, deeply grooved; fine pubescence showing under a lens, dense on pulvini.

BUD. Small, ovoid-conic, pointed, red-brown and shiny.

LEAVES. All round strong shoots, pectinate below on side-shoots, pointing forwards, slender, slightly curved, 2 cm bluish green, 2 narrow white bands above, (sometimes a third along the midrib) 2 broader white bands beneath; rounded or pointed but soft to the touch. Crushed foliage said to be foetid but the strong scent, after the first sniff, is sweet and like menthol or camphor.

GROWTH AND SPECIMENS. There are few specimens, and of the five in the 1932 *Report* only two have been found. One has grown very slowly and one very fast after an evidently slow start. This latter, the finest specimen by far, is at Dawyck and was brought from America as a seedling in 1904 and put out in 1908. In 1931 it was 29ft×1ft 6in. A. Bruce Jackson gave it a height of 42 feet in 1944 but by 1966 it was 86ft×6ft 5in. A second tree beside it with the same history was 80ft×6ft 6in in 1966. In the south growth is much slower. The other tree from the *Report* was planted at Blackmoor in 1913. In 1931 it was 9 feet tall, and in 1957 it was only 28ft×1ft 7in. At Speech House, Forest of Dean two trees planted in 1916 were 41ft×2ft 1in and 38ft×2ft 1in in 1959. At Edinburgh Royal Botanic Garden, planted 1937, 33ft×2ft 0in (1970); Powis Castle, 47ft×3ft 6in (1970). One planted in about 1916 at Wakehurst Place, 52ft×3ft 0in (1970). At Blairquhan, 42ft×2ft 11in (1970); and Woburn Abbey, 43ft×3ft 10in (1970).

cv. Fendleri. (Kew pre-1912.) A rare form with leaves over 2·5 cm long, bluer and spread all round pendulous shoots.

cv. Glauca (Probably from the natural population; pre-1891.) A slender, very blue-grey tree with an orange, shredding bark and soft lax leaves crowded forwards above the shoot. A rather superior version of *P. pungens glauca*, but rarely seen.

Dawyck, planted 1908, 63ft×4ft 2in (1966); Gordon Castle, 52ft×4ft 4in (1970); Powerscourt, 66ft×4ft 4in (1966); Fairburn (pinetum), 103ft×4ft 5in (1970).

RECOGNITION. The type resembles *Picea glauca* and its varieties and has a similar aroma when crushed (and is very closely related to them). It differs from *P. glauca* in the minute pubescence on the shoot and from this and its varieties in the soft, forward pointing leaves not upswept; brown or orange bark and the toothed margin to the cone-scales. cv. Glauca is very like a good bluish-grey form of *P. pungens* but differs in the orange bark; the leaves not radiating all round all the shoots but lying forwards on the upper side and in their softness. It differs very much also not only in the aroma of the crushed foliage but in the fact that crushing can be done without injury to the hand.

Picea glauca (Moench) Voss. White spruce

Alaska to Labrador and south to Dakota, the Lake States and Massachusetts. Introduced in 1700. Rare and almost confined to a few collections. Sometimes seen in shelterbelts.
BARK. Pink-grey stippled vertically with white and developing shallow, curving cracks. Big trees have bark like *P. sitchensis*, purplish dark grey, shallowly cracked into rounded scales which curl away from the stem.
CROWN. Narrowly conic; the oldest trees with level branches, except near the top where they are ascending. Occasionally misshapen and broader.
FOLIAGE. Shoot stout, relative to the length of leaf, white beneath but may be pale pink-buff above, or buff all over, shining and glabrous. Pulvini pink.
BUD. Conspicuous pale chestnut-brown, smooth, shiny.
LEAVES. Arising all round the main shoots but all upswept, vertical and curved inwards or slightly forward-pointing, rather even in length, 12–13 mm, stiff, ending in a blunt spine, pale blue-green or grey-looking, under lens dark shiny green with two narrow white bands above and below. When crushed a mixed aroma is emitted which some find disagreeable but others find like black-currant syrup or slightly mouldy grapefruit.
CONE. Long-ovoid, tapering droplet-shaped, 5–6×1·2 cm soft coppery pink-brown, smooth convex rather large, round-ended scales.

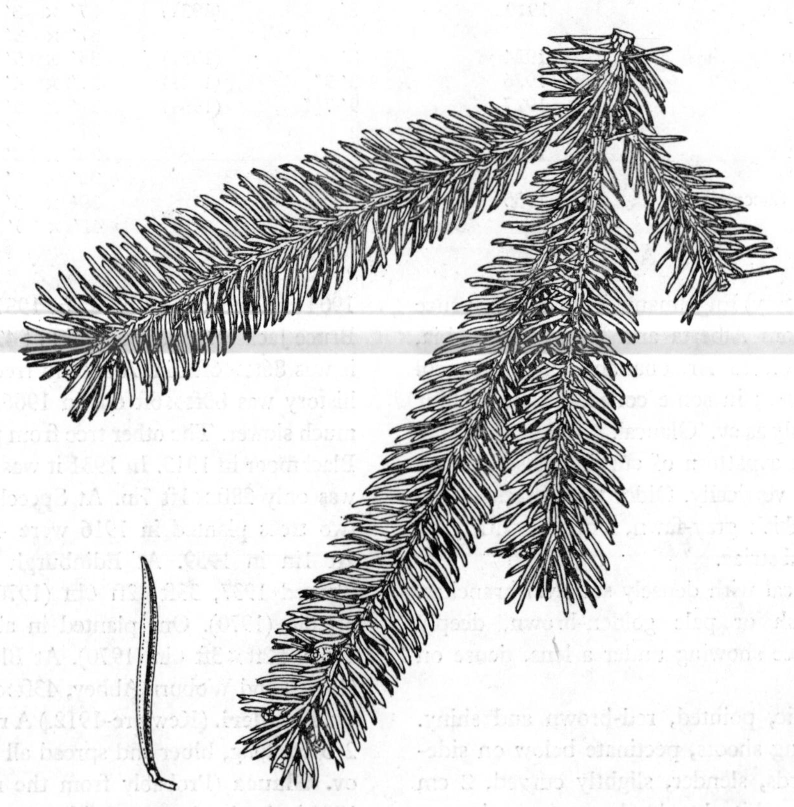

Picea glauca

Fig. 114
Foliage of *Picea glauca*, White spruce. The shoot is white or pink-buff and the pulvini are pink. The leaf (lower left ×2), stout and rhombic in cross-section, stands above the shoot.

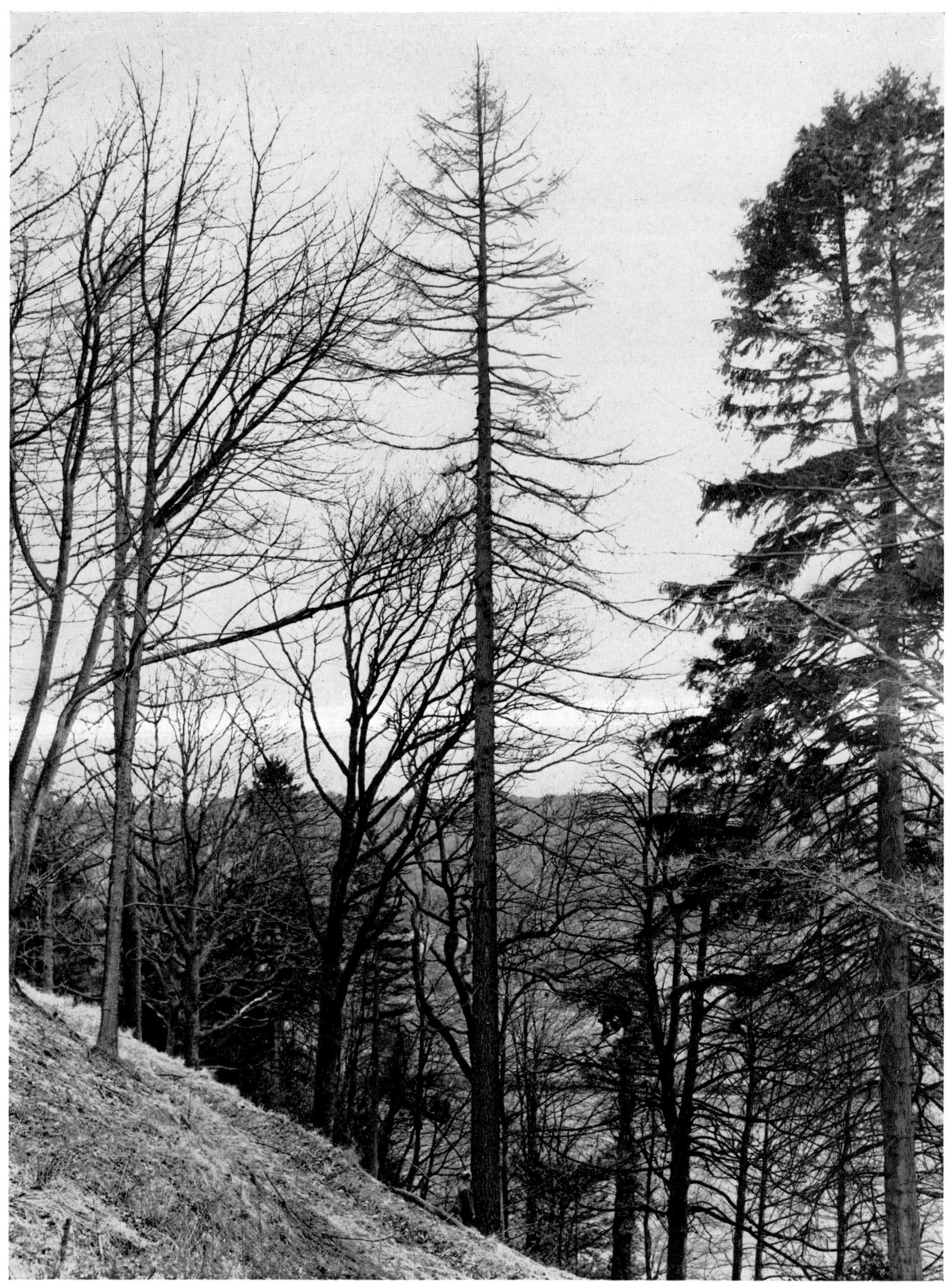

Plate 1.
Larix decidua. European larch. A young tree of outstandingly good form, at Grizedale Forest, Lancashire. D 4410

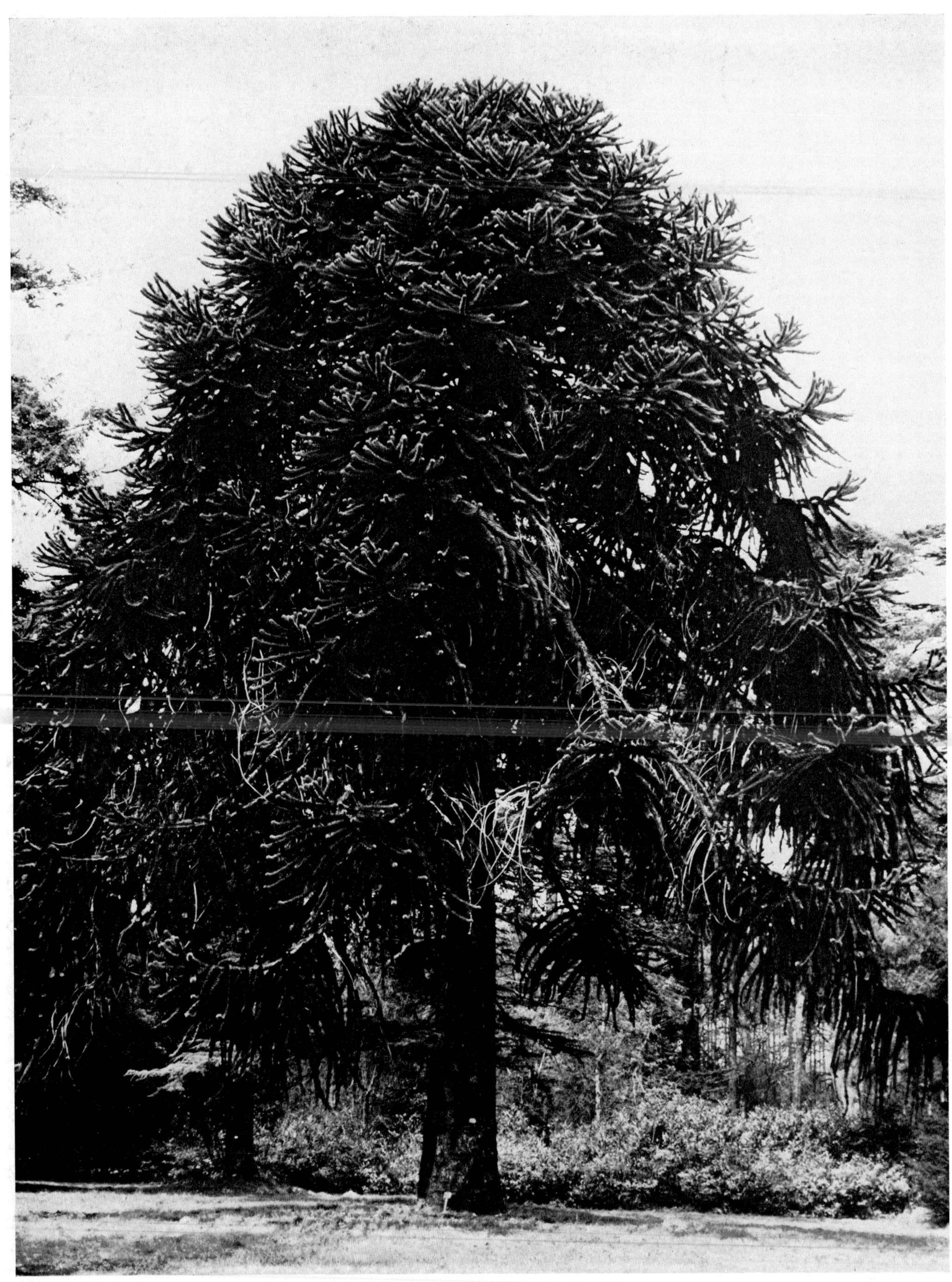

Plate 2.
Araucaria araucana. Chile pine. The specimen planted in 1840 by the drive at Dropmore, Bucks. It was 72ft × 10ft 5in in 1970 and among the largest in girth in the eastern side of the country. A 2658

Plate 3.
Calocedrus decurrens. Incense cedar. A line of typically narrow crowned trees at Eastnor Castle, Ledbury, Hereford. In Ireland and Scotland, crowns are much broader.

Plate 4.
Athrotaxis laxifolia. A Tasmanian tree of slow growth. The new shoots are pale yellow. This tree, at Bedgebury in Kent, is 44 years old and 23 feet tall.

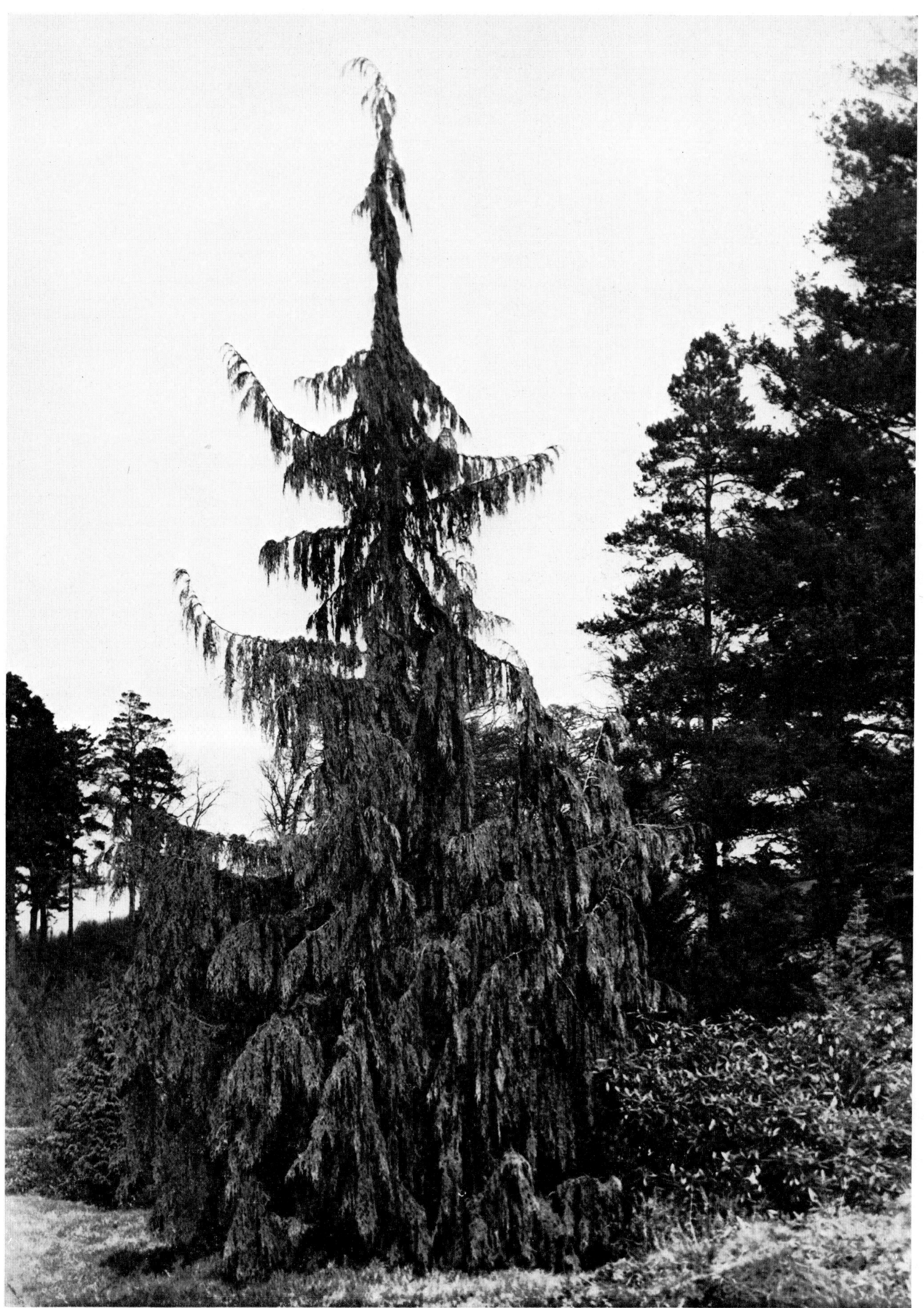

Plate 5.
Chamaecyparis nootkatensis. 'Pendula'. Weeping Nootka cypress. An imposing, if rather gaunt tree probably at its best when relatively young. This tree at Bedgebury was 30 years old when the picture was taken.

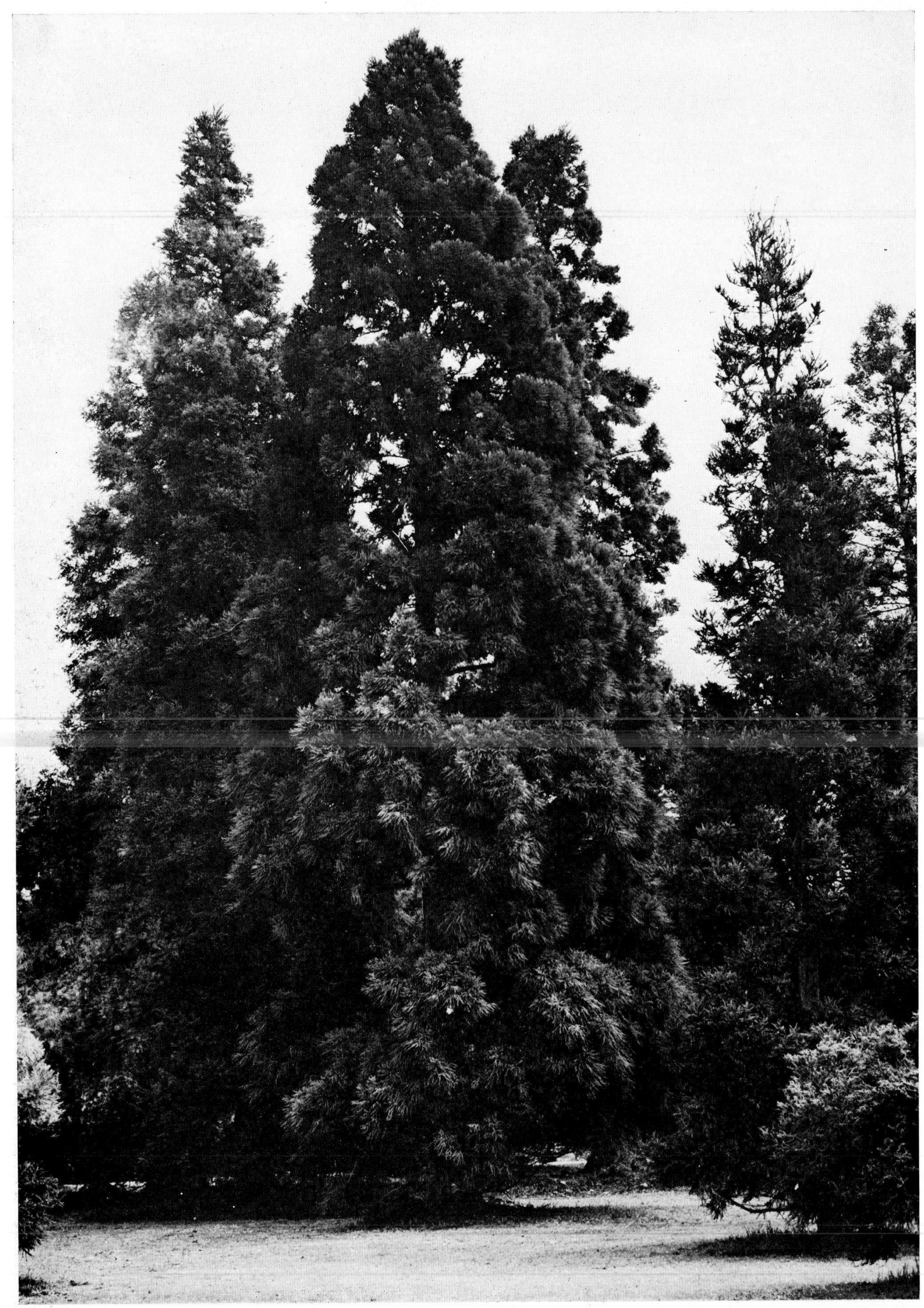

Plate 6.
Cryptomeria japonica. The Japanese 'Red Cedar' usually grows best in damp areas in the west and north, but this group, on a dry ridge at Bedgebury in Kent has grown well. Planted in 1925, the best trees in 1970 are 65ft × 6ft 8in and 58ft × 7ft 1in. C 4738

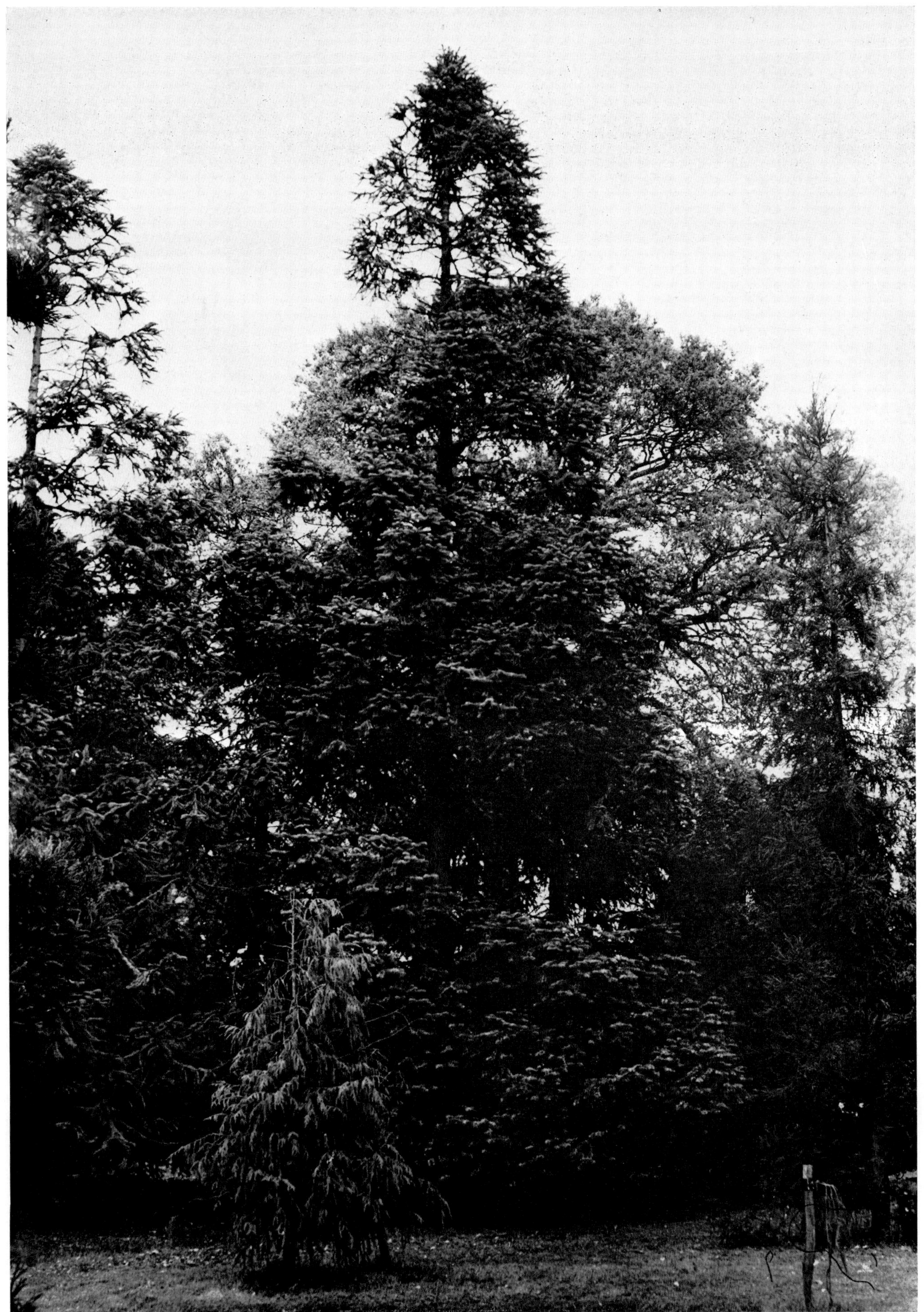

Plate 7.
Cunninghamia lanceolata. This Chinese species is more hardy than is often thought. The picture shows one of a group planted on a ridge at Bedgebury in 1925, which is now 50ft × 4ft 5in. In another group one is over 60ft. The orange-brown dead leaves are retained on the shoots for some years, contrasting with the exterior bright green foliage. The *Taiwania cryptomerioides* in front suffers annual frost-damage. C 4737

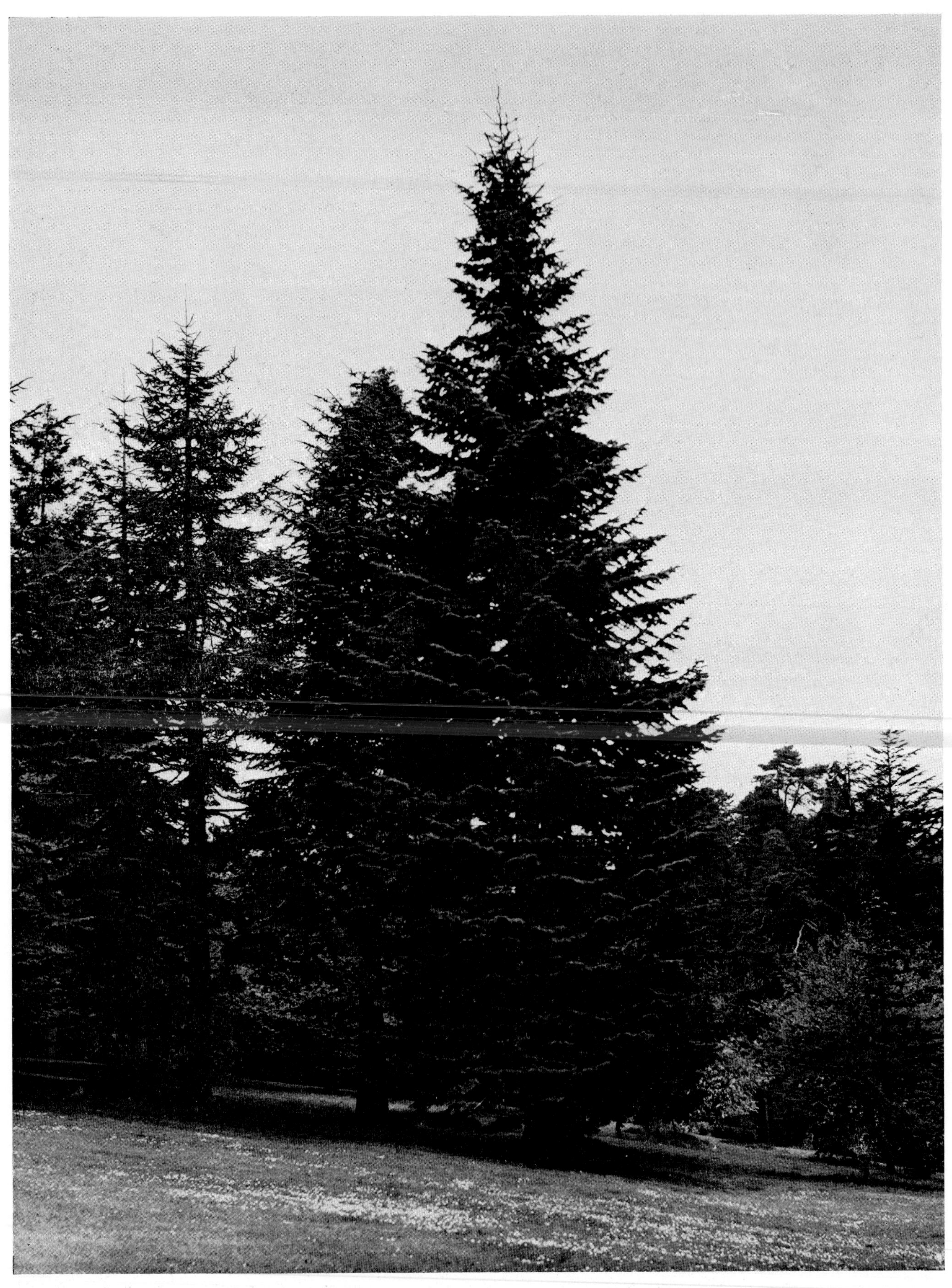

Plate 8.
Abies magnifica variety *shastensis*. Shasta fir. A tree at Bedgebury which was planted as one of the group of the type *A. magnifica* in 1925. It is 56ft × 5ft 0in. In 1969 it bore a cone with exserted bracts showing it to be v. *shastensis*, but the foliage is indistinguishable from those of the other trees in the group. C 4742

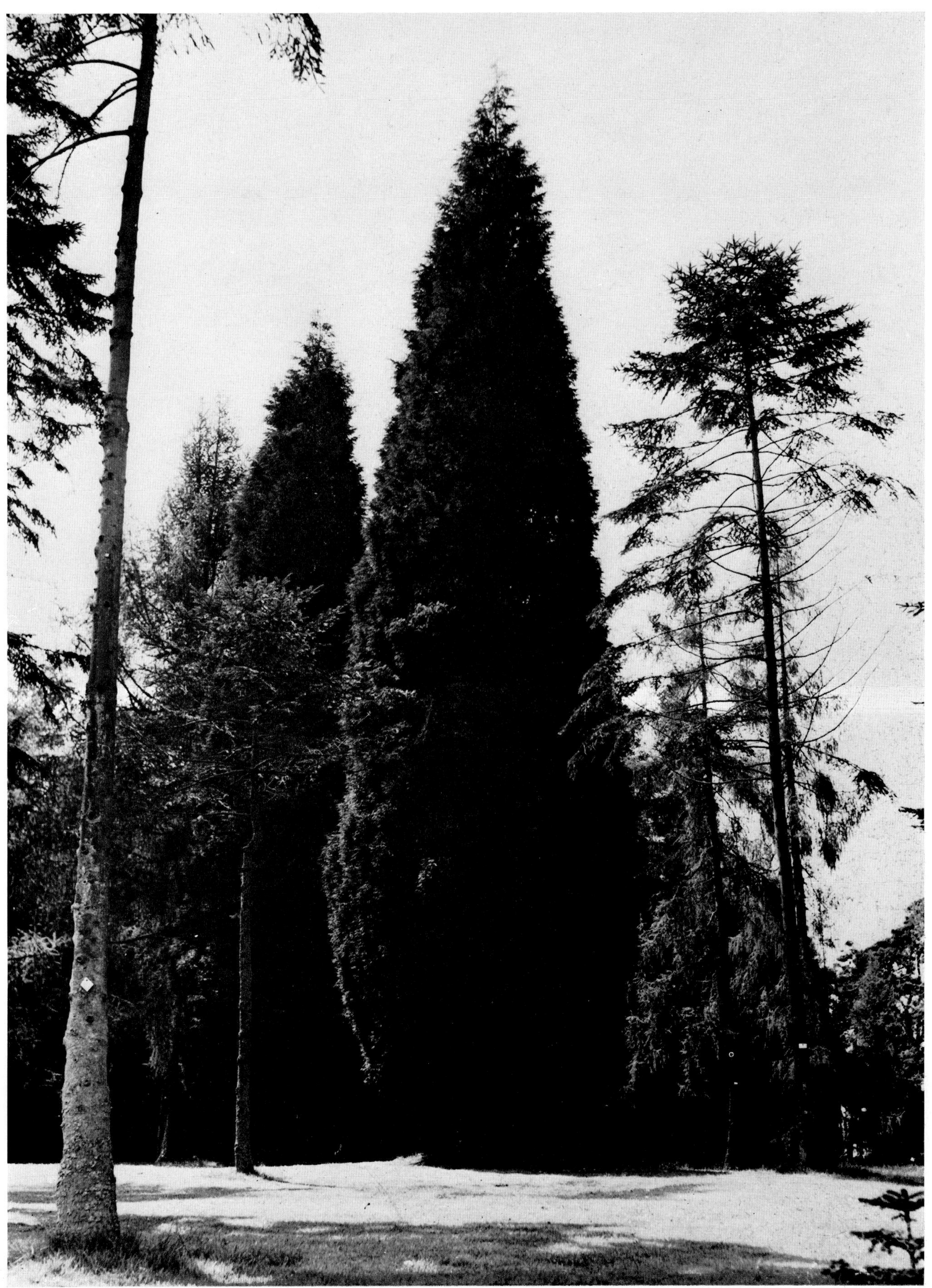

Plate 9.
×*Cupressocyparis leylandii*. Leyland cypress. Part of a short avenue planted in 1935 at Bedgebury with cuttings derived from one or more trees of the first hybrid. This arose at Leighton Hall in 1888, and the first trees were all sent to Haggerston Castle, Northumberland in 1892. In 1970 the trees in the Avenue, when 35 years planted, had mean dimensions of 70ft × 5ft 6in. C 4743

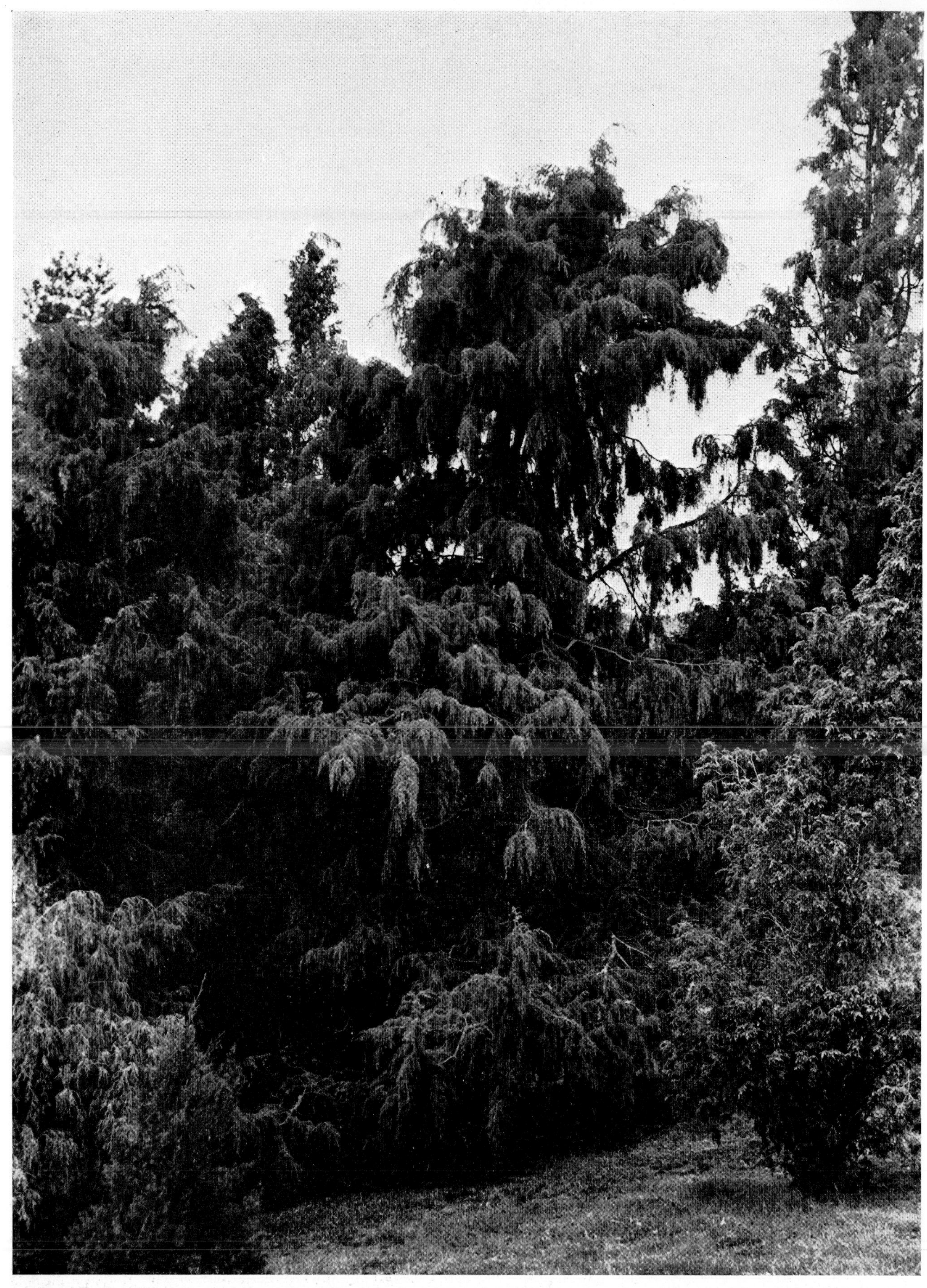

Plate 10.
Juniperus rigida. The long-leaved foliage, in well-spaced whorls of three, is pendulous in this Japanese juniper. This was planted in 1925 at Bedgebury and is 31 feet tall. C 4741

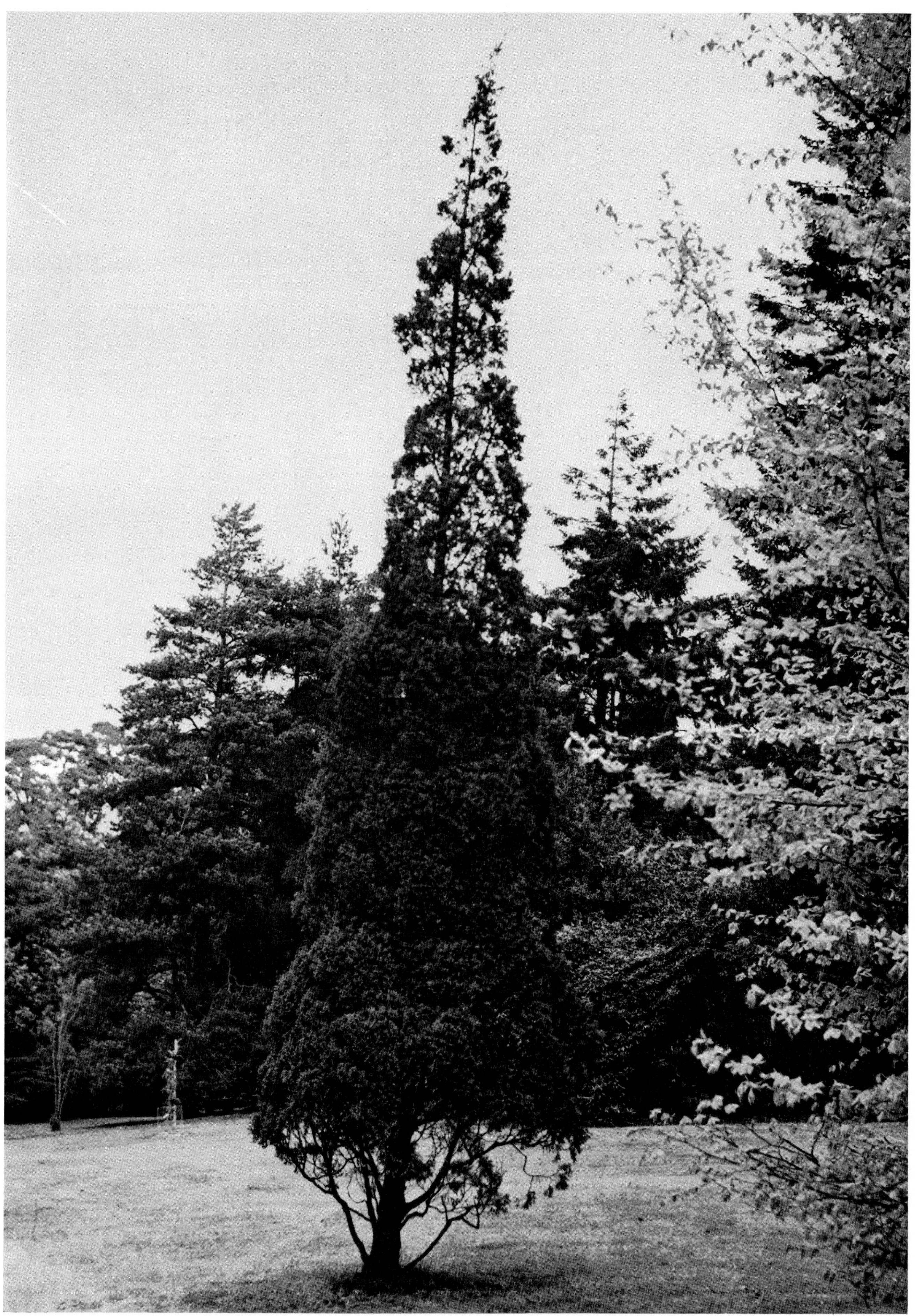

Plate 11.
Juniperus wallichiana. Typically narrow-conic crown of this grey-foliaged, black-fruited Juniper. This was planted in 1927 at Bedgebury and is 26 feet tall. C 4740

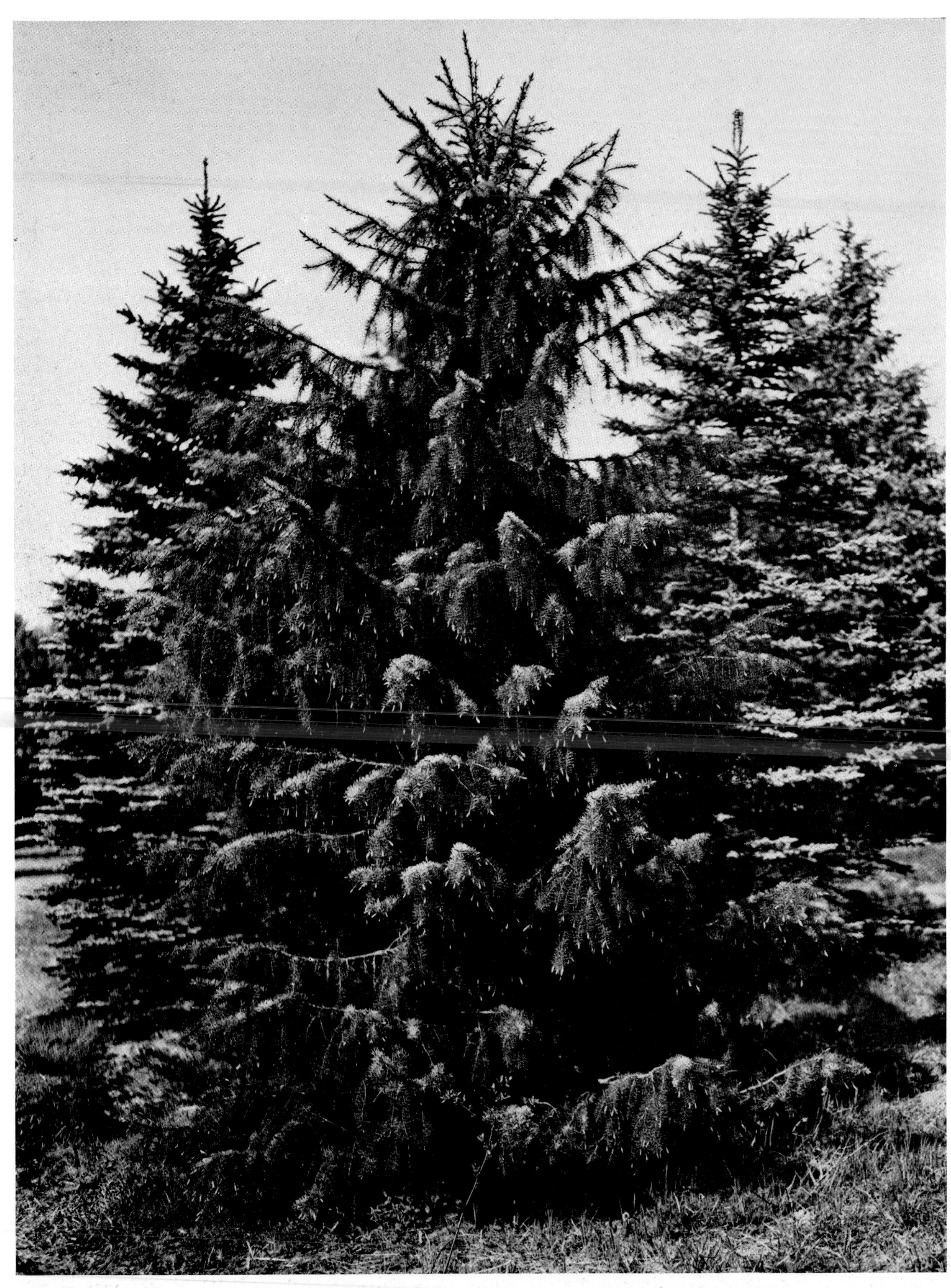

Plate 12.
Picea breweriana. Brewer's Spruce. A tree at Bedgebury when 27 years old and beginning to show well the hanging branchlets. D 3437

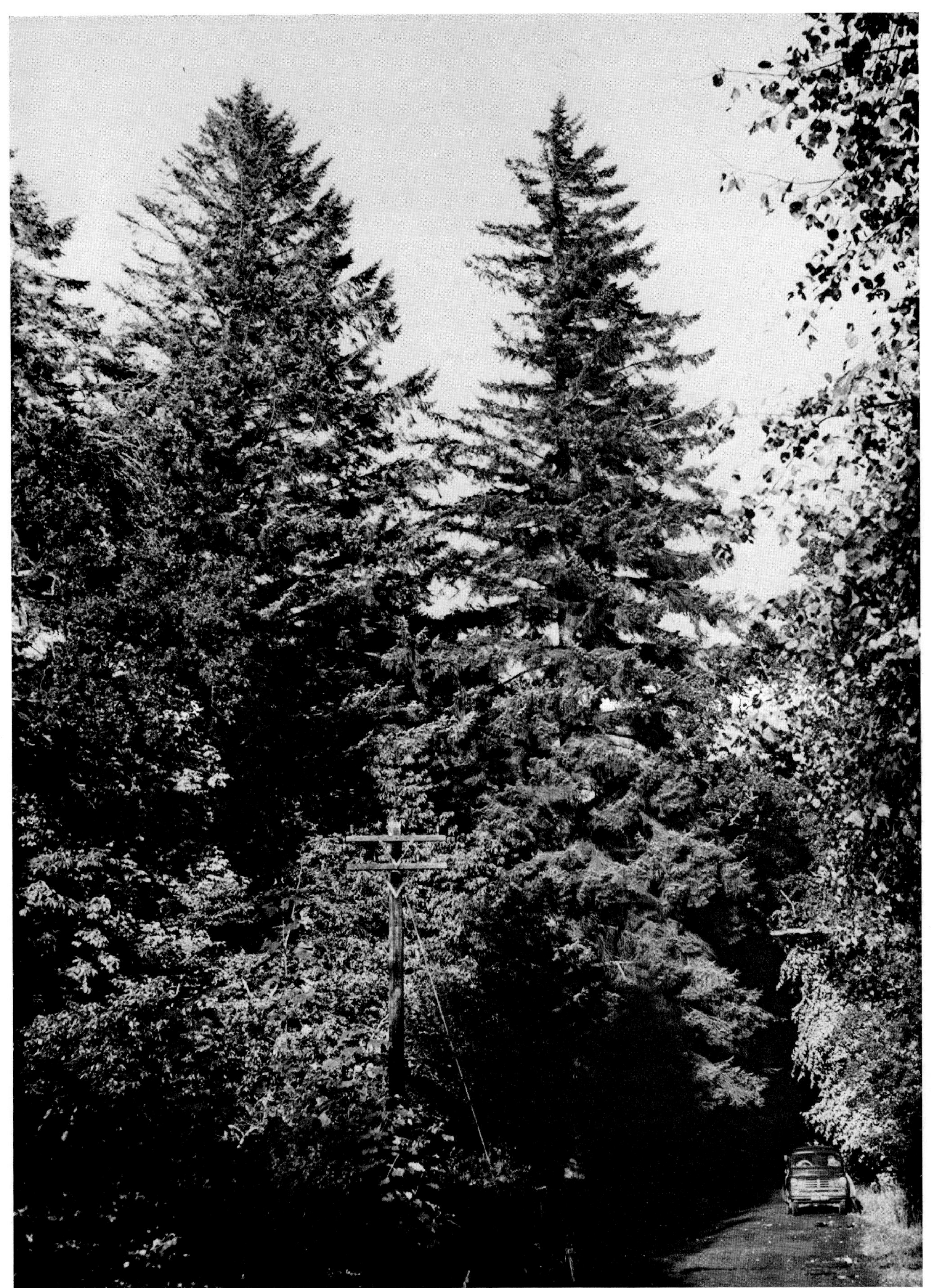

Plate 13.
Picea sitchensis. Sitka spruce. Two trees, each 140 feet tall but of contrasting crown-forms, at Novar, Ross and Cromarty.
B 3418

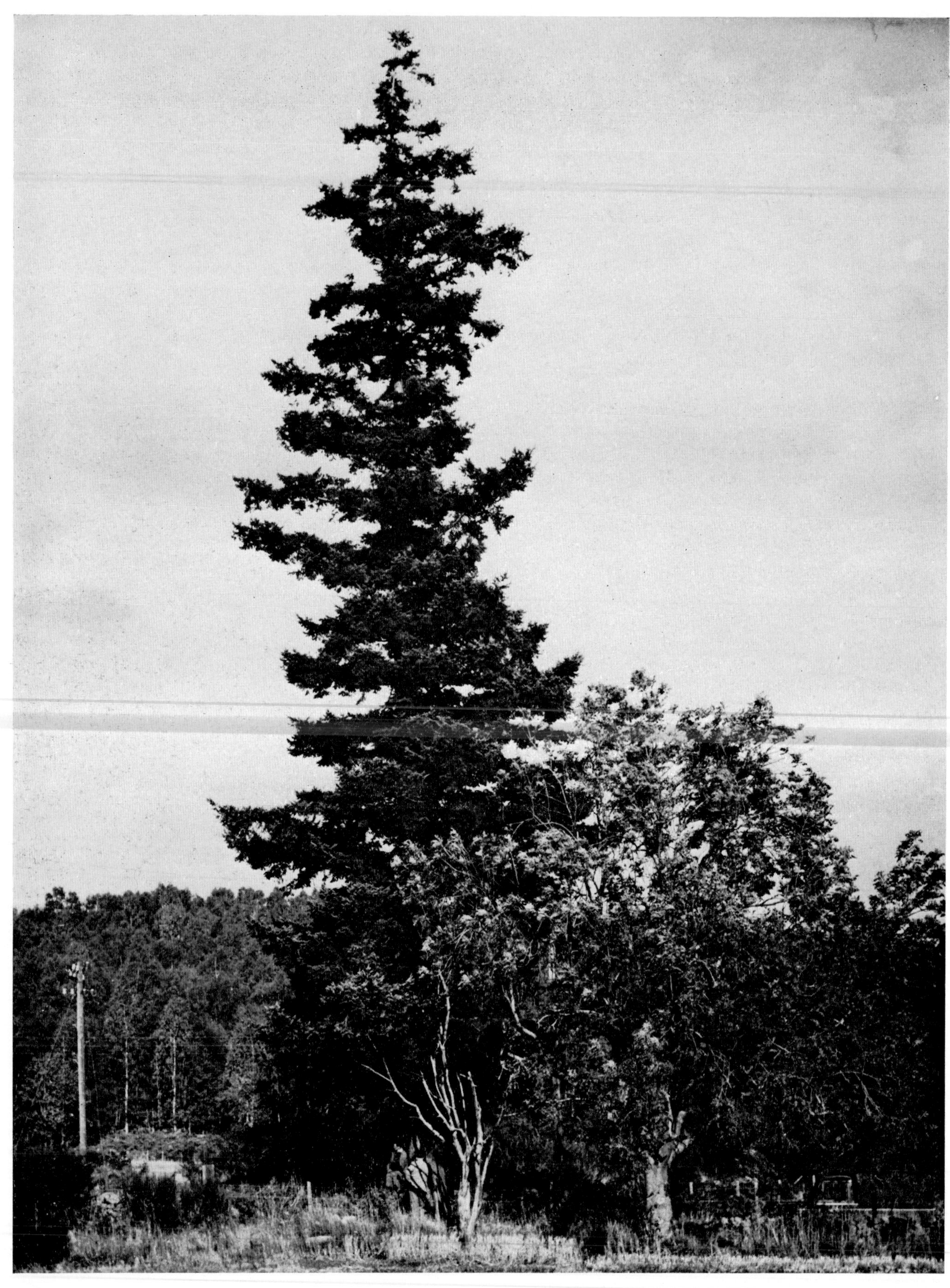

Plate 14.
Pseudotsuga menziesii. Douglas fir. A fine, narrow crowned tree in considerable exposure at Inchmarlo, Kincardineshire.
B 5216

Plate 15.
Sequoia sempervirens. Coast Redwood. A tree at Alice Holt, Hants, planted in 1876. The height, 100 feet, is exceeded only in sheltered places on damp soils. The large trees are nearly all in the far west and in the north. D 4589

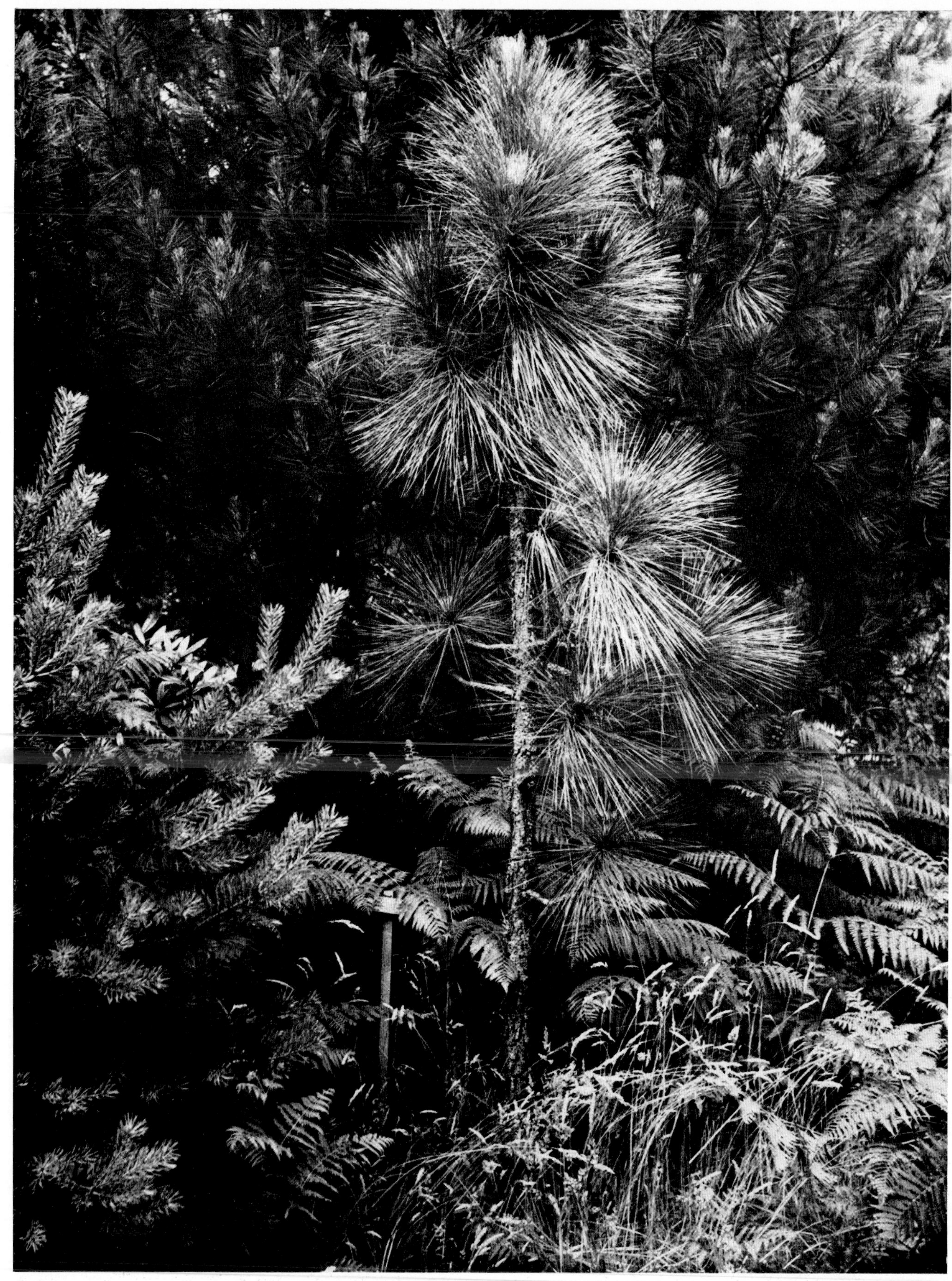

Plate 16.
Pinus palustris. Long-leaf pine. A tender species very rare in cultivation in Britain. This specimen was planted at Bedgebury in 1931 and is now 25 feet tall. The photograph was taken when the typical foliage could be well seen, when the tree was 20 years old. B 595

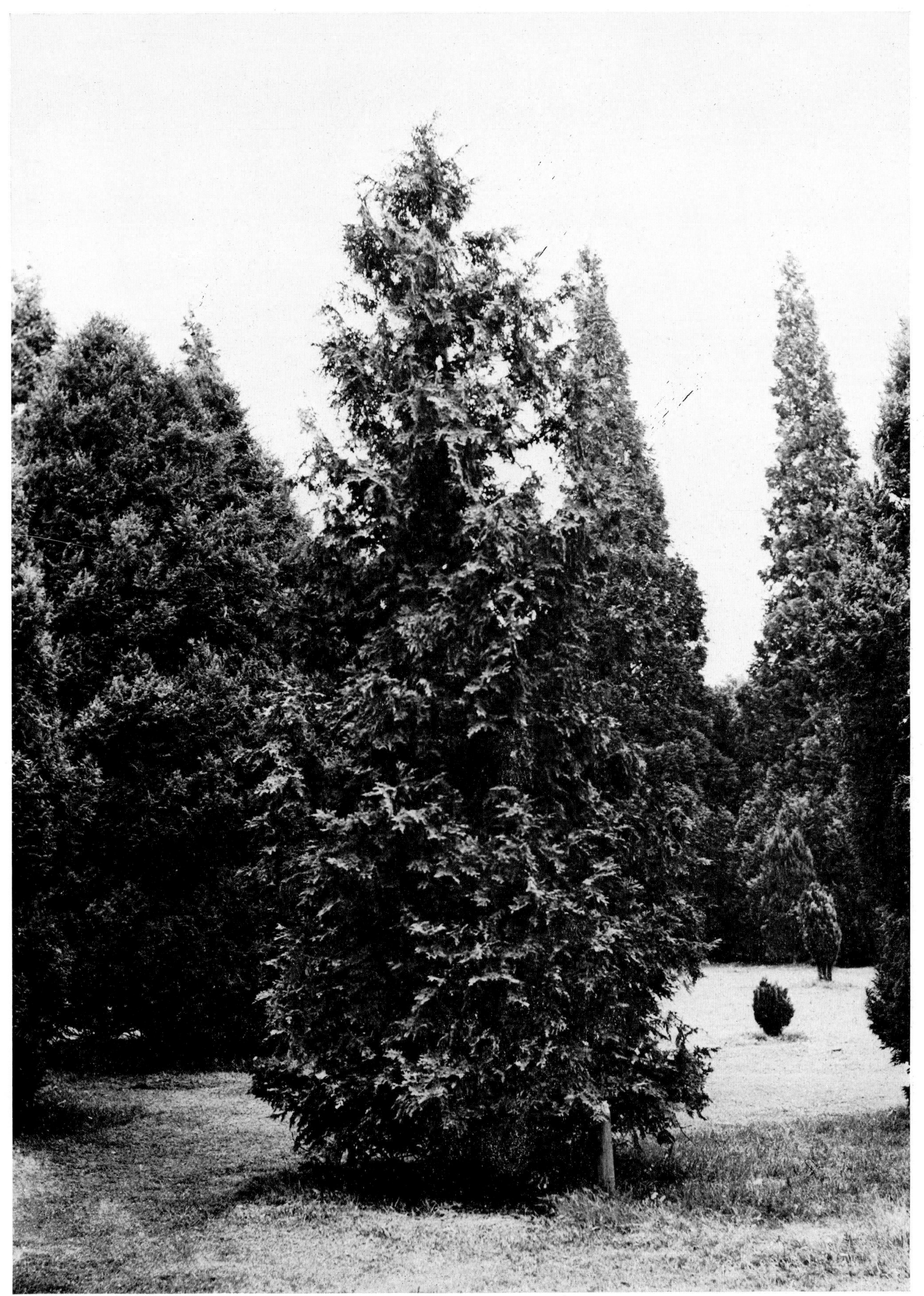

Plate 17.
Thuja koraiensis. This species has richly aromatic foliage which is heavily silvered on the underside, and is slow growing. The tree above was planted 45 years ago, at Bedgebury and is 22 feet tall. C 4735

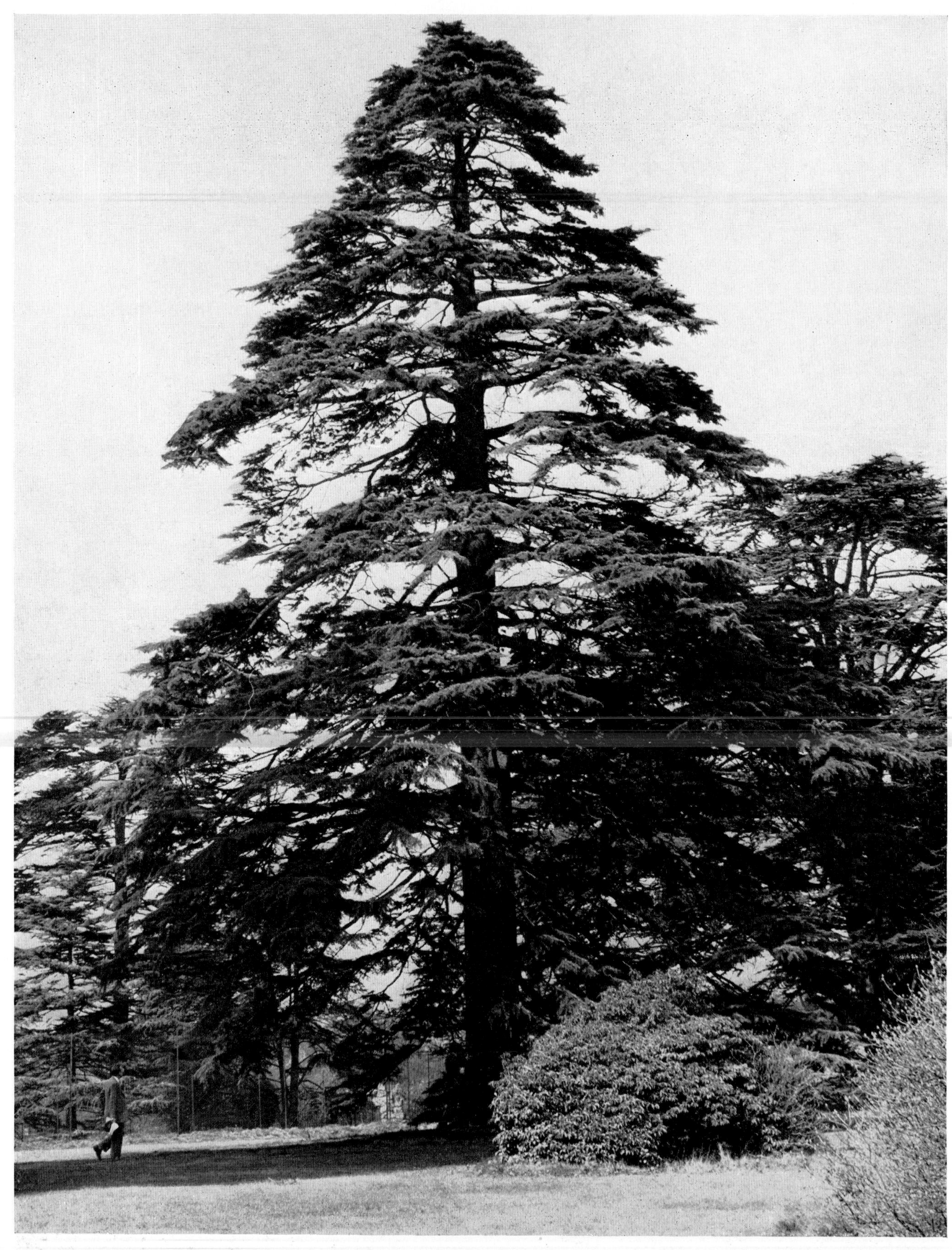

Plate 18.
Cedrus deodara. Deodar. A fine specimen, 98ft × 13ft 0in (1961) at Dropmore, Bucks. It was probably from the first seed imported in 1831. A 2669

Plate 19.
Pinus sabiniana. Digger pine. Typical open crown of the tree at Dropmore, planted in 1911. It was 72ft × 4ft 9in in 1970. It is a short lived species in Britain. A 2662

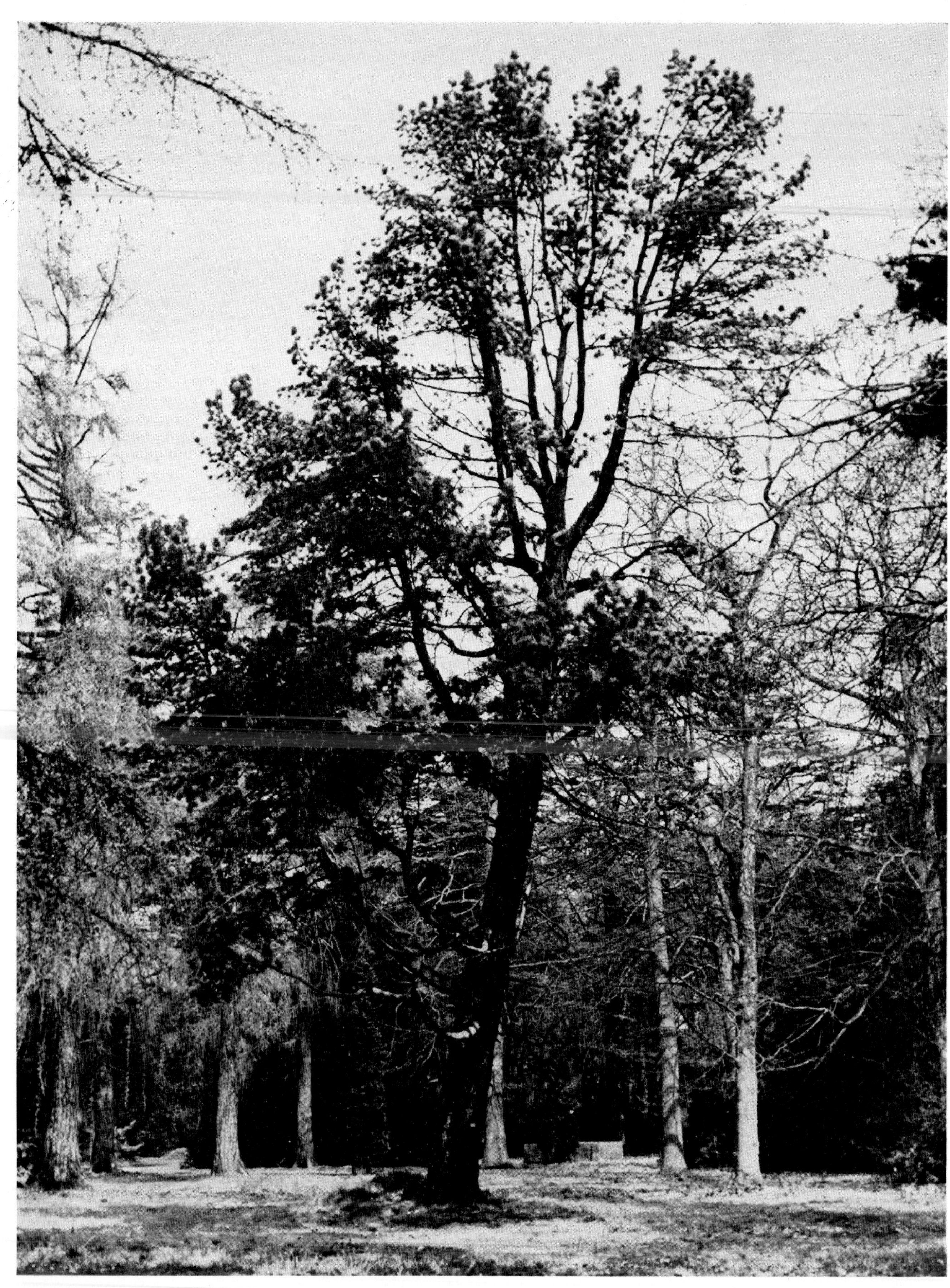

Plate 20.
Pinus cembra. Arolla pine. The oldest known specimen in Britain, planted in 1796 at Dropmore. The close, columnar crown is lost with age. A 2653

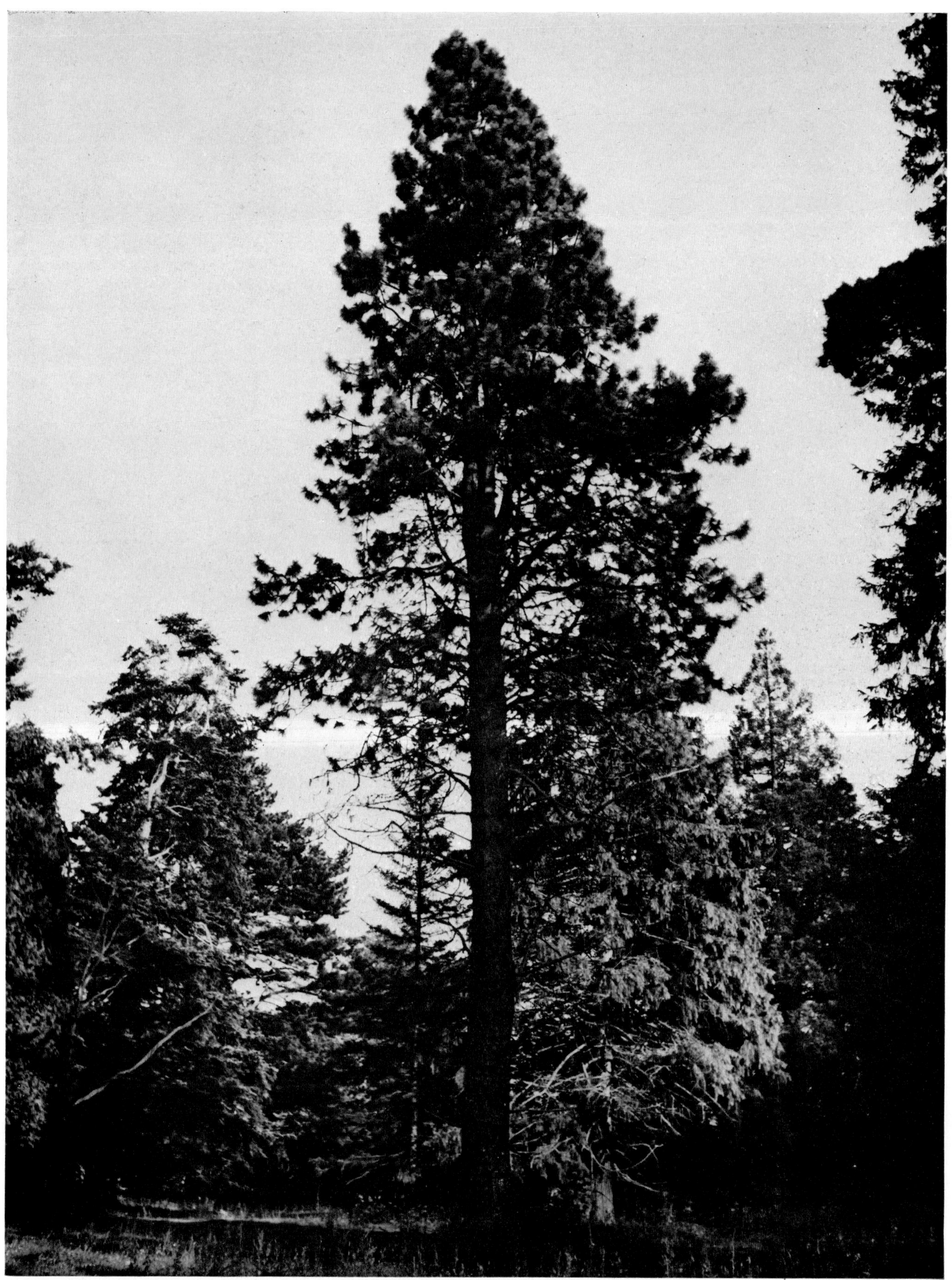

Plate 21.
Pinus ponderosa. Western yellow pine. A good specimen at Leighton Park, Montgomery, 98ft × 10ft 6in in 1970. B 5662

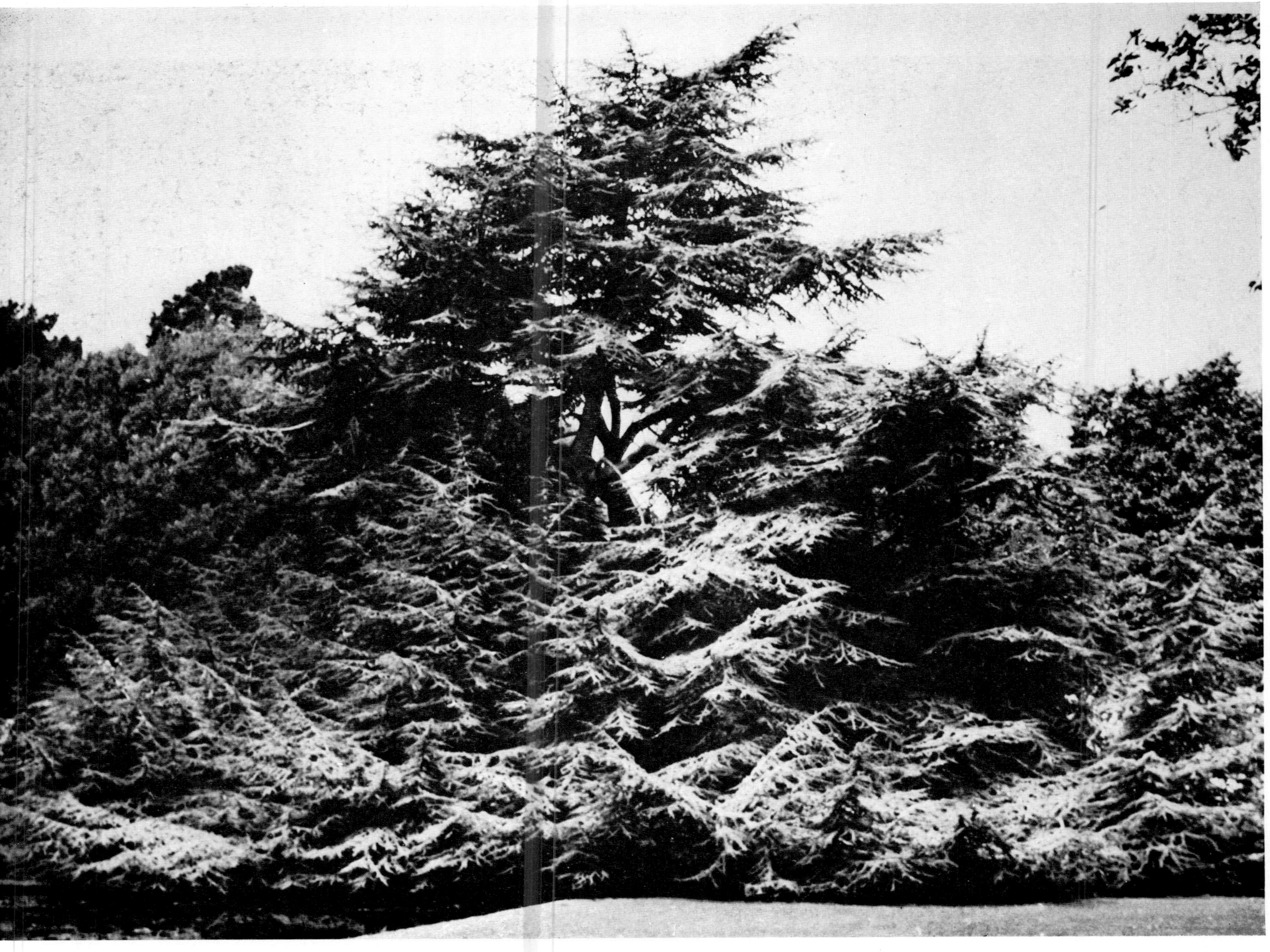

Plate 22.
Cedrus atlantica variety *glauca*. Blue Algerian cedar. The fine specimen in the Italian Garden at Bodnant, Denbighshire.

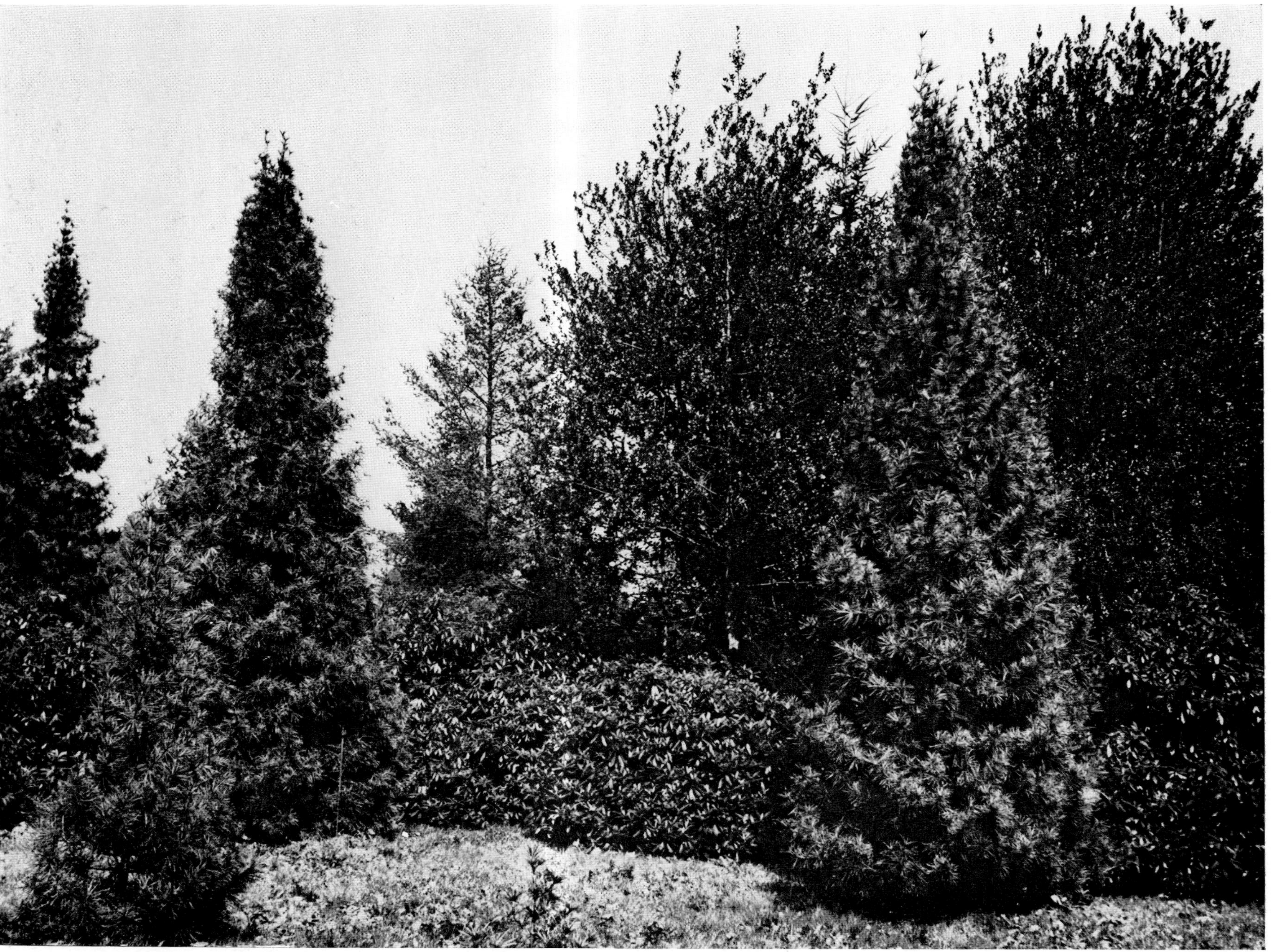

Plate 23.
Sciadopitys verticillata. A line planted in 1925 at Bedgebury. The picture was taken when they were 25 years old and shows the narrow conic form of single-stemmed trees. B 259

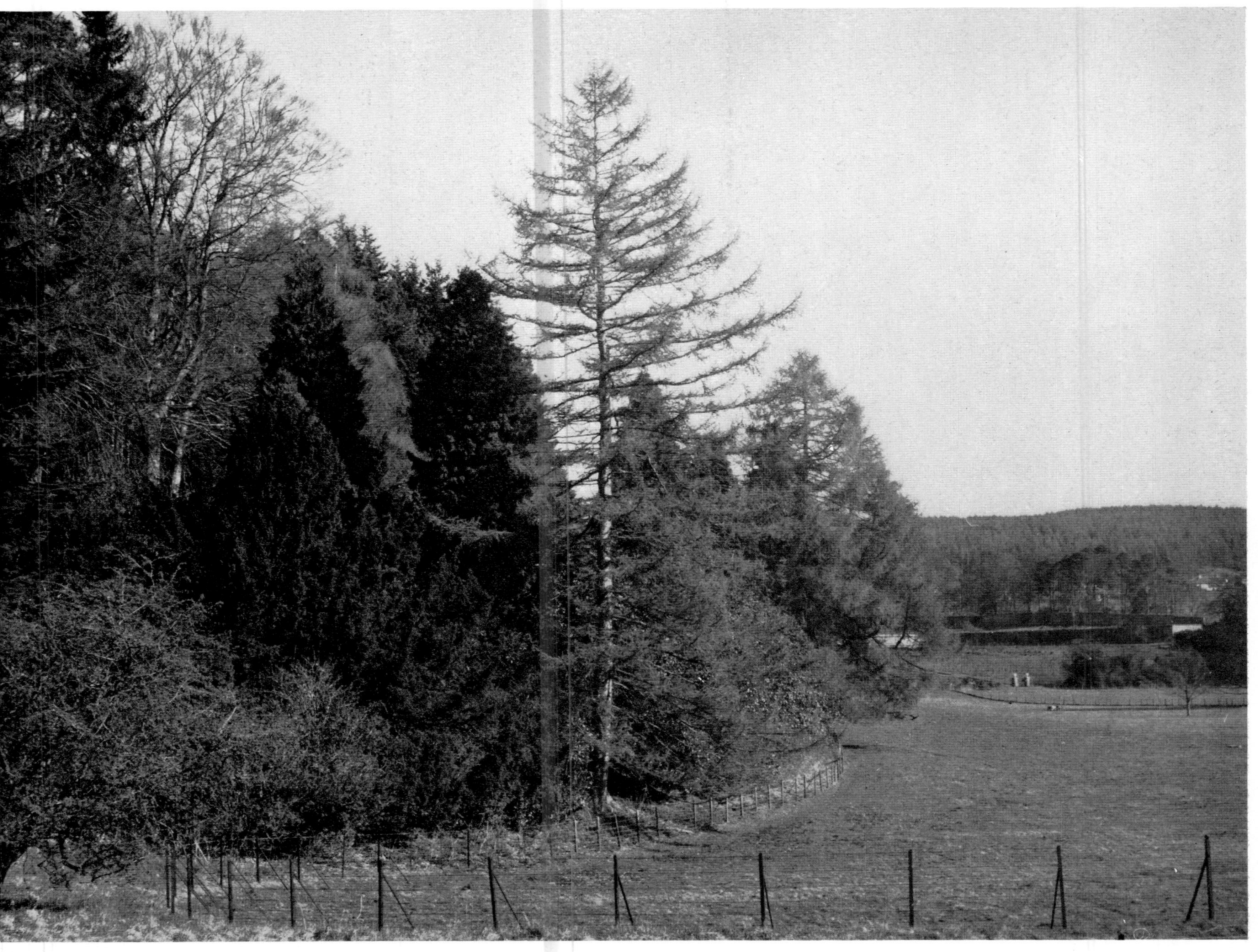

Plate 24.
Larix kaempferi. Japanese larch. Tree with the largest bole of this species so far known in Britain. 102ft × 9ft 8in (1970).
This tree was planted at Dunkeld House, Perthshire, in 1885.   B 2577

GROWTH. Among the earliest spruces into leaf; the buds often start to open in late March and shoot-growth starts between mid April and early May. It continues until the end of July with the maximum rate during June, of 3 inches in a week. Young plants can be very vigorous in height growth, a shoot of 3 feet 6 inches being noted on a 10 year old tree, but later growth in height, and all growth in girth is somewhat slow.

SPECIMENS. The only trees more than 100 years old known are the splendid trees along the Rhinefield Ornamental Drive in the New Forest. These were planted in 1861. In 1970 the best are 90ft × 5ft 8in; and 83ft × 5ft 0in. Apart from these, one of which was given by Elwes and Henry, and a different one in the 1932 *Report*, none of the older trees recorded earlier has been found. Three which were only young trees in 1931 are, however still alive.

Larger trees now known are: Hergest Croft, planted 1911, 60ft × 3ft 7in; planted 1911, 50ft × 3ft 7in (1969); Tubney Wood, planted 1906, 55ft × 2ft 3in (1966); Bicton, 54ft × 3ft 11in (1968); Abbeyleix, 55ft × 3ft 7in (1968); Crarae, 51ft × 2ft 9in (1969); Speech House, planted 1916, 64ft × 3ft 4in (1968); Little Hall, planted 1901, 51ft × 2ft 1in (1961); Bedgebury, planted 1929, 43ft × 2ft 10in (1970); Windsor Great Park, planted 1933, 45ft × 3ft 4in (1970); Eridge Castle, planted 1880, 69ft × 8ft 0in. (1971).

var. albertiana (Brown) Sargent. Alberta white spruce. Alberta to Montana. Introduced in 1906. Rare. Some collections only.

BARK. Dark purple-grey, much flaking.

FOLIAGE. Pulvini bright orange especially on second-year shoots and occasionally finely pubescent.

BUDS. Bloomed lilac with resin.

LEAVES. Stiff but more slender, denser, laid more forward over the shoot and longer, to 2 cm, bevelled to an abrupt, round-tipped spine; dark green above finely lined with stomata but two broad very white bands below giving a very two-coloured effect in most trees.

CONE. 7 × 4 cm, orange-brown.

Crushed foliage scented of pea-pods or of balsam.

SPECIMENS. Hergest Croft, planted 1915, 61ft × 3ft 2in; 60ft × 3ft 0in (1961); Bedgebury, planted 1925, 30ft × 2ft 10in; 31ft × 2ft 3in (1969); Westonbirt, 29ft × 1ft 5in (1969); Blairquhan, 40ft × 2ft 9in (1970); Borde Hill (Warren), 40ft × 1ft 1in (1958).

cv. Coerulea. Occurs among seedlings. Leaves short, dense and bluish white. Very rare. Fenagh House, planted 1897, 45ft × 2ft 2in (1968).

Picea glehnii (Schmidt) Masters. Sakhalin spruce

Sakhalin and North Japan. Introduced in 1877. Rare; in collections only.

BARK. Rich purplish brown, flaking finely, but also dull grey-purple and flaking coarsely on some trees.

CROWN. Narrowly conic, rather dense.

FOLIAGE. Shoot bright orange, densely hairy with red-brown hairs sometimes confined to shallow grooves; second year dark purple.

BUD. Ovoid or conic, purple-brown, slightly resinous and shiny. Dark, acute scales from the base extend half the length of the bud.

LEAVES. Pectinate and spreading below; all over the upper side, ascending forward 45°, 1–1·5 cm long, dark blue-green above with one central, or two fine bands of white stomata, and two broad, bright white bands beneath.

CONE. (ex Japan). To 6 cm bluntly cylindric, curved, 3 cm broad when dry, yellowish-brown, ±shiny, scales with wavy margin, frayed or toothed, turned inwards. (U.K.) fusiform, 5 × 2·5 cm, pinkish-purple; resinous.

SPECIMENS. The oldest trees are a group of four on Jubilee Terrace, Murthly, planted in 1897. The largest two were 69ft × 4ft 2in and 66ft × 3ft 10in in 1970. Other trees are: Hergest Croft, planted 1924, 45ft × 2ft 10in (1961); St. Clere, 38ft × 3ft 1in (1969).

RECOGNITION. Typically the bark, and bright-orange very hairy shoot with short bi-coloured leaves make this an easy species, but the first two can vary.

Picea × hurstii. A reputed hybrid between *P. engelmannii* and *P. pungens*, of unknown origin, but presumably American. As grown at Westonbirt, this handsome tree is distinguished by the following: bark, very smooth, brown, finely freckled. Shoot pale reddish brown, wrinkled, glabrous; greenish white when newly grown, in July. Leaves sparse, slender, curved, 2–2·5 cm upswept and forward above the shoot, a few spreading below; quadrangular, dark blue-grey green above; white bands below. Crushed foliage has a sweet, fruity scent, and, unlike *P. pungens*, is fairly soft.

SPECIMENS. Westonbirt (Morley), 45ft × 2ft 1in (1969); (Silk Wood), 30ft × 3ft 3in (1965); Borde Hill (The Tolls), 28ft × 1ft 1in (1957); Crarae, 23ft × 1ft 2in (1956).

Picea jezoensis (Siebold & Zuccarini) Carriere.

Eastern Siberia, Manchuria, Korea and Hokkaido; a variety in Honshiu. Introduced in 1861 but died out. The type tree is sometimes seen, stunted by repeated frost damage in a few collections. It has whitish shoots, and shining rich green leaves 1·3 × 0·1 cm with grey-white bands beneath, differing only in this last feature from the common var. *hondoensis*. The distinction is supposed to include brown shoots and shorter leaves duller and more curved in *hondoensis*, but the shoots in this variety are always nearly white, while the leaves vary greatly in length and curvature. They are, however brilliantly white beneath in *hondoensis*; this, and the difference in growth, seem to be the only reliable distinctions.

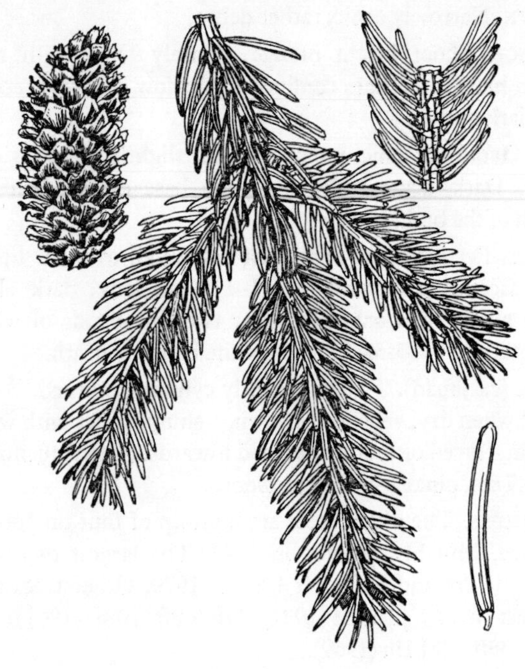

Picea jezoensis

Fig. 115
Picea jezoensis, Hondo spruce (var. *hondoensis*), showing the reddish-brown cone with crinkled scales; the stout white shoot as seen from below, and (×1⅓) the broad blue-white bands on the underside of the leaf.

Picea jezoensis var. hondoensis. (Mayr) Rehder. Honshiu, Japan. Introduced before 1871. Common in collections and large gardens all over the country, but very rare outside these.

Bark. Younger trees, smooth brown, roughened slightly by horizontal lines of whitish leaf-traces. Old trees, pale rather purplish grey, with ash-grey leaf traces and shallow, wandering cracks; sometimes deeper vertical cracks leaving brownish, white-flecked plates.

Crown. Conic; upper branches ascending, lower branches level all extending beyond the general crown with dense slightly hanging plumes of shoots, but much less markedly so than the ascending plumes of *P. bicolor.*

Foliage. Shoot shining white, especially from below, or pale buff; stout, grooved. Second year pale orange; third year grey-orange.

Buds. Ovoid, domed, shining orange-brown.

Leaves. Strongly pectinate below and upswept, slightly forward; those above dense and lying far forwards, tips curved forwards, 1·5 cm but variable; blunt, hard and flat, deep green above, two brilliant white bands beneath. Opening leaf-buds large, crimson in May.

Flowers. Females often abundantly borne over much of the crown, bright crimson. Males long cylindric, becoming curved.

Cone. Cylindric, tapered and slightly curved, 5×2·5 cm, reddish-brown; scales crinkled with 2–3 jagged teeth, curved inwards.

Growth. A very sturdy tree of remarkably even, steady growth, much the same in all parts of these islands. Growth in height is moderate; young plants may make shoots 2 feet long, but older trees at known age have average growth rates close to 1¼ to 1½ feet per year when 50–60 years old, and none has been found with more. Girth increase is vigorous and corresponds in inches with height increases in feet, that is about 1¼–1½ inches per year, but with wider limits.

Recognition. *P. bicolor* is superficially very similar. Apart from the rougher bark and much broader crown of slightly ascending, much protruding branches, its leaves are not flat but quadrangular, and stand up from the shoot more. *P. brachytyla* should be quite distinct with its short leaves depressed each side of the shoot, not upswept, and more pendulous shoots from an open crown.

TABLE 49. GOOD TREES OF PICEA JEZOENSIS VAR. HONDOENSIS

Locality	*Date Planted*	*Dimensions*	
Castle Kennedy	1871		76′ × 6′ 6″ (1967)
Eridge Castle (1)	1877		75′ × 9′ 11″ (1971)
Benmore	1880	52′ × 4′ 4″ (1905)	80′ × 10′ 8″ (1970)
Westonbirt	ca.1890	59′ × 4′ 11″ (1931)	72′ × 6′ 9″ (1968)
Fenagh House (1)	1896	44′ × 4′ 11″ (1931)	66′ × 7′ 6″ (1968)
Tregrehan		65′ × 5′ 7″ (1908)	100′ × 8′ 0″ (1971)
Tregrehan		50′ × 7′ 6″ (1927)	82′ × 10′ 2″ (1971)
Warnham Court		56′ × 5′ 0″ (1931)	72′ × 6′ 9″ (1957)
Melbury			64′ × 7′ 3″ (1970)
Lanrick			86′ × 8′ 2″ (1970)
Endsleigh			85′ × 7′ 10″ (1963)
Eridge Castle (2)			80′ × 8′ 10″ (1971)
Bodnant			70′ × 7′ 2″ (1959)
Ballimore			64′ × 7′ 4″ (1969)
Burnside			66′ × 6′ 0″ (1955)
Glenapp			75′ × 5′ 3″ (1970)
Highnam			80′ × 6′ 10″ (1970)
Dryderdale			70′ × 4′ 9″ (1958)
Brahan	1901		56′ × 5′ 3″ (1970)
St. Erth Station	1904		78′ × 5′ 9″ (1959)
Tilgate (1)	1905	27′ (1931)	43′ × 3′ 11″ (1961)
Leonardslee	ca.1905		90′ × 6′ 8″ (1969)
Leonardslee	ca.1905		85′ × 8′ 1″ (1969)
Leonardslee	ca.1905		90′ × 5′ 5″ (1969)
Eridge Castle (3)	1906		57′ × 6′ 3″ (1971)
Little Hall	1906	33′ × 2′ 7″ (1931)	56′ × 4′ 11″ (1961)
Tilgate (2)	1907	55′ × 2′ 9″ (1931)	80′ × 4′ 6″ (1961)
Fota			72′ × 8′ 0″ (1966)
Taymouth Castle			69′ × 4′ 10″ (1970)
Mount Usher			67′ × 5′ 6″ (1966)
Castle Milk			73′ × 6′ 5″ (1966)
Alnwick Castle		15′ (1931)	53′ × 5′ 0″ (1958)
Albury Park		29′ × 2′ 2″ (1931)	58′ × 4′ 6″ (1968)
Stourhead			75′ × 5′ 8″ (1970)
Herriard Park			65′ × 5′ 2″ (1961)
Blandsfort		21′ (1931)	62′ × 4′ 3″ (1968)
Avondale	ca.1910		50′ × 6′ 0″ (1968)
Wakehurst Place	ca.1914		65′ × 5′ 4″ (1968)
Headfort	1914	25′ × 1′ 10″ (1931)	53′ × 6′ 9″ (1966)
Fenagh House (2)	1918	18′ (1931)	54′ × 5′ 9″ (1968)
Fenagh House	1918	14′ (1931)	47′ × 5′ 0″ (1968)
Dawyck	1918	24′ × 1′ 6″ (1931)	68′ × 5′ 7″ (1970)
Bedgebury	1926		46′ × 3′ 5″ (1970)

Picea koyamai Shirasawa. Koyama's spruce.

Mount Yatsuga, Central Japan and probably Korea. Introduced in 1915. Rare; in collections only, in all parts except North and North-east Scotland.

BARK. Light purple, dark brownish or nearly black, with raised ashen-grey flakes.

CROWN. Conical, spiky from long branch-tips protruding and ascending.

FOLIAGE. Shoot stout, dull orange above, often paler below, deeply grooved, glabrous, or slight pubescence in the grooves visible under lens on main shoot, more readily seen and regular on side-shoots. Second year shoot dark orange above, purplish beneath.

BUD. Large 1·0–1·5 cm, ovoid-conic, sharply pointed, often surrounded by a ring of stiff forward pressed leaves; pale brown, slightly purplish or dark red-brown, always slightly resinous, but pale tips may be free; buds leave thick rings of dark brown papery scales at the nodes.

LEAVES. May radiate all round main shoots or be stiffly upswept from below; lower ones spreading perpendicular to shoot, upper ones lying 45° forwards, occasionally nearly upright; stiff, rigid, bevelled to a sharp pointed, short spine, 1·5–2·0 cm, quadrangular, dark blue-green; 1–2 fine stomatic lines above, two narrow bands of white stomata beneath. Crushing foliage is a harsh operation but releases a sweet, minty aroma, often like chrysanthemums.

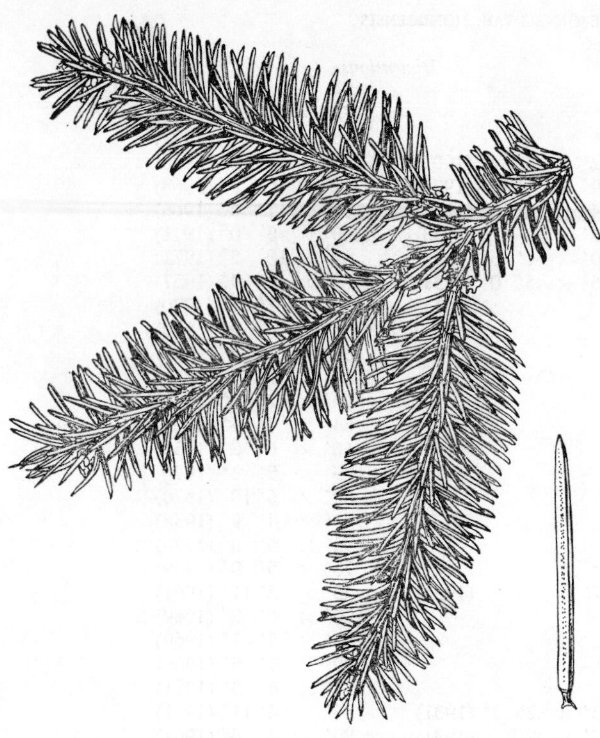

Fig. 116
Foliage of *Picea koyamai*, a rare Japanese spruce whose foliage differs from *P. abies* mainly in the stout orange shoot bearing rigid and short-spined leaves and stout, conic buds. Single leaf ×2.

CONE. Cylindric with short-domed top and flat base sometimes slightly oblique, 10×3 cm opening to 5 cm wide; numerous, striated, pale pink-brown scales, margins finely waved and toothed.

GROWTH. After, sometimes, a long, slow start, growth becomes steady and quite rapid. Some shapely trees have leading shoots of 2 feet or more in length.

SPECIMENS. There is an original tree at Dawyck, and (planted 1920) at Stanage Park. The largest trees are: Bedgebury, planted 1928, 57ft×5ft 0in; 48ft×3ft 10in; 45ft ×4ft 0in (1970); Stanage Park, 66ft×3ft 11in (1970); Borde Hill (Gores Wood), 58ft×4ft 0in; 56ft×2ft 11in (1968); Westonbirt, planted 1928, 46ft×3ft 7in; planted 1934, 51ft ×2ft 1in (1969); Dawyck, planted 1918, 48ft×2ft 9in (1966); Avondale, 54ft×4ft 4in; 46ft×3ft 8in (1968); Chandlers Ford (Hilliers Nursery), 50ft×2ft 5in (1967); Castle Milk, 38ft×3ft 6in (1966); Wisley Royal Horticultural Society Gardens, 44ft×2ft 7in (1969); Warnham Court, 60ft×4ft 0in (1971) (original tree).

RECOGNITION. A stiffly crowned, dark blue-green tree with stiff leaves on orange shoots, this is most like *P. abies*, differing in the above features and in the larger pointed buds, as well as the cones.

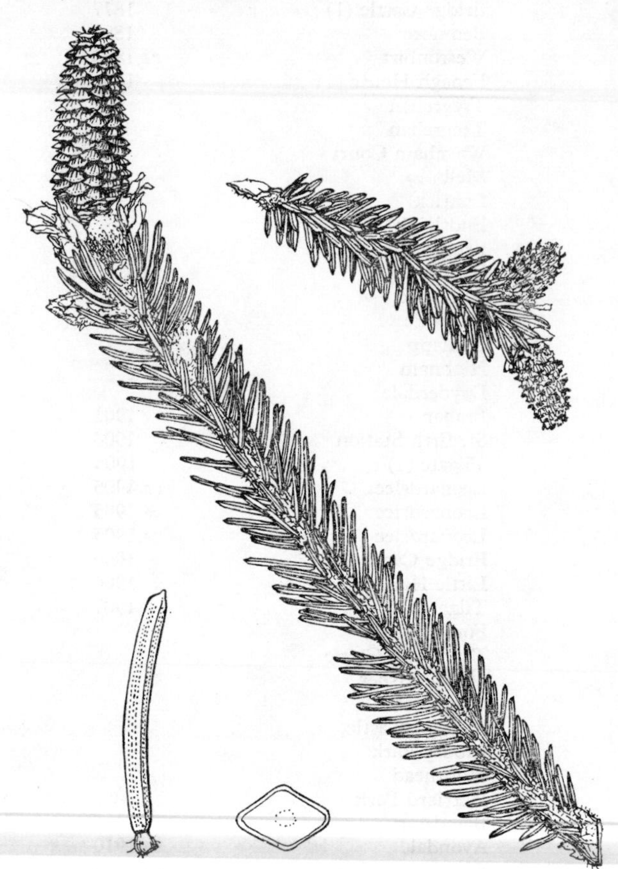

Fig. 117
Shoots of *Picea likiangensis*, the Likiang spruce. Left: strong shoot terminated by female flower which is bright red; right, weak shoot bearing male flowers, which are bright crimson until they shed pollen. The blue-grey leaves are flattened but rhombic in cross-section (×6) and have lines of stomata on each face, those beneath (×2) in broad bands.

Picea likiangensis (Franchet) Pritzel. Likiang spruce.

Western China; Yunnan, Szechuan and Kansu. Introduced in 1908. A variable tree, introduced from 1908 to 1910 under various names. Two of these survive as varieties, one of which is very distinct and almost a different tree (var. *purpurea*) but another which is no longer recognised even as a variety ("*yunnanensis*") is also distinct in its silvery blue foliage. Common in collections in England, Wales, Ireland and Southern Scotland, but not yet in parks and ordinary gardens.

Bark. Pale grey with a few, shallow, dark vertical fissures. (The blue Yunnan form has a more purplish and deeper fissured bark.) Occasionally with large flakes, or orange-grey with numerous narrow fissures.

Crown. Broadly conic and open with widely spaced level branches upturned towards the tips, or ascending and straight.

Shoot. Pink-buff to pale brown, slightly or more densely, soft pale pubescent, finely cracked rather than grooved. Second year pale pink-brown with very dark pubescence.

Bud. Ovoid, slightly pointed, shiny red-brown, purplish with resin at base, pale at tip where some scale-tips are just free, 6 mm, slightly resinous.

Leaves. Pectinate below and depressed below the shoot, arising from broad backward-curved pulvini, but bent some 30° forward; upper leaves strongly forwards, rising and well spaced, 1·5–1·7 cm long, with a short, blunt point, bevelled; upper side dark green or blue-green (grey-blue in Yunnan form) with two fine lines of stomata; underside with two very broad, bright white bands—a distinctly bicoloured leaf. Opening leaf-buds are tear-drop shaped, pointed.

Flowers and Cone. Flowers of both sexes profuse and well spread over 30 year old and older trees. Males large globular, brilliant crimson for weeks before they shed pollen (mid-May in Southern England). Females bright red, +1 cm long. Cone 9–13×2–4 cm, cylindrical, slightly tapered to a broad apex; scales pale brown with reddish bases; broad, waved, incurved tips; later purple-brown with broad margins red-brown.

Growth. In many places late frosts make this tree slow to establish, but once it can grow above danger, growth is steady and reasonably rapid. The average annual growth from planting date in all the trees of known date between 40 and 50 years old has been from slightly under one foot to slightly over 1½ feet per year. Since 1931 the seven trees remeasured have also grown between 1 foot and slightly under 1½ feet per year in the interval. Growth in girth has also been fairly consistently 1 to 1½ inches a year over both periods from planting or since 1931 as can be seen in Table 50.

Specimens. An original tree, planted in 1911 is at Warnham Court. Another survives at Stanage Park, planted in 1910. One at Glasnevin, planted in 1912 has died back severely and has a girth of 4ft 11in (1966). Several of the biggest undated trees probably derive from the original seed, as did that at Lamellan.

(There are at least 13 other trees at Wakehurst Place nearly as big).

var. balfouriana (Rehder & Wilson) Hillier. (Szechuan 1910). In a few collections. More like var. *purpurea* than the type, with brown scaly bark and narrowly conic crown, but more open than in var. *purpurea* and lacking the vertical shoots. Shoot grooved, pinkish-cream pubescent. Bud with outer scales free. Leaves 1·5 cm, slightly parted beneath, glossy, dark yellowish grey-green above, dull grey-green beneath; ill-defined stomatal lines on all surfaces. The leaf is thus not bicoloured.

Powis Castle (Pinetum), 50ft×3ft 2in (1970); Edinburgh Royal Botanic Garden, 46ft×3ft 2in (1970); Stanage Park, 72ft×4ft 4in; 57ft×4ft 5in (1970); Powerscourt, 53ft×4ft 0in (1966).

Table 50. Largest Trees of Picea likiangensis

Locality		*Date Planted*	*Dimensions*	
Stanage Park		1910		71′ × 6′ 0″ (1970)
Vernon Holme		1925	10′ 6″ × 5′ (1931)	48′ × 3′ 9″ (1961)
Bedgebury		1926	3′ 3″ (1931)	48′ × 6′ 3″ (1968)
Borde Hill Gores Wood			10′ (1931)	61′ × 5′ 1″ (1967)
Borde Hill Tolls		("Yunnanensis")		56′ × 5′ 4″ (1968)
Borde Hill Tolls		("Yunnanensis")		50′ × 5′ 0″ (1968)
Westonbirt Sand Earth			7′ (1931)	49′ × 4′ 8″ (1964)
Westonbirt Sand Earth		1930		61′ × 3′ 0″ (1969)
Hergest Croft		1916	14′ (1931)	50′ × 4′ 9″ (1961)
Hergest Croft		1928		54′ × 4′ 5″ (1969)
Bicton				66′ × 3′ 11″ (1968)
Edinburgh R.B.G.	F6746	1911		46′ × 4′ 9″ (1970)
Edinburgh R.B.G.	F6746	1911		41′ × 4′ 4″ (1970)
Kew		1914		37′ × 3′ 0″ (1969)
Lamellan				51′ × 4′ 9″ (1963)
Wakehurst Place				56′ × 5′ 3″ (1969)
Wakehurst Place				59′ × 4′ 11″ (1968)
Warnham Court		1911	30′ × 1′ 8″ (1931)	69′ × 5′ 7″ (1971)
Birr Castle		1916		47′ × 5′ 3″ (1966)
Powis Castle (Pinetum)				47′ × 4′ 6″ (1970)
Powerscourt				68′ × 6′ 2″ (1966)
Blandsfort			21′ (1931)	55′ × 4′ 6″ (1968)

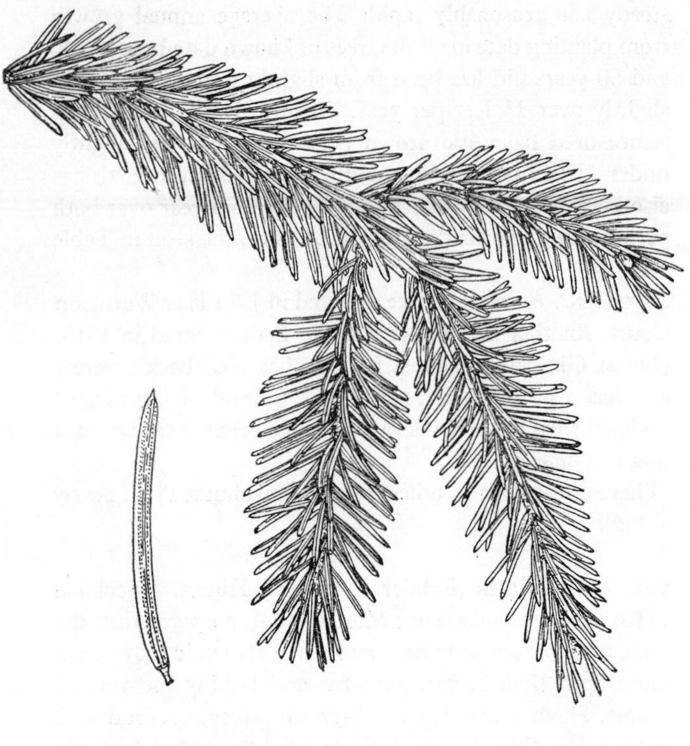

Fig. 118
Foliage of *Picea likiangensis* var. *purpurea*, a form very distinct in its flaky bark and dense dark green crown. The foliage is less distinct from the type, but the leaves are more spreading, often curved, and the stomatal bands beneath (left ×2) are duller, more grey-white.

var. purpurea (Masters) Dallimore and Jackson. (Szechuan and Kansu, 1910). Rather less frequent in collections than is the type. Distinguishable from a distance by the dense, dark green crown of numerous erect shoots, sprouting out all round the outside, those at the top competing with the leader or vertically alongside but below. The lower or shaded crown droops and smaller branches fan out each side in a downward spray. The bark also differs as it is flaky and dull orange-brown. The shoot is very pale pinkish grey with a long, soft, dense pubescence. The leaves are pressed down on to and below the shoot, as in *P. brachytyla* and (some) *P. obovata*, 1·5 cm long and are only pale grey beneath, not white. Cone, 5×2·5 cm, fusiform; rich plum-purple.

SPECIMEN. Westonbirt (Specimen Avenue), planted 1931, 62ft×3ft 6in (1969); Wakehurst Place, 51ft×2ft 8in; 46ft×3ft 6in (1964); Borde Hill (Pinetum), 47ft×2ft 10in (1961); Bicton, 55ft×3ft 9in (1968); Speech House, planted 1916, 38ft×2ft 3in (1959); Abbotswood, planted 1916, 47ft×2ft 1in (1966); Birr Castle, planted 1916, 49ft×3ft 3in (1966); Powerscourt, 51ft×4ft 1in (1966); Mount Usher, 45ft×3ft 10in (1966); Headfort, planted 1915, 42ft×4ft 3in (1966); Bedgebury, 44ft×2ft 5in (1969); Powis Castle (Pinetum), 55ft×3ft 8in (1970).

RECOGNITION. This spruce is one of the few with bicoloured leaves which are not fully flattened. The pinkish, pubescent shoots; the bicoloured leaves twisted forward from backward-bent pulvini and the lower leaves depressed below the stem, are distinctive when taken together, (for the type).

Picea × lutzii Little.

A hybrid between *P. sitchensis* and *P. glauca* found in 1950 where the ranges of the parents overlap in Southern Alaska. Interest was aroused here by the growth of early plantations in Iceland and seed was obtained in 1962. The plants have been quite vigorous, and resemble *P. sitchensis* but the leaves spread all round the shoot. It seems promising in Sutherland but not elsewhere.

Picea mariana (Miller) Britton, Sterns and Poggenberg. Black spruce (*P. nigra*)

Alaska to Newfoundland, south to mid British Columbia, the Lake States and West Virginia. Introduced in about 1700. Uncommon; almost restricted to collections.

BARK. Pink-grey, peeling into flakes; rough; becoming dark purple finely flaked in grey.

CROWN. Young trees are narrowly conic with slender leading shoots; old trees vary from narrow to broadly conic, very dense, often with the upper crown leaning or bent. Lower branches have layered at Borde Hill. Dark bluish black or blue-grey from a distance.

FOLIAGE. Shoot usually slender, pinkish or yellowish brown and pubescent. Second year orange-brown. Terminal bud 6 mm pale purple-brown; long, hairy, acute, keeled scales from base project beyond tip. Side buds ovoid, red-purple. Leaves densely set all round most shoots, slightly parted below in others, spreading below, forward above, very short, 1–1·5 cm slightly shiny dull green above, whitish blue bands below. Crushed foliage strongly scented of balsam or lemon-balm.

FLOWERS AND CONE. Male flowers small, crimson for a few weeks before shedding pollen. Female flowers, clustered on shoots just below the leading shoot even on young trees, red, ripening into dull purple cones which are ovoid tapered at each end, 3·5 cm (×2·5 cm open) shiny dark reddish brown, scales striated, with entire slightly incurved tips. They remain on the tree, dull grey-brown for several years after shedding their seeds.

GROWTH. Young plants may grow slender shoots 2 feet long but then decrease sharply in vigour and long-term growth is, with few exceptions, very slow. Growth in height is made between early May and the end of June. Few trees were measured for earlier works, and fewer still survive. In 35 years since 1931 a tree at Westonbirt added 10 feet to its

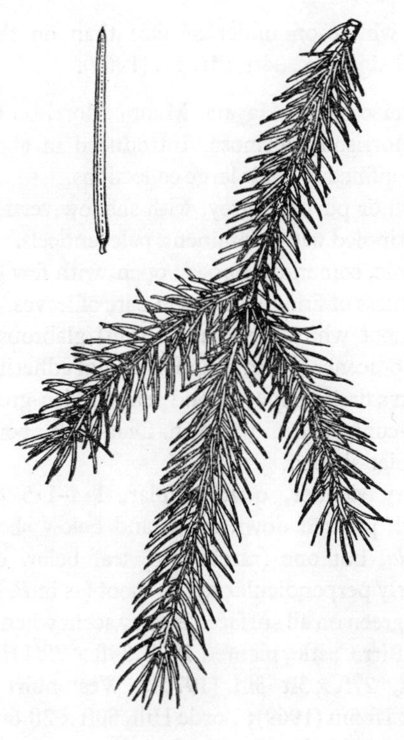

Fig. 119
Foliage of *Picea mariana,* Black spruce, which has a blue-grey colour in the mass although the upper surface seen closely is dull green with a few white stomata. The blue comes mainly from the underside (upper left ×2) which has two narrow blue-white bands.

height and 5 inches to its girth. In 31 years, a tree at Dawyck added 23 feet in height and 17 inches in girth. When 51 years old it was 51ft × 2ft 11in. Two trees have shown more vigorous growth; one at Nymans added 13 inches in girth in 9 years, and at Bodnant one 64 years old was 55ft × 4ft 6in.

Specimens. The oldest trees of known date were all planted in this century with the exception of two planted in 1861 in the Rhinefield Ornamental Drive, New Forest. One is now 69ft × 4ft 5in. A bigger one died in 1961 when 74ft × 7ft 2in. The biggest tree left is a fine specimen at Caerhayes Castle, 62ft × 6ft 9in in 1971. Other relatively big trees are: Westonbirt (Willesley), 61ft × 4ft 5in (1968); Nymans, 67ft × 5ft 6in and 63ft × 5ft 8in (1970); Cortachy Castle, 53ft × 4ft 1in (1962); Endsleigh, 50ft × 4ft 9in (1963); Wakehurst Place, 53ft × 4ft 1in (1964); Abbeyleix, 52ft × 5ft 1in and 56ft × 4ft 9in (1968); Bicton, 51ft × 3ft 8in (1968); Gurteen le Poer, 53ft × 2ft 9in (1968); Bedgebury, planted 1926, 39ft × 3ft 2in (1970).

Recognition. The dense, dark blue crown and short blue leaves on hairy pinkish shoots are distinct. The only spruce with shorter leaves and hairy shoots, *P. orientalis,* has green leaves, closely appressed to the shoot and a distant branchlet system. It also lacks the distinctive scent.

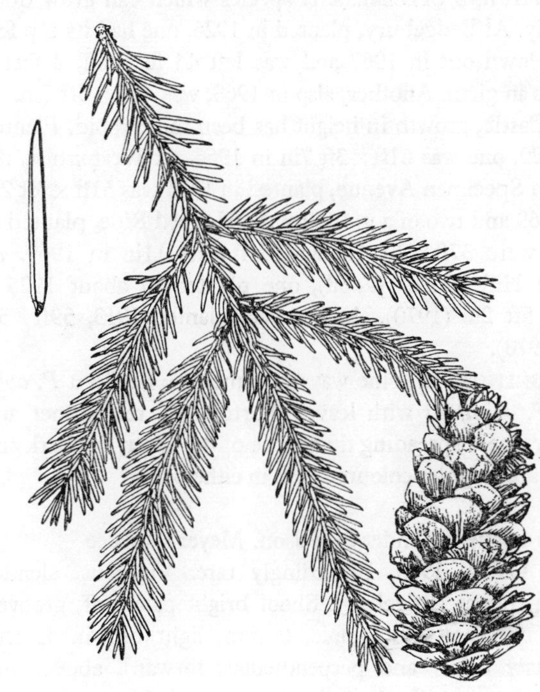

Fig. 120
Foliage, cone, and (left ×2) single leaf, of *Picea maximowiczii* a Japanese spruce with short leaves shining green on all four surfaces, and in several features intermediate between *P. abies* and *P. orientalis.*

Picea maximowiczii Regel ex Masters.

Central Japan. Introduced in 1865. Very rare; in a few of the biggest collections only.

Bark. Bright orange-brown, finely flaking, some larger trees buff-grey, smooth.

Crown. Narrowly conic, with projecting slender shoots, similar to *P. orientalis;* upper branches ascending in a curve.

Foliage. Shoot buff-brown to bright orange above, pale buff below; pulvini reddish purple; glabrous, rarely with fine, scattered pubescence; second year orange-brown.

Bud. Red-brown; resinous, 2 - 4 mm ovoid-conic with short, keeled basal scales.

LEAVES. Pectinate below, slightly forward, upper leaves well forward along shoot; very quadrangular and ridged; abruptly wedge-tipped, uniform in length, 1–1·3 cm, glossy dark green, finely lined with stomata on all faces.
CONE. Cylindric 4–7×2·5 cm, light red-brown, scales with red, low, rounded smooth margin.
GROWTH AND SPECIMENS. A species which can grow quite rapidly. At Bedgebury, planted in 1926, one had its top few feet blown out in 1967 and was left 44 feet tall, 4 feet 3 inches in girth. Another, also in 1968, was 46ft×3ft 7in. At Birr Castle, growth in height has been more rapid. Planted in 1929, one was 61ft×3ft 7in in 1966. At Westonbirt, the tree in Specimen Avenue, planted in 1935 was 51ft×3ft 2in by 1969 and two of a group by the Holford Ride, planted in 1946 were 37ft×2ft 1in and 34ft×1ft 11in in 1969. At Borde Hill (Gores Wood), one planted in about 1925 is 57ft×5ft 2in (1970). At Dawyck, planted 1913, 59ft×5ft 0in (1970).
RECOGNITION. In some ways intermediate between *P. abies* and *P. orientalis* with leaves shorter than the former and longer, more spreading than those of the latter, the bark and shoot are brighter coloured than in either.

Picea meyeri Rehder & Wilson. Meyer's spruce

W. China, 1910. Exceedingly rare. Vigorous, slender young tree at Bedgebury. Shoot bright pale buff, grooved and pubescent. Bud conic, 6 mm, light brown. Leaves pectinate below and perpendicular, forward, above, and rising, 2 cm, stiff, abruptly short-spined, blue-grey green with 2–3 stomatal lines above, 4 lines each side beneath. Crushed foliage has scent like chrysanthemums. Intermediate between *P. asperata* and *P. likiangensis*.

Picea montigena Masters.

West Szechuan, China. Introduced in 1908. Very rare indeed. Closely allied to *P. likiangensis,* but too distinct to be merged with that species. The tree described, at Bedgebury, is more like *P. asperata* in several features.
BARK. Orange-brown and purple-brown with thick grey flakes.
CROWN. A dark blue narrowly conic, spire-topped tree, rather dense.
FOLIAGE. Shoot pale orange, pubescent in well-marked grooves. Second year dark orange, pulvini contrasting bright orange.
BUD. Ovoid, purplish, very resinous.
LEAVES. Pectinate below, perpendicular to shoot and curved sharply upwards, upper leaves curved to nearly vertical; very quadrangular, short (1·0–1·5×0·2 cm) very blunt; deep blue-green with 2–3 fine lines of stomata above, two white bands of 5 lines each below. Unlike *P. likiangensis* in spreading pulvini (not decurved); in the stiff short, blunt, thick and upswept leaves, as well as in crown and bark. Differs from *P. asperata* in pubescent shoots, leaves pectinate below and whiter on under surface than on the upper.
SPECIMEN. Bedgebury, 24ft×1ft 5in (1969).

Picea morrisonicola Hayata. Mount Morrison spruce.

Mount Morrison, Formosa. Introduced in about 1926. Very rare; confined to a few large collections.
BARK. Brown or purplish-grey, with shallow vertical cracks and flakes, stippled with prominent, pale lenticels.
CROWN. Conic, sometimes broad; open, with few branches, but a dense mass of fine shoots, soon bare of leaves.
FOLIAGE. Shoot white, slender, (2 mm) glabrous or with scattered pubescence, arising from cluster of adhering orange bud-scales in a flask-shape; second year pinkish-grey.
BUD. Ovoid-conic, chestnut brown. Leaf-buds open narrow, pointed droplet-shaped.
LEAVES. Very slender, quadrangular, 1·4–1·5 cm long, long-pointed, pressed down on to and below shoot, as in *P. brachytyla,* but one (rarely two) leaf below each bud projects nearly perpendicular to the shoot (as in *P. obovata*); pale or dark green on all surfaces; grassy scent when crushed.
SPECIMENS. Birr Castle, planted 1929, 39ft×2ft 11in (1966); Castlewellan, 27ft×3ft 3in (1970); Westonbirt (Morley Ride), 30ft×1ft 5in (1969); Borde Hill, 50ft×2ft 6in (1968); Headfort, 34ft×2ft 8in (1966); Bedgebury, planted 1937, 36ft×1ft 11in (1970); Wakehurst Place, 46ft×2ft 7in and 45ft×2ft 6in (1970).
RECOGNITION. Allied to *P. glehnii,* but quite different in the white, slender shoot and the uniform colour on all surfaces of the leaf also in depressed leaves instead of rising. *P. morrisonicola* is more like *P. obovata,* but very distinct with its slender white shoot and very fine needles. *P. wilsonii* also similar, but stouter, shiny leaves and normal, dense crown.

Picea obovata Lédébour. Siberian spruce

From Northern Scandinavia across Russia and Siberia to East Asia. Introduced in 1908. From this vast range great variation would be expected, and is found in collections, but the similarity always remarked between most forms and *P. abies* is negligible, except presumably in trees from the parts of Scandinavia and Russia where they merge into one another. In collections the trees, often bushes, are usually more like *P. wilsonii* in shoot and foliage. Rare; in a few collections and large gardens.
BARK. Purplish-grey, flecked with white, flaking to leave pale red-brown patches, or may be smooth.
CROWN. Often a bushy, low tree with projecting arched-down shoots, but can be a conic tree with a broad base and a fine spire of ascending branches, sweeping upwards towards their tips and with foliage hanging from them.
FOLIAGE. Shoot buff with pale orange pulvini; pale brown, pale pink, or pale orange, grooved with fine scattered pubescence not always visible to the naked eye and sometimes absent; second year dull grey; dark brown bud-scales adhering at nodes.

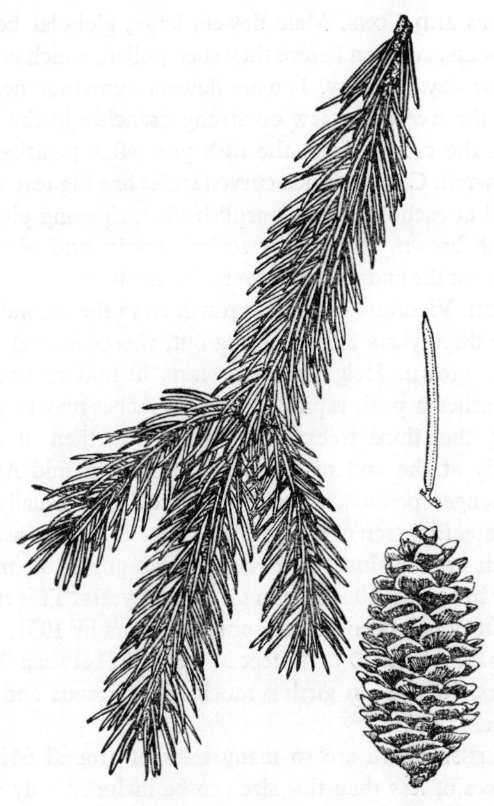

Fig. 121
Foliage, cone and (×1⅓) single leaf of *Picea obovata*, Siberian spruce. This tree is sometimes of a bushy form with more slender, arched shoots.

BUD. 6–7 mm ovoid, the orange-brown scales rounded but with minute free pointed tips.
LEAVES. Sometimes spreading below the shoot; usually pectinate below but depressed leaving a "V", as in *P. brachytyla*; very slender, pointing forwards, except a single leaf which projects widely from beneath each of the numerous side-buds; leaves above the shoot pressed forward closely to it; sparse on some trees, dense on others, abruptly acute to a bevelled tip with a short sharp point; shining green, above and below, (sometimes dull) with a few lines of stomata each side; 1·0–1·5 cm. Crushed foliage emits a sweet resinous aroma.
CONE. Cylindrical tapered each end, shining tan or light brown, 8·4 cm; scales smoothly rounded, some notched; often decurved.
GROWTH. The bushy form grows very slowly indeed. It seems to be damaged repeatedly by frosts and may be assumed to be from an interior Continental source. The more shapely trees have shown moderate growth but are variable in this respect. Two original trees are known and they differ considerably in vigour. The better tree, at Dawyck has a mean growth rate of 1 foot in height and one inch in girth for each year of its life since planting.
SPECIMENS. Dawyck, planted 1910, 59ft×4ft 10in (1966); 57ft×3ft 11in (1970); Blackmoor, planted 1911, 38ft×3ft 1in (1968); Wakehurst Place, 52ft×3ft 11in (1968); Bedgebury, planted 1926, 34ft×2ft 6in; 34ft×2ft 10in (1969); Abbeyleix, 30ft×2ft 1in; Edinburgh Royal Botanic Garden, 34ft×2ft 0in (1970).
RECOGNITION. Distinguished from all others except *P. morrisonicola*, by the slender leaves pressed downwards around the shoot and the single widely projecting leaf under each side-bud. From *P. morrisonicola* it is separable by the short-pointed far less fine leaves; stouter, darker, often pubescent shoot and dense crown.

Picea omorika (Pancic) Purkyne. Serbian spruce

The Drina Valley, Jugoslavia, (South-west Serbia). Introduced in 1889. Original trees known at Kew and probably

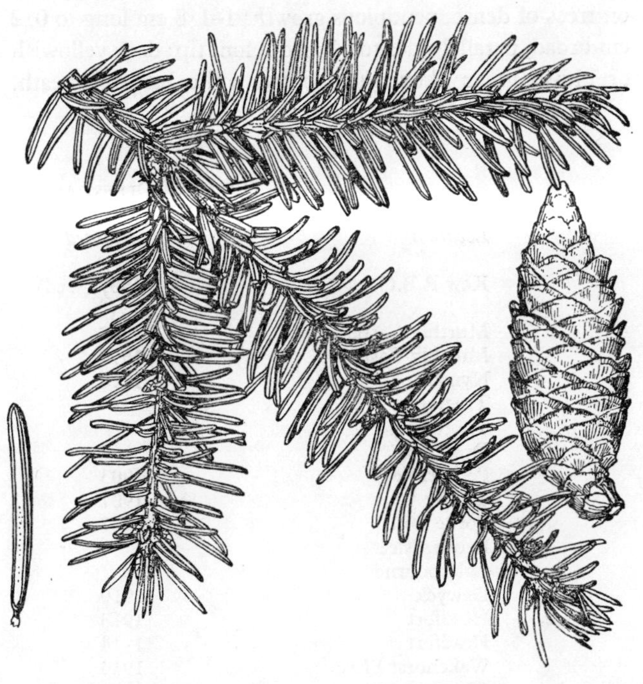

Fig. 122
Foliage and cone of *Picea omorika*, Serbian spruce, showing a form with somewhat upright leaves. The cone, which is pendulous, is purple, ripening to brown. The leaf (left×1⅓) shows the broadly rounded tip and broad, white stomatal bands on the underside.

at Dropmore, Murthly and Tregrehan. Frequent in many large gardens, parks and some small gardens even near towns.

BARK. Orange-brown or rufous; cracked into hard, square plates with a papery flaking surface.

CROWN. Very narrowly conic or columnar with a conic spire; occasional trees more broad. Some trees have a rather open crown of short branches which descend and then curve gently upwards, and carry rather sparse, bunched shoots. Others have a very dense crown, the exterior clothed in strongly ascending branch-ends from which hang dense sprays of pendulous shoots. The branches tend to arise from swollen bases where they join the bole. One tree known with layered branches.

FOLIAGE. Shoot dull pinkish-brown or orange, with a long pubescence. Second year dull, dark grey-brown.

BUD. Red-brown, often whitish at the base, from resin; ovoid, the acute tips of the scales just free. Buds on the sides of new shoots are numerous, dark brown and conic. Buds very late to expand—middle to end of May.

LEAVES. Pectinate below and spreading perpendicular to shoot, forward above, lying close and fanned out, slightly curved on trees of more open crowns, standing nearly erect on trees of dense, pendulous growth; 1–1·8 cm long to 0·2 cm broad, parallel sides to a broad, blunt tip; dark yellowish or bluish green above; two broad white bands beneath.

FLOWERS AND CONE. Male flowers large, globular beneath new shoots, crimson before they shed pollen, which is in the first few days of May. Female flowers numerous near the top of the tree and a few on strong branches in the upper half of the crown, from the fifth year after planting out; pinkish-red. Cone on thick curved stalk; like big tear-drops, tapered at each end, dark purplish-blue, ripening pink and purplish-brown, 6×3 cm; scales convex and shallowly rounded at the ends, with uneven, fine teeth.

GROWTH. Vigorous in height growth from the second year; two or three years after planting out, shoots of over 3 feet may be grown. Height-growth starts in mid or late May and reaches a peak rapidly so that 6 inches may be grown during the third week of growth, and then it ceases abruptly at the end of July, occasionally in mid-August. Over longer periods, mean height growth is usually only moderate. Eighteen of the trees given in 1931 can be assessed for their growth since. The youngest has grown the most—53 feet in height, 60 inches in girth in 36 years. This tree, at Bedgebury had been planted only five years by 1931. Seven more have added 40 to 46 feet in height in between 30 and 38 years. Increase in girth is much less vigorous and more variable.

SPECIMENS. There are so many trees of around 65ft×4ft that trees of less than this size can be included only where their age or growth have points of interest.

TABLE 51. OLDEST AND LARGEST TREES OF PICEA OMORIKA

Location	*Date Planted*	*Dimensions*	
Kew R.B.G.	1889 (seed)	23′ × 1′ 1″ (1931) (largest)	62′ × 2′ 9″ (1970) (largest)
Murthly Castle	1897	{ 45′ × 3′ 6″ (1931) }	{ 90′ × 6′ 2″ (1970)
Murthly Castle	1897		85′ × 6′ 3″ (1970)
Nymans	1898	49′ 6″ (1931)	68′ × 4′ 2″ (1966)
Tregrehan		45′ × 3′ 8″ (1927)	86′ × 4′ 10″ (1971)
Tregrehan			73′ × 4′ 3″ (1971)
Dropmore			79′ × 5′ 0″ (1970)
Pencarrow	1903	1′ 10″ (1927)	66′ × 3′ 11″ (1970)
Tilgate	1907	34′ × 2′ 5″ (1931)	67′ × 4′ 11″ (1961)
Borde Hill	1907	35′ × 2′ 2½″ (1931)	66′ × 3′ 1″ (1957)
Leonardslee			79′ × 4′ 2″ (1968)
Colesbourne			82′ × 3′ 9″ (1970)
Dawyck	1910	30′ 6″ × 2′ 2″(1931)	76′ × 4′ 6″ (1961)
Headfort	1913	27′ × 2′ 4″ (1931)	54′ × 6′ 1″ (1966)
Headfort	1914	27′ × 1′ 10″ (1931)	52′ × 5′ 10″ (1966)
Wakehurst Place	1914	25′ × 2′ 2″ (1931)	70′ × 4′ 7″ (1971)
Wakehurst Place	1914 ?		78′ × 4′ 7″ (1968)
Fenagh House	1918	17′ (1931)	60′ × 4′ 4″ (1968)
Keir House	1918		80′ × 4′ 0″ (1970)
Westonbirt	1921	28′ × 1′ 4″ (1931)	67′ × 2′ 10″ (1967)
Westonbirt	1933		68′ × 3′ 8″ (1969)
Bedgebury	1926	6′ 3″ (1931)	62′ × 2′ 10″ (1970)
Walcot Hall			73′ × 5′ 9″ (1959)
Sheffield Park	1910 ?		78′ × 5′ 0″ (1968)
Mells Park			69′ × 3′ 0″ (1962)
Endsleigh			71′ × 6′ 5″ (1963) at 4 feet
Ashbourne House			62′ × 5′ 9″ (1966)
Grange Road Woking			66′ × 3′ 1″ (1968)
Tongs Wood			65′ × 3′ 2″ (1968)

cv. Pendula. A small-growing tree with descending, long branches and pendulous foliage. Not usually particularly attractive as the crown is irregular.

Batsford Park, 40 feet; Vernon Holme, planted 1906, 34ft × 1ft 6in (1961).

RECOGNITION. The only other spruces with a comparable spired crown do not possess flattened leaves. Among flat-leaved spruces, the long, bluntly round-tipped leaves are distinct.

GENERAL. Serbian spruce has a remarkable range of tolerance in the soils on which it may flourish. Coming from a region of limestone mountains, it was to be expected that it would grow well on alkaline soils, but it does so also on acid, deep peats. Since the leaves emerge too late to be damaged by any normally late-season frost, and the form of the tree is so good, the ability to grow on soils where Sitka spruce is planted, made the Serbian spruce seem a likely substitute for Sitka in frosty hollows. There are a number of small plantations in several parts of England and Scotland. Despite the relatively slow increase in girth, volume production is at least equal to that of Norway spruce. Where Serbian spruce might have been planted the Norway spruce is preferred only because it is readily available and plants of Serbian spruce are not, in the quantities required.

Picea orientalis (L.) Link. Oriental spruce; Caucasian spruce.

Caucasus Mountains and southwards into Asia Minor. Introduced in 1839. Infrequent except in large gardens where it is common in all areas.

BARK. Young trees fawn-grey, smooth but roughened by pale, freckled leaf-traces. Old trees pink-brown or pink-grey; narrow curved cracks dividing it into hard rounded plates with horizontal lines of fine blisters, the plates being quite small and curling away.

CROWN. Narrowly conic until columnar with age, usually still slender-pointed. Young trees sparse, the long shoots unbranched, curving about at random, frequently with the leading shoot bowed. Crowns of older trees become very dense indeed, but around the apex remain open. Slender straight young shoots project, slightly ascending, from the general line of the crown in a distinctively spiky way. A few old trees have layered branches.

FOLIAGE. Shoot pale brown or yellowish-buff, pubescent, second year grey-buff.

BUD. Ovoid-conic 3–4 mm dull orange-brown; basal scales keeled with reddish points just free; finely pubescent.

LEAVES. On strong shoots very short, very closely adpressed to and growing all round the shoot. Smaller shoots have leaves pectinate beneath, lying forwards above and rising. Leaves notably the shortest of any spruce 0·6–0·8 cm deep shining green, with a glossy rounded tip, and 2 fine lines of stomata each side of midrib above, 5–7 each side below.

Fig. 123
Foliage and (×2) single leaf of *Picea orientalis*, Oriental spruce from the Caucasus Mountains. This has the shortest leaves of any spruce, abruptly bevelled to a short rounded tip.

FLOWERS AND CONE. Male flowers ovoid-conic, deep red before shedding pollen in the first two weeks of May. Cones freely borne over the upper crowns of the older trees, greyish-purple when young, ripening a distinctive ashen brown, fusiform, curved, and pointed, 6–10 cm long, the margins of the scales well rounded.

GROWTH. Young trees are slow for a few years but five or six years after planting out they may grow shoots nearly 3 feet long. Rapid height growth is maintained until about 70 feet is attained but after that it is very slow and even on favourable sites most trees are almost static when 90 or 100 feet tall. Growth in girth follows the same pattern, being very rapid from 1 foot until about 7 feet in girth but the biggest trees are scarcely adding to their girth now. Some examples of the slow growth of old trees and rapid growth of young trees can be seen from Table 52.

SPECIMENS. The tree at Stanage Park is from the original import of seed and that at Pencarrow probably is. The best trees are younger, some very fine specimens being those at Lowther Castle, Cortachy Castle, Leonardslee and Shroner's Hill.

TABLE 52. SOME SPECIMEN TREES OF PICEA ORIENTALIS

Locality	*Date Planted*	*Dimensions*	
Stanage Park	1840	90′ × 8′ 11″ (1931)	93′ × 10′ 7″ (1970)
Pencarrow	1846	40′ × 7′ 6″ (1927)	50′ × 8′ 1″ (1970)[1]
Highnam	1847		95′ × 9′ 7″ (1970)
Althorp	1851	76′ × 6′ 1″ (1931)	78′ × 7′ 3″ (1964)
Hewell Grange	1856	69′ × 6′ 8″ (1931)	85′ × 7′ 2″ (1963)
Dogmersfield		78′ × 7′ 8″ (1907)	99′ × 9′ 9″ (1961)
Stratfield Saye		76′ × 7′ 8″ (1907)	95′ × 10′ 1″ (1968)
Highnam (2)		67′ × 7′ 0″ (1905)	87′ × 9′ 7″ (1970)
Bedgebury House		90′ × 8′ 7″ (1931)	100′ × 9′ 1″ (1966)[2]
Westonbirt (1)		79′ × 8′ 6″ (1931)	98′ × 9′ 10″ (1971)
Woburn	1860	78′ × 7′ 5″ (1931)	76′ × 8′ 10″ (1970)
Broxwood Court			98′ × 11′ 7″ (1957)
Glamis Castle	1869	70′ × 6′ 4″ (1931)	92′ × 8′ 7″ (1970)
Titness Park			96′ × 10′ 7″ (1957)
Hallyburton			111′ × 7′ 8″ (1970)
Munches			82′ × 10′ 1″ (1970)
Inveraray (Lime Kilns)			96′ × 10′ 8″ (1969)
Stanway			80′ × 10′ 6″ (1964)
Inistioge			66′ × 10′ 3″ (1966)
Carton		65′ (1931)	76′ × 10′ 3″ (1968)
Cowdray Park	1870		82′ × 9′ 5″ (1967)
Cortachy Castle	1873		104′ × 10′ 1″ (1962)
Cortachy Castle			87′ × 10′ 6″ (1962)
Kinnettles	1891	41′ × 6′ 2″ (1931)	75′ × 9′ 5″ (1970)
Mells Park			103′ × 7′ 8″ (1962)
Bicton			100′ × 8′ 3″ (1968)
Rossie Priory		77′ × 7′ 9″ (1931)	94′ × 10′ 4″ (1970)
Dupplin Castle			106′ × 9′ 10″ (1970)
Petworth House			105′ × 8′ 11″ (1971)
Cultoquhey			98′ × 10′ 2″ (1970)
Strone			102′ × 7′ 7″ (1969)
Lowther Castle			102′ × 7′ 7″ (1967)
Fenagh House	1892	49′ × 4′ 2″ (1931)	75′ × 6′ 8″ (1968)
Blackmoor	1895	45′ × 4′ 8″ (1931)	99′ × 9′ 8″ (1957)
Nymans	1898	53′ × 4′ 3″ (1931)	79′ × 6′ 6″ (1970)
Hergest Croft	1898		87′ × 7′ 4″ (1969)
Leonardslee	ca.1905		81′ × 7′ 0″ (1969)
Little Hall	1906	49′ × 3′ 4″ (1931)	61′ × 5′ 10″ (1961)
Tilgate	1907	38′ × 4′ 2″ (1931)	75′ × 7′ 2″ (1961)
Tongs Wood	ca.1908		68′ × 9′ 3″ (1968)
St. Clere	ca.1908		52′ × 7′ 1″ (1969)
Benmore			108′ × 8′ 9″ (1971)
Shroner's Hill			78′ × 9′ 9″ (1966)
Lythe Hill			92′ × 9′ 1″ (1969)
Dawyck	1909	38′ × 2′ 8″ (1931)	84′ × 6′ 6″ (1961)
Knowefield	1911	22′ × 1′ 4″ (1931)	51′ × 2′ 10″ (1958)
Headfort	1914	26′ × 2′ 4″ (1931)	60′ × 7′ 2″ (1966)
Wakehurst Place	1914	30′ × 2′ 1″ (1931)	62′ × 5′ 11″ (1971)
Westonbirt (2)	1923		61′ × 5′ 0″ (1967)
Bedgebury	1932		39′ × 3′ 3″ (1968)

[1] Top leans out level for 20 feet
[2] Dying back at the top

RECOGNITION. The thick, curved blunt tips of the very short leaves and the hairy shoots distinguish *P. orientalis* from any *P. abies* in which ill health has caused the leaves to be very short and, from all other spruces.

GENERAL. A few of the largest trees have died back at the top. Many others have almost ceased growth. So it seems that despite the usual very healthy foliage and strong early growth, the ultimate age is being approached and that this is not much in excess of 100 years. The late opening of the leaf buds make it a very hardy tree and a few small trials have been made in plantations, but without much success.

cv. Aurea. (Bergedorf, Germany, pre-1892.) New shoots bright pale yellow, fading to dark green in mid-summer but until then contrasting beautifully with the very dark older foliage. Very rare. Three good trees at Bedgebury, 25–45 feet tall.

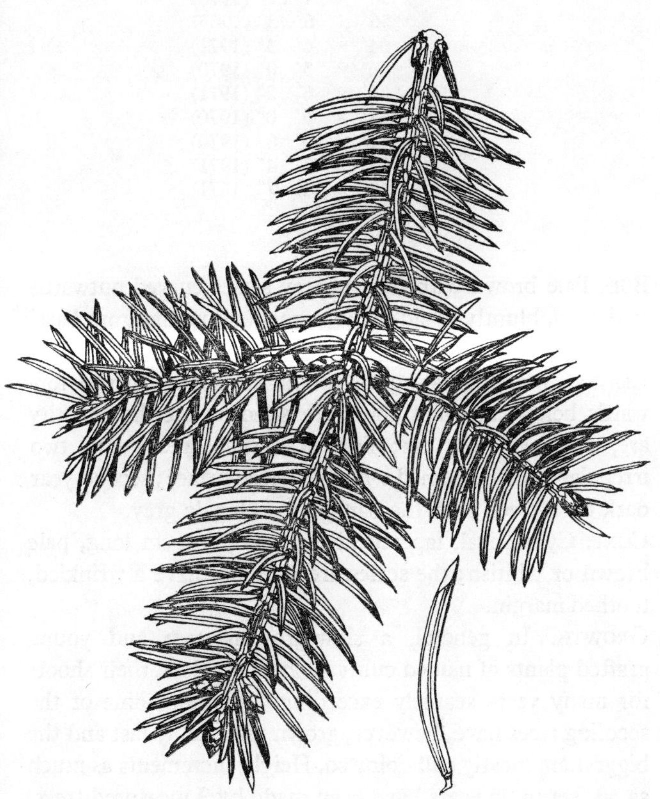

Picea polita

Fig. 124
Foliage of *Picea polita*, Tiger-tail spruce from Japan. The stout, rigid leaf curves to a very sharp point (right × 1⅓) and the buds are glossy chestnut-orange.

Picea polita (Siebold and Zuccarini) Carriere. Tiger-tail spruce

Honshiu Island, Japan. Introduced in 1861. Uncommon; present in most collections and many large gardens but rarely elsewhere.

BARK. Purplish brown to grey-brown, rough and scaly between coarse irregular cracks; ashen grey leaf-traces stipple the large flakes.

CROWN. Conical with narrow top; branches level protruding a little way in short spikes from the crown. Colour a distinctive dark yellowish green. Epicormic sprouts may grow on the bole.

FOLIAGE. Shoot stout, prominently ridged, creamy-white and glabrous; second year buff; third year pale orange.

BUD. Conic-ovoid 6 mm smooth, bright chestnut, leaving prominent scales at the nodes for three years.

LEAVES. Radiate all round the shoot, perpendicular to it except those on the upper side which curve forwards; 1·5–2 cm, stout, stiff, rigid and spined, dark shiny green with faint stomatal lines on all sides.

CONE. Long-ovoid, shining yellowish-brown, ripening reddish purple-brown then grey-brown 8–12×4 cm, curved, thin, leathery scales rounded and finely toothed with pale, waved margin; confined to near the top of the older trees only.

GROWTH. After a slow start, growth in height and girth is steady and moderate. Of fifteen trees re-measured since 1931, the greatest increments in height are 52 feet in 32 years (Endsleigh) and 32 feet in 30 years (Dropmore) and except for two the other increments lie between 14 feet and 29 feet in 26–35 years. The increments in girth of thirteen trees with earlier recorded dimensions lie mostly between 20 and 30 inches, the oldest tree having added the most—about 48 inches in 42 years (Pencarrow). More details can be seen in the table of specimens (Table 53). Short-lived.

SPECIMENS. No tree is positively recorded as an original tree, but from its size in 1927 and now, the larger tree at Pencarrow most probably is. Another tree at Linton Park is among other species planted in 1866 and its dimensions suggest it could well be from 1861 seed. The oldest and biggest trees, with earlier dimensions where known are given in Table 53.

TABLE 53. THE OLDEST AND BIGGEST PICEA POLITA

Locality	*Date planted*	*Dimensions*	
Pencarrow	?1865	50′ × 6′ 0″ (1927)	80′ × 9′ 10″ (1970)
Linton Park	?1866	38′ × 3′ 1″ (1931)	57′ × 5′ 6″ (1965)
Stourhead	1871	47′ (1931)	83′ × 7′ 7″ (1970)
Scorrier House	1878	35′ × 3′ 10″ (1928)	51′ × 6′ 0″ (1959)
Hewell Grange	1882	47′ × 4′ 4″ (1931)	61′ × 5′ 5″ (1963)
Eridge Castle	1883		57′ × 5′ 3″ (1971)
Eridge Castle	1886		52′ × 4′ 3″ (1971)
Endsleigh	ca.1900	20′ (1931)	74′ × 8′ 5″ (1970)
Dropmore	1902	26′ × 1′ 6″ (1930)	60′ × 4′ 8″ (1970)
Little Hall	1906	31′ × 2′ 1″ (1931)	48′ × 4′ 1″ (1961)
Petworth House			80′ × 7′ 2″ (1971)
Keir House		24′ × 1′ 0″ (1931)	52′ × 3′ 6″ (1970)
Westonbirt (Specimen Avenue)			69′ × 4′ 9″ (1971)
Melbury			67′ × 6′ 2″ (1970)
Trewidden			62′ × 6′ 5″ (1959)
Heckfield Place			67′ × 6′ 8″ (1969)
Castlewellan			53′ × 6′ 6″ (1966)
Shroner's Hill			60′ × 5′ 7″ (1966)
Ochtertyre (Perth)			51′ × 4′ 5″ (1970)
Batsford Park			59′ × 5′ 10″ (1963)
Scone			56′ × 4′ 11″ (1970)
Longleat (Heaven's Gate)			56′ × 6′ 3″ (1963)
Strone			64′ × 6′ 3″ (1971)
Murthly Castle			66′ × 5′ 0″ (1970)
Tregrehan			62′ × 6′ 2″ (1971)
Sindlesham (Bear Wood)			67′ × 6′ 0″ (1970)
Benenden			64′ × 4′ 8″ (1970)
Warnham Court			52′ × 3′ 4″ (1971)
Oakley Park			60′ × 4′ 7″ (1971)

RECOGNITION. Deep yellow-green, fiercely spined, stout, rigid, radiating leaves and bright chestnut, smooth buds are sufficient to separate this from all other spruces.

Picea pungens Engelmann. Colorado spruce

Colorado, New Mexico, Utah and Wyoming, South-west United States. Date of introduction thought to be about 1865 but the first known tree is a very glaucous var. *glauca* raised from a cutting in 1877 at Knaphill, and a fine tree today. The type is very rare, a narrow, densely crowned tree, predominantly a dark blue-green. Only two trees clearly of this form have been seen.

Westonbirt (Willesley Drive), 56ft × 4ft 0in (1969) and Leonardslee (Hill Garden), 49ft × 3ft 4in (1969).

cv. Glauca (Colorado, 1877). Blue spruce. Very common in parks and gardens of all sizes and in towns. This collective name covers the blue seedlings raised from seed of the natural population and a number of cultivars propagated vegetatively from selected, very blue seedlings. It thus includes "cv. Argentea".

BARK. Dark red-brown, rough with scales.

CROWN. Narrowly conic with short, level branches. Big trees are columnar in the lower crown, narrowly conic above, and the lower branches descend slightly and curve upwards towards their tips.

FOLIAGE. Shoot slightly shiny, pale yellow-brown, stout, glabrous and grooved; second year dark purple-brown.

BUD. Pale brown with free, papery scales curved outwards at the tip, bluntly ovoid-conic, some long points from basal scales may extend to the tip.

LEAVES. Stout, radiating all round the shoot, curved forwards below, upswept above the shoot where the majority are, stiff, 1·5–2·0 cm; first year rich green with two irregular bands bloomed white on each surface; second year dark blue-green with the bands on each side grey.

CONE. Cylindrical, tapered at each end, 5–8 cm long, pale brown or whitish; the scales are thin and have a wrinkled, toothed margin.

GROWTH. In general, a slow-growing tree and young grafted plants of named cultivars are very slow, their shoots for many years scarcely exceeding 6 inches. Some of the seedling trees have, however, grown reasonably fast and the biggest are mostly still doing so. Height increments as much as 30 feet in 25 years have been made by 3 measured trees.

SPECIMENS. The original tree at the Knaphill Nurseries, (G. Waterer's), raised in 1877 from a cutting, was 41ft × 4ft in 1931 and 62ft × 5ft 5in in 1961. An early tree at Westonbirt House was 40ft × 2ft 9in in 1931 and 73ft × 5ft 7in in 1967. Other good trees are: Borde Hill (Garden), 22 feet (1931), 61ft × 3ft 5in (1961); Patshull House, 76ft × 4ft 3in; 72ft × 4ft 5in (1970); Tring Park, planted 1906, 65ft × 6ft 0in (1965); Warnham Court, 86ft × 4ft 0in (1971); Dropmore, 64ft × 4ft 7in (1970); Hardwicke, planted 1913, 60ft × 5ft 5in (1952, M. Greville); Terling Place, 69ft × 3ft 1in

Fig. 125
Spray of *Picea pungens* cv. Glauca, Blue Colorado spruce. Many similar cultivars are widely planted. They differ in details of colour and arrangement of leaves; in many the leaves are more erect, but all have the leaves radiating all round the shoot and tapering to a sharply spined point (right × 1⅓).

(1953, M. G.); Eridge Castle, planted 1880, 69ft × 5ft 2in (1971); Highnam, 72ft × 4ft 0in (1970); Ramster, 57ft × 4ft 1in a fine silvery tree (1963); Batsford Park, 71ft × 5ft 5in; 62ft × 6ft 7in (1971); Shroner's Hill, 62ft × 3ft 10in (1966); Frensham Hall, 65ft × 6ft 2in (1967); Radley College, 78ft × 5ft 0in (1968); Highclere, 61ft × 3ft 7in (1968); Bagshot Park, 66ft × 5ft 6in (1963); Hergest Croft, planted 1897, 70ft × 5ft 11in (1969); The Frythe, 65ft × 4ft 0in (1969); Brahan, planted 1901, 50ft × 4ft 4in (1970); Pencarrow, planted 1899, 49ft × 4ft 2in (1970); Woburn Abbey, 64ft × 3ft 7in (1970); Leighton Hall, 70ft × 6ft 3in (1971).

Selected cultivars. The most frequently planted form is cv. Koster, which has the leaves very distinctly bloomed white and retains this colour in the winter. It was raised before 1885 by Arie Koster at Boskoop. In 1908 Van Nes selected and propagated ten of the best plants of Koster's stock and it is these which are in commerce—usually as "*P. pungens kosteriana*". This form is thus variable and all lie within the cv. Glauca. cv. Moerheim (1912) is similar with paler shoots and longer leaves (2·5–3 cm), perhaps a brighter blue-white. cv. Endtz (Boskoop, about 1925) is growing at Fota as a neat little tree, 14 feet high, with a dense shapely narrow crown; the new leaves are bright blue, contrasting with rich green leaves a year old.

Recognition. The two species which might be confused with *P. pungens* are *P. asperta* and *P. engelmanni*. The leaves of *P. asperata* are usually shorter (1·5 cm) and those beneath the shoot are bent backwards; the bark peels away in big papery flakes and the crown is more open inside. *P. engelmanni* differs in bark (q.v.) and the soft leaves lying forwards over the shoot; and pubescent pulvini.

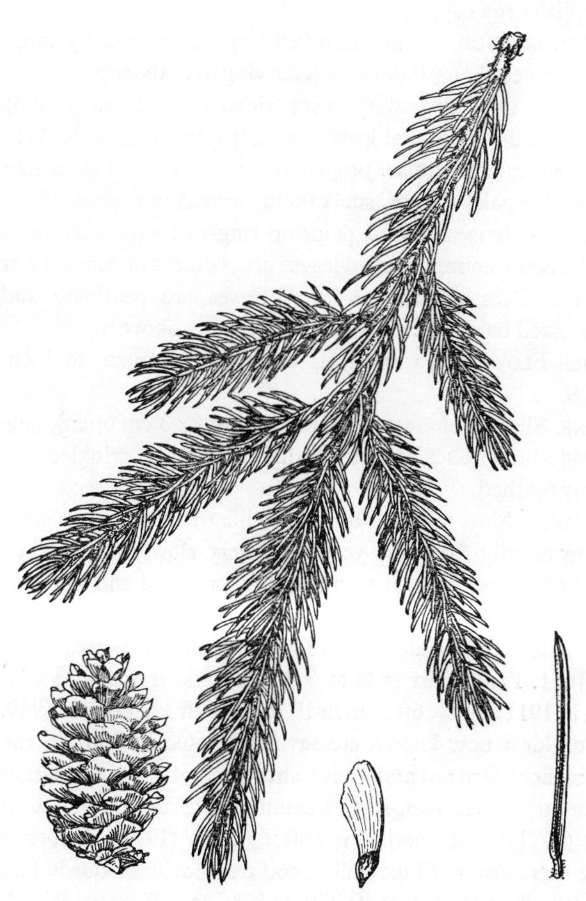

Fig. 126
Spray of foliage, cone, seed (below × 1⅓) and leaf (right × 2) of *Picea rubens*, Red spruce of N. America. The cone is a pale orange-brown. The leaves are usually very slender, curved upwards and bright grassy green, but some trees tend towards *P. mariana* and have less slender, bluer leaves.

Picea rubens Sargent. Red spruce.

Nova Scotia to North Carolina. Introduced before 1755. Rare; in collections only.

Bark. Young trees rich purplish-brown, scaling away in fine flakes. Somewhat older trees dark grey with fine brown flakes; old trees dark purplish-grey, red-brown in places, cracked into small (5×5 cm) concave plates.
Crown. Narrowly conic at all ages, tapering to a fine spire, very dense and an unusual, dark yellowish-green. Upper branches ascending, lower branches descend a little then curve upwards.
Foliage. Shoot pale orange or buff-brown with short pubescence, scattered or quite dense. Second year dark purplish brown.
Terminal Bud. 4 mm deep red-brown, covered by long-pointed very hairy basal scales, curving over the top.
Leaves. Typically, wiry, very slender (< 1 mm) lying forwards but all lateral leaves strongly curved inwards, 1·3–1·5 cm; quadrangular, bright grassy-green on all sides first year, to a pale, abrupt, short point, second year deep glossy green. A dense forward pointing ring of leaves surrounds each recent node. Crushed leaves are redolent of camphor or apples. Occasionally the lower leaves are pectinate and depressed below the shoot instead of swept above it.
Male Flowers. Crimson, up-curved when open, to 1 cm long.
Cone. Slightly elongated ovoid, 4·5 cm (×3 cm open), pale orange-brown; scales convex, slightly striated, crinkled and finely toothed.
Growth. Slow to start but in early life this species can grow quite rapidly for some years, but very slowly again when about 100 years old. It seems to be short-lived and to die or be blown down when over this age.
Specimens. The oldest tree of known date was blown down in 1961. Planted in 1836 at Stanage Park, it was 72ft×5ft 9in in 1911; 99ft×6ft 2½in in 1931 and 87ft×7ft 0in in 1959. The oldest now known are several planted in 1861 in the Rhinefield Ornamental Drive and three of these are larger than any others seen in this country. The best is 82ft×5ft 0in (1971); and another is 66ft×5ft 7in (1971). A forked tree there also is 73 feet tall. Good trees include: Borde Hill (Gores Wood), 65ft×4ft 8in (1967) and Warren Wood, 54ft×3ft 6in (1968); Wakehurst Place, 59ft×3ft 10in (1970); Walcot Park, 58ft×4ft 6in (1959); Bicton, 60ft×4ft 8in (1968); Bedgebury, planted 1925, 50ft×4ft 2in; 54ft×3ft 3in; 56ft×3ft 3in and 43ft×3ft 10in (1970).
Recognition. The bright green wiry, curved leaves on a hairy brown shoot are unlike those of any other tree. This species does, however, hybridise with *P. mariana* and hybrid swarms occur over wide areas where their ranges overlap. Some seed lots have yielded occasional trees with shorter, bluer, less curved leaves and some even more like *P. mariana.* The plot at Bedgebury contains some trees of these kinds.

Picea schrenkiana

Fig. 127
Foliage of *Picea schrenkiana* from Central Asia. The stout, ribbed shoot is glossy pale cream, as in *P. smithiana* but the buds are pale cream-brown. The leaf (right ×1⅓) is stout, and obtusely pointed and has an ill-defined pale band on each surface.

Picea schrenkiana Fischer and Meyer. Schrenk spruce.

Central Asia, from Turkmen to China. Introduced in 1877. Rare, and confined to large collections.
Bark. Dark purple-grey flaking away to leave orange-brown; fissured into rough, broken ridges.
Crown. Ovoid-conic and dense, with numerous close, level branches, ascending slightly at their tips, the side shoots radiating from them, those hanging are quite short, not long-pendulous.

Foliage. Shoot stout, 4–5 mm across, shallowly grooved or folded, shining pale cream, finely pubescent (under a lens) particularly on the pulvini; second year brownish-cream; third year, still shining but fawn.
Bud. Ringed by forward-pointing leaves on swollen pulvini, cream-brown, conic, 3–5 mm, leaving very pale brown scales at the nodes, running 5 mm up the shoot.
Leaves. 3–3·5×0·15 cm all round the shoot, pointing rather forwards, thick, abruptly pointed or obtuse, densely set; pale green or dark yellow-green with a pale green band on each surface.
Cone. Cylindric, slightly tapered to rounded tip, 5–8×2–3 cm, blackish-purple-brown, each scale fringed with white resin, convex broad, incurved.
Growth and Specimens. The only dated specimens, two in number, have made very slow growth. These are at Bayfordbury, planted 1907, 35ft×2ft 11in (1968) and Dropmore, planted 1911, 38ft×2ft 5in (1961). Others have evidently grown more rapidly. One at St. Clere, dating from about 1910 was 51ft×3ft 0in in 1954 but then lost its top, another there is 37ft×2ft 7in (1969). Other trees are at: Hergest Croft, 35ft×2ft 4in (1961); Wisley Royal Horticultural Society Gardens, 50ft×3ft 0in (1969); Warnham Court, 44ft×2ft 1in (1959); Wakehurst Place, 65ft×3ft 3in and 62ft×4ft 6in (1970); Castle Leod, 50ft×5ft 11in (1966).
Recognition. Closely similar to *P. smithiana* differing in bark; pale, few-scaled non-resinous bud; pubescent pulvini; long very pale adhering bud-scales at nodes; the leaves harder, stouter, more above the shoot, straighter and blunter. The crown is scarcely pendulous.

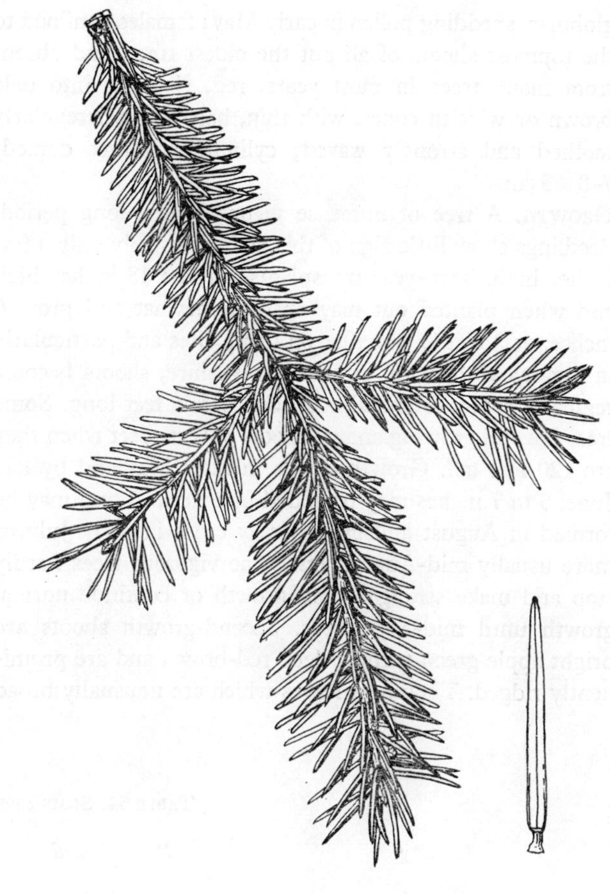

Picea sitchensis

Fig. 128
Foliage of *Picea sitchensis*, Sitka spruce, the main species used in afforestation in western and northern Britain. The shoot is white, and grooved, and the hard, flattened leaf (right ×$1\frac{1}{2}$) has a sharp tip and very broad, blue-white stomatal bands beneath.

Picea sitchensis (Bongard) Carriere. Sitka spruce

East Kodiak Island, Alaska; coast and islands in a narrow strip through British Columbia, Washington and Oregon to Caspar, North California. Introduced in 1831 by David Douglas and two original trees known in Ireland. Abundant as a plantation tree over huge areas of western Britain and Ireland, and in almost all large gardens and policies in those areas. Less widespread in the east and unusual in East Anglia and Yorkshire.
Bark. Young trees, dark purplish-brown; dark grey leaf-traces adhering as vertical flakes; pale brown lenticels horizontal. With age, large curving cracks appear. Old trees purple-grey, cracked into round, curling plates.
Crown. Narrowly conical and open, when young, with widely spaced, strongly whorled, ascending branches. Broadly columnar when old with arched branches splayed out, but usually retaining a short-pointed apex. Very large trees vary in their crown types. Some are dense with short branches and hanging foliage, whilst the majority have huge ascending branches arching out flat and wide, rather thinly clad with foliage. Epicormic shoots frequent, slender and bunched.

Foliage. Shoot white or pale buff, grooved and bumpy, glabrous; second year pale orange, more deeply grooved.
Bud. Small blunt ovoid, pale brown, purplish with resin.
Leaves. Pectinate and widely spreading below, but on main shoots several straight down or curved backwards below; upper leaves fanning out forwards, pressed flat, or rising very slightly; on second year shoots rising a little more, 2–2·5 cm ridged, ending in an abrupt spiny point, very flattened, stiff and hard, shining fresh dark green above, with two faint bands of stomata; two broad, very white or bluish bands beneath, leaving narrow midrib and margins. Occasional trees are surrounded by huge, layered branches.
Flowers and Cone. Male flowers seldom abundant,

globular, shedding pollen in early May; females confined to the topmost shoots of all but the oldest trees, and absent from many trees in most years, red, ripening into pale brown or whitish cones, with thin, hard scales irregularly toothed and strongly waved; cylindric, bluntly domed, 7–8×3 cm.

GROWTH. A tree of immense vigour over a long period. Seedlings show little sign of this and are usually only a few inches high. Two-year transplants may be 18 inches high and when planted out may check somewhat and grow 6 inches, or 2 feet. Thereafter on damp sites and particularly in regions with damp air, like Argyllshire, shoots become regularly three, four and occasionally five feet long. Some trees are still growing annual shoots of three feet when they are 120 feet tall. Growth begins in early May and by late June, 5 to 7 inches may be added in a week. A bud may be formed in August and growth may cease in early July or more usually mid-August, but some vigorous trees hardly stop and make strong second growth or continue normal growth until mid-September. Second-growth shoots are bright apple green turning deep red-brown and are prominently ridged. They bear leaves which are unusually broad at the base and longer than normal leaves. A whorl of short, slightly nodding shoots grow on the leading shoot at the point from which second growth begins.

The most vigorous growth by young plantation trees is shown by a planting in a much-flooded valley bottom at Culverwell, near Dunster. These were planted in 1928 and after 43 years growth the biggest trees are 120ft×9ft 10in; 131ft×7ft 11in and 124ft×7ft 4in (1970).

Trees re-measured since 1905 or 1931 have not shown increases of these dimensions, but the largest increases are well spread through the age-classes. The original tree at Curraghmore has grown 54 feet in height and 93 inches in girth in the 63 years since 1905, and 24 feet in height and 48 inches in girth in 37 years since 1931. Many more examples can be seen in Table 54.

SPECIMENS. The tree planted in 1841 at Dropmore was a 6-inch cutting which had been rooted from an original tree. At Curraghmore there is a group of Sitka spruces of similar sizes to the original tree (see Table 54). They may be contemporary with it, but being planted among *Sequoiadendron* and *Abies nordmanniana* they may date with these, from about 1856.

TABLE 54. SOME SPECIMENS OF PICEA SITCHENSIS

Locality	*Date Planted*	*Dimensions*	
Curraghmore	1835	106′ × 12′ 0″ (1905)	160′ × 19′ 9″ (1968)
Curraghmore			150′ × 19′ 11″ (1968)
Curraghmore			150′ × 18′ 4″ (1968)
Abbeyleix	1835	90′ × 11′ 4″ (1910)	125′ × 15′ 4″ (1968)
Dropmore	1841	73′ × 8′ 2″ (1891)	93′ × 12′ 8″ (1970)
Pencarrow	1842	90′ × 10′ 9″ (1927)	102′ × 12′ 2″ (1970)
Boconnoc	1843	86′ × 15′ 0″ (1905)	108′ × 21′ 1″ (1970)[2]
Murthly Castle	1846	132′ × 14′ 8″ (1931)	174′ × 16′ 3″ (1970)
Murthly Castle	1846		162′ × 16′ 9″ (1970)
Drummuir	1850		120′ × 15′ 9″ (1960)
Kilkerran	ca.1850	95′ × 11′ 8″ (1931)	131′ × 14′ 2″ (1970)
Heanton Satcheville	1851	112′ × 18′ 0″ (1928)	135′ × 19′ 6″ (1960)
Culzean Castle	1851	105′ × 14′ 0″ (1931)	136′ × 16′ 0″ (1970)
Culzean Castle	1851		115′ × 16′ 1″ (1970)
Albury Park	1851	92′ × 10′ 8″ (1931)	102′ × 11′ 3″ (1968)
Scone	1852	108′ × 14′ 4″ (1931)	131′ × 18′ 3″ (1970)
Scone	1852	101′ × 14′ 8″ (1931)	138′ × 18′ 3″ (1970)
Scone	1852	105′ × 14′ 8″ (1931)	146′ × 18′ 8″ (1970)
Scone	1852	106′ × 14′ 9″ (1931)	146′ × 19′ 0″ (1970)
Ballogie	1854	100′ × 14′ 2″ (1931)	115′ × 16′ 0″ (1961)
Murraythwaite	ca.1855	78′ × 8′ 10″ (1904)	101′ × 13′ 11″ (1966)
Dawyck	1856	89′ × 13′ 5″ (1930)	121′ × 17′ 11″ (1970)
Dawyck	1856	88′ × 11′ 4″ (1930)	137′ × 14′ 8″ (1966)
Dawyck	1856		124′ × 16′ 8″ (1970)
Kilravock Castle	1856	107′ × 19′ 3″ (1931)	135′ × 22′ 8″ (1970)
Kilravock Castle			138′ × 17′ 5″ (1970)
Munches	1856	100′ × 12′ 8″ (1931)	115′ × 15′ 7″ (1970)
Castlehill			138′ × 24′ 10″ (1970)
Fairburn			140′ × 22′ 0″ (1970)
Knightshayes			129′ × 19′ 9″ (1970)[1]
Drumtochty			154′ × 20′ 3″ (1970)
Cranford Farm			110′ × 18′ 10″ (1968)
Monk Coniston			115′ × 19′ 0″ (1971)
Castle Leod			150′ × 17′ 11″ (1966)
Bolderwood	1860	115′ × 11′ 2″ (1931)	135′ × 12′ 7″ (1970)

Locality	*Date Planted*	*Dimensions*	
Stourhead	1861	100′ × 11′ 4″ (1931)	131′ × 14′ 9″ (1970)
Cullen House	1861	103′ × 14′ 9″ (1931)	129′ × 17′ 5″ (1970)
Novar	1862		140′ × 15′ 6″ (1956)
Dupplin Castle	1863	98′ × 12′ 6″ (1931)	131′ × 15′ 7″ (1970)
Dupplin Castle	1863	114′ × 15′ 0″ (1931)	128′ × 16′ 2″ (1970)
Balmacaan			151′ × 20′ 4″ (1970)
Glamis Castle	1864	106′ × 12′ 3″ (1931)	126′ × 16′ 3″ (1970)
Glamis Castle			144′ × 15′ 9″ (1970)
Rossie Priory		105′ × 12′ 3″ (1931)	138′ × 14′ 8″ (1970)
Blair Atholl (Diana's Grove)			157′ × 12′ 0″ (1970)
Glenlee Park			159′ × 15′ 8″ (1970)
Lanrick Castle	1867		142′ × 15′ 10″ (1970)[2]
Powerscourt	1867	114′ × 16′ 3″ (1931)	145′ × 20′ 1″ (1966)[1]
Powerscourt	1867		151′ × 17′ 8″ (1966)
Shelton Abbey			162′ × 18′ 6″ (1968)
Blair Atholl (St. Brides)	1872	82′ × 11′ 2″ (1931)	141′ × 13′ 3″ (1970)
Dunans			162′ × 10′ 9″ (1969)
Dunans			158′ × 11′ 10″ (1969)
Dunans			145′ × 15′ 0″ (1969)
Inveraray (Dubh Loch)	1876		160′ × 13′ 1″ (1969)
Inveraray (Lime Kilns)			160′ × 15′ 4″ (1969)
Inveraray (Frews Br.)			155′ × 17′ 0″ (1969)
Skibo Castle			120′ × 16′ 3″ (1955)
Benmore			140′ × 17′ 11″ (1970)
Bicton		85′ × 11′ 6″ (1902)	124′ × 14′ 7″ (1968)
Penrhyn Castle		× 10′ 4″ (1904)	116′ × 14′ 11″ (1959)
Belladrum			157′ × 15′ 6″ (1970)
Ballimore		116′ × 16′ 0″ (1931)	120′ × 18′ 11″ (1969)
Castle Forbes		85′ × 11′ 9″ (1931)	100′ × 14′ 4″ (1968)
Fenagh House	1896	72′ × 5′ 6″ (1931)	108′ × 11′ 7″ (1968)
Humewood Castle			130′ × 14′ 2″ (1968)
Glenapp	ca.1900	59′ × 4′ 10″ (1931)	131′ × 9′ 11″ (1970)
Langholm		104′ × 7′ 11″ (1931)	120′ × 11′ 4″ (1955)
Brahan	1901		105′ × 13′ 2″ (1970)
Wakehurst Place	ca.1914		78′ × 11′ 6″ (1969)
Fonthill	1914		119′ × 6′ 9″ (1960)
Speech House	1916		90′ × 7′ 8″ (1960)
Bedgebury	1926	7 (1931)	74′ × 6′ 8″ (1970)
Speech House Walk	1937		86′ × 6′ 0″ (1967)

[1] Measured at 4 feet
[2] Dying back at the top (Knightshayes tree died and was felled in 1971)

General. Sitka spruce has shown remarkable ability to grow fast for long periods on a wide range of damp soils, from clay-loam to deep peat. It can yield higher volumes on most sites than any other species, particularly at moderate to high elevations and in exposure. The thinnings are among the most desired for the production of pulp. It is therefore the first choice among species for the afforestation of the western and northern upland areas. The recent tendency to more intensive treatment of sites before planting is justified economically by enabling Sitka spruce to establish itself rapidly where it would otherwise be too slow to be worth planting. As this trend increases, Sitka spruce will be planted on even more sites. The first trials of this species were encouraged by the observation, soon after 1920, that in policies and gardens over much of Scotland, the Sitka spruces, planted mostly from 1855 to 1880, were already very big trees and usually towered above most of the other trees planted with them, particularly on exposed sites and poor soils. Today this is even more marked, despite some losses from the severe gales since 1952, and the remarkable success of Sitka in many kinds of site from Cornwall to Caithness shows the validity of these observations. The greatest limitation to the growth, and therefore to the planting of this tree is that when under moisture-stress, whether from bad drainage restricting the root-system or from dry soils or atmosphere, bad attacks from the spruce aphid (*Elatobium abietinum*) develop. It is also badly checked in growth in frost-hollows.

Picea smithiana

Fig. 129
Foliage of *Picea smithiana*, Morinda spruce, a tree from the Western Himalaya with pendulous shoots. The foliage resembles that of *P. schrenkiana*, except in being pendulous; the purple-brown, resinous bud and longer, sharply pointed leaf (right × 1⅓).

Picea smithiana. (Wallich) Boissier. (*P. morinda* Link) Morinda Spruce.

Afghanistan to Nepal. Introduced in 1818 to Hopetown where the one original tree and one graft from it survive. Frequent. Common in collections and large gardens, uncommon in smaller gardens, parks and church-yards.

BARK. Dark purple-grey, shallowly cracked into hard rather square small plates which lift away from the bole.

CROWN. Columnar with a conic top, or rather broadly conic. Branches level and spreading far in broad trees, with shoots pendulous from them. Old trees open grown may have very large low branches, upswept. The narrower trees have usually dense crowns while some old, broad trees have very thin and open ones. In young trees the branches ascend and the hanging shoots are short.

FOLIAGE. Shoot pale brown or cream, rather stout, shiny with many shallow folds. Second year dull coffee-brown. Third year grey-pink or grey-brown.

BUD. Large, ovoid or conic-ovoid surrounded by leaves forward on swollen pulvini, red-brown and shiny with resin, 5–7 mm leaving bright chestnut-brown scales at the nodes 1–1·5 cm along shoot.

LEAVES. Slender, curving forwards and inwards 3·5–4 cm × 0·1 cm, all round the shoot, quadrangular, shiny dark green with faint stomatal lines on all sides, tapering to a sharp point.

FLOWERS AND CONE. Male flowers large, 2 cm, conic ovoid, terminal on pendulous shoots. Cones restricted to around the apex in all but the oldest trees, large, 12–17 cm × 3–4 cm cylindrical but markedly tapered at each end, very pale green in summer, bright brown when ripe; with shiny, smooth leathery scales, rounded margins entire but soon notched.

GROWTH. This species is difficult to establish being sensitive to late frosts when below about 5 feet in height. Once established, however, growth may be quite rapid. The two most vigorous young trees recorded recently have grown to 62ft × 3ft 8in in 35 years (Blounts Court, Henley), and 62ft × 6ft 1in in 42 years (Clonmannon). In height, growth slows markedly in old trees and the best increment on an old tree since 1902 is 42 feet in 66 years at Bicton. Since 1931 the best increases in height have been 45 feet in 26 years (Woodhouse) and 39 feet in 30 years (Little Hall), whereas many trees have grown less than 10 feet in over 30 years. In girth, the original tree at Hopetown had grown as well as any since 1911, adding 46 inches in 43 years. Since 1954, however, it has grown very slowly.

SPECIMENS. A tree at Woodhouse was 135ft tall in 1957 but had died by 1970.

TABLE 55. THE OLDEST AND THE LARGEST TREES OF PICEA SMITHIANA

Locality	Date Planted	Dimensions	
Hopetown	1821 (Original)	70′ × 6′ 2″ (1911)	90′ × 10′ 5″ (1971)
Hopetown	1826	77′ × 7′ 10″ (1931)	80′ × 9′ 0″ (1971)
Smeaton House	1840	67′ × 6′ 5″ (1905)	80′ × 9′ 3″ (1966)
Pencarrow	1842	57′ × 6′ 7″ (1907)	90′ × 8′ 5″ (1970)
Bicton (1)	1842	74′ × 15′ 2″ (1927)	80′ × 18′ 4″ (1957 Dead)
Dropmore	1843		75′ × 9′ 2″ (1970)
Stanage Park	1843	97′ × 7′ 1″ (1931)	98′ × 8′ 2″ (1970)
Fota	1847	67′ × 9′ 5″ (1931)	76′ × 10′ 4″ (1966)
Keir House	1850		85′ × 10′ 0″ (1970)
Highnam			80′ × 10′ 7″ (1970)
Castle Kennedy	1851	66′ × 5′ 9″ (1931)	85′ × 6′ 5″ (1967)
Cuffnells	1856	70′	118′ × 10′ 3″ (1970)
Cuffnells			113′ × 11′ 0″ (1970)
Melbury		85–90′ × 8′ 10″ (1906)	108′ × 12′ 3″ (1970)
Melbury			111′ × 11′ 4″ (1970)
Bicton (2)		65′ × 9′ 0″ (1907)	107′ × 10′ 4″ (1968)
Redleaf		75′ × 9′ 0″ (1907)	99′ × 10′ 2″ (1963)
Hardwicke		73′ × 7′ 0″ (1904)	105′ × 10′ 11″ (1954)
Bowood		100′ × 10′ 0″ (1931)	105′ × 11′ 4″ (1968)
Bowood			106′ × 10′ 6″ (1968)
Coldrennick			95′ × 10′ 5″ (1970)
Boconnoc		81′ × 10′ 6″ (1928)	100′ × 11′ 11″ (1970)
Taymouth Castle		76′ × 9′ 7″ (1931)	124′ × 12′ 10″ (1970)
Gordon Castle	1856	65′ × 9′ 1″ (1931)	83′ × 11′ 8″ (1970)
Fairburn			82′ × 13′ 6″ (1970)
Leighton Hall			79′ × 10′ 2″ (1960)
Nettlecombe			100′ × 9′ 0″ (1971)
Kilmacurragh		56′ × 8′ 10″ (1931)	65′ × 11′ 2″ (1966)
Castlewellan		49′ × 9′ 0″ (1931)	73′ × 12′ 3″ (1966)
Glenthorne			102′ × 7′ 0″ (1969)
Inistioge			90′ × 11′ 3″ (1966)
Dropmore (2)			80′ × 11′ 0″ (1970)
Bolderwood			111′ × 8′ 5″ (1970)
Oakley Park			95′ × 8′ 7″ (1971)
Castle Leod			94′ × 9′ 5″ (1966)
Holkham (Fox's Covert)			74′ × 10′ 3″ (1968)
Bodorgan			80′ × 10′ 7″ (1966)
Minterne			93′ × 10′ 6″ (1970)

RECOGNITION. Easily distinguished by the long, forward-curved, radiating, quadrangular leaves, from all except *P. schrenkiana*, which differs in its pale buds and harder, thicker leaves which are blunt and more densely held.

Picea spinulosa. (Griffith) Henry. Sikkim spruce

Sikkim and Bhutan, East Himalaya. Introduced in 1878. Rather rare and largely confined to collections in southern England, but a few in Wales, Scotland and Ireland.

BARK. Usually pinkish grey, marked by circular cracking into flat plates; the oldest tree has developed oak-like shallow fissuring (Castlewellan). Occasionally coarsely flaked and brown.

CROWN. Very open; long sparse branching, curved where new and vigorous near the top, ascending lower down arching out with pendulous shoots at the ends. The bigger trees are slightly tapering and broadly domed columns; young trees conical.

FOLIAGE. Shoot white to pale pinkish brown. Occasionally finely pubescent.

BUD. Pale red-brown shiny with resin, blunt, smooth ovoid.

LEAVES. All round the pendulous shoots, all pointing forwards at 45°, flattened, slender, straight, $2{\cdot}5 \times 0{\cdot}1$ cm abruptly spined, slightly keeled above, dark, slightly grey-green above; two broad, bright bluish-white bands beneath often coalesced. In the hand, a bunch of foliage looks clear fresh green and only when turned up to look back along the shoot does the blue-white become prominent.

CONE. Cylindric, blunt-topped, 6–8 cm long, green, the scales edged purple, ripening shining brown; scale margins finely toothed.

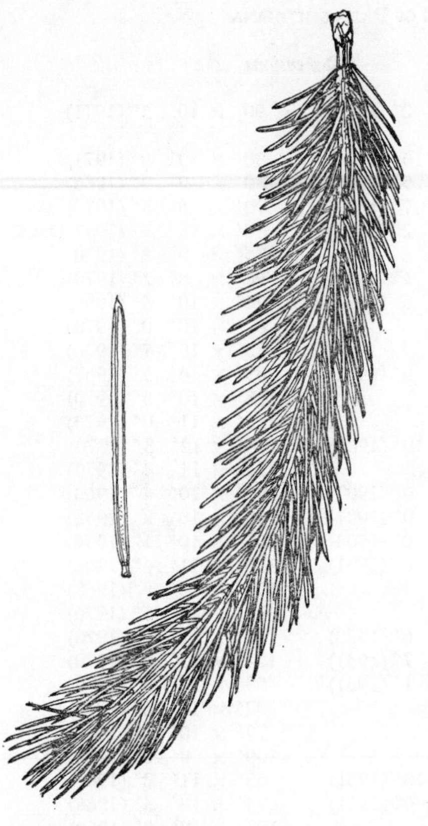

Fig. 130
Shoot and leaf (right × 1⅓) of *Picea spinulosa*, Sikkim spruce. The leaves point forwards all round the pendulous shoots, thus partly hiding their bright, blue-white stomatal bands on the inner surface.

GROWTH. A very vigorous species. The growth of the few earliest trees has not been spectacular, but many trees planted after 1910 have grown, and are still growing with great vigour. A fairly small tree at Bicton has grown 19 feet in height and added 12 inches in girth in a 9 year interval. As will be seen in Table 56, most of the younger trees have mean increments since planting of 1½ feet in height and about one inch a year in girth.

RECOGNITION. Among the flat-leaved spruces, only *P. brachytyla* has a similar, open, green crown and similar foliage, but the leaves of *P. spinulosa* differ from others which are brilliantly silvered beneath by being arranged radially and all pointing forwards. They are more slender and acute than those of *P. brachytyla*, which rarely, are radial on some shoots.

TABLE 56. THE LARGEST TREES OF PICEA SPINULOSA

Locality	*Date Planted*	*Dimensions*	
Castlewellan	1890	57′ × 8′ 6″ (1931)	84′ × 10′ 1″ (1970)
Melbury	1899	15′ (1909)	75′ × 9′ 2″ (1970)
Melbury	1899		85′ × 6′ 5″ (1970)
Borde Hill (1) Warren	1911	21′ (1932)	75′ × 6′ 11″ (1968)
Taymouth Castle	ca.1911	39′ × 2′ 4″ (1931)	75′ × 5′ 9″ (1957)
Lamellan	1911		50′ × 3′ 0″ (1963)
Fota	1914		71′ × 4′ 9″ (1966)
Bodnant	ca.1915		70′ × 5′ 7″ (1966)
Wakehurst Place	1916	22′ × 1′ 4″ (1931)	64′ × 4′ 8″ (1964)
Hergest Croft (1)	1916		62′ × 3′ 10″ (1961)
Sidbury Manor	1919		59′ × 5′ 6″ (1959)
Headfort	1921	20′ × 6″ (1931)	54′ × 4′ 10″ (1966)
Hergest Croft (2)	1922		52′ × 4′ 9″ (1969)
Chandlers Ford	1927		49′ × 3′ 1″ (1961)
Little Kingsmill Grange	1929		52′ × 4′ 0″ (1968)
Birr Castle	1929		46′ × 2′ 10″ (1966)
Birr Castle			45′ × 3′ 7″ (1966)
Borde Hill (2) Gores Wood			58′ × 4′ 6″ (1968)
Exbury		5′ 6″ (1931)	55′ × 4′ 7″ (1968)
Bicton			50′ × 2′ 10″ (1968)
Blandsfort		20′ (1931)	69′ × 4′ 9″ (1968)
Leonardslee			65′ × 4′ 9″ (1969)

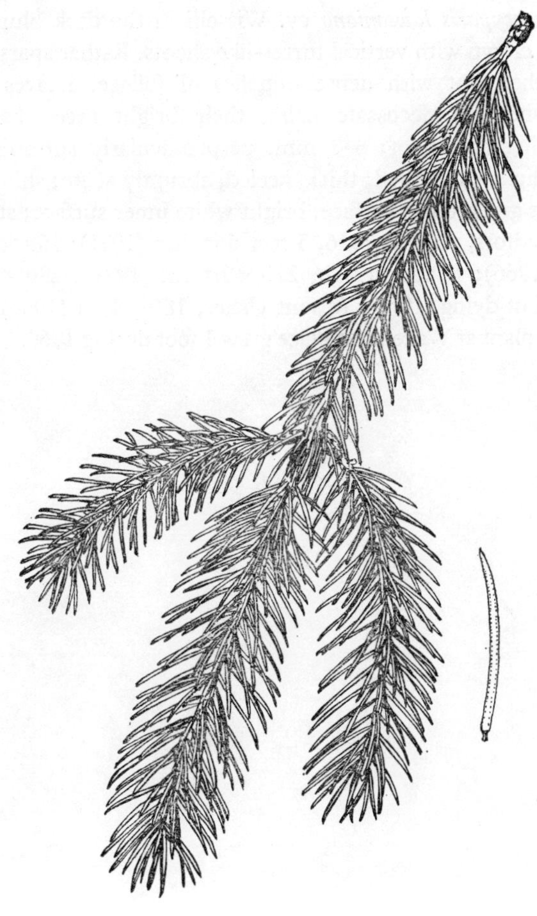

Picea wilsonii

Fig. 131
Foliage of *Picea wilsonii*, a rare Chinese spruce with shining white shoot and glossy chestnut-brown buds. The slender leaves are hard and glossy green on all four sides (right × 1⅓).

Picea wilsonii Masters. Wilson spruce.

North East Hupeh and North West Szechuan, Central China. Introduced in 1901. Rare and found only in some of the largest collections and occasionally in large gardens.

BARK. Greyish pink, sometimes copper-brown in places, shallowly cracked into flakes.

CROWN. Broadly conic but may have a narrow apex; dense at the top, open in lower parts, branches somewhat upswept in upper crown, others level, widely spaced, very bare inside the crown.

FOLIAGE. Shoot white, shiny, deeply but narrowly grooved; pulvini pale orange, second year the same, less shiny.

BUD. Ovoid, 3–4 mm chestnut, smooth and shining. Bud-scales remain at nodes of the previous year as bright chestnut-brown or dark red-brown bunches contrasting with the white shoot each side.

LEAVES. Pectinate below and slightly forward-pointing, 1·5–2·0 cm, above the shoot very close, forward-pointing, slender, hard, somewhat sparse, four-sided, shining mid-green with fine stomatal lines on all sides. Crushed foliage has an aroma like candle-wax.

GROWTH. Like most Asiatic mainland species, this is susceptible when young to damage from spring-frosts but perfectly hardy once established. Even then, growth is not rapid and one foot in height per year is the maximum recorded.

SPECIMENS. No trees are known that derive from the original seed. The table shows the size of the dated specimens and some others of similar size.

RECOGNITION. The white shoots and the leaves green on all surfaces and very slender are distinct but some trees of *P. obovata* are similar. In these, however, the shoot is usually greyish, not shiny, often pubescent, and the leaves are pressed below the shoot each side. The buds also have free tips to their scales in *P. obovata*. *P. morrisonicola* differs in more slender shoots and leaves, the latter pressed down on and below the shoot, one projecting widely at each bud.

TABLE 57. SPECIMENS OF PICEA WILSONII

Locality	*Date Planted*	*Dimensions*	
Hergest Croft	1914		46′ × 3′ 2″ (1969)
Hergest Croft	1914		35′ × 3′ 7″ (1969)
Headfort	1915	14′ × 1′ 2″ (1931)	38′ × 4′ 1″ (1966)
Birr Castle	1916		53′ × 4′ 6″ (1966)
Wakehurst Place	1917	12′ × 1′ 0″ (1931)	54′ × 3′ 10″ (1970)
Bicton	1920	9′ (1928)	49′ × 3′ 7″ (1968)
Dawyck (1)	1921	19′ × 1′ 0″ (1930)	36′ × 3′ 0″ (1961)
Bedgebury	1926		30′ × 2′ 6″ (1969)
Dawyck (2)	1931		25′ × 2′ 1″ (1966)
Stanage Park			39′ × 2′ 6″ (1970)
Chandlers Ford			45′ × 2′ 5″ (1967)

Pilgerodendron Florin (Cupressaceae)

A single species distinguished from *Libocedrus* by having leaves in four ranks and with widely spreading tips.

Pilgerodendron uviferum (D. Don.) Florin.

Southern Andes and Tierra del Fuego. Introduced in 1849. Very rare; almost confined to a few collections in Ireland. A narrowly erect tree, resembling from a distance *Chamaecyparis lawsoniana* cv. Wisselii in the dark bluish-black crown with vertical turret-like shoots. Rather sparsely branched but with dense bunches of foliage. Leaves in opposite and decussate pairs, their bright green bases covering the shoot; 3–8 mm, perpendicularly spreading, tips slightly incurved; thick, keeled, abruptly acute; shining bright green outer surface, bright white inner surface; stiff.

Headfort, planted 1916, 5 feet 6 inches (1931); 16ft × 1ft 3in (1966); Kilmacurragh, 22ft × 2ft 2in (1931); 28ft × 2ft 10in but dying (1966); Mount Usher, 18ft × 11in (1966). A small plant at Wakehurst Place grew 1 foot during 1969.

Pinus Linnaeus (Pinaceae)

A genus of about 96 species from all regions of the northern hemisphere southward to Central America, the West Indies, Mediterranean and Burma, but mostly confined to high altitudes towards the tropic. The foliage is distinct from all other conifers in being needle-like in clusters of 2, 3 or 5 from a single sheath. Juvenile leaves are spirally borne, slender and toothed. In all except five species these are confined to the first year's growth from seed. In most northerly species one whorl of shoots and one node on the stem is grown each year but some growing in or originating from more southerly regions (e.g. *P. contorta*) grow two or three whorls each year. Male flowers are small and globular and replace the leaf-bundles on the basal portion of weak shoots. Female flowers, usually red, are borne around the terminal buds of strong shoots and frequently of the leading shoot, opening as the shoot lengthens, sometimes in a whorl a third of the way down. The cones vary from globose to long-cylindric and from 3–4 cm to 45 cm long, and may be thinly woody and pliant or massively woody.

Pines are in general suited to thrive on rather dry sites and almost all are sensitive to poor drainage. Several will grow well on calcareous soils but the majority grow much better in slightly acid soils.

Key to the genus Pinus

1. Leaves in pairs — 2
   Leaves 3 or 5 per bundle — 26

2. Leaves 3–10 cm long — 3
   Leaves more than 10 cm — 17

3. Scales at apex of bud with tips free — 4
   Scales closely appressed to bud apex, or enclosed in resin — 9

4. Free tips of bud-scales bent outwards or rolled down — 5
   Free tips of bud-scales erect and straight — 6

5. Leaves crowded; deep green, shoot whitish-green — *densiflora*
   Leaves sparse, pale bright green, shoot grey-orange green — *halepensis*

6. Shoot orange-brown, becoming dark purple-brown; outer cone scales drawn down — *uncinata*
   Shoot pale, yellowish or greenish, becoming pink or brown, cone scales normal — 7

7. Bud white, scales with long silky fringes; shoot golden-brown — *thunbergii*
   Bud red-brown, scales not fringed; shoot pink-buff or whitish-green — 8

8. Leaf 9–(12) cm, bright shining green, slender, forward — *densiflora*
   Leaf 3–7 cm, blue-grey or grey-green, thick, broad, spreading — *sylvestris*

9. Bud broad ovoid, abruptly narrowed to long sharp point; scales papery, pale; leaves straight — 10
   Bud cylindric or ovoid, short pointed, scales not papery, leaves twisted — 11

10. Second year shoot orange-grey (immature cone bright deep blue, bark smooth); one year shoot bloomed glaucous at first — *leucodermis*
    Second year shoot dark brown (immature cone green or brown, bark scaly, fissured) one year shoot dark brown-green — *nigra nigra*

11. Shoot bloomed grey on pink-brown, second year purple, striped yellow, shoots with internodal branchlets — *virginiana*
    Shoot not bloomed; no internodal branchlets — 12

12.	Shoot pale greenish-white, second year pale orange, some bundles with 3 leaves amongst foliage; epicormic sprouts on main branches	*echinata*
	Shoot brown or dark green; bundles of 3 only at tips of vigorous shoots, rarely	13
13.	Bud contorted, 2–3 cm; second year shoot striped white on orange	14
	Bud straight 0·5–2·5 cm, second year shoot not striped; red or purple-brown	16
14.	Leaf 6–8·5 cm, flattened, broad, spreading	*contorta latifolia*
	Leaf 4–5 cm	15
15.	Leaves closely appressed to new shoot, very dense, persisting 3 years, bright or deep green (crown dense, vigorous)	*contorta contorta*
	Leaves spreading, blackish-green, persisting 1–2 years (crown open; slow)	*contorta murrayana*
16.	Shoot stout, red-brown for 2 years; bud red-brown with some white resin (cone pointing backwards, 8×5 cm, stoutly spined)	*pungens*
	Shoot slender, green-brown; second year dark purple-brown, bud pale brown (cone pointing forwards, 3 cm, soon quite smooth)	*banksiana*
17.	Upper scales of bud with free tips strongly decurved	18
	Upper scales of bud scarcely free, not decurved, tightly pressed to bud or enclosed in resin	21
18.	Leaf stout, stiff; foliage sparse, (cone 10 cm long)	19
	Leaf slender, flexible; foliage dense (cone 5–9 cm long)	20
19.	Leaf 10–15 cm, dark green (cone ovoid 10×10 cm, crown low-domed)	*pinea*
	Leaf 15–20 cm pale grey-green (cone oblique conic 10×5 cm, crown high-domed)	*pinaster*
20.	Shoot pink-buff or green-white, not stout; leaf 9–12 cm (cone 5 cm)	*densiflora*
	Shoot pale orange-brown, stout, leaf 12–15 cm (cone 9 cm on stalk 1 cm broad)	*halepensis brutia*
21.	Shoot bloomed pink on yellow-brown; bud long-ovoid, scale-tips just free; leaf stout, pairs remain close	*tabuliformis*
	Shoot not bloomed; orange or brownish, buds not ovoid, scale-tips appressed, leaf pairs well parted	22
22.	Bud cylindric, long-tapered, dark red-brown and whitish purple, leaf stout, (cone highly serotinous, stoutly spined)	*muricata*
	Bud abruptly and sharply pointed or encrusted in white resin (cones shed when ripe, soon smooth)	23
23.	Shoot shining yellow-brown, leaf 12–18 cm, twisted, slender; upper bud-scales red-brown fringed grey	*nigra maritima*
	Shoot orange or orange-brown, leaf 10–16 cm, straight	24
24.	Shoot orange; leaf very slender, snapping cleanly when sharply bent; foliage much whorled, dense, bud chestnut-red (bark of branches red-brown)	*resinosa*
	Shoot pale or brownish-orange, leaf not snapping cleanly however bent; foliage not whorled; buds soon caked in white resin	25
25.	Leaf 12–15 cm, slender, grey-green; shoot pale orange (cone fairly smooth)	*nigra cebennensis*
	Leaf 15–16 cm, moderately stout, dark green; shoot bright orange-brown (cone rough, knobbly)	*nigra caramanica*

26. Leaves 3 per bundle 27
Leaves 5 (or more) in a bundle 42

27. Leaf blue-grey or dull grey; shoot blue-grey bloomed on green-brown (cones $>$ 8 cm broad) 28
Leaf green, bright, deep or pale; shoot pink or white bloomed (cones $<$8 cm broad) 30

28. Shoot and leaf slender, bud scales appressed at tips (crown very open, upright) *sabiniana*
Shoot and leaf stout; scales on curve of bud free at tips 29

29. Bud bright and pale orange, to 6 cm; leaf 25–30 cm, usually crinkled, long bare shoot between annual foliage; (cone scales shiny, stoutly spined, massive and rigid) *coulteri*
Bud deep red-brown, 2–3 cm; leaf 15–23 cm, straight, whorls close; (cone scales thinly woody, not massive, slightly flexible, dull, with small spine) *jeffreyi*

30. Leaf 4–8 cm 31
Leaf more than 8 cm, nearly always more than 10 cm 32

31. Shoot chalky white; leaves very dense, fine, forward, 4 cm *nelsoni*
Shoot olive-green; leaves very sparse, stiff, spreading 6–8 cm *bungeana*

32. Shoot pink, brownish-pink or bloomed pink 33
Shoot greenish, whitish or brown 35

33. Shoot very stout, shining pink; leaf dark green, slender, 10–20 cm *tabuliformis yunnanensis*
Shoot not stout; brownish or bloomed 34

34. Leaves very slender, pendulous, bright grey-green, bud pale-brown without resin; shoot green bloomed pink (bark orange, papery) *patula*
Leaves not slender, stiff, spreading, twisted, mid-green; bud dark red-brown tip from solid white resin (bark scaly, grey and brown) *serotina*

35. Bud a huge rosette of papery scales which adhere at nodes; shoot very stout; leaf 20–45 cm, slender, bright green. (Crown very gaunt) *palustris*
Bud not very large nor papery; scales not persistent 36

36. Shoot whitish, tinged green or brown, leaves bright grass-green or darker greyish-green 37
Shoot dark, brown, orange, green or reddish 39

37. Leaves rather stout, stiff, twisted, dark grey-green (Epicormic shoot from) *rigida*
Leaves slender, new leaves bright grass-green 38

38. Leaf very slender and pendulous, foliage dense; bud dark red-brown and pale grey, not slender, old leaves deep green *radiata*
Leaf not very slender, rather stiff, not pendulous, foliage not dense, bud pinkish-grey with bright red-brown or chestnut scale-tips; old leaves bright green *greggii*

39. Leaf 8–9 cm, slightly yellowish-green, shoot orange-brown *rigida*
Leaf 10–22 cm 40

40. Annual whorls of foliage separated by long bare sector of shoot, leaf 10–15 cm (crown open, upswept; cones serotinous, long-conic, deflexed) *attenuata*
Foliage whorls not distant; leaf 15–22 cm 41

41. Leaf bright green, slender; bud non-resinous, scales free, bright chestnut-red *taeda*
Leaf dark mid-green or greyish; bud slightly resinous, pale brown *ponderosa*

42. Shoot pubescent 43
Shoot completely glabrous 55

43. Pubescence long and dense, hiding shoot, red-brown or orange 44
Pubescence very short and seldom hiding shoot, pale 47

44. Leaf to 4 cm, strongly incurved; basal sheath rolled down in second year 45
Leaf more than 7 cm, straight; basal sheath not rolled down 46

45. Leaf 2–4 cm, abruptly short-pointed; foliage with some large white resin-spots; second year shoot dark purple-grey (cone scale stoutly spined) *aristata*
Leaf 3·5–4 cm, tapering to slender point; foliage unspotted; second year shoot dark purple-brown (cone scale ± slender spine) *balfouriana*

46. Leaf 7–9 cm, with 2 resin-canals; main shoots abruptly upturned, leaves close, forward (crown densely columnar) *cembra*
Leaf 10–12 cm, with 3 resin canals; main shoots gently curved, leaves by second year widely spreading (crown open, conic) *koraiensis*

47. Pubescence confined to ridges just below pulvini; leaf 8–10 cm, bundles nearly closed, forward-pointing; shoot green-brown *strobus*
Pubescence evenly distributed over shoot 48

48. Leaf 8 cm or less 49
Leaf 9 cm or more 52

49. Leaf uniformly coloured, dark green; smooth margins 50
Leaf with inner side blue-white; serrated margins 51

50. Leaf 5–6 cm, curved outwards, very dense, evenly spaced; second year shoot shining dark brown (cone to 8 cm) *albicaulis*
Leaf 8 cm, twisted, fairly dense but each bundle of 5 separated from its neighbours, second year shoot dark grey-brown (cone 12 cm) *flexilis*

51. Shoot whitish-green, thinly pubescent, second year grey-green; leaves twisted, widely spread. (Cone squat ovoid, 5 cm) *parviflora*
Shoot pale fawn, densely pubescent; second year dark grey; leaves forward close to shoot. (Cone cylindric ovoid 8 cm) × *hunnewelliana*

52. Leaves about 10 cm long; shoot densely pubescent 53
Leaves 13–18 cm long; shoot with scattered pubescence 54

53. Shoot pale brown, bud with long, free-tipped scales, some bent outwards, leaves spreading *monticola*
Shoot dark olive-green; bud with long, dark, appressed scales, leaves appressed forwards *lambertiana*

54. Shoot pale pinkish-green; leaf 13–15 cm; (bark purple-grey deeply cracked into squares; cone narrow-conic, long-pointed 16–18 cm) *ayacahuite*
Shoot apple-green; leaf 14–18 cm; (bark orange-brown, deeply fissured; cone cylindric-ovoid 20–26 cm) × *holfordiana*

55. Leaves similar colour on all surfaces 56
Leaves blue-white on inner surfaces, dark on outer 62

56. Leaf dark blue-green, 5–6 cm, long; shoot dark brown, foliage in dense bunches hiding shoot *albicaulis*
Leaf pale green, grey or blue-grey; 8–28 cm, foliage spreading, lax 57

57. (The *Pinus montezumae* complex). Shoot very stout, dark orange-brown; leaves stout, 25–28 cm; pale blue-grey — *montezumae*
Shoot not unusually stout; blue-grey, bloomed or green-brown; leaves 10–22 cm — 58

58. Shoot green-brown, not bloomed; leaf 12–15 cm, bud orange-red — var. *rudis*
Shoot bloomed or grey-blue — 59

59. Shoot thinly bloomed, usually only below pulvini, elsewhere pale pinkish-green — 60
Shoot pale grey-blue uniformly — 61

60. Leaves 8–11 cm, densely set in nearly closed bundles; bud-scales just free at tip — *cooperi*
Leaves 16–22 cm, sparsely set in open, spread bundles; bud-scales appressed at tip — *durangensis*

61. Leaves 16–20 cm, very slender, pendulous, pale grey-green — *pseudostrobus*
Leaves 10–18 cm, not slender; spreading, dark grey-green often yellowish — (*montezumae*) var. *hartwegii*

62. Shoot whitish-green, bloomed violet; stout, long; leaf 18–20 cm very slender, pendulous (cone 15–20 cm, curved, cylindric) — *wallichiana*
Shoot deep or bright green, never bloomed, not stout, rarely long; leaves less than 15 cm long — 63

63. Leaves relatively stout, $\pm$pendulous in nearly closed bundles, dull grey-green (cone to 14 cm, barrel-shaped) — *armandii*
Leaves very slender, widely spread from bundles, forward pointing on main shoot, deep blue-green (cone to 12 cm, cylindric) — *peuce*

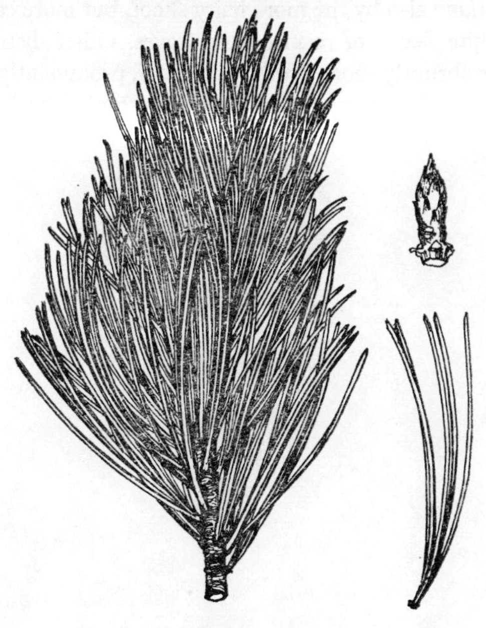

Pinus albicaulis

Fig. 132
Shoot and leaves of *Pinus albicaulis*, a 5-needle pine similar in aspect to the Fox-tail pines, but more closely related to *P. flexilis*. The bud ($\times 1\frac{1}{2}$) is dark red-brown with some grey wool.

Pinus albicaulis Engelmann. White-bark pine

Rocky Mountains from British Columbia to Mexico. Introduced in 1852 and re-introduced in 1900. Very rare indeed, one tree only known to survive. A tree like a "fox-tail pine" (see *P. aristata*, *P. balfouriana*) with densely bunched, closely held needles of dark bluish green, but somewhat more open in the upper crown. Bark smooth dark grey with pale freckling.

FOLIAGE. Shoot green, slightly shiny; glabrous; basal sheaths orange-brown. Second year shoot shiny dark brown; basal sheaths shed.

BUD. Dark red-brown covered in grey wool; scales not free.

LEAVES. Densely bunched, in fives, lying forwards then curving outwards, 5–6 cm ending in an acute or abrupt, fine tip; shiny dark green with fine bright white stomatal lines on each surface. Pale base where sheath has been shed. The margins are smooth.

SPECIMEN. Kew Royal Botanic Gardens, 18ft $\times$ 1ft 6in (1969).

RECOGNITION. Differs from the true fox-tail pines in the leaves being uniformly coloured on each surface, longer, and early shedding of basal sheaths. It differs in crown from the closely allied *P. flexilis*, and in lacking free tips to bud-scales and in shorter, more densely set leaves.

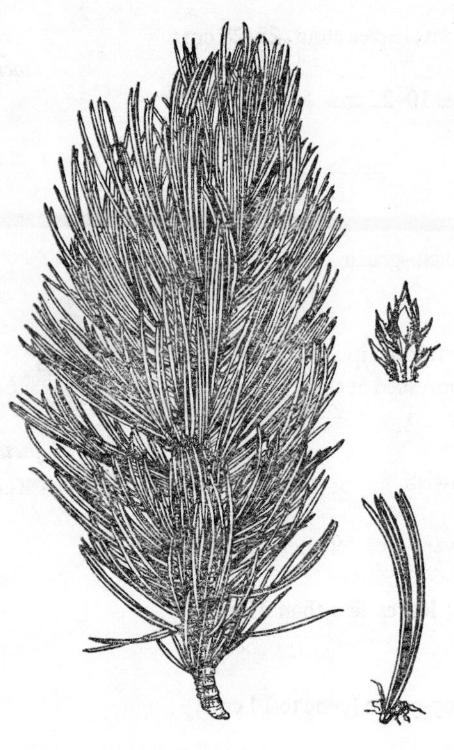

Pinus aristata

Fig. 133
Foliage and detail (×1$\frac{3}{8}$) of bud of *Pinus aristata*, Bristle cone pine. The thinly scattered white resin-blobs and the abrupt tip to the leaf distinguish this species from *P. balfouriana* which shares the rolled back sheaths and brown-pubescent shoots.

Pinus aristata Engelmann. Bristle-cone pine

Colorado, Arizona, New Mexico. [The trees in California, Nevada and Utah are separated as *P. longaeva*, D. K. Bailey, closer to *P. balfouriana.* They live to 5,000 years in the White Mountains, California, and lack white specks.] Very rare; a few collections. Introduced in 1863.

BARK. Black-grey, smooth.

CROWN. A "fox-tail" with widely spread, upturned branches densely lined with leaves and small shoots. Often leaning.

FOLIAGE. Shoot dark red-brown above; bright rufous beneath, covered in a dense, short white or pale brown pubescence. Second year dark purple-grey with dark grey, down-rolled basal sheaths largely covering it.

BUD. Dark red-brown, 4 mm, pointed, smooth with large incurved free basal scales, unfringed.

LEAVES. In fives very densely clustered on shoots for many years, 2–4 cm, abruptly short-pointed, curved in strongly for the first year, lying close along the shoot but later spreading more widely and curving inwards. First year bright green outer surface; blue white inner, but by second year dull dark green outside and often dull grey inside. The foliage is well speckled with large white resin-dots, but on some trees, they are few.

CONE. 1st year, 2 cm; ovoid, dull purple with spikes, linear, 5–6 mm long, spreading level, brown. Ripens 4–9 cm long, cylindric-ovoid.

GROWTH AND SPECIMENS. Growth is very slow and notwithstanding the 2,000 years achieved in Colorado, this is a shortlived tree here. The oldest known, dated tree is at Kew; planted in 1908 it is now 20 feet tall and 1 foot 7 inches in girth. Another planted in 1912 is now 9 feet tall (1969) but growth at Bedgebury has been less slow, and planted in 1932 one is already 13ft×8in (1971). Others are: Bells' Wood, Bayford (7 feet, 1931), 22ft×1ft 5½in (1962); Bayfordbury, 18ft×1ft 8in (1968); Leighton Hall, 27ft×1ft 2in (1960); Warnham Court, 30ft×1ft 3in (1961); Wisley Royal Horticultural Society Gardens, 20ft×1ft 6in (1968); Edinburgh Royal Botanic Garden, 29ft×1ft 6in (1970).

RECOGNITION. Easily distinguished as a "fox-tail" pine by the dense brushes of dark foliage, this is separable from *P. albicaulis* by the densely hairy shoot and from *P. balfouriana* also by the more hairy shoot, but more easily by the white flecks of resin on the leaves. Other distinctions are the abruptly short, blunt spined leaf, prominently spiked cone, and the entire scales around the bud. The foliage is also more dense and more curved.

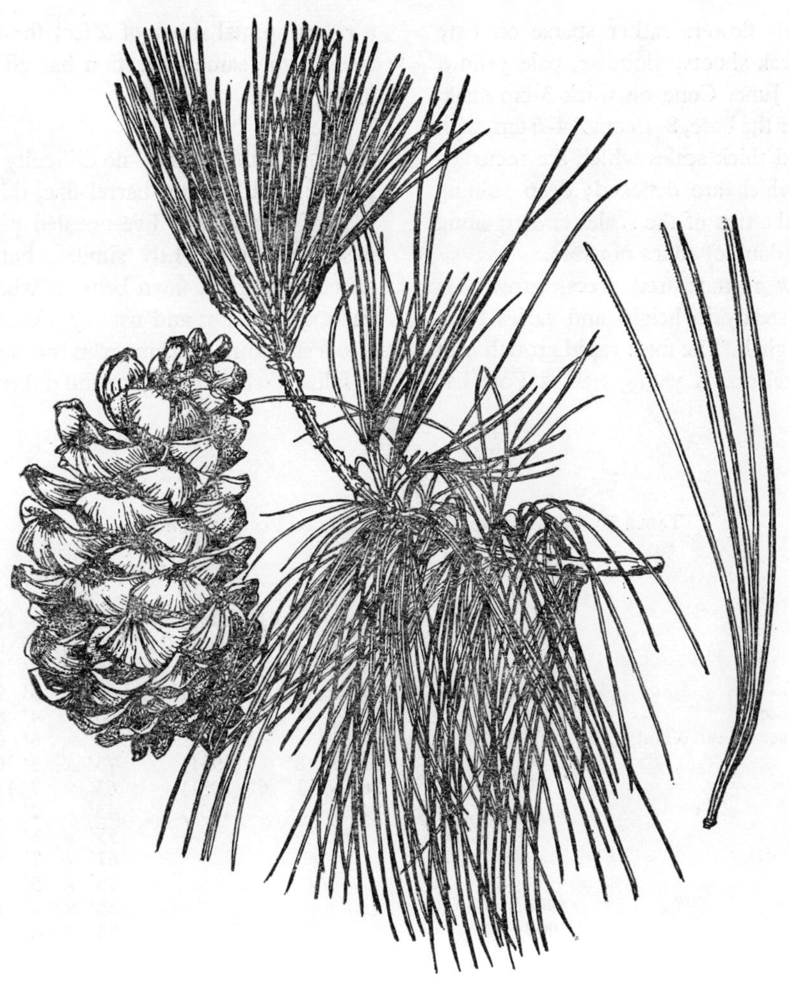

Pinus armandii

Fig. 134
Foliage ($\times\frac{1}{2}$) of *Pinus armandii* from China, showing bare length of stem with accretions of resin. The cone ($\times\frac{2}{3}$) has thick scales. Many bundles of leaves ($\times\frac{2}{3}$) are strongly crimped near the base.

Pinus armandii Franchet. Chinese white pine.

West China, Korea and Formosa. Introduced in 1897 to Kew, where the two original trees still stand. (See Table 58). Uncommon and mostly in collections in England and Ireland but a few in Southern Scotland.

BARK. Dull pale pinkish or dark purplish-grey, smooth, cracking deeply and coarsely into squarish plates which flake, and with deep vertical fissures at the base.

CROWN. Broadly conic, and open with very whorled branches, which are smooth, level and bare except at the tips.

FOLIAGE. Shoot deep green or olive-green, slightly bloomed, glabrous, partly covered by clusters of long brown papery sheaths and often with shiny translucent blobs of resin. Long bare basal part with small 2-3 mm, brown scales. Second year shoot shining olive-brown.

BUD. Cylindric or ovoid, usually blunt, 0·5 cm, red-brown and pale brown.

LEAVES. In fives, slender, long, 12–14 cm, drooping, all five sometimes in parallel crinkles (as in *P. wallichiana* also), serrulate to the touch, a pale green band on each inner surface, bright shining green on the outside.

Flowers and Cone. Male flowers rather sparse on bare lengths at the base of weak shoots, globular, pale yellow, shedding pollen in early June. Cone on thick 3 cm stalk, cylindric but broadest near the base, 8–15 cm × 4–6 cm, with a broad rounded apex and thick scales which are incurved except the basal scales which are deflexed; deep shining green, turning brown at the tips of the scales and ripening orange-brown. Twinned (double) cones not rare.

Growth. From the few re-measured trees, growth is uniformly moderate but steady in height and varies from rather slow to very fast in girth. The most rapid growth is in trees in Sussex and in Ireland. A young tree at Fota has a mean annual shoot of 2 feet for 18 years while an older tree on the same collection has added 77 inches of girth in 35 years.

Recognition. There is no difficulty when cones are present, for the broad, rather barrel-like, thick scaled cone is unlike that of any similar five-needled pine. In foliage alone *P. wallichiana* is slightly similar, but has a much-bloomed shoot, blue-grey, fawn beneath whereas *P. armandii* rarely has much bloom and usually none and is deep green. It is also less luxuriant, thinner in the crown; paler and more lax in foliage, which is thicker and duller.

Table 58. Oldest and Largest Trees of Pinus armandii

Locality	*Date Planted*	*Dimensions*	
Kew R.B.G.	1897	45′ × 3′ 0½″ (1931)	52′ × 3′ 10″ (1971)
Kew R.B.G.	1897	43′ × 2′ 8″ (1931)	60′ × 3′ 9″ (1971)
Bayfordbury	1908		45′ × 3′ 5″ (1962)
Borde Hill (1)	1909	27′ × 1′ 8″ (1931)	66′ × 3′ 9″ (1968)
Wakehurst Place	1914	20′ × 1′ 6″ (1931)	60′ × 4′ 8″ (1970)
Wakehurst Place (West Wood)			65′ × 6′ 0″ (1964)
Leonardslee		19′ × 8′ (1931)	73′ × 5′ 0″ (1969)
Fota (1)		26′ × 1′ 6″ (1931)	63′ × 7′ 11″ (1966)
Blandsfort		14′ (1931)	45′ × 2′ 9″ (1968)
Borde Hill (2)			55′ × 3′ 3″ (1968)
Tregothnan			67′ × 7′ 3″ (1971)
Tregrehan			75′ × 5′ 7″ (1971)
Little Hall	1906 ?		55′ × 3′ 1″ (1961)
Pencarrow	1908		54′ × 4′ 5″ (1970)
Garinish Island			60′ × 4′ 0″ (1966)
Mount Usher			55′ × 4′ 3″ (1966)
Kilmacurragh			56′ × 6′ 8″ (1966)
Avondale			56′ × 4′ 4″ (1968)
Bedgebury	1925	7′ (1931)	34′ × 3′ 7″ (1970)
Westonbirt	1936		31′ × 3′ 4″ (1966)
Fota (2)	1948		37′ × 2′ 6″ (1966)

Pinus attenuata Lemmon. Knobcone pine (*P. tuberculata*).

California and Southern Oregon. Introduced in 1847. Very rare and confined to a few collections in South England and one in North Wales.

Bark. Grey-pink, often smooth and finely flaking, but can become cracked, fissured and ridged. At Kew, dark brown, deeply fissured and scaly.

Crown. Very distinct, gaunt, open with wide-spreading, ascending, sinuous branches and long-conic cones retained down the branches, pressed against them, in backward-pointing whorls.

Foliage. Shoot green-brown.

Bud. Stout, cylindric, pointed, 4·5 cm, dark brown but covered in whitish resin.

Leaves. In threes, slender, grey-green, 14–16 cm; sheath brown 2 cm; leaves spreading widely on main shoots appressed on minor shoots.

Flowers and Cone. Male flowers profuse on a long basal portion of the shoot, often to about half the length, globular, pale yellow shedding pollen in the first half of May. Female flowers usually half way up strong shoots, pink-brown, ovoid, 1·5 cm, with upwards pointing prickles and on a very stout red-brown stalk 1 cm long. Fertilised flowers turn downwards and enlarge into long-pointed, large conic cones, pointing closely back along the stem in whorls of up to 5, dark brown, to 13 × 6 cm, with oblique bases where the scales have long drawn-out thick rounded points ending in a minute up-curved spine. Scales higher up nearly flat with a central prickle even smaller. The cones remain on the branches for 20 years or more and become grey with algae.

Growth. A reasonably fast-growing pine when young but

Fig. 135
Foliage and cone of *Pinus attenuata*, Knobcone pine from California. The cones are borne in whorls of three or more and are retained on the tree for many years.

failing early and short-lived. The two smallest trees of the four in the Report (1932) survive and in 37–38 years have added 30 and 32 feet in height and 36 and about 36 inches in girth.

SPECIMENS. No old tree is known, and the trees at Bedgebury are the only ones with known planting-dates, but several of those mentioned must be ten to twenty years older. The only trees of even moderate size are: Borde Hill, 28ft×2ft 3in (1931) 60ft×5ft 3in (1968) and 65ft×5ft 8in (1961); Wakehurst Place, 50ft×6ft 4in (1964); Bedgebury, planted 1926, 47ft×4ft 2in, 42ft×4ft 5in (1969); Kew Royal Botanic Gardens, 40ft×4ft 6in (1969).

RECOGNITION. The cones are unlike those which are serotinous in other species, in their long conic shape. Among three-needled pines the green-brown shoot and grey needles together are distinctive.

Pinus × attenuradiata Stockwell and Righter. (1927 Placeville, California).

Introduced in about 1952. A hybrid between *P. attenuata* (female) and *P. radiata* (male), and intermediate between them in all characters. At Alice Holt of two trees the larger (28ft×2ft 4in) planted in 1953 is nearly *P. attenuata* (leaf 14 cm, cone 9×4·5, bud 2·5 cm, white with resin) the other is closer to *P. radiata* (leaf 10 cm, cone ovoid 5×4 cm, bud 1·5 cm thinly resinous; dark red tips to scales). Both have broad, squat crowns with widely spread level branches, smooth grey-pink bark, cones mid-nodal in whorls 2–6, shoot orange or green with orange pulvini and ridges; long (6–12 mm) outward bent toothed scales on bare basal part of shoot; second year shoot purple-brown. Cone pale orange-brown, bloomed pink on the inner side, conic projections on outer basal scales with upcurved spines.

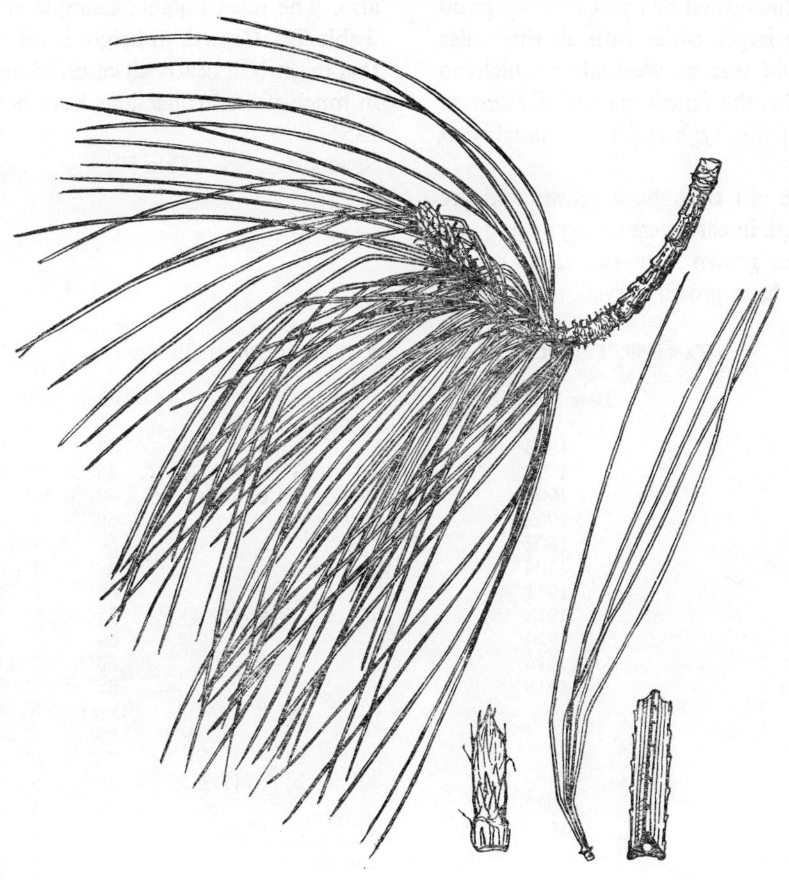

Pinus ayacahuite

Fig. 136
Foliage of *Pinus ayacahuite*, Mexican white pine, which has a finely pubescent shoot. Below, bud ($\times 1\frac{1}{3}$) bundle of 5 leaves ($\times \frac{2}{3}$) and enlarged ($\times 5\frac{1}{3}$) segment of a leaf.

Pinus ayacahuite Ehrenberg. Mexican white pine

Guatemala to Mexico. Introduced in 1840. Uncommon but in many collections everywhere except in East England and Central and North Scotland.

BARK. Young tree smooth dark grey, greenish with algae; small areas rupturing into vertical scales. Old tree dark purplish-brown with wide, shallow pink-buff fissures and densely flaking, rough ridges.

CROWN. Conic, maintaining a point even in most of the tallest trees, dense, with many, level, rather small branches.

FOLIAGE. Shoot green or green-brown with a pink tinge and a dense, fine pale brown pubescence; slender, around tip crowded with papery pale brown sheaths, narrow and to 2 cm long.

BUD. 6–7 mm ovoid with conic tip, smooth with a few free tips, pale brown and red-brown.

LEAVES. In fives, slender, straight, drooping, 13–15 cm, finely serrulate, bright pale shiny green; faint stomatal lines on outer surface, bright blue-white narrow bands on inner.

CONE. First year, 2–3 terminally, stalked, club-shaped, $2{\cdot}5 \times 1{\cdot}5$ cm, pink and green. When ripe, in second year, cylindrical, tapering from half way to a narrow point, slightly oblique from a curved, stout stalk 2 cm long; pale orange-brown ripening cream-brown 18×5 cm (to $+30$ cm); scales convex, striated on their lower parts, with an obtuse point and a purple-brown triangular patch at the apex; incurved except for the basal whorl or two which are strongly decurved and the next whorl which is spreading.

var. veitchii Shaw. Distinguished by short seed wings on large seed, but better by larger cones with all the scales strongly recurved. The old tree at Westonbirt which no longer bears cones, but was the female parent of *Pinus* × *holfordiana*, bore cones of this type and is presumably of this variety.

GROWTH. Although some old trees have grown and are growing very slowly, growth in early years is very rapid and many of those which had grown very fast from known planting dates until 1931 have grown very fast since then also. The most notable example is a tree at Bodnant (see Table 59). Growth in height is relatively less vigorous than that in girth in nearly all cases. Many trees recorded in 1931 in much-visited collections have been missing since before 1954.

SPECIMENS. See Table 59.

TABLE 59. THE OLDEST AND LARGEST TREES OF PINUS AYACAHUITE

Locality	*Date Planted*	*Dimensions*	
Kew R.B.G.	1873		47′ × 3′ 7″ (1968)
Pencarrow	1900	× 5′ 2″ (1927)	75′ × 7′ 9″ (1957)
Bodnant	1902	49′ × 5′ 0″ (1931)	62′ × 10′ 3″ (1966)
Bodnant	1902		60′ × 9′ 6″ (1966)
Fota	1902		60′ × 7′ 10″ (1966)
Kew R.B.G.	1904		49′ × 4′ 6″ (1968)
Dawyck	1911		65′ × 4′ 6″ (1966)
Dropmore	1913	47′ × 2′ 9″ (1931)	75′ × 6′ 7″ (1970)
Headfort	1914		60′ × 5′ 2″ (1966)
Hergest Croft	1916		60′ × 5′ 11″ (1961)
Fenagh House	1918		38′ × 3′ 3″ (1968)
Westonbirt		62′ × 6′ 8″ (1909)	(Top out) 8′ 6″ (1971)
Bicton			88′ × 7′ 6½″ (1968)
Bicton			78′ × 8′ 8″ (1968)
Tregrehan		30′ × 2′ 8″ (1931)	70′ × 5′ 5″ (1957)
Woburn	1922		52′ × 4′ 7″ (1970)
Bedgebury	1926	20′ × 3′ 9″ (1931)	52′ × 4′ 3″ (1963)
Wisley R.H.S.G.			62′ × 7′ 2″ (1969)
Stanway			64′ × 6′ 3″ (1965)
Wayford Manor			60′ × 4′ 7″ (1967)
Curraghmore			54′ × 4′ 8″ (1968)
Little Kingsmill Grange	1929		48′ × 4′ 5″ (1968)

RECOGNITION. From *P. wallichiana*, this species is distinguished by the pubescent, unbloomed, more slender shoot and by the more pointed cone with more basal scales reflexed than just the first whorl. From *P. lambertiana*, which has dense pale reddish-brown hairs on the shoot and seldom now, if ever, has a cone, distinction is more difficult, but the buds of *P. ayacahuite* lack the dark tipped scales and the leaves are paler and droop where those of *P. lambertiana* are held close to the shoot.

From the hybrid *P.* × *holfordiana*, distinction is even more difficult and sometimes, in second generation hybrids, not really possible. The cones of most of the hybrids are usually less pointed, more a broad cylinder, and the bark has orange fissures in reddish brown.

Pinus balfouriana Jeffrey ex Murray. Fox-tail pine

Northern Coast Range and Southern Sierra Nevada, California; two well-separated populations. Introduced from the northern area in 1852. Very rare indeed.

BARK. Purple-grey, cracked into squares; younger stems horizontally striated.

CROWN. A very dense "fox-tail" with spreading upcurved branches.

FOLIAGE. Shoot deep orange-brown, very finely pubescent with dark hairs; ridged. Second year dark purple-brown; third year black-purple with down-curled, dark grey-purple basal sheaths crowded on it.

BUD. Ovoid-conic, sharply pointed, red-brown; large free scales around the base fringed with grey-white hairs.

LEAVES. In fives; first year in closed bundles, lying nearly flat forwards, second year rising almost straight from the shoot; 3·5–4 cm long, hard, tapering to fine sharp point; first year shining light green outside, brilliantly white inside, second year dark green outside; still bright white inside. Broken shoots or foliage release a scent of marmalade.

GROWTH AND SPECIMENS. Growth is very slow. A thirty-one year old tree at Borde Hill is 8 feet tall, but at Edinburgh one grew 5 feet in height and 4 inches in girth between 1955 and 1967. The best trees are at Edinburgh Royal Botanic Garden, 33ft×2ft 2in; 31ft×2ft 4in (1970). At Bodnant, a tree planted in 1915 was 18ft×1ft 1in in 1959. At Prested Hall, Essex, the Hon. Maynard Greville found one 25ft×1ft 7in in 1954.

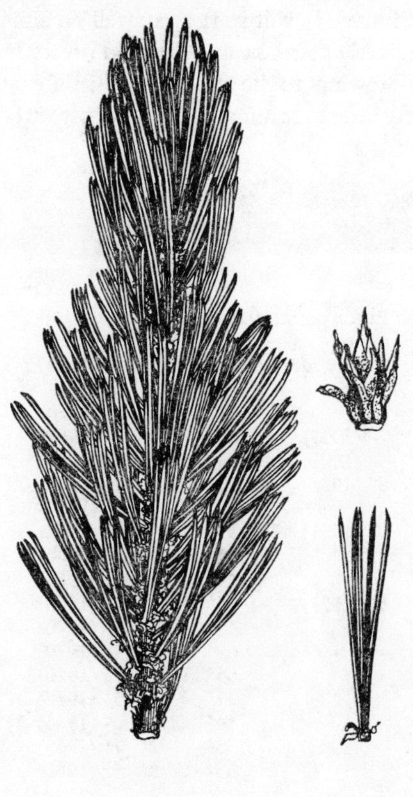

Pinus balfouriana

Fig. 137
Foliage and detail ($\times 1\frac{1}{3}$) of bud of *Pinus balfouriana*, Fox-tail pine, showing enlarged basal bud-scales and fine tips to the needles.

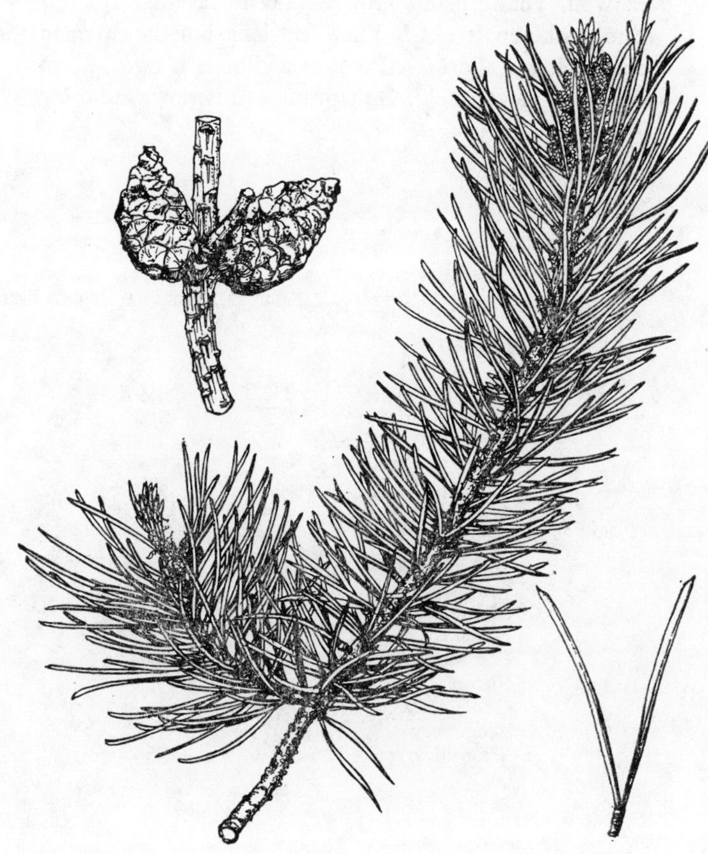

Pinus banksiana

Fig. 138
Foliage, unopened male flowers and serotinous cones several years old of *Pinus banksiana*, Jack pine. The cones point upwards or outwards along the shoots, those of the similar *P. contorta* point downwards or inwards. The leaves ($\times 1$) are broad and twisted.

RECOGNITION. Only the other fox-tail pines resemble this. *P. aristata* has slender prickles on the cone, resin-dots on the leaves, paler pubescence; leaves rather shorter, more curved and abruptly short spined. *P. albicaulis* has longer leaves, less incurved, and with stomatal lines on the outer surface.

Pinus banksiana Lambert. Jack pine

Alaskan border to New York State. Introduced before 1783. Rare but in several collections each in England, Wales and Scotland.

BARK. Orange-grey striped with darker vertical fissures.
CROWN. Broadly conical but irregular with slender and curved branches spreading wide and drooping slightly. Open and thin but full of a dense mass of bare twigs. Small smooth cones adhere to the branches for at least 20 years, pointing forwards in a curve, projecting or close.
FOLIAGE. Shoots spindly, green-brown, two-noded (a whorl of short branchlets in the middle third) sometimes purplish on the upper side. Second year shoot dark purple-brown.
BUD. Cylindric light brown, shining with resin, 1 cm.

LEAVES. In twos from a red-brown sheath 4–5 mm long; each leaf 4 cm long, broad, flat and twisted yellowish green.
FLOWERS AND CONE. Male flowers clustered densely at the base of short, small shoots, borne from an age of about 5 years, shedding pollen in May. Female flowers dull red several on each terminal shoot and on the leading shoot of young plants, small 5 mm with erect prickles. Cone irregular, bumpy conic, pointed and curved, pale green becoming yellow-brown, 3–4 cm long. Some open on the tree but most remain closed, lose the minute prickle which was on each scale and become very smooth and often covered in algae.

Growth. Young plants grow rapidly in height for a few years, with shoots nearly three feet long but they remain spindly. It is a short lived species and none is now known more than 75 years old. Growth in girth is slow, so no big boles are found. It will start away well on almost any soil, poorly drained or shallow and dry, and is very hardy but it is too slow-growing to be of any use in forestry and has remarkably little to recommend it for ornament.

Table 60. The Oldest and Largest trees of Pinus banksiana

Locality	*Date Planted*	*Dimensions*	
Murthly Castle	1897		47′ × 3′ 1″ (1970)
Blackmoor	1906	30′ (1931)	62′ × 4′ 1″ (1968)
Borde Hill (Pinetum)	1911	31′ (1931)	53′ × 3′ 2″ (1957)
Borde Hill (Warren)		28′ × 1′ 8″ (1931)	58′ × 4′ 4″ (1968)
Wakehurst Place	1912		49′ × 4′ 1″ (1964)
Wakehurst Place		30′ × 2′ 0″ (1931)	57′ × 3′ 9″ (1964)
Wakehurst Place			52′ × 3′ 6″ (1964)
Wakehurst Place (West Wood)			44′ × 3′ 7″ (1965)
Tregrehan		30′ × 2′ 6″ (1931)	35′ × 3′ 1″ (1965)
Blairquhan			43′ × 5′ 4″ (1970)
Nymans			69′ × 3′ 9″ (1970)
Fairburn (Pinetum)			66′ × 3′ 7″ (1970)
Bicton			47′ × 3′ 5″ (1968)
Castle Milk			44′ × 3′ 0″ (1966)
Bedgebury	1926	8′ 4″ (1931)	35′ × 2′ 7″ (1969)
Westonbirt	1943		35′ × 2′ 5″ (1969)

Recognition. *P. contorta* differs in that the cones point in the opposite direction, downwards, and retain their prickles, also in bark and narrow, dense crown. *P. virginiana* differs in bloomed shoots and straight cones with retained spines. A hybrid between *P. banksiana* and *P. contorta* was raised in 1952 (pollination done 1949) at Alice Holt and is known to occur in the natural populations where they overlap in North West Canada. The hybrids are vigorous and vary between the parental types but are mostly intermediate in all characters. Very conveniently, the angle of the cone on the shoot indicates the type of the hybrid—ascending in *P. banksiana* types, descending in *P. contorta* types and spreading perpendicular to the shoot in the true intermediate types. The largest tree at Alice Holt is now 15 years planted and is 35ft×2ft 0in. Bud dark purple-grey, very resinous, bulbous with male flowers. Leaf 4–5 cm×0·1 cm, twisted pale shiny green then dark blue-green. Cone 4×2·5 conic, serotinous, some open or partly so, others closed; minute prickles soon shed; pale orange-brown.

Pinus bungeana Zuccarini. Lace-bark pine

East and Central China. Introduced in 1846. Rare but in a few small as well as a few large collections.

Bark. The most beautiful of any pine; smooth grey-green with shallow rounded scales falling to leave pale yellow areas which turn green, olive-brown, reddish and purple.

Crown. Usually a broad, bushy tree, but occasionally narrow and slender, from a broad base. Branches long, slender and strongly ascending.

Foliage. Shoot pale olive-green; second year dark grey-green; third year dark grey-brown.

Bud. Projecting on shoot well forward of terminal leaves, ovoid, pointed; the dark red-brown scales bent outwards at the tips all over the bud.

Leaves. In threes spread widely on side-shoots, forward on main shoots, shiny, smooth, hard and stiff, 6–8 cm long, dark yellow-green on outer surface, inner surface paler, with grey-green stomatal lines.

Cone. Short-stalked ovoid, 4×3·5 cm, dark brown, few-scaled, each thick and wrinkled with a spreading spine 3 mm long.

Growth and Specimens. Very slow growing, but in the absence of trees of known date, the actual rates achieved can be known only from the recent measurements of the very few specimens which have previously been measured, where they survive. At Kew one tree has added 8 feet to its height over a period of 46 years but has added about 34 inches in

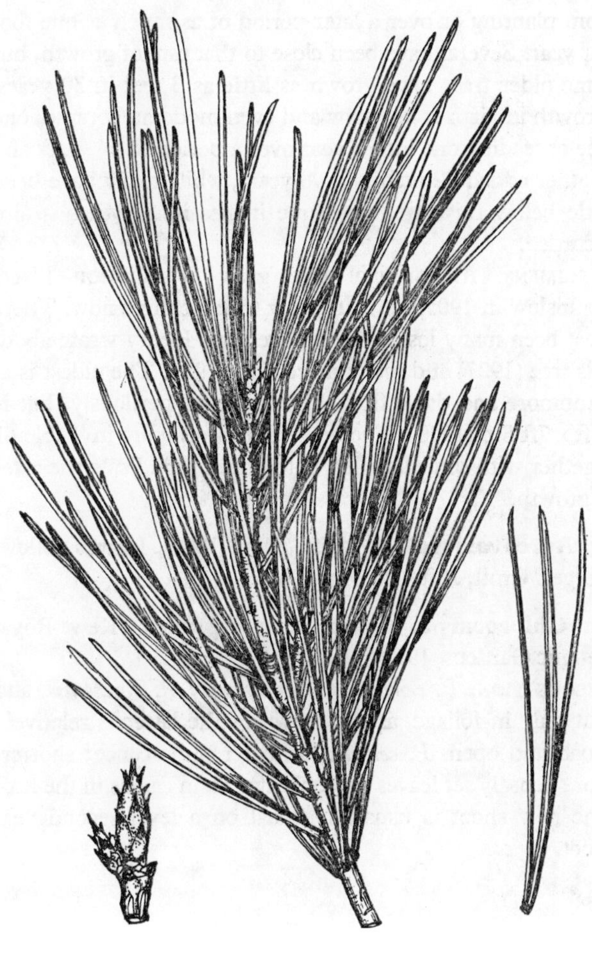

Pinus bungeana

Fig. 139
Foliage of *Pinus bungeana*, Lace-bark pine, is hard but smooth, shiny and dark yellowish-green. The bud (×1⅓) projects slightly ahead of the terminal leaves. The bark sheds scales and the bared area goes through a long series of colour changes, from white to purple and grey.

girth. At Bayfordbury 15 feet has been grown in 31 years and at Patshull one tree added three inches to its girth in 24 years and another in the same time added 7 inches.

Kew Royal Botanic Gardens, 33ft×4ft 9in at 6 inches (1969); 40ft×3ft 7in; 40ft×3ft 2in, 30ft×3ft 1in (1970); Bayfordbury, 25ft×2ft 6in (1968); Wisley Royal Horticultural Society Gardens, 41ft×1ft 10in, a slender spire (1969).

Pinus canariensis Smith. Canary Island pine

Canary Islands. Introduction not recorded, but before 1890. Very rare indeed; far S.W. and in Ireland. Bark grey-pink, widely and deeply fissured, very like that of Corsican pine, but the bole bears epicormic shoots. Crown narrow with few, level branches; shoot yellow; leaves in threes 20–30 cm, grass-green. Seedlings, which seldom survive more than one year in the open in England nowadays (a tree was 57ft×4ft 3in in 1928 at 37 years at Heligan) have long silvery blue juvenile leaves, which foliage is continued in the next year also. This pine regenerates from coppice-shoots.

Mount Usher, 39ft×2ft 6in (1966); Tresco Abbey, 85ft ×7ft 6in (1970); Casa di Sole, 7 feet (1970).

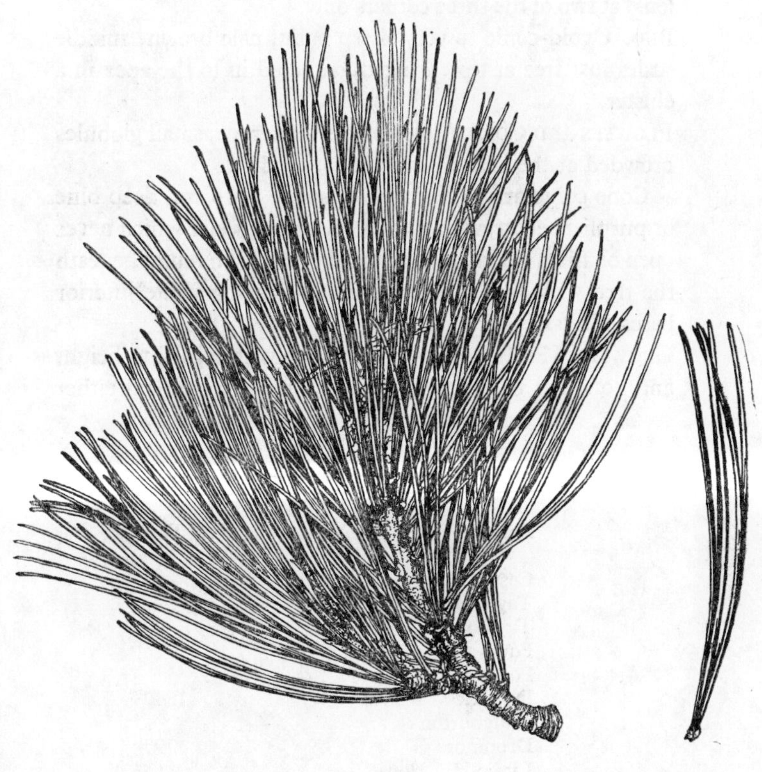

Pinus cembra

Fig. 140
Foliage of *Pinus cembra*, Arolla pine, a tree of dense and columnar habit. The shoot is closely covered by a thick, pale brown pubescence.

Pinus cembra Linnaeus. Arolla pine.

Central Alps and Carpathians. The Siberian form is now regarded as a separate species. Introduced in 1746 or before. Common in collections, and large gardens; occasional in smaller gardens and in parks.

Bark. Dark grey with coarse vertical scales curling away, fissured in red-brown; or orange-brown with coarse purplish scales, curling away.
Crown. Narrowly and densely columnar, with short, level branches abruptly upturned at their tips, and looking very black from a distance. The oldest trees are more open and broader with a flat top composed of upcurved branches.
Foliage. Shoot visible with some difficulty among densely crowded leaves and loose sheaths, green with pale-brown, dense pubescence. Second year shoot, dark brown with pale matted pubescence. Needles in fives, the bunches only partially opened, densely crowded, 8 cm (7–9) dark shining green with a few stomatal lines outside, bright bluish-white inside. Cut across and squeezed, resin-blobs appear (under lens) at two of the three corners only.
Bud. Ovoid-conic to very sharp point, pale brown, middle scales just free at tips, fringed, gathered in to the apex in a cluster.
Flowers and Cone. Male flowers numerous, small globules crowded at the base of weak shoots, yellow.

Cone conic or cylindric and blunt, 6·8×6 cm, deep blue or purplish, erect, with thickened, obtuse scales which never open on the tree; fall in their third year. Often found beneath the tree with seed cleanly eaten out leaving white interior bases of husks.
Growth. This is a slow-growing tree with regard to height and none has been found to have a mean increment either from planting or over a later period of as much as one foot per year. Several have been close to that rate of growth, but some older trees have grown as little as 3 feet in 30 years. Growth in girth is less slow and even moderately rapid, one tree exceeding one inch a year over a period of 54 years and another added 92 inches in 98 years, while many have been little below this rate, but three inches in 27 years is also recorded.
Specimens. An original tree grew at Whitton Place, Hounslow in 1905 but is unlikely to exist there now. There have been many losses since Elwes and Henry wrote about this tree (1907) and many more since 1931. The oldest is at Dropmore and dates from 1795. It leans perilously, but is 65ft×7ft 8in (1970). The biggest trees seen are in Table 61 together with some smaller, dated trees to indicate the rates of growth.

cv. Aureovariegata (France, about 1865). Leaves yellow. Hergest Croft, 20ft×2ft 9in (1961).

cv. Chlorocarpa. Cones yellowish green. Kew Royal Botanic Gardens, 19ft×11in (1969).
Recognition. *P. cembra* resembles only *P. koraiensis*, and that only in foliage, as the crown of the latter is relatively broad and open. *P. cembra* has paler pubescence; shorter, more densely set leaves and only two resin canals in the leaf. The new shoot is usually vertical on a level second year shoot.

Table 61. The Largest Trees of Pinus cembra and some dated specimens

Locality	*Date Planted*	*Dimensions*	
Castle Milk			86′ × 7′ 3″ (1966)
Taymouth Castle		72′ × 9′ 9″ (1931)	90′ × 10′ 11″ (1970)
Taymouth Castle			72′ × 8′ 10″ (1970)
Powis Castle			71′ × 8′ 0″ (1970)
Powis Castle			60′ × 9′ 1″ (1970)
Dawyck	1840		50′ × 8′ 4″ (1966)
Hallyburton			75′ × 5′ 2″ (1970)
Dropmore	1795		65′ × 7′ 8″ (1970)
Lythe Hill House			70′ × 6′ 1″ (1969)
Dupplin Castle			77′ × 5′ 0″ (1970)
Murthly Castle			80′ × 7′ 11″ (1970)
Kilkerran			71′ × 6′ 3″ (1970)
Capenoch	1860		72′ × 5′ 5″ (1970)
Cullen			67′ × 5′ 11″ (1970)
Herriard Park			64′ × 6′ 4″ (1961)
Eridge Castle			57′ × 6′ 4″ (1971)
Keir	1889	40′ × 4′ 6″ (1931)	56′ × 5′ 6″ (1970)
Nunwick			65′ × 5′ 8″ (1958)
Walcot Hall			59′ × 7′ 2″ (1959)
Holkham (Fox's Covert)			63′ × 6′ 6″ (1968)
Westonbirt		48′ × 4′ 5″ (1931)	63′ × 5′ 0″ (1967)
Blairquhan	1856	45′ × 6′ 11″ (1931)	55′ × 8′ 1″ (1970)
Brahan	1901	31′ × 3′ 2½″ (1931)	59′ × 5′ 6″ (1970)
Leonardslee		52′ × 4′ 1″ (1931)	60′ × 4′ 10″ (1960)
Little Hall	1906	28′ × 2′ 6″ (1931)	51′ × 3′ 11″ (1961)
Blackmoor	1899	37′ × 3′ 3″ (1931)	55′ × 4′ 2″ (1961)
Wakehurst Place	1913	20′ × 1′ 2″ (1931)	45′ × 3′ 9″ (1964)
Bedgebury	1926	7′ (1931)	42′ × 3′ 1″ (1969)
Bedgebury	1926		35′ × 2′ 10″ (1969)

Pinus cembroides Zuccarini. Pinyon.

Mexico, Arizona and California. Introduced in 1846. Very rare indeed. A three-needle pine with the scales rolled back at the base of the needles, slender glaucous shoots, leaves incurved, pointed, to 5 cm long. A tree at Bell's Wood, Bayford is probably of the type, 27ft×1ft 10in in 1962.

var. edulis (Engelmann) Voss. (Introduced in 1848). Leaves mostly in pairs. A young tree at Cambridge Botanic Garden, 14 feet (1969).

Pinus cembroides v. monophylla

Fig. 141
Pinus cembroides var. *monophylla,* Single-leaf pine, a form of the Edible-nut pine, has solid, nearly rounded needles, pale grey-green with fine white bands on all sides.

var. monophylla (Torrey and Fremont) Voss. Single-leaved Nut pine. Introduced in 1848. Very rare.

BARK. Very dark purplish grey, finely and deeply cracked into squares.

CROWN. Tall ovoid—a rather narrow, domed top, branches upswept.

FOLIAGE. Leaves somewhat whorled by bare lengths between annual growths occupied by male flowers, single, solid circular in cross-section, 5 cm long, stiff curved forwards, pale grey-green first year, striped by white lines all round, older leaves dark grey-green.

SPECIMENS. The tree at Cambridge Botanic Garden which was 5 feet tall in 1910 and 15ft 9in×2ft 1in in 1931 is now 33ft×3ft 6in. It has been male-flowering only so far. A young one at the same place is 2ft 9in tall. At Trent College one is 18ft×2ft 0in at four feet (1962), at Kew there is a tree 13ft×10in (1963), and at Edinburgh, 25ft×1ft 8in (1970).

Pinus contorta Douglas. Lodgepole pine; Shore pine; Beach pine

South West Alaska, Mackenzie, Alberta and south along the Pacific Coast to Northern California, inland along the Sierra Nevada and Rocky Mountains to Dakota and Colorado. Introduced in 1855. Three of the four varieties have been much confused in their naming and time of introduction. The varieties will be treated separately here.

var. contorta Douglas. The Pacific Coast, in a belt about 100 miles broad, from the Alaska Pan-handle to Point Arena in California. Introduced in 1831 but lost and re-introduced, perhaps in 1855. Uncommon in collections or large gardens, but widely used in young plantations in the west.

BARK. Typically light reddish-brown or yellowish-brown deeply fissured into darker squares but biggest trees dark red-brown with deep vertical fissures, close, leaving narrow, short plates.

CROWN. Young trees have a broad bushy base with upswept branches and often a swept stem but soon produce a long, vigorous, straight, narrow spire with densely set appressed leaves hiding the stem. Old trees may be dense, ovoid bushes or columnar with flat or pointed top. The outside is densely covered by upturned yellow-green foliaged shoots. Young trees from Lulu Island and a few other areas at the mouth of the Fraser River are spindly and open-crowned with long thin branches curving up to become vertical.

FOLIAGE. Shoot greenish-brown, wrinkled. Second year orange-brown striped whitish, third year shining orange-brown.

BUD. Cylindrical, pointed, the terminal buds surrounded by a whorl of vertical side-buds, 3 cm but lengthening during March to twice that, when they often show the contortions from which the name is derived; dark red-purple with some white resin. Buds on side-shoots are usually bulbous at the base where they contain the male flowers.

LEAVES. In twos, 4-5×0·1 cm dull very deep green in Oregon trees, bright green, yellowish at the base, in trees from further north, twisted; basal sheath dark red-brown, 3-5 mm. Under a lens the convex outer side and the flat inner side are lined finely with stomata. The leaves are held closely along the shoots.

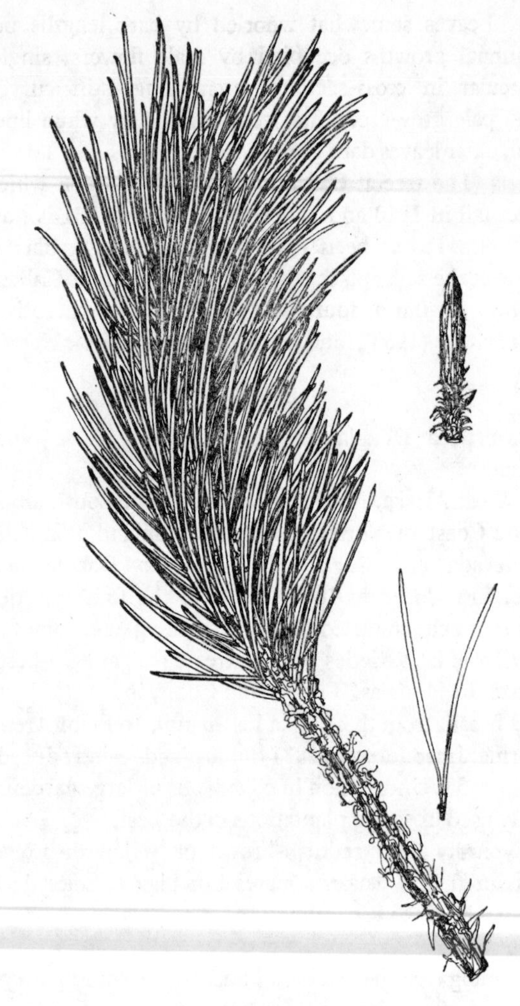

Fig. 142
Foliage and bud of *Pinus contorta* var. *contorta*, Shore pine, the very vigorous form from the coastal regions of North West America. The closely appressed needles are bright or deep green. The swollen base of the bud contains male flowers.

FLOWERS AND CONE. Male flowers abundant from an early age; on every side-shoot of trees from Lulu Island, from their fourth or fifth year, but later and fewer on some other provenances; crowded in a shallow ring at the base of the new shoots, pale yellow, shedding pollen in early May.

Female flowers abundant, often on the tips of the leading shoot and main branch shoots from the third year, in whorls of 2–5, dull pink, opening in early May.

Cone 4·5×2 cm long-conic, ripening light pink-brown then darkening, shiny at the base, matt above, each scale with a small straight or upcurved prickle. The cones point back along the shoot and are often retained on the tree, mainly open, for many years.

GROWTH. The Coastal form is exceedingly vigorous as a young tree on a wide variety of sites, which are acid and damp, including deep peats, and in fairly severe exposure. Annual shoots of 3 feet are usual in any thriving plantation and four and even five-foot shoots may be found. The older specimen trees have not shown such vigour for long enough to have made spectacular growth over the periods between measurements, but probably few of them have come from the coastal Washington and Oregon sources which provide the trees used in forestry. The three trees found of the ten given by Elwes and Henry have grown only 15 to 22 feet in around 50 years, and of eight comparisons possible since 1931 the two largest increases in height have been 30 and 29 feet in 37 years. Growth in girth is not at first rapid, but, in open-grown trees it does become so and even large old trees have added as much as 64 inches in 58 years and the largest in girth is 12 feet 2 inches when only 84 years old. Height growth starts with the bud lengthening by 3–4 inches in March without spreading the bud-scales noticeably. The bud opens in mid-April and maximum growth-rate is soon achieved, up to 5 inches being grown in a week in early May even on shoots finally only three feet long. Growth ends in early July.

Many trees from the northern parts of the range grow two nodes, shown by a whorl of shoots about half-way up the leading-shoot. This is in no sense second growth—these shoots can be seen already in the bud as a swelling half way up it.

SPECIMENS. The largest tree known to have grown in Britain was blown down two years ago. It was at Bicton and was 103ft×11ft 3in. The oldest and largest now known are shown in Table 62.

Table 62. Oldest and Largest Pinus contorta var. contorta

Locality	*Date Planted*		*Dimensions*
Bodnant	1876		88′ × 9′ 10″ (1966)
Ashford Castle	1884		88′ × 12′ 2″ (1968)
Ashford Castle	1884		90′ × 11′ 1″ (1968)
Ashford Castle	1884		90′ × 10′ 11″ (1968)
Ashford Castle	1884		80′ × 11′ 6″ (1968)
Grayswood Hill	1886	25′ × 3′ 1″ (1906)	66′ × 8′ 9″ (1971)
Bodnant	1888	73′ × 7′ 6″ (1931)	92′ × 9′ 5″ (1966)
Wakehurst Place (Pinetum)	1913	35′ × 1′ 8″ (1931)	70′ × 5′ 9″ (1970)
Wakehurst Place (Pinetum)			64′ × 5′ 7″ (1970)
Wakehurst Place (Oaks)			67′ × 7′ 5″ (1968)
Wakehurst Place (West Wood)			60′ × 7′ 6″ (1964)
Leonardslee			83′ × 4′ 7″ (1969)
Woburn Abbey			82′ × 6′ 5″ (1970)
Warnham Court		56′ × 7′ 1″ (1931)	73′ × 9′ 3″ (1971)
Bowood		59′ × 5′ 8″ (1931)	88′ × 9′ 1″ (1968)
Bowood			70′ × 7′ 10″ (1968)
Bowood			73′ × 6′ 11″ (1968)
Westonbirt (Pool Avenue)		59′ × 4′ 7″ (1909)	72′ × 7′ 7″ (1971)
Westonbirt (Broad Drive)			61′ × 9′ 0″ (1970)
The Frythe			85′ × 6′ 3″ (1969)
Errol			74′ × 10′ 6″ (1970)[1]
St. Clere		50′ × 5′ 3″ (1955)	53′ × 6′ 9″ (1969)
Oakley Park			72′ × 5′ 8″ (1971)
Melbury			66′ × 9′ 10″ (1971)
Melbury			79′ × 5′ 9″ (1971)
Trentham Park			63′ × 5′ 4″ (1968)

[1] Measured at 3 feet

Fig. 143
Shoot with cones of *Pinus contorta* var. *latifolia*, Lodgepole pine from inland regions. The leaves are much longer and more spreading than those of the coastal form var. *contorta*.

var. latifolia (Engelmann) Critchfield. Inland range of the species except Oregon and California. The inland and coastal forms intergrade along their mutual boundary from Alaska to Southern Washington. Introduced in 1855. Rare in collections and large gardens but has been used in plantations since 1930, usually at high altitudes and in the east as well as the west.

BARK. Typically red-brown, scaly with fine, curled flakes, but the square-cracked bark of var. *contorta* also occurs mixed with this in some inland populations.

CROWN. Young trees open-crowned narrowly conic, with few short, level slightly twisted branches, and leaves widely spread. Older trees neatly conic with whorled somewhat ascending branches.

FOLIAGE. Leaves 6–8·5 cm, spreading or pointing rather forwards but not tightly around the shoot; fresh green.

FLOWERS AND CONE. As the type; the cone more likely to be ovoid and rather bright coppery brown and the spines on the scales spread and 3 mm long.

GROWTH. In forest plantations, this is very much slower than is the type except on some particular sites, inland and at high altitudes where it can be superior. As a specimen or garden tree this inland tree is more shapely but less impressive and the thinner crown shows in the slower increase in girth. In height, they are much the same, but leading-shoots of young trees seldom exceed three feet. The growth of a few dated trees can be seen from the table under 'Specimens'.

SPECIMENS. No old tree is known, and this may be a short lived tree here.

TABLE 63. SPECIMEN TREES OF PINUS CONTORTA VAR. LATIFOLIA

Locality	*Date Planted*	*Dimensions*	
Bodnant	1901		55′ × 5′ 8″ (1966)
Bodnant	1902		61′ × 4′ 9″ (1966)
Borde Hill	1910	29′ × 3′ 10″ (1931)	66′ × 4′ 11″ (1961)
Borde Hill			74′ × 4′ 2″ (1968)
Kew R.B.G.			36′ × 5′ 4″ (1969)
Dropmore	1914	40′ × 1′ 6″ (1930)	72′ × 5′ 1″ (1970)
Speech House	1916		55′ × 3′ 0″ (1963)
Speech House	1916		49′ × 4′ 10″ (1959)
Fenagh House	1918	16′ 6″ (1931)	47′ × 3′ 1″ (1968)
Bedgebury	1926	7′ 9″ (1931)	30′ × 2′ 5″ (1969)
Bedgebury	1931		38′ × 4′ 0″ (1969)

var. murrayana (Balfour) Critchfield. Mountains of Oregon and California. Introduced in 1853. Differs as a young tree in its neat narrow shape and very dark leaves. The branches curve up at the end and the small tree resembles *Pinus cembra* but with branches bare of leaves after the first year. It grows very slowly indeed. The leaves are as long as, and rather broader than, var. *latifolia*; the cones are rarely retained on the tree when ripe.

var. bolanderi (Parl.) Critchfield. Mendocino plains, California. An outlying population a little to the south of the end of the range of the var. *contorta*. It differs mainly in leaves being narrower than 1·5 mm and lacking resin-canals in all leaves whereas other forms lack them in some leaves only. Included in several experimental plantings since 1959.

GENERAL. Lodgepole pine is now the second most widely planted species in Commission forests, due to its ability to grow rapidly on very poor soils and exposed sites at high altitudes. The area of origin of the seed used to raise the plants is a vital factor in the success or failure. On most sites trees from coastal Washington and Oregon grow much the fastest and the dense broad lower crowns suppress the strongest ground vegetation rapidly. Unfortunately in many places the basal lengths of stems are badly bowed and since this is a result of their fast early growth which is otherwise highly desirable, this causes difficulties. To plant deliberately more northerly and slower growing provenances seems to defeat one of the prime aims of the forester. Inland trees grow straight and more slowly but seldom suppress *Calluna* properly, whereas a northern coastal provenance will do this rapidly. The miserable performance of trees from Lulu Island area is an unfortunate disappointment. Thousands of acres were planted with this when such a middle-latitude coastal provenance held every prospect of being successful.

RECOGNITION. All forms of *P. contorta* are distinguished among two-needle pines by their deflexed short-spined small cones. Var. *contorta* is unlike any other in its dense, forward, short, often yellowish green needles, but var. *latifolia* is very like *P. uncinata* (*P. mugo uncinata*). It differs in its red-brown bark, less dense branches and foliage, less stiff and more green needles and narrower cone with prickles, and without long drawn out basal scales.

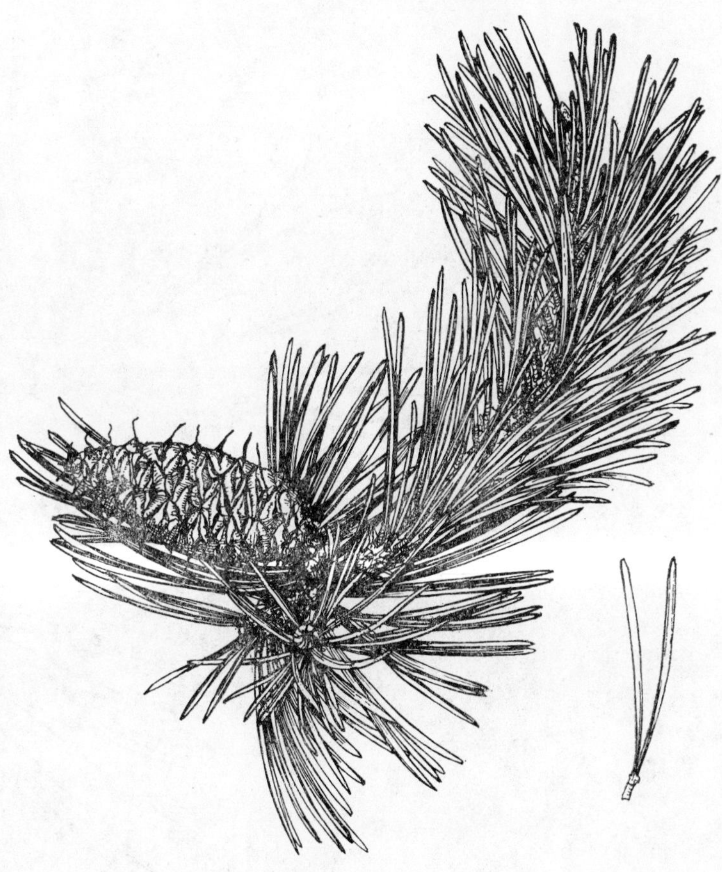

Pinus contorta v. murrayana

Fig. 144
Foliage and cone of *Pinus contorta* var. *murrayana*, the form of Lodgepole pine found in the western mountains south of the Columbia River. It is a slow, neat tree with short, dark needles, seen only in forest trial plots in Britain.

Pinus cooperi Blanco.

Mexico. Introduced in 1962. Closely allied to *P. montezumae* var. *hartwegii*. Plants in a trial at Plym Forest are now 3 feet tall, after 3 years, and making shoots of 1 foot.

Shoot stout (5–7 mm) at first bluish-white, later green-brown, tinged pink, bloomed lilac-grey below the pulvini, which are purple.

BUD. 1·4–1·7 cm dark red-brown or chestnut, cylindric, tapered to a blunt point or abruptly short pointed with a few scales free at their extreme tips. Leaves rather dense (15–20 bundles on 5 cm of shoot), in fives but scarcely parted so may, at first appear as a single, round needle, 8–11 cm long with a red-brown basal sheath 5 mm long with a further 5 mm papery white. Greyish dark blue-green; about 10 crowded fine stomatal lines on the outside; inner side paler blue-grey. Thick, rather stiff, to a small clear abrupt point.

Pinus coulteri

Fig. 145
Spray (× $\frac{1}{3}$) and fascicle of needles (× $\frac{2}{3}$) of *Pinus coulteri*, the Big-cone pine. The shoot is very stout and is bloomed blue-grey. The bud depicted is expanding, at which time they are pale orange.

Pinus coulteri D. Don. Big-cone pine.

Southern California to North West Mexico. Introduced in 1832. Infrequent; mostly in collections but in a few gardens, and largely confined to South England and the Welsh borders.

BARK. Young trees, pale grey with wide vertical and narrow horizontal cracks, later more fissured and darker. Old trees, black or dark purplish-brown, divided by wide fissures into flaking, thick, broad, intercrossing ridges.

CROWN. Gaunt as a young tree, with few branches curved up at their ends. Some young trees more dense and conical. Old trees conic with wide-spreading level branches upturned at their ends, bare of foliage except for the branch-ends where rather sparse, very long, pale grey needles stand out straight all round.

FOLIAGE. Shoot very stout, pale blue-grey bloom on green-brown; dark red below pulvini; basal length bearing only dark brown, curved scales, may be four fifths of shoot.

BUD. Cylindric-conic to a fine point, 2–6 cm, bright orange; long dark chestnut scales at side with free tips.

LEAVES. In threes, stout, 25–30 cm long, spreading, usually crinkled; pale or dark grey-green; many stomatal lines on each surface; acute.

FLOWERS AND CONE. Male flowers spread rather widely on the bare lower half of the new shoot, dark purple then yellow. Female flowers ovoid, dark pink, borne at first on the leading shoot beneath the apex, on trees about 10 years old.

Cone massive, long-ovoid 20–35 × 15-20 cm, oblique at base, deflexed down the shoot; light brown with dark red-brown points on the scales. These points are longest on the outer side of the base, to 2 cm long, broad, flattened, ridged, spreading and upcurved at the shortly-spined tip. They remain closed on the tree and may weigh five pounds when fresh. Kept in a warm room for a year or so they open and when dry weigh more than one pound. On opening they may eject the large seed explosively over a period of weeks.

GROWTH. This is a short-lived tree here, the two oldest, probably original trees are dying and the trees recorded earlier have largely gone. Elwes and Henry noted twelve (they did not note the two oldest and largest mentioned above), seven of these being in Hertfordshire. None is now known but three may survive. The 1932 *Report* noted 13 and only one, which was then but 6 feet tall, has been found since. Hence the evidence for the rates of growth rests on the trees now known with fixed planting dates and a few re-measurements over short periods. These both show height increments of 1 to 1½ feet per year, but very considerable vigour in growth in girth, exceeding one inch a year in all but one measured tree and nearly two inches a year in several. (See Table 64).

SPECIMENS. The first trees were raised from seed sent by Douglas in 1831. They were thus three years younger than the original trees of *P. ponderosa. P. coulteri* has similar but often slightly more rapid growth than *P. ponderosa.* The original trees of *P. ponderosa* now range from 10 feet to 14 feet in girth. It thus seems highly probable that the two *P. coulteri,* which are very much bigger than any others known and both with a girth of over 12 feet, are original trees, planted in about 1835.

RECOGNITION. When bearing cones, *P. coulteri* is quite distinct; the only tree at all similar is *P. sabiniana* and the cone of that tree is shorter, broader, less woody and has strongly down-curved points. In foliage, the big orange buds and stout shoot of *P. coulteri* and its very dark bark differ from *P. sabiniana.* As a large tree without cones, *P. coulteri* can be very like *P. jeffreyi* but the ridged bark, wide-spreading branches, the bud and sparse, longer crinkled leaves distinguish it.

TABLE 64. THE LARGEST TREES OF PINUS COULTERI

Locality	*Date Planted*		*Dimensions*
Titley Court, Hereford			98′ × 12′ 7½″ (1963)
Bankfield House, Hereford			75′ × 12′ 4″ (1966)
			Dying 1969
Stanway			66′ × 7′ 8″ (1964)
Tilgate	1906		67′ × 7′ 1″ (1964)
Tubney Wood	1906		68′ × 4′ 6″ (1966)
Broxwood Court			66′ × 6′ 1″ (1957)
Dropmore	1915		56′ × 7′ 3″ (1970)
Tibberton Court	1921		53′ × 4′ 8″ (1967)
Edinburgh R.B.G.			59′ × 4′ 9″ (1970)
Penrhyn Castle	1922		52′ × 5′ 10″ (1959)
Powerscourt			56′ × 6′ 2″ (1966)
Wakehurst Place (Valley)			58′ × 5′ 1″ (1968)
Wisley R.H.S.G.			45′ × 3′ 9″ (1969)
Bedgebury	1926	35′ × 2′ 11″ (1956)	47′ × 3′ 8″ (1969)
Bedgebury (plots)	1935		45′ × 4′ 3″ (1967)
Chandlers Ford	1927		44′ × 4′ 11″ (1961)
Youngsbury			55′ × 3′ 2″ (1966)
Alice Holt	1953		31′ × 3′ 3″ (1971)

Pinus densiflora

Fig. 146
Pinus densiflora, Japanese red pine, resembles *P. sylvestris* in the bark, but has longer, darker needles and retains the cones, which are more pointed, on the branches in whorls of three for many years.

Pinus densiflora Siebold and Zuccarini. Japanese red pine.

Japan. Introduced in 1861. Rare. Found only in some collections, mainly in South England and in Ireland, but there are two trees in Edinburgh Royal Botanic Garden.

BARK. Grey-pink and scaly, widely fissured with orange-brown.

CROWN. Broadly and irregularly conic with wide, level then upswept branches which are orange-red with heavy dark brown flakes. The dense foliage is dark and often does not spread but points forward, making the shoots narrow as in *P. strobus* but at other times it is more spreading.

FOLIAGE. Shoot pale whitish-green or bloomed pinkish, narrowly grooved, the weak shoots smooth and whitish. Second year, pale pinkish-brown, narrowly grooved.

BUD. 0·5 to 1·5 cm cylindric-conic, chestnut brown, slightly resinous but free tips of scales point straight forward or curve open in a rosette.

LEAVES. In pairs, 9–10 cm slender, bright green with fine

lines of scattered stomata on each side. Basal sheath 1 cm with long pale filaments, soon lost.

CONE. Female flower turns purple-brown when 1 cm long and ripens into a cone 5×3 cm, ovoid-conic, long pointed, pinkish brown or purplish, the smooth scales with very minute prickles in the centre. The cones are borne in whorls of 3 to 5 and remain for many years on the tree, pointing about 45° backwards. Males small, pale, open in June.

GROWTH. Of the five trees in the 1932 Report only one, then only 5 feet 8 inches tall, survives. Early growth is quite rapid, particularly in girth, but the height increment soon falls off and a low-crowned tree results.

SPECIMENS. The biggest tree and the only one dating from before this century, has died. It was at Nuneham Court and was 48ft×7ft 0in in 1966.

RECOGNITION. Resembles *P. sylvestris* in bark and crown, but cone and details of foliage readily distinguish it.

TABLE 65. THE LARGEST TREES OF PINUS DENSIFLORA

Locality	*Date Planted*	*Dimensions*
Bedgebury	1925	5′ 8″ (1931) 44′ × 3′ 0″ (1969)
Bedgebury	1925	33′ × 2′ 7″ (1971)
Westonbirt	1926	45′ × 3′ 3″ (1967)
Westonbirt	1926	37′ × 3′ 0″ (1967)
Garinish Island		44′ × 3′ 6″ (1966)
Garinish Island		48′ × 4′ 6″ (1966)
Powerscourt		42′ × 3′ 2″ (1966)
Bicton		48′ × 5′ 9″ (1968)
Wakehurst Place		37′ × 2′ 7″ (1964)
Edinburgh R.B.G.	1908	49′ × 3′ 8″ (1970)
Muckross Abbey		48′ × 3′ 4″ (1968)
Jermyn's House	1954	30′ × 2′ 7″ (1969)

Pinus durangensis Martinez. Durango pine.

Mexico. Introduced in 1962. Closely allied to *P. montezumae.* Plants in a trial at Plym Forest are now 3 feet tall after 3 years planted out and have shoots of 15 inches. In the nursery they had a "grass" stage for two years. Now the shoots are slender, at first bright white, then pale green and greenish-brown, bloomed lilac or blue-white especially below the pulvini, and ridged.

BUD. 1·5 cm dark red-brown, slightly white with resin at the base, bright red-brown to orange at the tip, cylindric, bluntly conic at the tip. The leaves, in fives, are sparsely or very sparsely set (6–10 bundles in 5 cm of shoot); the bundles remain nearly closed; leaves 16–18 cm, sheath 2 cm basal half red-brown, upper half paper-white. Leaves light grey-green, three widely spaced stomatal lines outside, a grey band on each inner surface; soft, slender to a fine, clear point.

Pinus echinata Miller. Short-leaf pine.

From New York to Florida and Texas, north to Illinois. Introduced in 1739. Very rare; one old tree at Dropmore and a few small trees in some collections in South England only.

BARK. Dark grey-orange-purplish with coarse, short flaking ridges.

CROWN. Poorly developed in this country, with level, then depressed, long branches from a sinuous bole, the branches bearing many short epicormic sprouts on their basal portions, and ordinary foliage in flattened sprays.

FOLIAGE. Shoot pale whitish-green; pulvini orange-brown; second year shoot pale orange-brown.

BUD. Narrowly cylindric-ovoid, 4 mm, dark brown.

LEAVES. In pairs but scattered bundles of threes, 5–7 cm, fresh green with a pale base; fine stomatal lines on each surface; abruptly and bluntly pointed.

CONE. (Not seen). Sessile or on stalk to 6 cm, conical-oblong, 4–6 cm×2·5–3 cm blunt, light brown with thin, rounded scales, thickened at the ends, with slender deciduous prickle (Den Ouden and Boom).

GROWTH AND SPECIMENS. The old tree at Dropmore was planted in 1821. It was 50ft×3ft 4in in 1908 but now leans and in 1970 it measured 55ft×4ft 2in. In the Pinetum at Borde Hill a tree is 45ft×3ft 1in (1961) and in The Tolls another is 26ft×2ft 1in (1957). At Blackmoor a tree is 47ft× 3ft 10in (1959). At Bedgebury three planted in 1932 are now 31ft×2ft 7in; 26ft×1ft 6in and 28ft×2ft 0in (1969); one at Bicton is 34ft×1ft 10in (1968).

RECOGNITION. The whole tree is recognised by the sprouts along the branches, (a feature-shared by *P. rigida* which has them also thickly on the bole) the short needles mostly in pairs and the pale shoot.

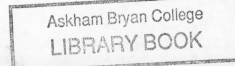

Pinus engelmannii Carriere. Engelmann pine.

Mexico and South West United States. Introduced in 1962. Shoot green. Leaves in threes, 20 cm.

Pinus flexilis James. Limber pine

South-West United States and northwards along the eastern Rocky Mountains to Alberta. Introduced in 1851. Very rare but in some widely scattered collections, and most appropriately, some of the best are at Brocklesby Park which is near the village of Limber. It is closely allied to *P. albicaulis* and in the wild they are very similar, but in this country the whole aspect of the tree is different.

BARK. Smooth, dull pink-grey wrinkled horizontally, later cracked horizontally and with wide, shallow vertical fissures.

CROWN. Broadly conic with wide, level, branches slightly curved up at the ends; upper branches projecting far, upswept, with close, dark foliage.

FOLIAGE. Shoot pale apple-green with short brown pubescence. Second year dark grey-brown.

BUD. Cylindric with a long conic point of red-brown free scale-tips, the lower part paler and grey; to 1·3 cm long. The short shoots are very flexible and will not snap however sharply they are bent. This would be a more useful character if one knew that the same were not true of other five-needle pines. In those tried, it isn't.

LEAVES. In fives, the bundles remaining nearly closed and widely separated from adjacent bundles—which is quite untrue of *P. albicaulis*. They are laid very forward along the shoot in the first year, but spread from it in the second year; dark green, 8 cm long, basal sheath slender, red-brown, soon shed. The pulvini are large, wrinkled, dark grey and resemble small spur-shoots.

CONE. Long-ovoid-conic, tapering from near the base; 8–15 cm × 5 cm, erect at first, rather few scales which are thick, dark orange-brown and round-ended, the lower ones elongated and reflexed strongly; much covered in resin.

SPECIMENS. A tree at Brocklesby Park was 87ft × 5ft 11in in 1931 but was blown down soon afterwards. The best there in 1956 were 46ft × 4ft 1in and 46ft × 1ft 11in. One of these, presumably the larger was 17ft × 8in in 1931 so it has grown quite rapidly. Others are: Edinburgh Royal Botanic Garden, 46ft × 2ft 5in; 35ft × 1ft 10in (1970); Leighton Park, 36ft × 5ft 0in (1970); Kew Royal Botanic Gardens, 54ft × 4ft 8in (1970); Westonbirt (Sand Earth), 34ft × 3ft 5in (1970); Killerton, 23ft × 1ft 4in (1959); Bedgebury, planted 1926, 30ft × 1ft 1in (very slender, 1969); Cambridge Botanic Garden, 37ft × 2ft 3in (1969); Windsor Great Park, planted 1933, 48ft × 5ft 1in; 45ft × 4ft 1in (1970).

RECOGNITION. Of the five-needled, short-leafed pines none other has uniformly dark green needles held closely in their bundles.

Pinus gerardiana Wallich.

North Afghanistan, Kashmir and Tibet. Introduced in 1839. Very rare indeed—in effect a single tree at Cambridge Botanic Garden. This tree was probably planted in about 1900. It was 15 feet tall in 1910 and is now 39ft × 2ft 9in (1969). The bark is pink-grey, which flakes off in papery scales and leaves patches of green, yellow and brown. It is similar to that of *P. bungeana* but darker.

This small tree has an open crown with few branches but dense foliage, the weaker shoots pendulous. Leaves in threes, 9 cm long, dull green all round and spreading, making the shoots look spiky.

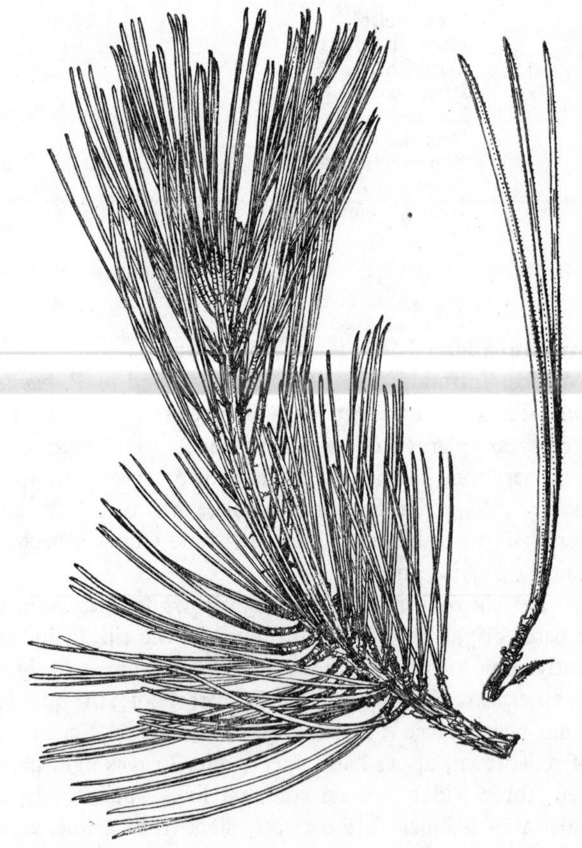

Pinus greggii

Fig. 147
Foliage of the Mexican *Pinus greggii*, with bright green leaves and nearly white new shoots. Fascicle with basal sheath (right × 1⅓).

Pinus greggii Engelmann. Gregg pine.

Mexico. Introduced in about 1905. Very rare indeed; trees of any reasonable age known in only three collections, Bedgebury, Leonardslee and Fota, but young plants have been distributed more widely in recent years.

Bark. Pale grey, with thick, deep, flaking intercrossing ridges. Young trees have pale grey bark with wide, brown fissures.

Crown. Bright green broad-conic with level, slightly upswept branches, open on the inside but dense with hanging leaves on the outside. Young trees are very narrow and upright with strong leading shoots.

Foliage. Side-shoots glaucous whitish green and glabrous but main shoots often more olive-green slightly bloomed pinkish white. Second year pale orange-brown.

Bud. Prominent bright deep chestnut, very slender and cylindrical, pointed with vertical free tips to the scales; 1·5 cm or more.

Leaves. In threes, pointing forwards 45° on young shoots, spreading perpendicular in the second year and recurved on older shoots; 9–12 cm long, finely serrated, bright green with a few widely separated lines of stomata on each side, slender; basal sheath grey and dark brown, 1·3 cm long.

Flowers and Cone. Male flowers at the base of short shoots, becoming pale yellow in July and shedding pollen either then or in August and fairly regularly in October. (By far the latest of the pines.) Female flowers in whorls of up to 8 on strong shoots; dull red when open in July or August. Cone reflexed along branch, very oblique base; irregular, curved conic, 10×4 cm; small flat scales with waved margin, shiny cream-brown, dark pink-brown centres, minute spine.

Specimens. In 1926 two trees were brought to Bedgebury from the Temperate House at Kew. One was then 15 feet tall. They grew well until the hard winters after 1940 and one died after 1962. The other, 53ft×5ft 7in (1970) shows still the point from which it made new growth at Bedgebury, but has grown quite fast. It is now giving some concern. A tree at Leonardslee Pinetum, an area planted in about 1905, was 9 feet tall in 1913. By 1962 it had run into a branch of an oak and was 47ft×6ft 1in. At Fota, the tree was planted in 1911 and was 54ft×5ft 10in in 1966.

Recognition. The white shoots with rather appressed bright green leaves and slender chestnut buds are quite distinct.

Pinus halepensis

Fig. 148
Foliage of *Pinus halepensis*, Aleppo pine, which has smooth, slender bright green leaves on a green shoot which becomes orange and grey. Detail of bud (×1⅓) showing strongly recurved scales.

Pinus halepensis Miller. Aleppo pine

Mediterranean to South West Asia and Afghanistan. Introduced in 1683. Very rare and confined to a few collections in South England.

Bark. Young trees deep purple-brown with wide, shallow dark orange fissures. Old trees dark red-brown fissured into small plates which scale away to leave orange.

Crown. Domed with large contorted branches and a dense mass of fine shoots with cones adhering in whorls.

Foliage. Shoot smooth, pale green, second year ashen above, orange-grey beneath.

Bud. Red-brown, cylindric, 1 cm, with scale-tips free, widely fringed grey and recurved.

Leaves. In pairs, sparse, bright fresh green, shiny and smooth, 6–9 cm long; basal sheath 1 cm, grey-brown.

CONE. Deflexed, pointing back along the shoot, long-conic, curved, 7×3 cm, scales orange to red-brown, (purple-brown in S. Europe) centre raised, pale grey.

SPECIMENS. Kew Royal Botanic Gardens, 32ft×10ft 1in at 6 inches (1969) and 45ft×4ft 8in (1971); Wisley Royal Horticultural Society Gardens, 34ft×3ft 6in (1968); Bicton, 45ft×2ft 7in; 24ft×1ft 5in (1968); Tresco 50ft×4ft 2in (1970).

RECOGNITION. The smooth green of the shoots and leaves, with the colour of the cone are distinct from other 2-needle pines.

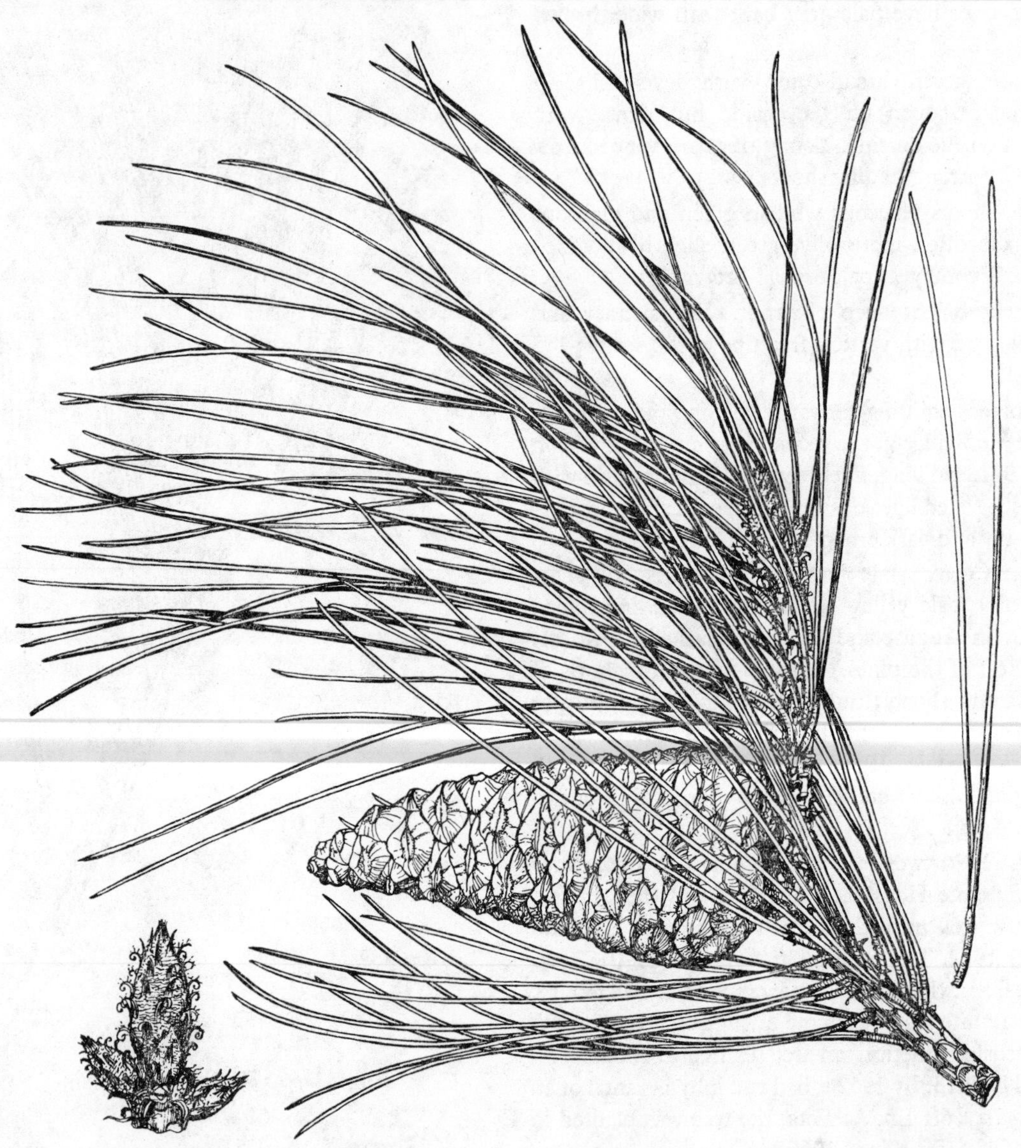

Fig. 149
Pinus halepensis var. *brutia* with cone and (inset) buds. The leaves are about twice as long as in the type and the cone also much bigger.

var. brutia (Tenore) Elwes and Henry. Southern Italy to Syria. Introduced in 1836. This differs from the type in having stout orange shoots; darker, stiffer leaves 10–15 cm long and forward pointing larger cones, 9×4·5 cm on stalk 1 cm *thick*. Found only at Kew, Royal Botanic Gardens, 44ft ×6ft 1in (1971) and Bowood, 45ft×2ft 9in (1957. Not seen 1968).

Pinus heldreichii Christ

Balkan Mountains. Introduced in 1884. Regarded by many botanists, including those from the countries where it grows, as the same species as *P. leucodermis*. *P. leucodermis* is a very distinct tree when grown here, very handsome and far from rare. It is treated as a full species and under *P. heldreichii* are included only two specimens. These are rough trees with dark bark coarsely flaking and irregular crowns of spreading branches bearing foliage as described under *P. leucodermis*. One is at Bicton, where it is 91ft × 9ft at 6 feet (1968) and the other at Wakehurst Place, 49ft × 5ft 4in (1964).

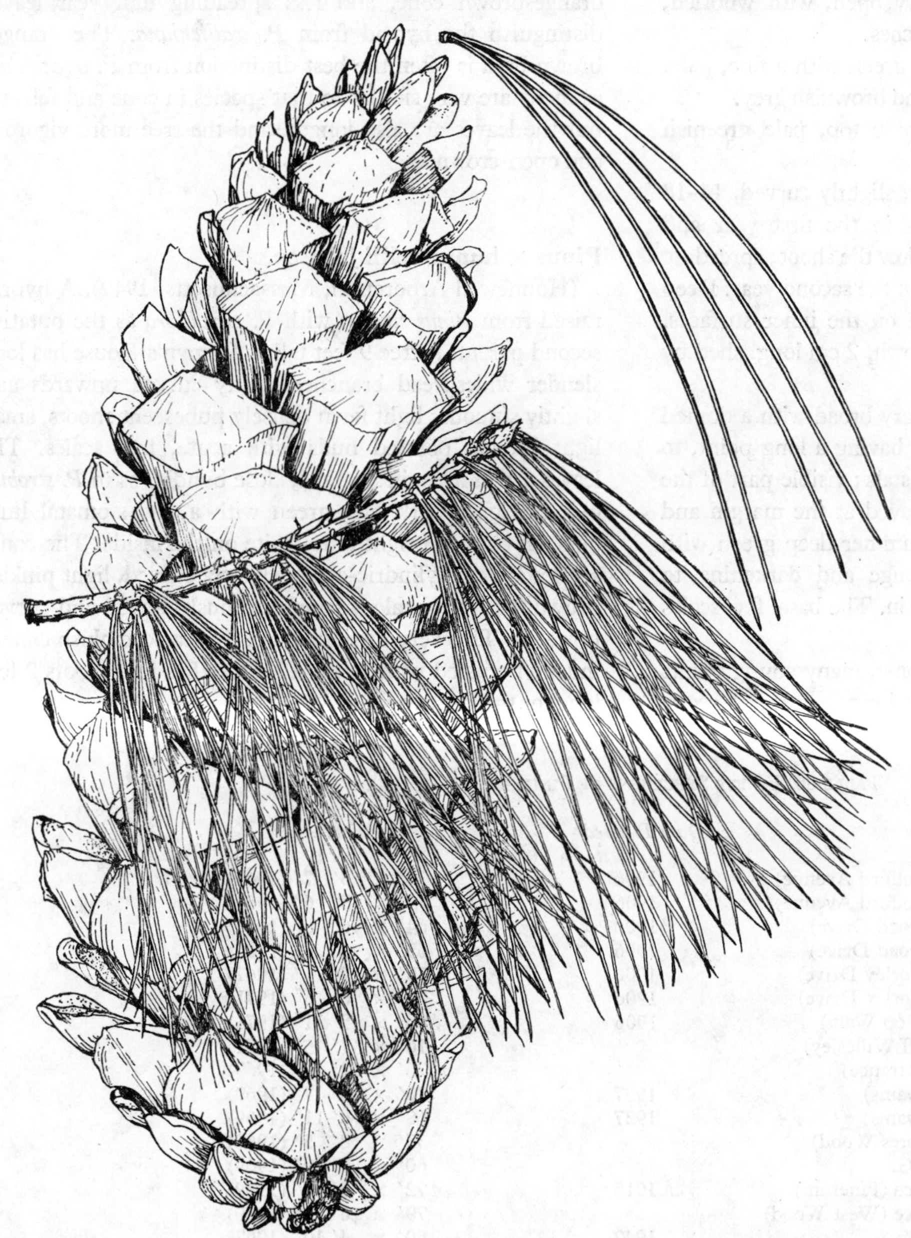

Fig. 150
Pinus × *holfordiana*, a hybrid between *P. ayacahuite* and *P. wallichiana*, raised at Westonbirt (×⅗.) The cones can vary from narrowly tapering to a long point, to broad and less pointed as here.

Pinus × holfordiana Jackson. Holford's pine.

A hybrid raised at Westonbirt in about 1904 when seed was taken from a *P. ayacahuite* standing near a *P. wallichiana*. Trees from the first crossing were planted in several parts of Westonbirt Arboretum and Silk Wood, and either more of these or others raised immediately subsequently were sent to a number of estates in South England. Later trees may have been raised from the earlier hybrids, for they show much variation between the parental types, but mainly towards *P. ayacahuite* (q.v.).

BARK. Orange-brown or red-brown, with scaly narrow plates between deep complex fissuring.

CROWN. Rather broadly conic, very open, with whorled, long, wandering, sinuous, level branches.

FOLIAGE. Shoot slender, pale apple-green with a fine, pale, pubescence. Second year greenish and brownish grey.

BUD. Broad cylindric base and conic top, pale greenish brown, 6–8 mm on side shoots.

LEAVES. In fives, long, very slender, slightly curved, 14–18 cm, close together in the bundles in the first year and pointing forwards, arching down below the shoot; spreading in open bundles and often reflexed in the second year. Deep glossy green outside, a white band on the inner surfaces. Basal sheath pale brown or pink-brown, 2 cm long, shed by the second year.

CONE. Variable, from long-ovoid, very broad with a domed apex, to more like *P. ayacahuite* in having a long point, to 25×8 cm, or 30×5 cm, on a 4 cm stalk; visible part of the scale broadly triangular, slightly waved at the margin and with a thickened tip; during the summer deep green with brown-tipped scales; ripening orange and darkening to brown, much crusted with white resin. The basal few scales are very thick, short and recurved.

GROWTH. This is a very vigorous pine, many young plants growing shoots of more than 3 feet long for several years. Growth in girth is also rapid. One of the original trees at Westonbirt has increased in girth by 13 inches in 11 years recently and several younger trees have maintained a mean increase of 2 inches a year since planting, for over 30 years.

RECOGNITION. Confusion is likely only with each parent species. The downy shoot; broader or more pointed and orange-brown cone, and less spreading first year leaves distinguish the hybrid from *P. wallichiana*. The orange-brown bark is often the best distinction from *P. ayacahuite* as many are very similar to that species in cone and foliage; but the leaves are also longer, and the tree more vigorous and open-crowned.

Pinus × hunnewellii Johnson.

(Hunnewell Arboretum, Massachusetts. 1949). A hybrid raised from *Pinus strobus* with *P. parviflora* as the putative second parent. A tree 9 feet tall at Jermyn's House has long slender widespread branches gently curved upwards and slightly sinuous; light fawn densely pubescent shoots, small light brown, pointed buds with acute, free scales. The leaves are in fives, in forward, close bundles as in *P. strobus*, 6–7 cm long, dark blue-green with a few stomatal lines outside, banded bright blue-white on the inside. The cones are 8×3·5 cm cylindric-conic, slightly curved, light pinkish brown, with the scale margins curiously waved and curved upwards. This very distinctive, curly-scaled pinkish cone is much encrusted with resin. This tree has had shoots 2 feet long for the last two years.

TABLE 66. FINEST SPECIMENS OF PINUS X HOLFORDIANA

Locality	*Date Planted*	*Dimensions*
Westonbirt (Holford Avenue)	1906	78′ × 5′ 7″ (1967)
Westonbirt (Holford Avenue)	1906	73′ × 5′ 6″ (1967)
Westonbirt (Broad Drive)	1906	64′ × 6′ 8″ (1966)
Westonbirt (Broad Drive)	1906	65′ × 6′ 0″ (1966)
Westonbirt (Morley Drive)	1906	75′ × 7′ 1″ (1967)
Westonbirt (Morley Drive)	1906	80′ × 6′ 6″ (1971)
Westonbirt (Loop Walk)	1906	80′ × 5′ 11″ (1971)
Westonbirt (Off Willesley)		76′ × 7′ 5″ (1971)
Westonbirt (Entrance)		76′ × 4′ 0″ (1969)
Westonbirt (Byams)	1937	70′ × 5′ 7″ (1969)
Westonbirt (Byams)	1937	68′ × 6′ 11″ (1969)
Borde Hill (Gores Wood)		55′ × 8′ 5″ (1968)
Wisley R.H.S.G.		60′ × 9′ 2″ (1969)
Wakehurst Place (Pinetum)	ca.1915	72′ × 6′ 7″ (1969)
Wakehurst Place (West Wood)		79′ × 6′ 11″ (1970)
Redleaf Wood	1942	60′ × 4′ 10″ (1967)
Lythe Hill		60′ × 8′ 1″ (1969)

Pinus jeffreyi Murray. Jeffrey's pine

Southern Oregon to Lower California. Introduced in 1853. Some trees of earlier planting-dates previously said to be this species have been found to be, in fact, *P. ponderosa*. Uncommon but widespread and occasionally in small gardens.

BARK. Nearly black, smooth over all but with areas, often dark grey, traversed by numerous fine, deep fissures. Rarely coarsely fissured.

CROWN. A most splendidly straight tall cone or column with a conic pointed top, even in some of the oldest and biggest trees. The bole is usually clear for a good length then bears

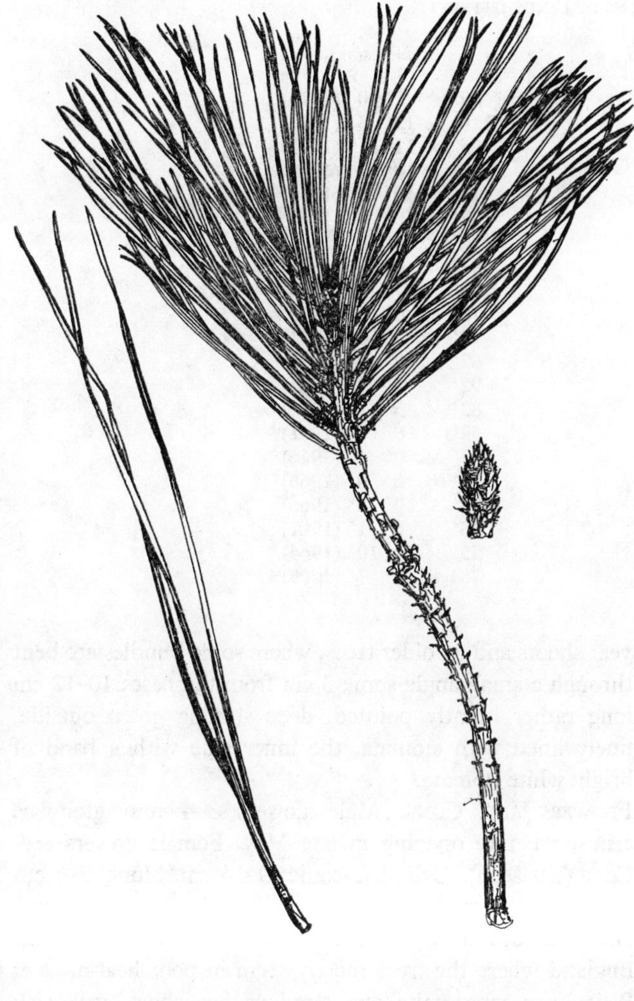

Pinus jeffreyi

Fig. 151
Shoot and leaves ($\times\frac{1}{3}$) of *Pinus jefffreyi*, Jeffrey's pine, a shapely tree with blackish bark. The shoot is bloomed violet. The leaves (single fascicle $\times\frac{2}{3}$) are grey-blue from numerous lines of stomata. The bud ($\times\frac{2}{3}$) is dark red-brown with the tips of the scales free.

regular whorls of short, level branches curved up at the ends. Young trees can be dense, but older trees have open crowns, caused by the branches dividing into few shoots and the leaves on these falling away in their third year. Some big trees have wide spreading branches, the upper ones ascending.

FOLIAGE. Shoot stout, greenish grey, bloomed violet; pulvini orange; second year pale orange-brown.

BUD. Ovoid-cylindric, pointed apex, 3 cm or more, the dark red-brown acute scales having short free, vertical tips.

LEAVES. Grey-green, with indistinct stomatal lines on both sides, 16–18 cm (26) long; spreading. Basal sheath dark grey and brown, 1 cm adhering. When a shoot is broken, a very strong lemon scent comes from the resin.

CONE. First year dark purplish-brown, long-conic with oblique rounded base, to 18×7 cm with short curved prickles and weighing one pound when fresh; opening to 15 cm across and very flat broad base, while still on the tree, and pale brown with very flat scales each with a sharp, small reflexed spine in the middle of the under part of the margin. When shed or picked the cone has a deep hollow in its base, the size of the hollow depending on how many basal scales remain on the tree.

GROWTH. This tree is often short-lived. Several big trees are dying and are excluded from the table, and of 21 specimens measured in 1909 or 1931 only four have been found since 1950. One of these grew 27 feet and increased by 30 inches in girth in 45 years, another added 28 feet and 16 inches in 30 years and the third added 28 feet and 24 inches in 35 years. Young trees of known date of planting show that vigorous growth can be maintained for many years; the best noted being a tree only 29 years old of 55ft×4ft 10in. The finest by far is that at Scone, which was much admired in the 1890's but omitted from the Report of 1932.

SPECIMENS. There is no tree surviving which is certainly an original tree but several may be, despite the early death of many specimens. Growth is usually similar to that of *P. ponderosa* and trees of that species dating from 1855–60 are mostly 9 to 10 feet in girth. An interesting group of the only *P. jeffreyi* in England more than ten feet in girth occurs just south of the Hog's Back in Surrey. Here four trees on two nearly adjacent estates near Elstead, exceed ten feet in girth and these may well be original trees from 1853 seed.

RECOGNITION. From *P. ponderosa*, this tree is distinguished by its black, smoother bark (in Britain; in Oregon some *P. ponderosa* have bright orange bark and *P. jeffreyi* in California have deep orange-red at high altitudes); by the paler, longer leaves, usually larger cones, broad at the base when open; by glaucous bloomed shoots, and the bud scales free at the tips. All these features, except the cones, are more like *P. coulteri* and distinction here, in the absence of cones is less easy. The deeply ridged bark and wide-spreading, heavy branches of *P. coulteri* are distinctions, and its needles are far less dense and more stout, and longer, and the orange bud is very different.

TABLE 67. NOTABLE SPECIMENS OF PINUS JEFFREYI

Locality	*Date Planted*	*Dimensions*
Gordon Castle		89′ × 7′ 10″ (1970)
Scone Palace	1860	118′ × 12′ 5″ (1970)
Peper Harrow		95′ × 11′ 1″ (1971)
Hampton Park		90′ × 10′ 1″ (1969)
Hampton Park		75′ × 10′ 5″ (1969)
Hampton Park		72′ × 10′ 2″ (1970)
Powerscourt	1866	116′ × 10′ 8″ (1966)
Powerscourt	1866	107′ × 8′ 7″ (1966)
Ochteryre (Crieff)	1875	102′ × 7′ 7″ (1970)
Sidbury Manor	1885	72′ × 6′ 1″ (1959)
Blackmoor	1896	75′ × 6′ 2″ (1961)
Eastnor Castle		82′ × 9′ 5″ (1970)
Warnham Court		92′ × 7′ 7″ (1971)
Borde Hill (Garden)		82′ × 5′ 11″ (1968)
Knaphill Nurseries		58′ × 8′ 6″ (1961)
Castle Leod		108′ × 9′ 4″ (1966)
Trentham Park		88′ × 6′ 0″ (1968)
Shelton Abbey		95′ × 9′ 2″ (1968)
Little Hall	1906	48′ × 6′ 1″ (1961)
Holdfast Lane, Grayswood	1935	55′ × 4′ 10″ (1964)
The Frythe		78′ × 5′ 7″ (1969)

Pinus koraiensis Siebold and Zuccarini. Korean pine

East Siberia, Manchuria, Japan and Korea. Introduced in 1861. Very rare; in a very few collections in England, Wales, Scotland and Ireland.

BARK. Young trees smooth, dark grey, freckled paler; older trees pink-grey or pink-brown with wide shallow fissures and big grey or purplish scales curling away.

CROWN. Young trees neatly narrow-columnar with branches curved up at the ends. Old trees widely columnar and open with level branches.

FOLIAGE. Shoot brownish-green but largely covered by dense pale orange-brown, curly, pubescence. Second year dark grey above, orange beneath, with matted woolly hairs.

BUD. Ovoid with a sharp point of long free scale-tips which are dark red-brown, pale edged.

LEAVES. In fives fairly densely bunched and forward on new shoots of young trees, more spreading and lax on second year shoots and on older trees, where some bundles are bent through a small angle some 3 cm from the base; 10–12 cm long rather bluntly pointed, deep shining green outside, finely lined with stomata, the inner side with a band of bright white stomata.

FLOWERS AND CONE. Male flowers 3–4 mm globular, crimson before opening in late May. Female flowers red. Cone (not seen). Cylindric-conic; 9–14 cm, blunt, 5–6 cm broad; lurid brown, convex scales (Den Ouden and Boom).

GROWTH AND SPECIMENS. Growth is slow in South East England where the trees mostly seem in poor health, as at Bedgebury where the one survivor has short, yellowish leaves. But in the west and north health is good and growth can be quite rapid. A tree at Crarae added 11 feet to its height and 17 inches to its girth in 13 years, whereas the tree at Bedgebury has added 2 feet and 2½ inches respectively in 12 years.

TABLE 68. NOTEWORTHY SPECIMENS OF PINUS KORAIENSIS

Locality	*Date Planted*	*Dimensions*	
Westonbirt (Willesley Drive)	1880	35′ × 2′ 4″ (1931)	56′ × 2′ 9″ (1967)
Dawyck	1919	14′ 6″ (1930)	60′ × 4′ 2″ (1970)
Bodnant			42′ × 3′ 6″ (1959)
Sidbury Manor			37′ × 3′ 3″ (1959)
Windsor Great Park			30′ × 1′ 8″ (1967)
Fota			50′ × 4′ 8″ (1966)
Nymans (Rough Ground)			36′ × 2′ 2″ (1968)
Crarae			39′ × 3′ 7″ (1969)
Moundsmere	ca.1945		36′ × 2′ 7″ (1971)

RECOGNITION. The foliage is very like *P. cembra*, but the habit of the tree differs in being more open, wider and with level branches. The leaves are slightly longer, brighter blue and green, and more spreading and lax. As a last resort, if a leaf be torn across and squeezed, a lens will show three clear resin-drops from the resin canals one at each corner of the triangular cross-section, whereas there are only two in *P. cembra.*

Pinus lambertiana Douglas. Sugar pine.

Mountains of Oregon and California. Introduced in 1827. Very rare indeed. Thirty years ago there were large trees in many collections but every one has died. At Dropmore a tree dating from 1843 died in 1950 when it was 95ft × 11ft 6in. This was the only one of the 21 given by Elwes & Henry or the 1932 Report to have been seen since these were published. One found in Bagshot Park in 1957 when 70ft × 7ft 2in was dead by 1958. The cause of most, if not all, of these losses is the white pine blister-rust, *Cronartium ribicola*. In the last few years healthy plants have been acquired by a number of collections.

CROWN. Young trees have broad, dense bases, and, when growing strongly, open upper crowns. The shoots from the base of the leading shoot make a wide "U", being level for a length then curving upward to the vertical.

FOLIAGE. Shoot slender, dark olive-green densely covered in a pale reddish-brown short pubescence.

BUD. Cylindric with pointed top, pale brown with dark-tipped long, acute scales.

LEAVES. In fives, pressed closely forward on strong shoots, spreading on weaker ones, bases of terminal leaves densely cluttered with pale papery sheaths which have been shed by the other leaf bundles; 10 cm long; outer surface deep green with two pairs of faint stomatal lines; inner surfaces with bright bands of brilliantly white stomata in 4–5 close lines. The leaves are slightly twisted and when handled, or when a shoot is broken a sweet grapefruit-like scent arises.

CONE. (Dry specimen from California) 30–35 × 11 cm (open), faintly tapered cylinder; scales thin relative to the size of the cone, except for thick short ones near the base, the basal ring deflexed down the stem; pale pinkish-brown; a few deep striations at the sides, curving gently to a thickened, resinous, broadly rounded apex. Cones were first borne in European trees on an original tree at Dropmore in 1872, but it is very doubtful if any are being borne now or will be for many years.

GROWTH. Growth was, and is on young plants, very vigorous. A tree planted five years at Chobham, Surrey, has a leading shoot three feet long. The second tree at Dropmore, which died in 1950, was 85ft × 10ft when 65 years old.

SPECIMENS. Weasenham, planted about 1909, 53ft × 3ft 6in (1957); Ripley Castle, Yorks, planted 1926, 37ft × 3ft 1in (1958).

RECOGNITION. The five-needle pine most resembling this is *P. ayacahuite*, in which the foliage, shoot, bud and leaves are very similar. The leaves of *P. lambertiana* are, however, straighter, stouter, shorter and held forward near the shoot.

The distant aspect is more like *P. strobus*, but the dense pubescence distinguishes it from that species.

Pinus leucodermis Antoine. Bosnian pine

Northern Italy, Jugoslavia and the Balkan Mountains. Introduced to Kew in 1890 where the original tree still stands. Uncommon, but in many collections and large gardens.

BARK. Smooth greenish-grey, becoming dark grey with whitish patches in older trees and finely cracked vertically. Trees of 1000 years old within the native range, have their bark very deeply but narrowly cracked into small squares of remarkably uniform size.

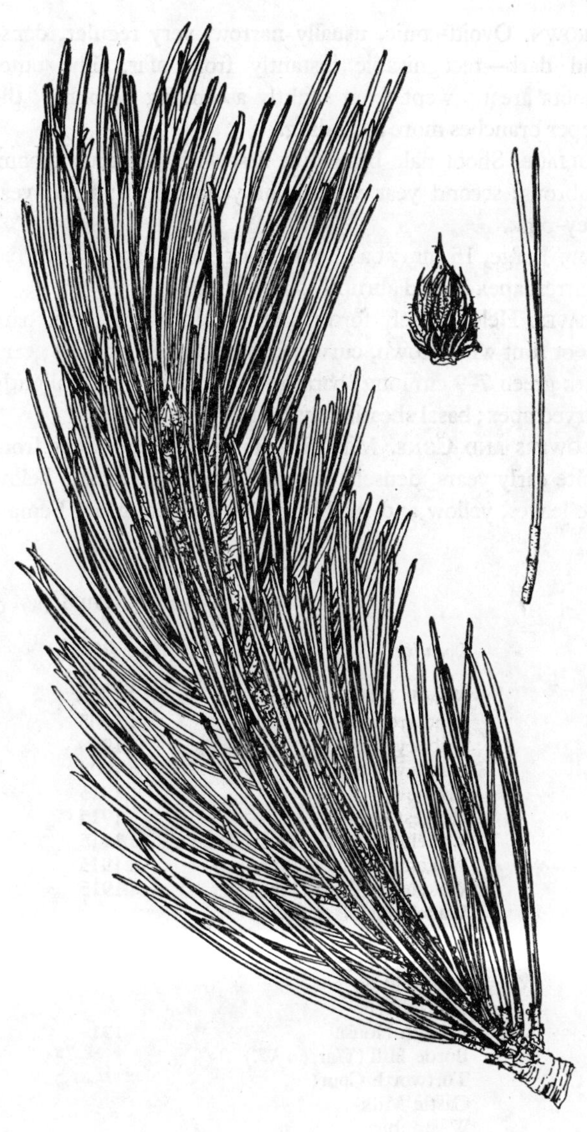

Fig. 152
Foliage and (×1⅓) bud of *Pinus leucodermis*, Bosnian pine. This dark neat tree bears cones of bright cobalt-blue in the summer. The bark is finely cracked but smooth greenish-grey.

Crown. Ovoid-conic, usually narrow, very regular, dense and dark—recognisable instantly from afar. The outer shoots are upswept from slightly ascending branches; the upper branches more ascending.

Foliage. Shoot pale brown, at first with glaucous bloom, glabrous; second year whitish or yellow-fawn; third year grey-pink.

Bud. Large, 15 mm; basal scales large and papery with red centres, apex of bud abruptly sharp pointed.

Leaves. Held densely forward at 45°, in whorls with bare shoot (but with brown, curved scales) between whorls; very dark green 7–9 cm long; hard and stiff; with blunt, slightly curved apex; basal sheath grey 1 cm.

Flowers and Cone. Male flowers usually abundant from quite early years, densely bunched along new shoots below the leaves, yellow and shedding pollen in late May. Female flowers also abundant, at the tips of new main shoots, red. In June they turn outwards, enlarge and become bright deep cobalt blue 1·8×1·3 cm, with spreading spines. Next summer they are full size and the same colour; by September they are dark purple but ripen finally dull orange-brown, ovoid-conic, 5–8 cm long, 4 cm broad, each scale with a down-curved spine.

Growth. The original tree at Kew has grown very slowly, but elsewhere this is a sturdy tree of steady growth, and of uniformly splendid health. All seven trees previously recorded have been found, although one was blown down. Re-measurements and measurements of dated trees give the same patterns—increase in height up to, but usually somewhat below, one foot per year; increase in girth from one half to one and a half inches a year, usually close to one inch. (See Table 69).

Table 69. The Largest Trees of Pinus leucodermis

Locality	*Date Planted*	*Dimensions*		
Kew R.B.G.	1890	3′	(1907)	41′ × 3′ 0″ (1968)
Pencarrow	1905			46′ × 3′ 7″ (1970)
Tubney Wood	1908			58′ × 2′ 10″ (1964)
Tubney Wood	1908			56′ × 2′ 2″ (1964)
Crarae	1915	8′	(1931)	36′ × 3′ 10″ (1969)
Hergest Croft	1915			41′ × 2′ 10″ (1961)
Wakehurst Place (West Wood)	ca.1915			44′ × 6′ 7″ (1966)
Wakehurst Place (Pinetum)	ca.1915			53′ × 4′ 0″ (1964)
Wakehurst Place (Pinetum)	ca.1915			54′ × 6′ 0″ (1971)
Wakehurst Place (Serps)				55′ × 3′ 10″ (1970)
Tyninghame				47′ × 6′ 9″ (1967)
Stratfield Saye				62′ × 5′ 11″ (1968)
Stratfield Saye				48′ × 5′ 10″ (1968)
Colesbourne				56′ × 4′ 0″ (1971)
Fenagh House	1918	12′	(1931)	36′ × 3′ 6″ (1968)
Borde Hill (Warren W.)		19′	(1931)	58′ × 3′ 6″ (1968)
Tortworth Court		12′ × 10″	(1931)	35′ × 4′ 6″ (1964)
Castle Milk		5′ 6″	(1931)	40′ × 4′ 5″ (1966)
Westonbirt		6′ 9″	(1931)	36′ × 3′ 1″ (1970)
Woburn				46′ × 3′ 6″ (1970)
Headfort	1925	9′	(1931)	37′ × 3′ 7″ (1966)
Bedgebury	1926	4′ 9″	(1931)	38′ × 3′ 4″ (1970)
Birr Castle	1927			34′ × 3′ 6″ (1966)
Castlewellan				54′ × 4′ 4″ (1966)
Mount Usher				50′ × 5′ 8″ (1966)
Killerton				62′ × 4′ 10″ (1970)
Blackmoor				42′ × 3′ 7″ (1968)
Blackmoor				44′ × 2′ 11″ (1968)
Wisley R.H.S.G.				54′ × 3′ 4″ (1969)
Bowood				53′ × 3′ 7″ (1968)

Specimens. There are many fine and some large trees at Wakehurst Place, and one at Colesbourne but the two best all round are one at Tyninghame and one at Stratfield Saye —respectively a cold, dry easterly climate and a warm, fairly dry southerly one.

Recognition. The ovoid, neat crown and smooth bark are unlike those of any other two-needle pine, while the blue cones in summer are unlike any other pine of any sort. Foliage away from the tree is like that of *P. thunbergii* but the bud is distinct, the shoot whiter, and the leaves shorter, and like *P. nigra nigra* but the shoot is paler, often bloomed and less rough.

General. This singularly attractive pine is not only extremely hardy but it also thrives on limestone or chalk and on dry sites, as well as on acid soils and high rainfall. It is thus suitable for all gardens in any region and on any soil, even in very small gardens in view of the neat crown and slow growth in height.

Pinus montezumae Lambert.

Mexico. A very variable tree with at least fourteen forms which hover between being regarded as varieties or separate, full species. (*P. cooperi* and *P. durangensis* have been treated in this work as separate species, since they are new to this country but this is not a taxonomic judgement, it is done merely to give them more prominence.) Introduced in 1839. Uncommon; in some collections and large gardens in South and South-west England, North Wales, South-west Scotland and Southern Ireland.

BARK. Pinkish-grey, rough, with wide brownish vertical fissures leaving ridges which are transversely cracked into short, rough lengths.

CROWN. The type is distinguishable from the varieties given, by the crown, on its own. It is gaunt with few up-curved very stout branches as a young tree, similar to but stouter and less branched than the varieties. But with age it becomes hugely low-domed, closely covered by upturned shoots bearing immense blue-grey brush-like foliage.

FOLIAGE. Shoot very stout, ridged, rich dark greenish or orange-brown with persistent sheaths orange-brown; second year orange-brown.

BUD. Cylindric-conic, large and fat, 2 cm long on side-shoots of old trees, larger on more vigorous growth, crusted in white resin; deep red-brown at the pointed apex.

LEAVES. In fives, or more on young trees, and occasionally in threes; 25–30 cm long, grey-blue, spreading perpendicularly to the shoot; rather sparse.

CONE. Disappointingly small for a tree with such large parts; usually in this country little blackish or dark purple barrels with small spines and about 6 cm long but in Mexico at least they range up to 25 cm long.

TABLE 70. THE LARGEST TREES OF PINUS MONTEZUMAE

Locality	*Date Planted*	*Dimensions*	
Endsleigh		50′ × 9′ 6″ (1906)	65′ × 14′ 0″ (1957)
Endsleigh			40′ × 10′ 0″ (1970)
Grayswood Hill	1881	25′ × 2′ 10″ (1906)	55′ × 9′ 3″ (1968)
Tregrehan		60′ × 6′ 8″ (1931)	70′ × 7′ 7″ (1971)
Pencarrow			72′ × 4′ 3″ (1970)
Glasnevin B.G.	1899	19′ × 3′ (1931)	33′ × 6′ 6″ (1966)
Bicton	1900	40′ (1931)	69′ × 5′11″ (1968)
Sidbury Manor	1902		48′ × 10′ 4″ (1959)
Bodnant	1905	34′ × 3′ (1931)	50′ × 7′ 8″ (1959)
Mount Usher	1909		54′ × 9′10″ (1966)
Mount Usher	1925		29′ × 5′ 0″ (1966)
Powerscourt			67′ × 6′ 6″ (1966)
Powerscourt			68′ × 5′ 3″ (1966)
Sheffield Park			50′ × 7′ 1″ (1968)
Culzean Castle		13′ × 1′ 5″ (1931)	50′ × 5′ 4″ (1970)
Cairnsmore			30′ × 5′ 9″ (1956)
Tregothnan	1937	31′ × 3′ 9″ (1959)	37′ × 4′10″ (1971)

GROWTH. For about 60 years this tree, where suited, can grow with great vigour with regard to girth but culminates early in height. After about 60 years, casualties become rather frequent and several old and some not so old trees have died, but those still living beyond 60 years have grown slowly thereafter where records can provide comparisons. Three trees show increments in girth of 2 inches per year.

SPECIMENS. It is possible that the largest tree at Pencarrow was an original tree planted out when 10 years old from seed. It was 70ft × 11ft 3in in 1957 but died before 1970. None other is known to date from before 1881.

var. hartwegii (Lindley) Engelmann. (Mexico 1839). Rather less common than is the type. Although from colder regions of Mexico and thought to be hardier, it is confined now to collections in South and West England and in Ireland. The most obvious distinctions are:—

BARK. Dull, dark purple grey, shallowly fissured dark-brown.

CROWN. Gaunt, narrow and tall, with few low branches; not a broad dome.

FOLIAGE. From a distance a dull grey-green more yellowish than blue. Shoot pale green bloomed violet, less stout.

BUD. Scales with finely pointed tips free, pale pink-brown.

LEAVES. Grey-green, 10–12 or 16–18 cm depending on vigour.

GROWTH. Height is achieved more rapidly than in the type, but girth increases much more slowly.

TABLE 71. LARGE TREES OF PINUS MONTEZUMAE VAR. HARTWEGII

Locality	Date Planted	Dimensions	
Eastnor Castle		55′ × 4′ 8″ (1909)	82′ × 6′ 7″ (1970)
Strete Ralegh (House)	1855	52′ × 5′ 7″ (1909)	75′ × 7′ 0″ (1970)
Strete Ralegh (Pinetum)			55′ × 5′ 3″ (1964)
Kilmacurragh			70′ × 8′ 5″ (1966)
Inistioge			85′ × 8′ 8″ (1966)
Wakehurst Place (Pinetum)			52′ × 5′ 3″ (1964)
Bolderwood	1860		88′ × 6′ 7″ (1970)

var. rudis (Endlicher) Shaw (Mexico. Introduced before 1855). Since the large tree at Westonbirt died in 1963, this is known only as young plants recently distributed to a few collections in South West England and Ireland, and a 15 year plant at Jermyn's House. The foliage of these have shoots green-brown or bright pale green, bloomed white, bud, ovoid-conic orange-red and variably resinous, and leaves 10 cm long on the youngest, 12–15 cm long on the established plant.

RECOGNITION. *P. montezumae* type is unique, in aspect and foliage—resembling somewhat only the three-needled *P. jeffreyi* and *P. coulteri* in foliage. Var. *hartwegii* is the only five-needled pine with this gaunt aspect and yellowish grey-green foliage.

Pinus montezumae × patula

A hybrid which arose at Fota, probably in about 1910, and has not been noted elsewhere. It has a crown like a *P. montezumae* in which the grey spreading leaves have been replaced by the green hanging leaves of *P. patula.*

BARK. Interwoven pink-grey large ridges with orange fissures between them.

FOLIAGE. Shoot pale brownish-cream.

BUD. Globular with an abrupt point; orange, scales free at their tips.

LEAVES. Bright green, hanging, 25 cm.

This appears to be very vigorous at Fota, and the date suggested above is based on an assumed rate of growth rather greater than that of *P. montezumae* there. The only tree is 67ft×9ft 10in at 3 feet (1966).

Pinus monticola Douglas. Western white pine

Southern British Columbia, south to California and east to Montana. Introduced in 1831. Earliest now known dates from 1847 and only one other is of earlier planting than 1900. Very rare; in a few of the larger collections in all parts.

BARK. Dark grey, smooth and blistered, becoming purplish, cracked and scaly in old trees.

CROWN. A shapely tree at all ages, narrowly conic when young with short, ascending branches in regular whorls; narrowly columnar-conic in middle age with a sturdy, straight stem and a dense crown of slightly ascending branches: finally broadly columnar, level-branched and rather open. Although dark, nearly black from a short distance, this tree looks bright and clean because the shiny leaves are borne by clean shoots which remain smooth and grey until quite big.

FOLIAGE. Shoot brownish-green, or copper-brown finely pubescent.

BUD. Cylindric-ovoid, sharply pointed; dark orange-brown; long free scale-tips, mostly point forwards, a few curve out.

LEAVES. In fives, bunched above a length of bare shoot, 7–10 cm, straight, palish green outer surfaces with faint stomatal lines, inner surfaces with 3–4 thick bright white lines.

CONE. Usually frequent on trees of moderate size; in bunches on branch-tips; pale brown, long-pointed narrow-conic, tapering evenly from near the base, slightly curved, 15 cm, scales with spreading tips.

GROWTH. A vigorous tree in height and girth for many years. At over 1,000 feet above sea level at Vivod, North

TABLE 72. THE LARGEST TREES OF PINUS MONTICOLA

Locality	Date Planted	Dimensions	
Hamwood	1847	76′ × 7′ (1905)	95′ × 10′ 7″ (1968)
Pencarrow			72′ × 7′ 11″ (1970)
Scone Palace	1852	82′ × 7′ 9″ (1904)	(80′) × 9′ 8″ (1970)
Avondale	ca.1908		73′ × 7′ 2″ (1968)
Kelburn Castle			80′ × 7′ 2″ (1970)
Bicton			70′ × 8′ 4″ (1968)
Bicton			68′ × 4′ 11″ (1968)
Dawyck	1913	30′ × 2′ 4″ (1931)	78′ × 6′ 6″ (1966)
Edinburgh R.B.G.			62′ × 4′ 1″ (1970)
Redleaf Woods	1942		43′ × 3′ 6″ (1967)
Arley Cottage			50′ × 2′ 9″ (1966)

Wales, young trees have grown shoots of 2–2½ feet a year for several years and are considerably taller than any of a great range of species planted with them. Older trees show only moderate growth in height, but mean annual increases in girth are mostly around 1½ inches.

SPECIMENS. The tree at Hamwood is now very thin. It is remarkable that it lives at all, for it is the only one out of thirteen large trees given by Elwes and Henry (1904–1908) to survive. Of 16 trees given in the 1932 Report only four, including one then only 5 years planted, have been found. The loss of these trees is due to the susceptibility of this species to white-pine blister-rust (*Cronartium ribicola*). Like *Pinus lambertiana*, the larger trees have been almost completely destroyed. This disease precludes the wider use of the tree, but it is now thought that infection occurs only when the trees are young in this country, and clean stock planted in isolated areas where the alternate host of the disease, species of currants, are remote, may well be worth planting.

RECOGNITION. Among the five-needle pines with pubescent shoots, *P. ayacahuite* has much longer, less densely set leaves, drooping and more slender. *P. lambertiana* has twisted leaves more closely pressed to the new shoots.

Pinus mugo Turra. Dwarf mountain pine. (*P. montana* Miller).

Alps and South-east Europe. Introduced in 1779. Rare in gardens but sometimes planted to shelter plantations at high altitudes.

A scrubby bush of upwards curving, sparsely branched stems, dull grey and scaly at the base.

FOLIAGE. Shoot dull grey-brown; second year blackish-purple-brown.

BUD. 5 mm cylindric bluntly conic at tip, scales free at tips until encrusted by resin.

LEAVES. In pairs, each pair widely spread from other pairs but remaining nearly closed, curved forwards, 5 cm long, dark green sometimes shiny; many fine stomatal lines each side. Sheaths persist grey and dark brown.

GROWTH AND SPECIMENS. Neither worth mentioning.

var. uncinata. See *Pinus uncinata*.

Pinus muricata D. Don. Bishop pine

Coast of California, in 7 scattered areas from Big Lagoon, Humboldt Co. to Lompoc; and on Santa Rosa, Santa Cruz, and Cedros Islands. Discovered by Coulter in 1832 at San Luis Obispo which accounts for the English name. Intro-

TABLE 73. LARGE EXAMPLES OF PINUS MURICATA

Locality	*Date Planted*	*Dimensions*	
Ebernoe			88′ × 13′ 1″ (1971)
Bayfordbury	1850	45′ × 4′ 7″ (1909)	45′ × 8′ 4″ (1962)
Claremont		71′ × 7′ (1907)	77′ × 10′ 0″ (1965)
Eastnor Castle		40′ × 6′ (1907)	83′ × 10′ 8″ (1970)
Castle Kennedy	1856	35′ × 5′ 7″ (1904)	76′ × 9′ 0″ (1967)
West Dean			85′ × 9′ 6″ (1971)
Ashness			95′ × 9′ 8″ (1955)
Dupplin Castle			92′ × 10′ 11″ (1970)
Sandling Park			80′ × 10′ 1″ (1965)
Grayswood Hill			76′ × 10′ 1″ (1968)
Ashford Castle			80′ × 12′ 5″ (1968)
Blackmoor	1867	63′ × 7′ 4″ (1931)	70′ × 9′ 3″ (1968)
Blackmoor			74′ × 8′ 4″ (1968)
Leighton Hall			93′ × 8′ 11″ (1970)[1]
Muckross Abbey (Garden)			95′ × 8′ 6″ (1968)
Muckross Abbey (Drive)			90′ × 8′ 3″ (1968)[1]
Muckross Abbey (Drive)			95′ × 7′ 1″ (1968)[1]
Westonbirt (Morley Ride)		69′ × 5′ 8″ (1931)	76′ × 9′ 1″ (1971)
Bicton		63′ × 5′ 5″ (1957)	82′ × 6′ 10″ (1968)
Albury Park		82′ × 6′ 6″ (1931)	84′ × 7′ 10″ (1960)
Borde Hill (Warren Wood)		40′ × 3′ (1931)	80′ × 8′ 2″ (1968)
Bodnant	1905	42′ × 5′ 6″ (1931)	74′ × 9′ 11″ (1966)
Crarae	1916	13′ (1931)	40′ × 6′ 2″ (1969)
Wakehurst Place (Pinetum)	1917	25′ × 2′ 1″ (1931)	75′ × 9′ 3″ (1971)[1]
Wakehurst Place (Pinetum)			65′ × 8′ 8″ (1970)
Wakehurst Place (Valley)			73′ × 7′ 5″ (1965)[1]
Hergest Croft	1924		55′ × 5′ 2″ (1961)
Bedgebury	1926		52′ × 6′ 6″ (1969)
Birr Castle	1927		59′ × 6′ 3″ (1966)

[1] Blue-leaved, narrow, northern form

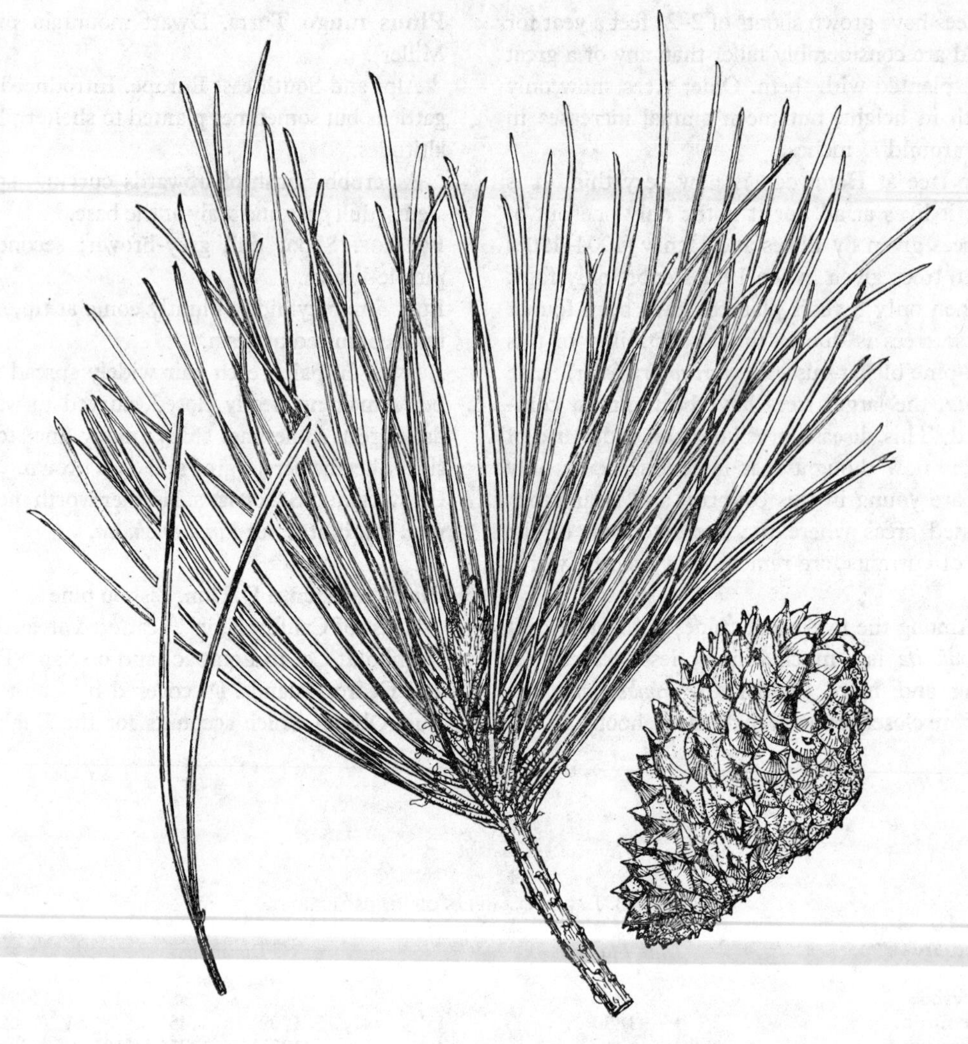

Pinus muricata

Fig. 153
Foliage and cone of *Pinus muricata*, the Bishop pine. The cones are clustered along the branches and adhere for up to 70 years. The buds are cylindric and deep red-brown, purple and white with resin. (Leaf-pair $\frac{2}{3}$ natural size, as for main drawing.)

duced in 1846. Uncommon, but in many collections and large gardens throughout these islands and occasionally in smaller gardens.

Bark. Dark grey, coarsely wrinkled or deeply fissured into long parallel plates extending far up the bole, where they are more brown.

Crown. Two forms occur. The more usual is broadly domed with strong level branches upturned at the ends but descending with age, ringed at close intervals throughout their length with whorls of backward pointing ovoid cones. The general colour of the foliage is dark yellowish grey-green, paler near the buds, making a pattern in the crown.

Less frequent is the form from the two most northerly areas of the range. This is tall-domed, rather narrow, with smaller branches and dark blue-grey leaves.

FOLIAGE. Shoot green turning orange-brown. A long segment below the foliage is bare except for long, pointed, broad-based bracts which curve backwards at the base then straight forwards.

BUD. Deep red-brown, bloomed purple and white, cylindric, tapering towards the tip, 2 cm long. Leaves in pairs, 15 cm long, crowded, stiff, spreading widely, dull grey-green or bluish grey, with fine stomatal lines both sides. Sheath 2 cm.

FLOWERS AND CONE. Male flowers abundant, spread over the bare part of the shoot below the leaves, shedding pollen in June. Female flowers at the tips of most shoots and often many inches below the tip of the leading shoot, in whorls, dull dark pink, globose, spiny. Cones oblique, ovoid-conic, dull orange-brown, to 8×4·5 cm, all the scales with a stout spine, those near the apex ascending; in the middle spreading level and at the base pointing downwards. Scales on the outer base, which is very oblique, have long drawn-out conic points tipped by the spine, projecting in all 6–8 mm. Old cones adhering can be counted back for 67 whorls on the tree at Castle Kennedy, and more at Ebernoe. They become nearly smooth.

GROWTH. An exceedingly vigorous tree, but varying with provenance. Young trees of southern provenances soon make bushy, broad crowns with leading shoots 3–4 feet long. Plants raised from seed collected from some northern-type trees at Muckross Abbey, when growing on very poor acid silts and sands at Bedgebury have made shoots more than 6 feet long in a year. Height growth slows down fairly early in the southern forms, but growth in girth remains vigorous except in some of the oldest trees.

This species has shown itself to be very resistant to sea-wind and with its rapid and bushy growth it is an invaluable tree for early shelter in gardens exposed along the western seaboard.

RECOGNITION. Superficially like *P. radiata* (bark, crown and serotinous cones) and, rather like *P. pinaster*; the paired needles and very prickly cone distinguish *P. muricata* from *P. radiata*, while the prickly cone and shorter, less stout needles distinguish it from *P. pinaster*, and the purple, resinous, long narrow buds distinguish it from either.

Pinus nelsonii Shaw. Nelson's pine.

North East Mexico. Introduction not recorded. A single tree growing out of doors since 1910 at Kew, with an irregular bushy crown and curving, spreading branches, and bark shallowly cracked into dark red-brown scales.

FOLIAGE. Shoot peculiarly chalky white, tinged green on main shoots, pink on side-shoots; second and third years chalky purplish-white; slender, short; densely covered in leaves and their rich brown basal sheaths which curl down by the second year and remain for the third.

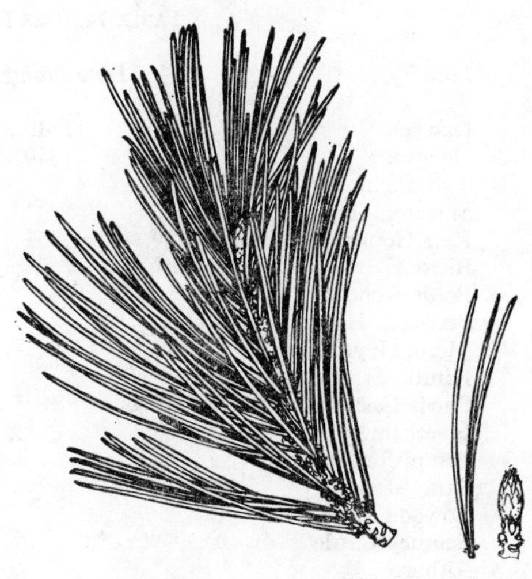

Pinus nelsonii

Fig. 154
Foliage of *Pinus nelsonii*, an extremely rare pine with chalky white shoots and (far right × 1⅓) pale pink-brown buds.

BUD. Slender ovoid, 1 cm, yellowish at first, later pale pink-brown with dark recurved free tips.

LEAVES. In threes, very slender and dense, pointing forwards, 4 cm long; first year leaves bright light green outer surface, grey-blue inner surface; second year dark green outside.

CONE. Globose, 4×4 cm, few shiny, deep green scales with large orange umbos.

Kew Royal Botanic Gardens, planted 1910, 32ft×2ft 4in (1969).

RECOGNITION. In aspect like a 'fox-tail' pine, the short fine leaves in threes and the chalky white shoots distinguish this from all other pines. The leaves occasionally remain partially united, but this is not a prominent feature in this specimen.

Pinus nigra Arnold. Black pine

Pyrenees, Cevennes, Alps, Corsica and South East Europe to Crimea and Asia Minor. The geographical forms are silviculturally and arboriculturally distinct and since *Pinus nigra* is not an entity there will be no general description.

var. nigra (Harrison) Austrian pine. (*Pinus nigra austriaca*) (Hoess) Aschers & Graebner. Austria to Central Italy, Jugoslavia and Greece. Introduced in 1835. Common as a shelter and windbreak tree, park tree and around the larger gardens on the Victorian outskirts of towns and on railway embankments. Uncommon in Ireland.

TABLE 74. THE LARGEST TREES OF PINUS NIGRA NIGRA

Locality	*Date Planted*	*Dimensions*	
Dawyck	1840		95′ × 9′ 6″ (1961)
Dawyck	1840		75′ × 8′ 0″ (1961)
Tynninghame			88′ × 12′ 9″ (1967)
Smeaton House			88′ × 10′ 11″ (1966)
Keir House	1851		75′ × 12′ 11″ (1970)
Bicton			88′ × 13′ 3″ (1968)
Bolderwood			115′ × 12′ 7″ (1970)
Petworth House			112′ × 11′ 7″ (1961)
Monk Hopton			98′ × 11′ 5″ (1971)
Hinton St. Thomas			84′ × 11′ 11″ (1959)
Powis Castle (Pinetum)			111′ × 11′ 7″ (1970)
Elvetham			92′ × 11′ 7″ (1963)
Pampisford		78′ × 9′ 1″ (1931)	95′ × 10′ 9″ (1969)
Pampisford		78′ × 8′ 3″ (1931)	70′ × 9′ 10″ (1969)
Bowood		90′ × 7′ 6″ (1931)	86′ × 12′ 11″ (1968)
Scotney Castle			85′ × 10′ 11″ (1963)
Althorp			82′ × 11′ 2″ (1964)
Gwysaney			80′ × 12′ 1″ (1966)
Welford Park			90′ × 10′ 5″ (1966)
Sidbury Manor	ca.1880		70′ × 10′ 10″ (1959)
Westonbirt (Specimen Avenue)			90′ × 10′ 8″ (1966)
Bedgebury	1926	7′ 1″ (1931)	39′ × 4′ 6″ (1969)

BARK. Dark brown and blackish, widely split by flaking fissures into scaly plates.

CROWN. Domed irregularly, with wide, spreading branches. Some old trees have upswept branches and a more conic crown. As often seen in shelterbelts the upper stem leans.

FOLIAGE. Shoot stout, shiny green, soon rich brown, crowded with basal sheaths.

BUD. On side shoots squat, broad-ovoid with abrupt very tapered sharp point, 1·2 cm×1·2 cm, surrounded by white, papery basal scales.

LEAVES. In pairs, straight, 8–10 cm, very dark, blackish green.

FLOWERS AND CONE. Male flowers clustered in a shallow ring at the base of small shoots, very abundant, conic, large, to 1·3 cm long, after pollen is shed in May. Female flowers at the ends of main shoots, dull pink; Cones ovoid-conic, yellow-brown ripening brown, pale whitish brown when old, 5–8 cm long, scales flexible, with transverse ridge sometimes minutely spined in the middle.

GROWTH. A vigorous but rough tree, taller growing for several years than the Corsican pine but rapidly falling behind after 5 or 6 years. Growth in girth is maintained with some vigour, due to the large crown, at least in open grown trees. This tree is useful for shelter as it not only grows vigorously at first and is bushy, but it will do this on alkaline soils, on dry sites and in considerable exposure.

SPECIMENS. Several trees at Dawyck are probably originals from Lawsons of Edinburgh who imported the seed, as may be the next two in the list, also near Edinburgh. Some of the trees recorded earlier as Austrian pine are in fact Corsican. The only one of the four given by Elwes and Henry which has been found so far, is one of these. Only four of the 23 given in the 1932 Report have been found, so this is a short-lived species for none was then 100 years old. Losses are probably mainly from windblow.

RECOGNITION. Distinguished from var. *maritima* (Corsican pine) generally by the heavily branched wide crown and darker bark, but the aspect of the foliage is different, being in dense bunches separated by short bare lengths of shoot, the bunches opaque and blackish, with straight, short needles.

From var. *caramanica* the dense, short foliage is a distinction.

var. caramanica (Loudon) Rehder. Crimean pine. (*Pinus pallasiana* Lambert) Crimea and Western Asia Minor. Introduced in 1790 (Lee and Kennedy, Hammersmith). Rare and mainly confined to collections in England, but a few elsewhere.

BARK. As in var. *maritima*, but oldest trees have large plates which scale away in cinnamon and yellow flakes.

CROWN. As a young tree more strongly branched than var. *maritima;* the ends curved up. Old trees, possibly from Crimean seed (for in Asia Minor the tree is of excellent form) have numerous vertical branches close to the bole and of equal size, rather like organ-pipes, as well as others, further out curving strongly upwards.

FOLIAGE. Shoot shiny yellow-green; 2nd year orange-brown.

TABLE 75. THE LARGEST TREES OF PINUS NIGRA CARAMANICA

Locality	*Date Planted*	*Dimensions*	
Arley Castle	1820		124′ × 11′ 6″ (1961)
Dropmore	1821	108′ × 11′ 5″ (1904)	118′ × 13′ 5″ (1970)
Bury Hill	1840	93′ × 13′ 7″ (1931)	102′ × 14′ 9″ (1971)
Fota	1847		100′ × 13′ 3″ (1966)
Ickworth			137′ × 12′ 8″ (1955)
Ickworth			99′ × 12′ 1″ (1955)
Bicton			105′ × 11′ 11″ (1968)
Bicton			88′ × 10′ 8″ (1968)
Rossie Priory		87′ × 10′ 6″ (1931)	121′ × 13′ 2″ (1970)
Leaton Knolls		93′ × 10′ (1909)	112′ × 11′ 7″ (1954)
Westonbirt Park		81′ × 12′ 3″ (1931)	75′ × 13′ 7″ (1966)
Cuffnells	ca.1856		124′ × 12′ 2″ (1970)
Tetton House			102′ × 16′ 10″ (1959)[1]
Stratfield Saye			86′ × 10′ 3″ (1969)
Bolderwood	1861		115′ × 12′ 4″ (1970)
Oxenfoord Castle	1863		98′ × 9′ 2″ (1967)

[1] Three stems, dividing low

BUD. Conic pale, whitish brown; grey scale-tips fringed and some recurved.

LEAVES. Appressed to shoot, stout, hard, stiff 12–15 cm, slightly shiny dark green with many fine stomatal lines; abruptly narrowed to yellow spine point.

CONE. Narrowly conic, evenly tapered, 6×3 cm, shining purplish-green before fully ripe; rough outline and knobbly apex from protruding centre and transverse ridge of each scale.

GROWTH. The old trees are very vigorous and are disproportionately represented among the biggest Black pines in the country considering how few specimens there are.

RECOGNITION. The vertical branches or multiple upper stem distinguishes old trees. The dark leaves are shorter, straighter more dense and whorled than in var. *maritima*, but longer than var. *nigra* and less whorled. The rough cone is another distinction from both forms.

var. cebennensis (Grenier and Godron) Rehder. Pyrenean pine. The Cevennes and Pyrenees Mountains; Central and Eastern Spain. Introduced in 1834. Rare and in only a few collections.

BARK. Deeply fissured into wide, flaking ridges which are brown, pink-brown and greyish, with layers of irregularly rounded flakes coming away.

CROWN. Domed, rather low and broad with descending, long branches; rather open.

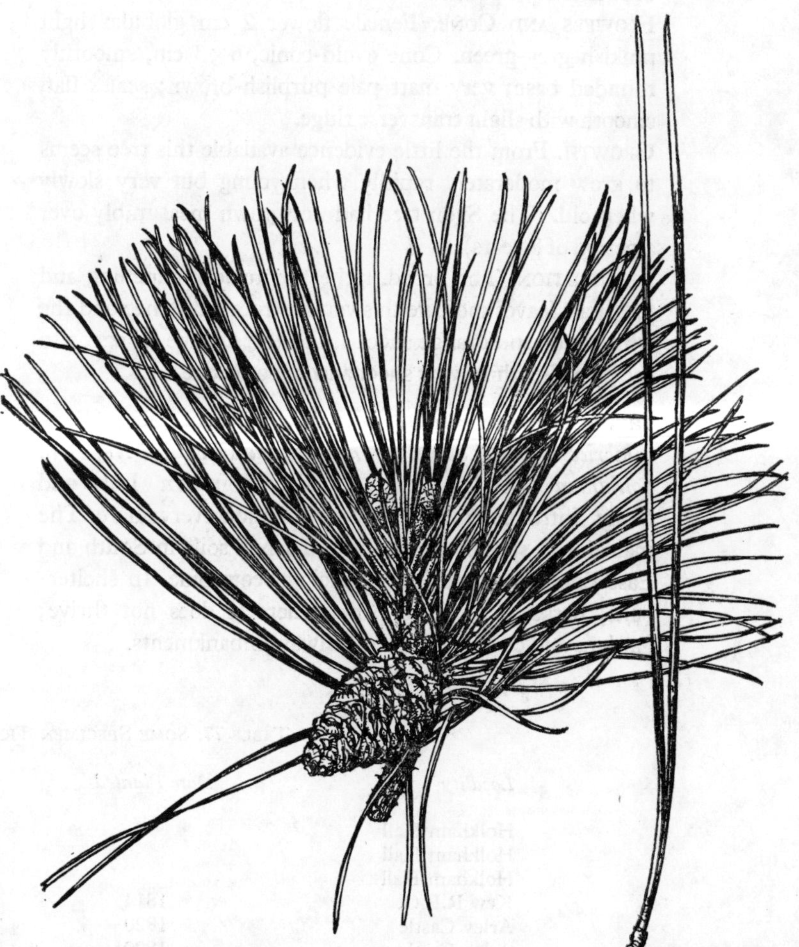

Fig. 155
Shoot, one-year cone and two conelets ($\times\frac{1}{2}$) of *Pinus nigra* var. *cebennensis*, a form of black pine from Central Southern France and the Pyrenees. The leaves (single pair $\times\frac{2}{3}$) are more slender than those of other forms of *P. nigra*.

TABLE 76. LARGE TREES OF PINUS NIGRA CEBENNENSIS

Locality	Date Planted	Dimensions
Syon House		53′ × 8′ 3″ (1969)
Cambridge B.G.		72′ × 8′ 2″ (1969)
Pampisford		65′ × 9′ 0″ (1969)
Fenagh House	1897	77′ × 8′ 2″ (1968)
Bodnant	1902	50′ × 7′ 0″ (1966)
Bedgebury (Plot)	1932	47′ × 3′ 2″ (1965)

FOLIAGE. Shoot bright orange-brown; glabrous, somewhat ridged, pulvini purple-brown; second year deep brown-orange, third year large brown scales fall to leave pale pink.

BUD. Ovoid-cylindric, caked in white resin.

LEAVES. Grey-green, slender, to 15–17 cm long, with short, brown oblique point.

FLOWERS AND CONE. Female flower 2 cm globular light pinkish grey-green. Cone ovoid-conic, 6×3 cm, smoothly rounded base; very matt pale purplish-brown; scales flat, smooth with slight transverse ridge.

GROWTH. From the little evidence available this tree seems to grow moderately rapidly when young but very slowly when old. (The Syon tree had not grown measurably over a period of 8 years).

RECOGNITION. The broad, rather depressed branching and fine, pale leaves indicate this variety from a distance and the white buds and orange shoot are features of the foliage, also the pale pink third year shoot and smooth cone.

var. maritima (Aiton) Melville. Corsican pine. (*P. n. calabrica* (Loud.) Schn.; *P. n. corsicana* (Loud.) Hyl; *P. n. poiretiana* (Loud.) Schn.). Corsica, Southern Italy and Sicily. Introduced in 1759. Very common everywhere. The main forest species on heaths and sandy soils in South and East England where it is replacing Scots pine. In shelter-belts, parks, even town parks where it does not thrive; gardens and churchyards; on railway embankments.

BARK. Young trees soon fissured and ridged pink and grey; in plantations dull pink. Old trees heavily ridged, dark grey or with wide plates pale pink and scaly.

CROWN. Narrowly conic then narrowly columnar with a conic top. This form is maintained with a little broadening to a considerable age; but oldest trees are very flat-topped and where grown quite in the open they may have stout, broadly upswept lower branches. Branches regular and very level, with dark grey foliage sparse enough to let much light through.

FOLIAGE. Shoot: pale yellow-brown, stout, grooved. Second year dark orange-brown.

BUD. Narrowly conic to sharp point; 1·5–2 cm, basal scales large, free, erect; main bud red-brown, grey-fringed, heavily encrusted with white resin.

LEAVES. In pairs, remote, especially on young vigorous trees, each pair spreading widely apart and twisted, pale grey-green, or light green; shiny and dark on old trees, 11–18 cm, sheath 1–1·5 cm, dark grey.

FLOWERS AND CONE. Male flowers abundantly produced, clustered in shallow rings at the base of small, often hanging, shoots, shedding pollen in late May to mid-June. Female flowers dull pink, on the tips of expanding shoots, curving down when fertilised. Cone ovoid-conic, slightly curved, 6–7×3·5 cm, scales pale grey-brown with small red-brown centres, transverse ridge and very short spine.

TABLE 77. SOME SPECIMEN TREES OF PINUS NIGRA MARITIMA

Locality	Date Planted	Dimensions	
Holkham Hall		85′ × 11′ 0″ (1907)	100′ × 13′ 10″ (1968)
Holkham Hall		80′ × 9′ 11″ (1907)	98′ × 12′ 4″ (1968)
Holkham Hall		80′ × 9′ 4″ (1907)	98′ × 11′ 6″ (1968)
Kew R.B.G.	1814	86′ × 9′ 3″ (1903)	89′ × 9′ 6″ (1970)
Arley Castle	1820	+100′ × 10′ 8″ (1905)	125′ × 14′ 3″ (1961)
Arley Castle	1820	+100′ × 9′ 8″ (1905)	120′ × 12′ 1″ (1961)
Arley Castle	1820		110′ × 12′ 3″ (1961)
Hewell Grange	1821	102′ × 9′ 7″ (1931)	108′ × 10′ 3″ (1963)
Stanage Park	1828	118′ × 8′ 7″ (1931)	144′ × 10′ 11″ (1970)
Dropmore (1)	1829	100′ × 13′ 0″ (1931)	120′ × 14′ 0″ (1970)
Dropmore (1)			115′ × 12′ 4″ (1970)
Warnham Court	1834	90′ × 9′ 8″ (1931)	100′ × 11′ 0″ (1971)
Albury Park		+100′ × 6′ 9″ (1905)	110′ × 12′ 2″ (1966)
Canford House		83′ × 9′ 0″ (1904)	90′ × 11′ 8″ (1967)
Linton Park		103′ × 10′ 10″ (1931)	98′ × 11′ 9″ (1965)
Leaton Knolls		102′ × 11′ 0″ (1931)	115′ × 13′ 4″ (1970)
Leaton Knolls			131′ × 10′ 10″ (1970)

Locality	*Date Planted*	*Dimensions*	
Eastnor Castle		111′ × 9′ 6″ (1931)	100′ × 11′ 4″ (1970)
Vinney Ridge	1855		120′ × 6′ 1″ (1971)
Cuffnells	1856	est.120′ × 8′ (1931)	130′ × 10′ 0″ (1970)
Nuneham Court			112′ × 12′ 5″ (1966)
Nr. Llanfacreth			70′ × 15′ 4″ (1968)
Nr. Llanfacreth			80′ × 13′ 6″ (1968)
Fota			75′ × 12′ 6″ (1966)
Bicton			96′ × 14′ 2″ (1968)
Bicton			93′ × 13′ 2″ (1968)
Riccarton		86′ × 9′ 11″ (1931)	85′ × 11′ 4″ (1967)
Culzean Castle	1871	69′ × 6′ 4″ (1931)	110′ × 10′ 4″ (1970)
Kirkennan	1876	87′ × 5′ 5″ (1931)	108′ × 6′ 11″ (1954)
Puck Pits			132′ × 6′ 5″ (1969)
Fonthill			128′ × 5′ 10″ (1960)
Adhurst St. Mary			119′ × 11′ 6″ (1964)
Monk Hopton			113′ × 13′ 6″ (1971)
Broxwood Court			103′ × 12′ 3″ (1957)
Mells Park			125′ × 13′ 3″ (1962)
Knightshayes			111′ × 10′ 3″ (1970)
Escot			105′ × 11′ 9″ (1965)
Tubney Wood	1908		75′ × 6′ 9″ (1966)
Speech House	1923		65′ × 5′ 5″ (1963)
Bedgebury	1926	5′ 9″ (1931)	61′ × 6′ 1″ (1969)
Bedgebury	1926	4′ 6″ (1931)	60′ × 5′ 11″ (1969)
Dropmore (2)	1929		61′ × 4′ 11″ (1970)

GROWTH. This form makes a puny seedling and small transplant, but starts away rapidly when planted out. Shoots of 3 feet are normal after 2–3 years, but seldom much more. Growth in height occurs between early or mid-May and mid-July. It grows well on sands, gravels, well-drained clays, shallow peats or thin soils over chalk and limestone, but it will suffer a bad die-back from *Brunchorstia destruens* if grown where summer temperatures are insufficiently high. Despite this, there are some good individual trees as far north as Skibo Castle in Sutherland. Growth in height is maintained well to 90–100 feet in most districts and growth in girth is rapid, for a pine, for about 50 years.

SPECIMENS. The only probable original trees are the three at Holkham. The tree at Kew, planted in 1814 is claimed to be the first planted, but this was 55 years after the introduction by Philip Miller.

RECOGNITION. The columnar crown and short, light, level branches distinguish a good specimen from any other pine. In the foliage, the pale yellow-brown shoot and long leaves are distinct among 2-needle pines.

Pinus palustris Miller. Long leaf pine; pitch pine

Virginia to Florida, U.S.A. Introduced in 1730. Very rare; found only in a very few collections in South East England and in Ireland. A gaunt tree with very few, stout branches level at first then curving upwards. The bark is dull grey widely fissured. The bud is large, to 5 cm, and white with long, reflexed scales. At the joint with the previous years growth these bud-scales persist in a large bunch.

LEAVES. Light grassy-green, very long, to 45 cm, slender, on very stout orange-brown shoots. Cone. (Not seen) cylindrical, 15–25×5–7·5 cm, dull brown with thin flat scales with recurved spines; basal scales left on tree when cone shed (From Den Ouden and Boom).

RECOGNITION. The shape, long leaves and unusual buds with ring of persistent scales, identify this tree.

TABLE 78. LARGE TREES OF PINUS PALUSTRIS

Locality	*Date Planted*	*Dimensions*	
Borde Hill (Warren Wood)		15′ (1931)	50′ × 3′ 9″ (1968)
Borde Hill (Warren Wood)		12′ (1931)	48′ × 2′ 3″ (1968)
Glencormac	(planted 1920 as *P. canariensis*?)		48′ × 3′ 8″ (1968)
Glencormac			60′ × 3′ 3″ (1968)
Glencormac			47′ × 4′ 4″ (1968)
Mount Usher			39′ × 2′ 1″ (1966)
Bedgebury	1931		23′ × 1′ 1″ (1969)

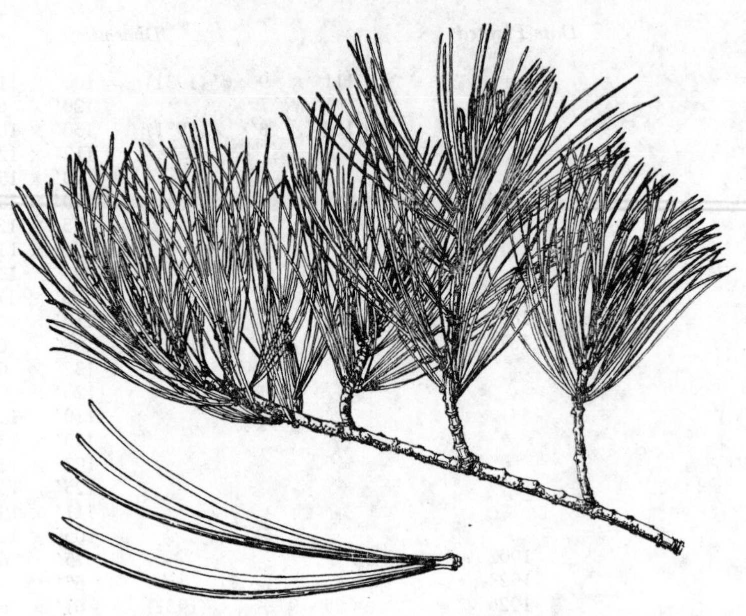

Pinus parviflora

Fig. 156
The flattened spray of *Pinus parviflora*, Japanese white pine, is composed of short, twisted leaves (below × 1⅓) with bright blue-white inner surfaces.

Pinus parviflora Siebold and Zuccarini. Japanese white pine

Mountains of Japan. Introduced in 1861. Uncommon but in collections and large gardens, also in Japanese-style gardens. The form first introduced and usually now seen, is thought to be a Japanese semi-dwarf cultivar. The wild species is known here by the fine tree at Stourhead and a few others. Spontaneous seedlings are found in some gardens.

BARK. Dark purplish with black scales in patches, or with a few wide, spiralled cracks.

CROWN. In the common form, low and broad with wide, level branches and the foliage, short, blue and twisted, laid out in wide plates. In the tree form conic, rather round-topped, with small level branches carrying less dense foliage. Usually bearing numbers of upright cones.

FOLIAGE. Shoot pale greenish-white minutely pubescent.

TABLE 79. SOME SPECIMENS OF PINUS PARVIFLORA

Locality	*Date Planted*	*Dimensions*	
Ochtertyre	1879	28′ (1931)	44′ × 5′ 1″ (1970)
Boconnoc		25′ × 3′ 6″ (1927)	49′ × 7′ 6″ (1970)[1]
Boconnoc			36′ × 5′ 8″ (1970)[1,2]
Edinburgh R.B.G. (1)	1890		(35′) × 2′ 8″ (1967)
Edinburgh R.B.G. (1)			40′ × 3′ 8″ (1967)
Trentham Park			45′ × 4′ 0″ (1968)
Stourhead			69′ × 6′ 6″ (1970)
Leonardslee			60′ × 4′ 1″ (1962)
Leonardslee		36′ × 2′ 4″ (1958)	44′ × 3′ 6″ (1969)
Leonardslee			43′ × 4′ 7″ (1969)
Bodnant	1904	28′ × 2′ 6″ (1931)	38′ × 2′ 11″ (1966)
Tilgate	1905	20′ (1931)	38′ × 2′ 8″ (1961)
Dropmore	1906		37′ × 3′ 1″ (1970)
Bayfordbury	1907		36′ × 2′ 8″ (1962)
Edinburgh R.B.G. (2)	1907		34′ × 4′ 4″ (1967)
Westonbirt		17′ 6″ × 1′ 2″ (1931)	36′ × 2′ 1″ (1971)
Stanage Park			46′ × 3′ 9″ (1970)
Mells Park			50′ × 3′ 6″ (1962)[3]

Locality	*Date Planted*	*Dimensions*	
Highclere Park			45′ × 3′ 9″ (1968)
Garinish Island			40′ × 4′ 0″ (1966)[2]
Headfort	1914	17′ (1931)	39′ × 3′ 11″ (1966)
Headfort	1922	11′ 6″ (1931)	25′ × 3′ 0″ (1966)
Curraghmore		22′ × 2′ 4″ (1931)	40′ × 3′ 5″ (1968)
Bedgebury	1926	8′ 3″	35′ × 3′ 7″ (1969)
Bedgebury	1926		31′ × 3′ 4″ (1969)
Bedgebury	1929		34′ × 3′ 11″ (1969)

[1] Grafted on *P. strobus*
[2] Measured at 2 feet
[3] Thirteen other stems

BUD. Small, ovoid, pale orange-brown with scales free at the tips.
LEAVES. In fives, spreading widely from their bundle and twisted, 5 cm long in the low-growing form; to 8 cm in the larger tree form; dark blue-green outer surface (greyer green in the tree form) the inner surface brightly banded blue-white.
CONE. A tall bun shape (ovoid) standing up from the flat array of branchlets, dark brownish-purple with a few big, leathery incurved scales; 5 cm high, 3·5 cm broad; when open, 4 cm wide; scales pale orange-brown margins, bloomed purple-grey at apex; striated.
GROWTH. The low form is predictably of slow growth, although it maintains a moderate increase in girth to a considerable age. The tall form is more rapid in both dimensions.
RECOGNITION. No other five-needle pine has such short, twisted, spreading leaves; and the blue appearance of the flat-plated crowns with numerous cones erect from them is unlike any other tree.

Pinus patula Schlechtendal and Chamisso. Spreading-leaf pine.

Central and Eastern Mexico. Introduced between 1820 and 1837. Rare and confined to collections across the extreme south of England and in Ireland.
BARK. Orange, rolling into darker vertical flakes which adhere for some time.
CROWN. Widely ovoid with branches leaving the bole, slightly downwards, spreading straight and level then curving slightly upwards, the grey-green leaves hanging from the upcurved sector.
FOLIAGE. Shoot pale greenish-brown bloomed pink-white.
BUD. Slender, long-cylindric to 2·5 cm, curved upwards on side branches; pale brown; the scales free at the tips.
LEAVES. In threes, very slender, all lying forwards along the shoot then hanging down each side, 18–20 cm grey-green from a distance, bright grassy green in the hand; fine lines of stomata visible under a lens, on the outer surface, few on the inner; finely serrated.
CONES. Persist on the branches, in whorls, oblique, curved,

TABLE 80. SPECIMENS OF PINUS PATULA

Locality	*Date Planted*	*Dimensions*	
Fota		22′ × 2′ 3″ (1931)	54′ × 6′ 6″ (1966)[1]
Powerscourt			45′ × 5′ 2″ (1966)
Shelton Abbey			52′ × 5′ 2″ (1968)
Headfort	ca.1918		35′ × 5′ 1″ (1966)
Wakehurst Place	1918	25′ × 1′ 9″ (1931)	46′ × 3′ 5″ (1971)[2]
Tregrehan			52′ × 5′ 7″ (1971)
Tregothnan			57′ × 7′ 5″ (1971)
Heligan			40′ × 3′ 6″ (1959)
Garinish Island			46′ × 3′ 11″ (1966)
Mount Usher			32′ × 4′ 8″ (1966)
Dunloe Castle			47′ × 3′ 10″ (1968)
Sidbury Manor			30′ × 2′ 9″ (1957)
Jermyn's House	1954		25′ × 1′ 9″ (1969)

[1] Large limb missing
[2] Another stem, ×2ft 11in

ovoid-conic, shining pale brown, 8–10 cm long, minutely prickled.

GROWTH. Early growth is quite rapid, but in England once trees reach a good size they blow down or die. Before this happens several trees have been increasing in girth at about one inch a year.

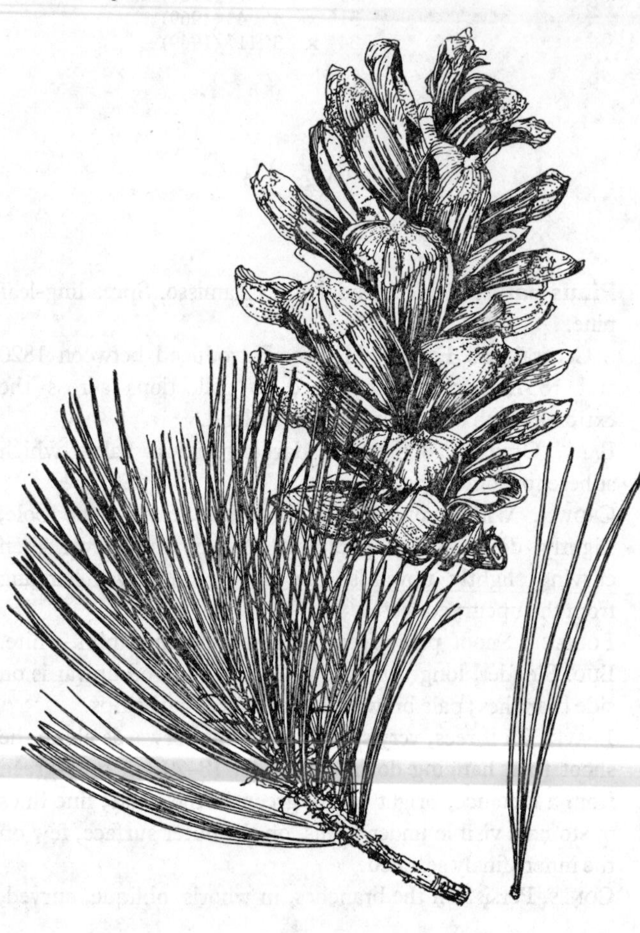

Pinus peuce

Fig. 157
Foliage and fully opened cone of *Pinus peuce*, Macedonian pine. The foliage is densely held on glabrous bright green shoots.

Pinus peuce Grisebach. Macedonian pine.

South and West Balkan Mountains. Introduced in 1864. Uncommon but in many collections and large gardens and occasionally as a small trial plantation at high altitude.

BARK. Young trees; grey-green finely cracked with red-brown fissures. Old trees dark purple with big smooth areas between fissures, or pale grey finely fissured into very short plates.

CROWN. Neatly narrow ovoid, or columnar, broader in old trees; upper branches strongly ascending; middle and lower level; occasional heavy low branches strongly upswept. Very dense and dark.

FOLIAGE. Shoot bright green, sometimes brown on upper side; second year, overlaid by orange-brown.

BUD. Cylindric, abruptly pointed, grey-white with hairy fringes to the scales; tips of scales free. Leaf-sheaths densely on shoots, rich brown, papery 1–1·5 cm, loose.

LEAVES. 7–9 cm in fives, very densely pointing forwards on young shoots and closely so on leading shoots, spreading on weak shoots; slender, straight; outer surface deep blue-green finely lined with white stomata; inner surface with two broad bands but a wide dark green margin.

FLOWERS AND CONE. Male flowers freely borne, ovoid, pale yellow shedding pollen in June when they become long-conic. Female flowers dark red at tips of strong shoots, becoming pale green cone with some clear or white resin exuded, 12×3·5 cm, strongly curved from the stalk and slightly curved at the tip, straight between, cylindrical but tapered slightly to the apex; ripening dark red-brown, the scales grey-tipped and shallowly striated. They open to 6 cm across when dry.

GROWTH. An extremely sturdy tree of uniform, steady growth on almost any site, often in the best of health when other species around are sickly or dying. Growth in height is not rapid, but young trees may grow annual shoots of 2 feet, starting late in May and ending in early July. Growth in girth is usually more than one inch a year and is well maintained with age.

SPECIMENS. No original tree is known, but those that are grafts are presumably of very early planting, and the largest tree, at Stourhead, is likely to be an original.

RECOGNITION. The shapely dense dark crown is only like *P. monticola*, or *P. cembra*, from both of which the green, smooth shoots easily distinguish *P. peuce*. *P. armandii* is another five-needled pine with green smooth shoots, but its long, lax, pale leaves are quite distinct.

TABLE 81. SPECIMENS OF PINUS PEUCE

Locality	*Date Planted*	*Dimensions*	
Stourhead			93′ × 11′ 11″ (1970)
Stourhead			80′ × 8′ 7″ (1970)
Nymans			80′ × 6′ 2″ (1966)[1]
Woburn		50′ × 3′ 11″ (1931)	79′ × 9′ 3″ (1970)[1]
Bicton		42′ × 3′ 8″ (1906)	94′ × 7′ 11½″ (1968)
Kew R.B.G.		42′ × 3′ 10″ (1909)	59′ × 6′ 1″ (1969)
Warnham Court		50′ × 5′ 9″ (1931)	72′ × 8′ 0″ (1971)
Melbury			75′ × 7′ 8″ (1971)
Westonbirt (Willesley)	1876		75′ × 7′ 9″ (1971)
Westonbirt (Willesley)	1876		70′ × 7′ 8″ (1971)
Bayfordbury		25′ (1931)	62′ × 6′ 10″ (1968)
Nuneham Court		50′ × 6′ 4″ (1931)	75′ × 6′ 8″ (1966)
Alnwick Castle		49′ × 3′ 10″ (1931)	69′ × 6′ 1″ (1958)
Glamis Castle			82′ × 4′ 8″ (1970)
Rednock			76′ × 6′ 9″ (1955)
Brahan			71′ × 7′ 10″ (1970)
Petworth House			93′ × 6′ 10″ (1971)
Strete Ralegh (Pinetum)			72′ × 7′ 2″ (1964)
Hergest Croft			63′ × 7′ 0″ (1969)
Trentham Park			64′ × 6′ 8″ (1968)
Glasnevin B.G.		60′ × 4′ 9″ (1931)	66′ × 6′ 0″ (1966)
St. Clere	ca.1908		54′ × 5′ 7″ (1969)
Borde Hill (Warren)		22′ (1931)	60′ × 5′ 3″ (1968)
Borde Hill (Gores Wood)	1910		53′ × 4′ 10″ (1967)
Dawyck	1910	19′ × 1′ 3″ (1930)	64′ × 5′ 2″ (1961)
Wakehurst Place	1915	25′ × 1′ 8″ (1931)	65′ × 6′ 4″ (1970)
Headfort	1926	7′ 6″ (1931)	47′ × 5′ 5″ (1966)
Bedgebury	1926	7′ 3″ (1931)	45′ × 5′ 0″ (1969)
Bedgebury	1949		37′ × 3′ 4″ (1969)

[1] Grafted plant

Pinus pinaster Aiton. Maritime pine

Western Mediterranean east to Greece. Introduced before 1596. Uncommon except locally in the far south of England, where there are a few areas of plantations and small areas of heathland on which it seeds itself freely. Elsewhere a few trees in collections and large gardens; (notably good trees in Herefordshire), and a few shelterbelts by the coast.

BARK. Young trees and plantation-trees, orange-brown, widely fissured; purple in places. Old trees dark purple, deeply cracked into small squarish plates which scale away and leave dark red.

TABLE 82. SOME SPECIMENS OF PINUS PINASTER

Locality	*Date Planted*	*Dimensions*	
Curraghmore	prob.1770	91′ × 7′ 10″ (1907)	102′ × 9′ 8″ (1968)
Sheffield Park	ca.1800		85′ × 15′ 0″ (1968)
Sheffield Park	ca.1800		85′ × 9′ 4″ (1968)
Hewell Grange	1811	80′ × 9′ 9″ (1909)	95′ × 10′ 3″ (1963)
Holme Lacey			92′ × 10′ 11″ (1962)[1]
Garnons			114′ × 10′ 4″ (1969)
Dropmore			75′ × 10′ 3″ (1961)
Garinish Island (Co. Kerry)		72′ × 8′ 8″ (1931)	60′ × 10′ 0″ (1966)
West Lavington Rectory			75′ × 11′ 9″ (1967)
North West of Wareham			50′ × 10′ 10″ (1968)
North West of Wareham			70′ × 9′ 7″ (1968)
Leonardslee		76′ (1910)	94′ × 8′ 10″ (1961)
Brocklesby Park		81′ × 8′ 1″ (1931)	90′ × 8′ 8″ (1956)
Exbury		67′ × 10′ 4″ (1931)?	80′ × 10′ 8″ (1955)
The Hendre			97′ × 8′ 10″ (1962)
Caerhayes Castle			80′ × 12′ 2″ (1971)
Bolderwood	1861		90′ × 8′ 7″ (1970)
Wakehurst Place	1913	35′ × 3′ 6″ (1931)	76′ × 7′ 8″ (1970)
Bedgebury	1926	7′ 6″ (1931)	62′ × 5′ 8″ (1966)

[1] Bole 80 feet with only one branch

Fig. 158
Foliage of *Pinus pinaster*, Maritime pine, with leaves stouter and longer than any other 2-needle pine. The bud ($\times 1\frac{1}{3}$) has very decurved scale-tips.

CROWN. Young trees often leaning at the base; long vigorous upswept branches and a long, stout leading-shoot, very open and sparse. Old trees with a long bare bole, slightly curved or sinuous and a broad, flat-domed head of level branches lined with whorls of adhering cones. Trees in plantations are often all bent at the base, in the same direction. They have very open crowns and big, stout leaves.
FOLIAGE. Shoot stout, pink-brown above, pale olive-green beneath; long shoots on young trees become deep red-purple in summer. Pulvini on upper side purple-brown, on lower side of shoot orange-brown. Second year shoot dull grey-brown.
BUD. 1–2 cm, more on strong shoots, sharply conic; bright red-brown acute scales broadly edged pale brown and fringed with long, curling silvery hairs; basal scales with apices, rolled outwards and down.
LEAVES. In pairs, stout, stiff but not rigid, about 17 cm, short-pointed; first year shining grey-green, very convex outer surface, plane inner, both finely lined with white stomata; second year glossier deep green; finely serrated.
FLOWERS AND CONE. Male flowers usually abundant, clustered in shallow rings beneath the leaves; shedding pollen in mid- or late May. Female flowers on the tips of expanding shoots, dull red. Cone nearly sessile, very oblique at base, slightly curved ovoid-conic; 10×5 cm when closed; shining dark olive-green, ripening orange-brown; scale with broad transverse ridge rising to a central, small, upcurved prickle.
GROWTH. This species grows very fast when young, on a variety of soils including very poor sands, and in some exposure, but is liable to be laid over from the base by strong winds. It bends back to the vertical and continues growing as fast but the bend remains in the stem. Shoots over 3 feet long are common. It is not usually long-lived and none of the 16 British trees given by Elwes and Henry has been found, but the trees 169 years old at Sheffield Park seem to be in very good health, and one Irish tree given by Elwes and Henry survives. Very few of those given in the 1932 Report have been found (and one that was is now dead).
SPECIMENS. The fine tree at Curraghmore is among Scots pines planted in 1770 and was probably planted with them, which would make it the oldest known Maritime pine. It measured 98ft × 8ft 10in in 1931.
RECOGNITION. Old trees may be recognised at once by their bark and open crown. The foliage is recognised by the long stout leaves, unlike any other 2-needle pine, and the outward rolled bud-scales.

Pinus pinea Linnaeus. Stone pine

Mediterranean region. Introduced before 1548. Uncommon and although seldom found anywhere but in the south of England, it is perfectly hardy in South-east Scotland. Largely confined to big gardens but occasional in unexpected places like the railway embankment at Dunglass, East Lothian, and a field near Calne, Wilts.

BARK. Young trees very early fissured orange in dull grey. Old trees with dark, deep vertical, slightly spiralled fissures between big long flat plates which are orange and pink-brown and scaly.

CROWN. Very distinctively wide-domed on few stout branches ascending steeply from low on a short, sinuous bole then dividing into radiating and ascending small branches to make a dense head. The leaves are distinctively separated from each other, as in the three-needled *P. bungeana*.

FOLIAGE. Shoot pale greenish buff with orange-brown pulvini, smooth and curved.

BUD. Bright chestnut-red, scales acute, deeply fringed with white hairs and reflexed at the tips; cylindric-ovoid, 1 cm long.

LEAVES. Rather sparse, forward on young shoots, with a neat basal sheath brown and grey, 1 cm long; shiny dark green, 10–12 cm long, twisted and sharply pointed, stout, with 10–12 fine stomatal lines on the outer surface and 5–6 on the inner surface.

CONE. Symmetrical, flat-based ovoid, 12×9 cm weighing 10–12 oz, shining pale brown and smooth, remaining closed for three years; scales convex, with 5 slender ridges radiating from an orange-brown rough centre, which becomes pale grey on the margin and dark grey centrally.

GROWTH. A short-lived tree with very few remaining from records of 1903-9 or from 1931. Growth in height is moderate for some years until the form of the crown precludes long shoots, but growth in girth is quite vigorous for longer, although it falls very low in old trees despite their large crowns.

SPECIMENS. The big old trees at Hurn (Heron) Court, Christchurch have all long gone.

RECOGNITION. The umbrella-crown; big orange-red plates on the bark and big smooth cones identify the tree. The foliage is sparse and dark green which, with the bud and the needle-length separate it from that of other two-needled pines.

TABLE 83. SOME SPECIMENS OF PINUS PINEA

Locality	*Date Planted*	*Dimensions*	
Fota	1847		54′ × 8′ 0″ (1966)
Embley Park		59′ × 9′ 10″ (1931)	72′ × 11′ 2″ (1971)
Kew R.B.G.		31′ × 7′ 7″ (1903)	42′ × 8′ 8″ (1958)
North Manor, Crickhowell			60′ × 10′ 9″ (1971)
Curraghmore		61′ × 7′ (1931)	67′ × 8′ 4″ (1968)
Dartington Hall			55′ × 9′ 5″ (1968)
Glenthorne			50′ × 9′ 4″ (1969)
Pylewell Park			46′ × 8′ 2″ (1968)
Gurteen le Poer			65′ × 6′ 10″ (1968)
Glencormac			50′ × 6′ 2″ (1968)
Tregothnan	ca.1900		49′ × 7′ 5″ (1971)
Leonardslee			51′ × 8′ 7″ (1961)
Tetton House			50′ × 7′ 4″ (1959)
Chiswick House			50′ × 5′ 11″ (1964)
Cambridge B.G.			45′ × 4′ 0″ (1969)
Bowood		23′ × 1′ 9″ (1931, Estate Record)	48′ × 3′ 7″ (1968)
Exbury	1925	20′ × 4′ 2″ (1955)	32′ × 5′ 3″ (1968)
Dropmore			45′ × 5′ 2″ (1970)
Chandlers Ford	ca.1927		30′ × 4′ 7″ (1967)

Pinus ponderosa Douglas. Western yellow pine

Western North America from the lower Fraser River in British Columbia, south to northern Mexico and east to Nebraska. Introduced in 1827. Some original trees still survive. Uncommon but frequent in collections and large gardens, particularly in the west and in Central Scotland. Very rare in Ireland.

BARK. Young and middle-sized trees, pale purple-grey deeply fissured into scaling vertical ridges. Old trees with wide, scaling fissures and very large plates, often slightly concave; scaling and cinnamon, yellow-brown and pink.

CROWN. As a young tree, narrow, conic with short, stout branches. As an old tree, variable in shape. Many retain a good conic top with ascending branches and a long, straight bole. Others, and most of those growing in the open, have a few big lower branches which make the crown irregular. At all ages the dense brushes of long leaves are a feature. Bare branches are smooth and whippy. Long, pendulous branchlets hang from many old trees, bare for 10ft or more, curling up at the tip with a brush of foliage.

FOLIAGE. Shoot shining dark brown; second year dark orange-brown striped yellowish green between plates.

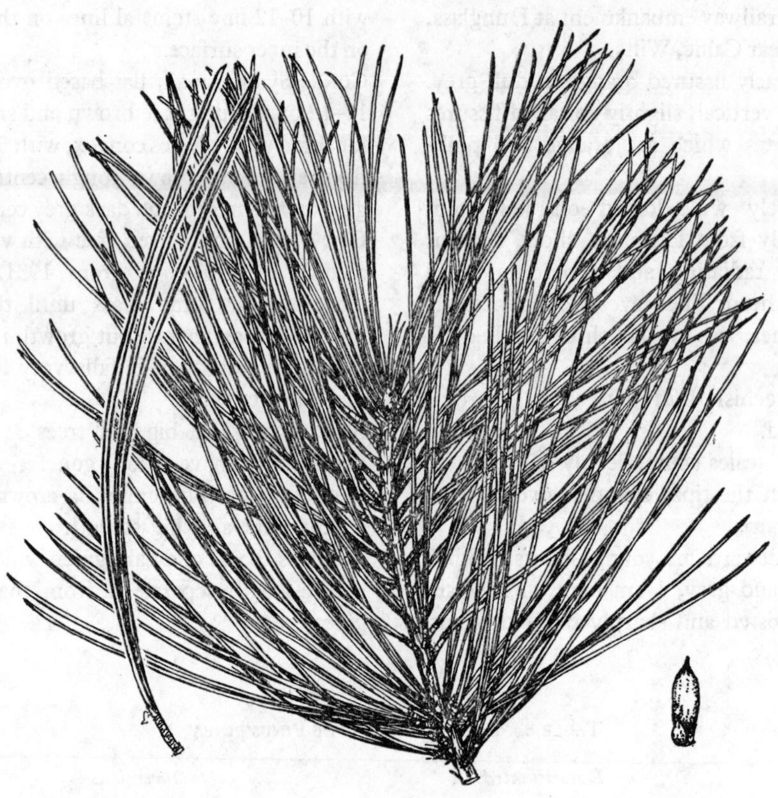

Pinus ponderosa

Fig. 159
Foliage and shoot of *Pinus ponderosa,* Western yellow pine, ($\times \frac{1}{3}$) with detail of bud ($\times \frac{2}{3}$) and leaf fascicle ($\times \frac{2}{3}$). The shoot is bright yellow-green, becoming brown. The bark of old trees is in huge, often concave, flaking plates of pink and cinnamon.

Bud. Cylindrical, pointed, 4 cm long on side-shoots, crusted with white resin; bud-scales pale red-brown partly free of resin.

Leaves. Densely crowded, lying forward on leading-shoots, to 15 cm long on some trees, 20–22 cm on others.

Cone. Ovoid, 7–9×4–5 cm, ripening dark brown, each scale transversely ridged, with a central, short spreading spine. Males crowded, purplish, open to 3 cm.

Growth. Young trees soon make vigorous shoots up to 3 feet long, and a fine tree at Leonardslee has grown from 75 feet to 90 feet in 8 years, but few trees have made growth for long at more than an average of 1 foot in a year. Growth in girth has been rapid in young trees and remains moderately so in some of the oldest, while in others the growth is very slow indeed. The table of specimen trees shows that the largest are not found in the west, nor in the east, but largely in a belt from Kent through the Midlands and the Welsh borders to North Wales, and again in Southern Scotland. No trees were seen in Ireland. This seems to be a long-lived healthy species, as a high proportion of trees recorded earlier has been found.

Specimens. The trees at Dropmore, Arley Castle and Bowood are known to be original trees from David Douglas's seed. It is very probable that this is true of the largest tree at Powis Castle, and probably also those at Eastnor Castle and Bicton. The original tree at Bayfordbury noted by Elwes and Henry is taken to be the one that was blown down in 1951 when 124ft×11ft 0in but another there is now of larger girth and may well have been planted at the same time.

TABLE 84. SOME SPECIMEN TREES OF PINUS PONDEROSA

Locality	*Date Planted*	*Dimensions*	
Dropmore	1829	99′ × 8′ 9″ (1909)	98′ × 9′ 10″ (1970)
Arley Castle	1829	96′ × 6′ 7″ (1909)	114′ × 7′ 7″ (1961)
Bowood	ca.1829	99′ × 10′ 10″ (1931)	120′ × 13′ 5″ (1968)
Powis Castle	?1829	105′ × 10′ (1908)	128′ × 14′ 0″ (1970)
Powis Castle			122′ × 13′ 1″ (1970)
Powis Castle			118′ × 10′ 2″ (1970)
Eastnor Castle		65′ × 8′ 4″ (1909)	105′ × 10′ 8″ (1970)
Leighton Hall			98′ × 10′ 6″ (1970)
Bayfordbury			93′ × 11′ 10″ (1962)
Highnam	1844	72′ × 9′ 4″ (1909)	85′ × 12′ 11″ (1970)
Bicton		89′ × 9′ 11″ (1928)	104′ × 11′ 7″ (1968)
Bury Hill	1834	98′ × 9′ 1″ (1931)	100′ × 9′ 3″ (1971)
Dawyck	1837		105′ × 9′ 5″ (1966)
Escot		94′ × 7′ 8″ (1904)	96′ × 10′ 2″ (1965)
Brahan			107′ × 11′ 2″ (1970)
Dropmore (2)	1843		105′ × 11′ 1″ (1970)
Albury Park	1850	84′ × 7′ 5″ (1931)	92′ × 9′ 0″ (1966)
Coppid Hall		80′ × 10′ 0″ (1931)	88′ × 10′ 3″ (1968)
Scotney Castle			120′ × 10′ 9″ (1971)
Silia			121′ × 10′ 4″ (1970)
Nuneham Court			117′ × 10′ 8″ (1970)
Oxenfoord Castle	1856	57′ × 4′ 8″ (1931)	67′ × 9′ 10″ (1967)
Highnam (2)	1856		90′ × 10′ 5″ (1970)
Stratfield Saye			90′ × 11′ 9″ (1968)
Glamis Castle	1861	67′ × 5′ 8″ (1931)	90′ × 9′ 7″ (1970)
Dunorlan Park			91′ × 10′ 7″ (1954)
Chatsworth			85′ × 8′ 10″ (1971)
Oakley Park			87′ × 11′ 1″ (1971)
Glendoick		68′ × 6′ 6″ (1931)	105′ × 8′ 7″ (1970)
Windsor Great Park			77′ × 11′ 1″ (1967)
Blackmoor	1869	65′ × 5′ 10″ (1931)	105′ × 8′ 0″ (1968)
Westonbirt (Specimen Avenue)			105′ × 8′ 3″ (1967)
Leonardslee		75′ × 5′ 4″ (1961)	90′ × 6′ 5″ (1969)
Smeaton House		28′ × 1′ 5″ (1931)	64′ × 5′ 6″ (1971)
Bodnant	1901		80′ × 7′ 6″ (1966)
Borde Hill	Seed 1911		68′ × 4′ 8″ (1957)
Tibberton Court	1920		60′ × 4′ 7″ (1967)
Speech House	1921		70′ × 4′ 3″ (1963)
Little Kingsmill Green	1929		54′ × 4′ 4″ (1968)
Bedgebury	1930		54′ × 3′ 11″ (1969)

var. scopulorum Engelmann. A not very distinct form from the South-east part of the range, with shorter leaves, 15–16 cm, rather twisted, sometimes in pairs. Seen only at Kew, planted 1889, 49ft×3ft 1in (1970).

RECOGNITION. An old tree of *P. ponderosa* is distinguished by the pink-brown bark in large scaling plates, long leaves in dense brushes and long, hanging branchlets. Pointed apex to crown with dark, upright brushes often useful at distance. Foliage features are yellow-brown shoot and resinous bud. See also *P. jeffreyi.*

Pinus pseudostrobus Lindley.

Mexico and Central America. Introduced in 1839. Four trees known of some size, one in Ireland and three in South England, of which one was dying ten years ago. The species shows wide variation in its cones in different parts of its range and can be separated thereby into at least five varieties. The species itself is part of the *P. montezumae* complex with bloomed shoots like *P. cooperi* and *P. hartwegii.*

BARK. Grey-purple, scaling and with deep vertical scaly fissures, rather like that of *P. nigra maritima.*

CROWN. Irregular, with stout, sinuous branches.

FOLIAGE. Shoots slender, heavily bloomed grey-blue.

BUD. Distinctively stalked (Powerscourt tree), cylindric-ovoid, scale-tips adhering.

LEAVES. In fives, slender and pendulous, 18–20 cm long rather grey, grassy green, like *P. patula.*

SPECIMENS. Pencarrow, planted 1849, 47ft×5ft 8in (1906); 65ft×7ft 0in (1957, dying—dead before 1970); Borde Hill, 12 feet (1931), 40ft×2ft 5in (1958, dying); Blackmoor, planted 1913, 22ft×1ft 10in (1931), 56ft×4ft 11in (1968); Powerscourt, 40ft×5ft 7in (1966); Tresco Abbey, 10 feet (1970).

RECOGNITION. The *P. patula*-like leaves but glaucous shoot and rough bark together distinguish this, and so do the stalked buds if the Powerscourt tree be typical.

Pinus pungens Lambert. Prickle pine

New Jersey to Georgia, Eastern United States, in the mountains. Introduced in 1804. Very rare—three large trees and a number of small trees known.

BARK. Young trees dark brown and scaly, widely fissured with orange. Old trees like *Pinus nigra maritima*, coarsely fissured into grey-pink scaly plates on wide pink ridges.

CROWN. The older trees have sinuous boles, leaning, with long slender descending branches whorled by large adhering cones. Young trees sturdy with ascending branches.

FOLIAGE. Shoot stout in young plants, shiny red-brown, darker in the second year.

BUD. Narrowly conic; those on older trees with a base swollen by male flowers; whitish shiny red-brown.

LEAVES. In pairs, thick, twisted and broad, 4·5 cm long, rather dark green. The resin from a broken shoot has a scent like lemon-curd.

CONE. Tightly held to the shoot in pairs on leading shoots of young trees and whorls of 3–5 on branches of old trees, pointing backwards, ovoid-conic, slightly curved 8 cm×5 cm, yellowish-green ripening green-brown (October) then pink-brown; scales smoothly convex, rounded margin, transverse and vertical ridges crossing at the centre where there is a broad, flat-based, hooked, sharp spine.

SPECIMENS. Leonardslee, planted circa 1905, 49ft×2ft 6in (1958) growing to 52ft×3ft 2in (1969) and 57ft×3ft 8in (1969); Bedgebury, 9ft (1969); Rhinefield Arboretum, 7 feet (1969). There is a large tree at Castlewellan.

RECOGNITION. The crown is like that of *P. banksiana* but the bark differs (q.v.) and the retained cones are much larger and are fiercely prickly. As young trees cone within a few years of planting this usually suffices, but without cones the bark and dense foliage distinguish *P. pungens*.

Pinus radiata D. Don. Monterey pine

Small areas of Monterey County, California, around Swanton, Monterey and Cambria towns. As var. *binata* Engel. on the islands of Santa Rosa and Guadelupe.

Introduced in 1833. Very common in the south-west, where it fringes many fields, parkland and estates, particularly along the south coast from the New Forest westwards. In the north and east mainly confined to large gardens; rare in Central and North-east Scotland.

BARK. Young and middle-aged trees have purplish grey bark deeply fissured into long parallel ridges. Old trees often dark grey or pale with algae, the ridges very deeply separated by fissures up to 15 cm deep, and red-brown; inside; the ridges shorter, 1–2 m long. On large branches the bark is smooth dark grey-green broadly fissured pink-brown.

CROWN. Young trees with long, strong shoots and ascending branches rising from a rather bushy base; soon conic. Older trees with a huge, dark, domed crown high on a bole which becomes rough and bears big short, ascending bases of broken branches. In the open they may be widely domed, sometimes low; with very big branches low on the bole. From a distance the crowns look blackish but from nearer they are bright deep green.

FOLIAGE. Shoot light grey-green becoming grey-brown.

BUD. 1 cm, much bigger on strong shoots, dark red-brown; purplish-grey with resin, cylindric with an abrupt conic tip. They lengthen early in spring and become conspicuously light yellow-green shoots.

LEAVES. In threes, very densely set, rather forward but spreading widely, very slender 10–15 cm; bright shining deep green; basal sheath grey to red-brown, 1 cm long first year, 0·5 cm second year.

FLOWERS AND CONE. Male flowers conspicuously bright yellow in March or April, densely whorled in broad rings at the base of emerging shoots; shedding pollen in March usually, but in January in sheltered parts of Cornwall.

CONE. Ovoid, on a curved stalk 1 cm long, very oblique at base; as the cone is held close to the branch and pointing backwards or downwards, the upper outer part (the base of the cone) is grossly distorted by swollen scales, convex and round-pointed like acorns, pale reddish or yellowish brown with roughened dark grey centres; normal scales flat, wavy edged with a thin transverse ridge through the roughened dark grey centre. The cones (10–12×8–9 cm) are held tightly in whorls along the branches for 30 years or more and often rot and break up on the tree.

GROWTH. The most vigorous conifer of all in these countries, with annual shoots of eight feet recorded, and 4–5 feet quite common. It has grown to 202 feet in 51 years in New Zealand. In the far south-west, growth hardly stops in the winter and buds have been measured which grew 6 inches during January. It is the only common pine, and probably the only pine, in these countries to make growth in late summer and autumn. Young trees not in the south-west take some years to settle to a proper pattern of growth and until then they may rest for the winter with a half-expanded shoot. In spring this will expand early but soon stops with a true bud. This expands in June and grows rapidly until September when a new bud is set, only to begin expanding until stopped by cold weather. Other trees grow normally but slowly until July then rapidly until mid-September. The height of trees of known planting date does not show the rapid growth of which the young tree is seen to be capable, because this growth slows down after some 20 years and no dated examples have been measured as young as this. The most rapid growth in height among the trees given in Table 85 is 79 feet in 28 years at Albury Park in Surrey, and although this is not in the region of the best growth for the species, this is more rapid than any noted in the 1931

Pinus radiata

Fig. 160
Foliage and mature cone of *Pinus radiata*, Monterey pine. The very oblique cones adhere in clusters to the branches for up to 30 years. They differ from the similar cones of the two-needled *Pinus muricata* in lacking spines.

figures. The most vigorous tree recorded by Elwes and Henry had reached 52ft × 4ft in 16 years growth at Whiteknights, Reading. Growth in girth is very vigorous indeed in youth although it is exceeded by several other conifers. The greatest increases from planting noted in the Table 85 are 126 inches in 47 years at Whites, Goudhurst, Kent, 169 inches in 66 years at Bodnant and 193 inches in 79 years at Sidbury Manor, Devon. That these figures are not the fastest growth and that this speed of growth can fall rapidly in old trees is shown by the tree at Castle Horneck, Penzance, which grew 234 inches in its first 78 years but in the subsequent 31 years increased by only 7 inches. Growth is not greatly affected by the kind of soil but it must be well drained. The foliage can be badly burned by cold dry winds but with little apparent ill-effect. The tree is so far very long-lived; only one tree of the 18 visited that were recorded from 1903 to 1908 was missing, although another one was only a stump. The main losses of old trees seem to be from breakage low down. Natural seedlings are found in a number of places, but are usually in too much shade to grow properly.

SPECIMENS. The tree at Dropmore was a cutting raised at Lee's Nursery in Hammersmith, presumably from an original seedling.

RECOGNITION. The dense, green leaves in threes resemble only those of *P. greggii* but the buds and shoots differ. The crown, bark and adhering cones resemble *P. muricata*, but *P. radiata* differs in the needles in threes, of a different colour, and un-spined cones.

TABLE 85. LARGEST RECORDED TREES OF PINUS RADIATA

Locality	*Date Planted*	*Dimensions*	
Dropmore	1839	77′ × 15′ (1909)	90′ × 17′ 2″ (1970)
Adare Manor (1)	1841	72′ × 7′ 6″ (1891)	100′ × 16′ 3″ (1968)
Upcott	1845		75′ × 14′ 6″ (1970)
Highnam	1846		80′ × 10′ 3″ (1970)
Fota	1847		85′ × 19′ 11″ (1966)
Sandling Park	1848	85′ × 15′ 10″ (1907)	95′ × 17′ 5″ (1965)[2]
Castle Kennedy	1849	68′ × 9′ 4″ (1904)	102′ × 15′ 1″ (1967)
Castle Kennedy	1849	68′ × 8′ 6″ (1904)	90′ × 13′ 5″ (1967)
Castle Horneck	1850	90′ × 19′ 6″ (1928)	82′ × 20′ 1″ (1959)
Keir House	1850	68′ × 12′ 5″ (1927)	88′ × 15′ 4″ (1970)
Coollattin	1851	61′ × 11′ (1931)	90′ × 16′ 9″ (1968)
Blandsfort	1851	73′ × 11′ 8″ (1931)	73′ × 14′ 3″ (1968)
Hamwood		70′ × 17′ 0″ (1905)[3]	85′ × 29′ 0″ (1968)[4]
Muckross Abbey		85′ × 14′ 10″ (1909)[1]	90′ × 17′ 10″ (1968)
Derreen		70′ × 14′ (1931)	85′ × 20′ 5″ (1966)
Kelburn	1850	90′ × 14′ (1931)	110′ × 16′ 11″ (1970)
Bicton	1855		104′ × 22′ 6″ (1968)[2]
Dropmore	1855		79′ × 12′ 1″ (1970)
Cuffnells	1856	116′ × 8′ 6″ (1907)	144′ × 12′ 2″ (1970)
Cuffnells	1856		128′ × 13′ 9″ (1970)
Northerwood House		106′ × 14′ 6″ (1907)	108′ × 18′ 3″ (1969)
Knowle Hotel		83′ × 14′ 2″ (1907)	78′ × 18′ 11″ (1965)
Heanton Satcheville		92′ × 14′ (1905)	98′ × 17′ 5″ (1960)
Haldon Grange		90′ × 14′ 6″ (1903)	94′ × 19′ 3″ (1967)
Bury Hill		98′ × 14′ 6″ (1908)	100′ × 16′ 7″ (1971)
Embley Park		86′ × 17′ 6″ (1931)	98′ × 19′ 6″ (1971)
Trebah		95–100′ × 12′ 5″ (1906)	105′ × 15′ 4″ (1959)
Bodorgan		75′ × 17′ 10″ (1906)[3]	70′ × 23′ 11″ (1966)[3]
Bodorgan			105′ × 17′ 8″ (1966)
Powerscourt	1859	99′ × 12′ (1931)	103′ × 15′ 9″ (1966)
Holnest			75′ × 20′ 5″ (1968)
Inistioge			125′ × 18′ 1″ (1966)
Ashford Castle			118′ × 15′ 6″ (1968)
Emo Park			100′ × 15′ 11″ (1968)
Headfort			65′ × 20′ 6″ (1966)
Errol House			100′ × 13′ 9″ (1970)
Bolderwood	1861		111′ × 15′ 8″ (1970)
Killerton			115′ × 14′ 7″ (1970)
Killerton			124′ × 12′ 9″ (1970)
Luscombe Castle			95′ × 15′ 7″ (1971)
Powderham Castle			92′ × 17′ 6″ (1970)
Heligan			100′ × 17′ 4″ (1959)
Boconnoc		72′ × 21′ (1927)	95′ × 25′ 0″ (1957)[5]
Bowood		91′ × 17′ (1931)	95′ × 19′ 1″ (1968)
Hurn Court		111′ × 13′ 5″ (1915)	105′ × 17′ 5″ (1968)
Sidbury Manor	1880		88′ × 16′ 1″ (1959)
Whiteknights	1888	52′ × 4′ 0″ (1904)	67′ × 10′ 6″ (1971)
Lytchett Heath			101′ × 16′ 3″ (1967)
Goodwood Park		83′ × 9′ 0″ (1906)	93′ × 13′ 5″ (1965)
Adare Manor (2)		87′ × 6′ 10″ (1905)	100′ × 14′ 0″ (1968)
Muckross Abbey			95′ × 14′ 11″ (1968)[6]
Blackmoor	1896	70′ × 6′ 11″ (1931)	100′ × 9′ 6″ (1961)
Bodnant	1900	68′ × 7′ 0″ (1931)	82′ × 14′ 1″ (1966)
Bodnant	1902	71′ × 7′ 6″ (1931)	93′ × 12′ 4″ (1959)
Wayford Manor	ca.1902		65′ × 12′ 8″ (1961)
White's	1906		81′ × 10′ 6″ (1953)
Bodnant	1907		80′ × 9′ 9″ (1960)
Little Hall	1907	56′ × 7′ 2″ (1931)	60′ × 8′ 10″ (1961)
Wakehurst Place	1911	50′ × 4′ (1931)	77′ × 8′ 3″ (1964)
Albury Park	1926	79′ × 5′ 11″ (1954)	95′ × 8′ 4″ (1970)
Bedgebury	1926	9′ (1931)	50′ × 6′ 5″ (1969)
Bedgebury	1929		62′ × 6′ 1″ (1969)
Westonbirt (Sand Earth)	1933		80′ × 8′ 4″ (1969)
Westonbirt (Pool Avenue)	1935		82′ × 8′ 0″ (1970)

1 Measured at 2 feet
2 Measured at 6 feet
3 Measured at 0 feet
4 Measured at 1 foot
5 Measured at 3 feet (Died before 1970)
6 Clear bole for 50 feet

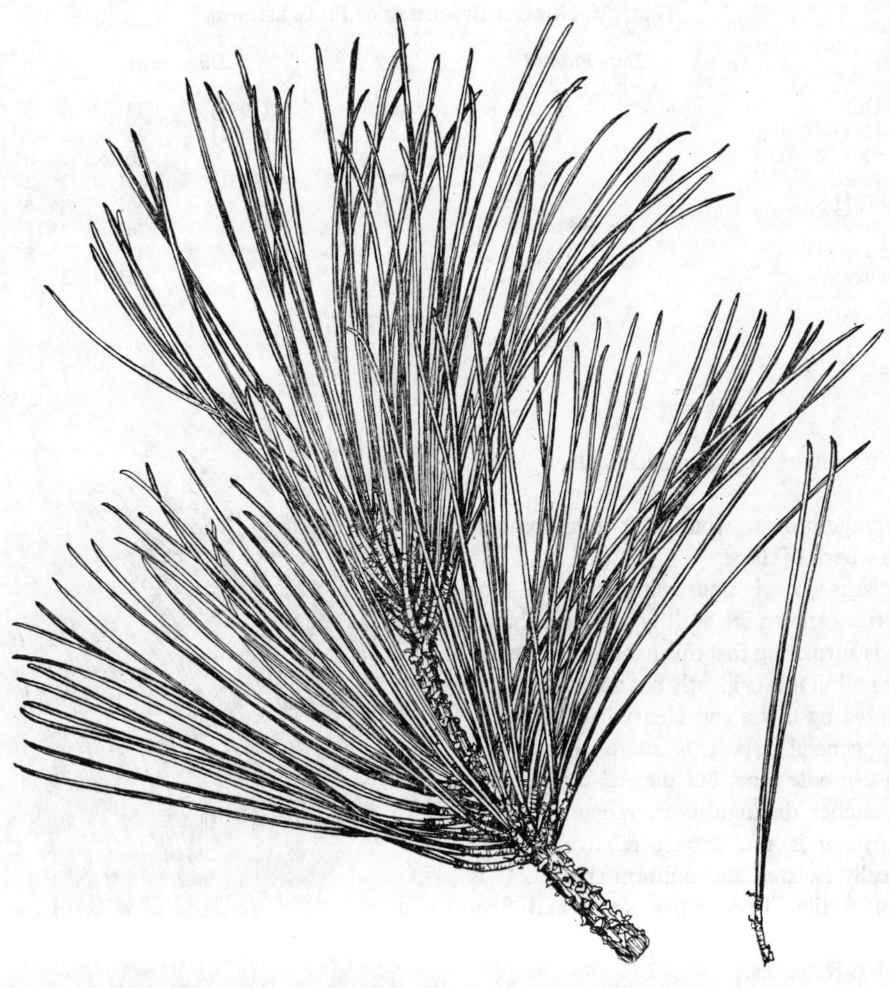

Fig. 161
***Pinus resinosa*, Red pine, showing the slender needles in whorls on the shoot, which is orange. The needles snap cleanly when bent sharply.**

Pinus resinosa Aiton. Red pine

Eastern North America, from Nova Scotia to Pennsylvania. Introduced in 1756. Very rare and apparently now growing only in collections in South East England.

BARK. Lower bole pink-grey and shredding, higher up, red-brown with dark, small curling scales.

CROWN. A sturdy, conic tree with large dense brushes of dark foliage on stout branches with upcurved ends and on upswept top branches.

FOLIAGE. Shoot rather stout, orange.

BUD. 2 cm long a stout-based long-pointed cone of chestnut scales on pale brown, some basal scales with free papery tips.

LEAVES. Whorled with a length of bare shoot at the base of each year's growth, dense, shining dark green, slender, snapping cleanly when bent in a loop (leaves of Corsican pine will only crack and stay in one piece when the loop is squeezed flat) 10–12–15 cm long; many fine stomatal lines on the outer side, few on the inner side. Basal sheath 1·5–2·0 cm first year, very pale brown, second year 0·5 cm

TABLE 86. NOTABLE SPECIMENS OF PINUS RESINOSA

Locality	*Date Planted*	*Dimensions*	
Borde Hill		16′ (1931)	53′ × 3′ 6″ (1968)
Borde Hill		18′ (1931)	44′ × 2′ 9″ (1957)
Borde Hill (Warren)			48′ × 3′ 0″ (1957)
Leonardslee		33′ × 2′ 4″ (1931)	49′ × 3′ 2″ (1962)
Wisley R.H.S.G.			46′ × 4′ 6″ (1969)
Bedgebury	1931		36′ × 2′ 11″ (1969)
Bedgebury	1931		43′ × 3′ 8″ (1969)
Bedgebury	1931		35′ × 2′ 10″ (1969)

long dark grey. Resin from broken shoots has a strong scent of lemon-balm.

CONE. Pale shiny orange-brown, ovoid-conic long-pointed, 4-5 cm × 2·5 cm; in whorls of three.

GROWTH. Young plants are vigorous with strong 2-foot shoots, and the few trees known are healthy and have shown moderate vigour. It is surprising that this handsome tree has not been planted more, but it is evidently not very long-lived for the four trees noted by Elwes and Henry have all gone.

RECOGNITION. The general aspect is more that of *P. ponderosa* than of a 2-needle pine, but the red bark on the upper bole and branches distinguish *P. resinosa* from a distance. *P. n. maritima* is the nearest relative, but *P. resinosa* is a genetically isolated and uniform species. It is also remarkably self-fertile. The orange shoot and fine, dense leaves which snap cleanly and readily (see under 'Foliage') distinguish this species.

Pinus rhaetica Bruegger. Central Europe.

A plant of this close relative of *P. sylvestris*, at Grayswood Hill, 5 feet tall, is like *P. sylvestris* but has grey leaves and the buds coated in white resin.

Pinus rigida Miller. Northern pitch pine

Eastern North America from New Brunswick to Georgia and west to Kentucky. Introduced in about 1743. Rare; in many collections in southern England but very few in the rest of the country or in Wales, Scotland and Ireland.

BARK. Orange-brown, coarsely fissured into parallel ridges.

CROWN. Broadly conic or ovoid, rather irregular; branches spreading widely and ascending. The bole and the larger branches bear bunches of epicormic sprouts, some short, some a few feet long and hanging down, grassy-green, or grey-green.

FOLIAGE. Shoot pale orange-brown, crinkled.

BUD. Cylindric-conic with a sharp point, dark red-brown, often with some whitish resin; some tips of scales decurved.

LEAVES. In threes, thick, serrate to the touch, 8–9 cm long

Pinus rigida

Fig. 162
Foliage and cone of *Pinus rigida*, Northern pitch pine, which has twisted leaves and large sprouts on the bole. The cones vary from ovoid to cylindric and are spiny.

TABLE 87. SPECIMENS OF PINUS RIGIDA

Locality	*Date Planted*	*Dimensions*	
Bolderwood	1861		73′ × 7′ 6″ (1970)
Blackmoor			72′ × 6′ 8″ (1968)
Blackmoor (Moat)			67′ × 6′ 8″ (1968)
Kew R.B.G.		51′ × 4′ 0½″ (1931)	56′ × 5′ 0″ (1970)
Wisley R.H.S.G.			66′ × 8′ 1″ (1970)
Batsford Park			56′ × 6′ 6″ (1963)
Shroners Hill			60′ × 4′ 5″ (1966)
Borde Hill (Warren)		22′ (1931)	64′ × 5′ 2″ (1968)
Borde Hill		20′	58′ × 3′ 11″ (1958)
Wakehurst Place	1913	20′ × 2′ 1″ (1931)	48′ × 6′ 3″ (1964)
Streatham Hall			49′ × 4′ 6″ (1967)
Castle Milk			36′ × 4′ 1″ (1966)
Bedgebury	1926	5′ 8″ (1931)	41′ × 3′ 9″ (1969)
Bedgebury	1926		40′ × 3′ 7″ (1969)

slightly twisted, dark grey-green. Basal sheath 0·5–1 cm red-brown. Strong epicormics may have greenish-white shoots and longer leaves, to 12 cm.

CONE. Varying from cylindric to barrel-shaped or ovoid, 3–4 cm long, borne in bunches, dull pale brown with a short decurved prickle; opening on the tree to irregular shapes. Males open to 3 cm, long-conic; late May.

GROWTH. A sturdy but rough young tree, this species grows quite fast for some years. Where suited it continues rapid growth but elsewhere it loses vigour and scarcely increases in size at all.

SPECIMENS. None of the six big trees recorded by Elwes and Henry now survives, but five of the seven smaller ones noted in the 1932 Report have been found.

RECOGNITION. The tree itself is easily recognised by the grassy shoots on the bole and by the clustered adhering cones. The needles are short and thick for a three-needled pine. *P. echinata* also has shoots on big branches, but the shoots are white, the leaves mainly in pairs and shorter.

Pinus sabiniana Douglas. Digger pine

California, in the Sierra Nevada and Coast Range. Introduced in 1832. Very rare; in a few collections in South England and at Glasnevin, Dublin.

BARK. Grey-pink, scaly and deeply fissured.

CROWN. Very irregular, light and open with ascending long branches thinly foliaged and slender, curving, whippy, largely bare, branchlets; quite unlike any other tree.

FOLIAGE. Shoot slender, pale green bloomed white, crowded with long, rich copper-red or orange-brown sheaths among the leaves and dark brown acuminate scales 2 cm long on the bare shoot between whorls of foliage. These large scales are still prominent and curled on four-year wood with no leaves.

BUD. Ovoid-conic to 3·5×1·5 cm, pointed yellowish and red and brown, slightly resinous.

LEAVES. In threes, straight, 17–25 cm long, dark yellowish green, or pale grey-green, the bundles remaining nearly closed.

CONE. Very large ovoid, 15–20 cm×8–10 cm but lighter and softer than that of *P. coulteri*, pale coffee-brown; scales with elongated blunt, rounded tips bent down and curled up at the ends. Basal scales bent down to the stalk, all deeply striated.

GROWTH. A short-lived tree of rapid early growth. The oldest tree recently known was one planted in 1899 at Kew, but it was a poor tree, leaning badly and has been felled. Rates of growth can be seen from Table 88.

RECOGNITION. The open crown is quite distinct with the long, fine leaves, held very level.

TABLE 88. SPECIMEN TREES OF PINUS SABINIANA

Locality	*Date Planted*	*Dimensions*	
Dropmore	1912	36′ × 2′ 0″ (1931)	72′ × 4′ 9″ (1970)
Wakehurst Place	1913	40′ × 3′ 0″ (1931)	66′ × 5′ 8″ (1971)[1]
Wakehurst Place			55′ × 2′ 6″ (1964)
Glasnevin B.G.			58′ × 5′ 4″ (1966)
Wisley R.H.S.G.			62′ × 5′ 0″ (1968)
Bedgebury	1926	4′ 4″ (1931)	32′ × 2′ 1″ (1957)
Bedgebury	1935	25′ × 1′ 4″ (1957)	42′ × 2′ 3″ (1969)

[1] Measured at 4 feet

Pinus serotina Michaux. Pond pine

South East United States, from Northern Carolina to Florida. Introduced in 1713. Very rare indeed. Possibly a form of *P. rigida*; shoot dark pink-brown, slightly ridged and shiny; bud narrowly cylindric; acute red-brown tip with vertical free scales protruding from thick white resin. Leaves in threes, 15 cm, hard, slightly twisted, shiny mid-green; basal sheath 1–1·5 cm. A few sprouts on the bole. Borde Hill (Gores Wood) 30ft×11in and 15ft (top lost)× 1ft 3in (1960); Windsor Great Park, 11 feet (1969).

Pinus × schwerinii Fitschen. *P. wallichiana × strobus*

Found as a 26-year-old tree near Berlin in 1931. This cross was made again, by controlled pollination at Alice Holt in 1955. One tree resulting is 20 feet tall, having grown more than 10 feet in the last 3 years.

BARK. Very smooth, light grey.

BUD. Cylindric-conic, purplish white with resin, sharply pointed; scales at the side with points minutely free, curved in towards the bud-tip.

SHOOTS. Somewhat greenish orange-brown, conspicuous as basal half of new shoot is bare; exceedingly minute scattered pubescence most visible near tip.

LEAVES. Slender, spreading, slightly drooping, 10–12 cm; shining light green outer surface with 2 widely spaced stomatal lines; blue-grey inner surfaces with 4–5 close lines.

CONE. (Not seen) 8–15×4–5 cm on stalk 2·5 cm, curved, tapering cylindric (Den Ouden and Boom, text and photo).

Pinus strobus Linnaeus. Weymouth pine, White pine (U.S.A.).

Newfoundland to Manitoba, south to Georgia. Introduced in 1705. Still quite frequent, despite the loss of many old trees from blister-rust (*Cronartium ribicola*). Rather ragged trees occur in broadleaved woods on many estates and in parks, and small trees are seen in town parks and in some gardens.

BARK. Young trees smooth dark grey, green with algae, stippled by horizontal lenticels. Old trees dark blackish purple or dark grey-pink, with short, deep fissures, finely roughened but not scaling or flaked.

CROWN. Young trees slenderly conic with slender upcurved branches, and leading shoot slightly sinuous; open in the upper parts. Old trees densely twigged, flattened domes with slender vertical shoots arising all over them, often on a long bole bearing stumps of broken branches.

FOLIAGE. Shoot slender, pale green-brown, faintly ribbed; a fine pubescence, often requiring a lens to be plainly visible, is restricted to the rib just below each pulvinus or a little way down the rib. Pulvini pubescent red-brown.

BUD. Ovoid-conic, pointed, orange-brown with dark red-brown appressed points on the scales.

LEAVES. In fives held closely forward along the shoot, the bundles not opening appreciably for the first year; 8–10 cm long, slender and soft, dark green outside, faintly lined white; grey-white with stomata on inner surfaces. Ends of shoots abruptly widened as terminal leaves spread, not appressed.

TABLE 89. SPECIMEN TREES OF PINUS STROBUS

Locality	*Date Planted*	*Dimensions*	
Ombersley Court		90′ × 16′ 6″ (1906)[1]	90′ × 18′ 1″ (1964)[1]
Stratfield Saye			102′ × 16′ 10″ (1968)[2]
Woburn Park		90′ × 7′ 6″ (1904)	98′ × 12′ 7″ (1970)[2]
Nuneham Court		95′ × 7′ 9″ (1908)	83′ × 10′ 0″ (1966)
Bury Hill	1850	80′ × 6′ 5″ (1931)	105′ × 9′ 10″ (1954)
Albury Park	1851	84′ × 9′ 6″ (1931)	98′ × 10′ 1″ (1954)
Westonbirt		72′ × 8′ 10″ (1931)	96′ × 10′ 2″ (1969)
Penrhyn Castle		81′ × 8′ 2″ (1931)	95′ × 9′ 11″ (1959)
Cannop			120′ × 11′ 3″ (1959)
Cannop			110′ × 10′ 11″ (1959)
Tregrehan			100′ × 6′ 8″ (1971)
Bicton			94′ × 12′ 6″ (1968)
Chatsworth House			121′ × 7′ 11″ (1971)
Puck Pits			128′ × 8′ 5″ (1969)
Puck Pits			126′ × 7′ 5″ (1969)
Cardross			92′ × 9′ 5″ (1954)
Fonthill			112′ × 11′ 0″ (1965)
Lowther Castle			80′ × 10′ 2″ (1967)
Inistioge			88′ × 9′ 9″ (1966)
Rhinefield Terrace			110′ × 9′ 8″ (1970)
Bowood	1926		60′ × 3′ 10″ (1957)
Bedgebury	1931		60′ × 4′ 3″ (1967)

[1] Measured at 2 feet

[2] Measured at 3 feet. Dying back

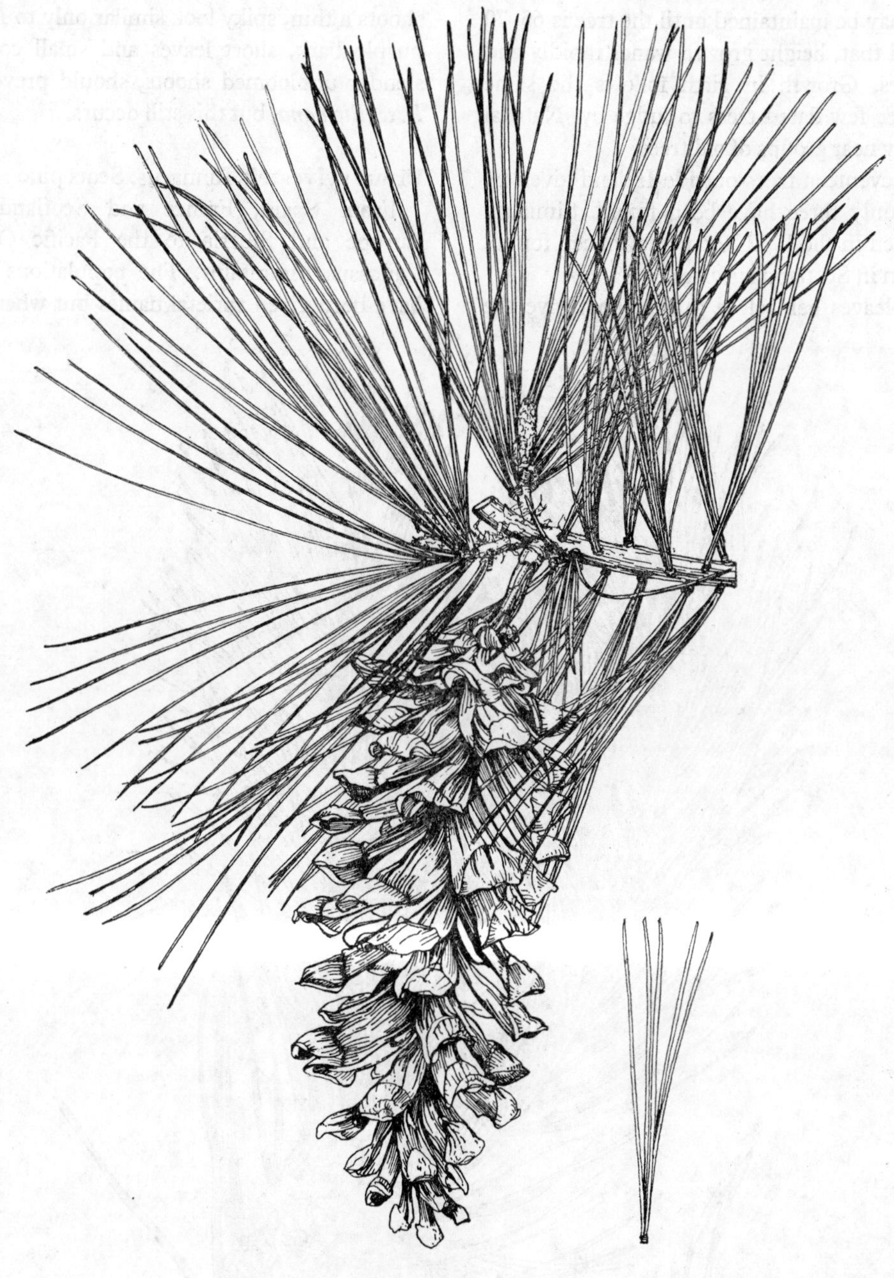

Fig. 163
Spray and mature cone of *Pinus strobus*, Weymouth pine. On new shoots, the leaves lie forward close to the shoot.

CONE. Slender, slightly curved and tapered cylindric, 12–15 ×4 cm (open) on a smooth curved stalk 1 cm long; scales very convex, tips curving outwards when open; slightly ribbed, light reddish-brown but often purplish-grey on one side, thickened to a very slight point; very resinous.

GROWTH. Early growth is rapid, with annual shoots to 3

feet long, and this may be maintained until the tree is 65–70 feet tall, but beyond that, height growth wanes rapidly and soon virtually ceases. Growth in girth follows the same pattern, but there are few dated trees to judge by. Natural seedlings occur freely near groups of old trees.

SPECIMENS. Of the seventeen trees outside Ireland given by Elwes and Henry, only three have been found. Similarly only seven of 23 given in the 1932 Report have been found, and none of the seven in Scotland survives.

RECOGNITION. The leaves held close to the shoot give the shoots a thin, spiky look similar only to *P. lambertiana*. The purple bark, short leaves and small cones, together with slender unbloomed shoots, should prevent confusion with *P. wallichiana*, but this still occurs.

Pinus sylvestris Linnaeus. Scots pine

From Spain, France and Scotland across Northern Europe and Siberia to the Pacific Ocean; also in the Caucasus Mountains. The populations in various regions have been given varietal names but when grown away from

Pinus sylvestris

Fig. 164
Shoots with 1-year old cones of *Pinus sylvestris*, Scots pine. The broad, twisted needles are blue in the native form.

their native region few of them can be distinguished. Native to parts of Argyll, Inverness-shire, Perthshire and Wester Ross (var. *scotica*). Abundant where re-introduced, and seeding itself extensively on heathlands in Devon, Dorset, Hampshire, Surrey, Berkshire, Kent, Suffolk and Staffordshire especially. Extensive plantations have been made in Norfolk, Suffolk, Northumberland and Morayshire particularly. The best native woods left are the Black Wood, Loch Rannoch and around Loch Morlich and Loch Maree.

BARK. Young trees green-grey, soon a smooth but scaling pink-orange. Old trees with branches scaling pink-orange or dark red, but boles variable in colour. When deeply fluted and fissured, the bark is usually black or dark brown. Smooth trees even when 200 years old are equally frequent and have "alligator-skin" bark, finely cracked into variously shaped flat scales, dark pink or cinnamon. Intermediate forms are shallowly fissured into dark red, scaling long vertical plates.

CROWN. Conic and open when young. Old trees scattered in native or wild-sown open woodland have low, broadly domed crowns and low, heavy branches. Old trees in tended plantations or in gardens and woods frequently have long, clean boles, usually slender, and flat, shallow, domed crowns. Branches usually level in old trees, particularly in the natural areas ("var. *horizontalis*") but semi-fastigiate forms occur. In old trees the twigs become very slender, short and crowded, making a dense crown.

FOLIAGE. Shoot, slender on old trees, stout on young, vigorous trees; pale green-brown: the most vigorous shoots pinkish and faintly grooved; second year dull pink-brown.

BUD. Cylindric ovoid, short-pointed bright red-brown and rather resinous; bright shining dark red, bulbous at base with male flowers in old trees; a few tips free of resin on strong buds.

LEAVES. In pairs, stiff, twisted, 5 cm or less on old trees, 7 cm or more on strong young trees; abruptly short-spined, bluish grey-green or yellowish grey-green, strongly marked on both sides by white lines of stomata. Basal sheaths orange-brown at base, dark grey outer end; blackish brown by second year.

FLOWERS AND CONE. Male flowers on weak, hanging shoots, and thus not borne by vigorous young trees; globular, sometimes scattered rather up the shoot, pale yellow, shedding pollen in mid-May. Female flowers on the tips of expanding strong shoots, opening dark red in mid-May, in whorls of 2–5, bending down and turning brown when pollinated; soon green, and remaining small all that year. They expand next spring into shining dark green ovoid-conic cones, 4–5 cm long. Late that year they ripen to pale brown or red-brown, with diamond-shaped scales, each with a vertical and a transverse ridge crossing at a raised centre without a spine.

GROWTH. Early growth is vigorous on almost all soils, with shoots commonly 2–3 feet long, sometimes 3 feet 6 inches. Growth in height remains fairly rapid until the tree is 50–60 feet tall but soon becomes very slow. Growth in girth is seldom rapid and soon becomes very slow. The old tree at Curraghmore has added four inches to its girth in 37 years, and another nearby of the same age, is only 78 inches round after 198 years. Some of the youngest trees have exceeded one inch average for each year of life. Further details can be seen in Table 90. Shoot growth starts in early May and finishes in early July.

SPECIMENS. A tree dating from about 1620 was blown down at Inveraray in 1951 when more than 128 feet tall and 16 feet 1 inch in girth. None is now known to be so old (nor so big). The 'Raven fir' at Spye Park may be about as old; it forks into two stems from ground level which separate at a height of 12 feet. Several trees around Bramshill Park are said to date from 1660 but gravel-workings there have destroyed them. Two of the same age are in the churchyard at Eversley nearby. Of the groups planted in 1746 at Hurn Court, given

TABLE 90. SPECIMEN TREES OF PINUS SYLVESTRIS

Locality	*Date Planted*	*Dimensions*	
Hurn Court	1746		75′ × 9′ 4″ (1968)
Hurn Court	prob.1746		70′ × 11′ 7″ (1968)
Novar	1750	105′ × 10′ 3″ (1904)	115′ × 10′ 10″ (1953)
Kilkerran	1757	86′ × 12′ 5″ (1931)	102′ × 13′ 2″ (1970)
Curraghmore	1770	110′ × 7′ 0″ (1907)	120′ × 9′ 9″ (1968)
Curraghmore	1770		108′ × 6′ 6″ (1968)
Castle Grant	1770		80′ × 10′ 11″ (1961)
Shambellie Wood	1780		105′ × 6′ 11″ (1954)
Hartrigge	1800		93′ × 11′ 10″ (1954)
Keir House	1827	80′ × 10′ 6″ (1931)	93′ × 11′ 9″ (1970)
Holywell Hall			90′ × 15′ 8″ (1952)[1]
Munches			82′ × 13′ 1″ (1970)
Longleat			75′ × 17′ 6″ (1959)[2]
Forde Abbey			60′ × 13′ 10″ (1960)
Hartrow Manor			× 16′ 8″ (1965)

[1] Measured at 3 feet
[2] Measured at 1 foot

(continues)

Table 90 (*continued*) *Specimen Trees of Pinus sylvestris*

Locality	*Date Planted*		*Dimensions*
Compton Chamberlayne			85′ × 14′ 4″ (1960)
Dubs House			104′ × 13′ 0″ (1961)
Dupplin Castle			92′ × 13′ 5″ (1970)
Tittenhurst Park			70′ × 12′ 5″ (1963)
Snowdenham House			80′ × 12′ 3″ (1964)
Bicton			84′ × 12′ 3″ (1968)
Studley Royal			100′ × 11′ 6″ (1966)
Tetton House			82′ × 11′ 4″ (1959)
Muckross Abbey			50′ × 11′ 11″ (1968)
Creech Grange			75′ × 11′ 7″ (1968)
Castle Forbes			85′ × 11′ 0″ (1968)
Adare Manor			75′ × 10′ 10″ (1968)
Strone			90′ × 10′ 10″ (1969)
Stonefield			80′ × 12′ 2″ (1969)
Knole Park			80′ × 11′ 5″ (1969)
Ravensbury Park			70′ × 10′ 6″ (1969)
Oakley Park			118′ × 8′ 0″ (1971)
Oakley Park			113′ × 10′ 5″ (1971)
Oakley Park			88′ × 12′ 9″ (1971)
Westonbirt	1829	90′ × 8′ 10″ (1931)	79′ × 10′ 1″ (1967)
Bowood		114′ × 9′ 10″ (1931)	112′ × 10′ 2″ (1957)
Albury Park	1850	89′ × 10′ 2″ (1931)	75′ × 10′ 8″ (1961)
Hewell Grange		108′ × 9′ 6″ (1909)	98′ × 10′ 5″ (1963)
Hewell Grange			105′ × 10′ 4″ (1963)
Raehills			107′ × 10′ 10″ (1954)
Chatsworth			95′ × 9′ 11″ (1971)
Wakehurst Place			85′ × 10′ 4″ (1965)
Smeaton House			62′ × 10′ 5″ (1966)
Kidbrooke Park			105′ × 7′ 7″ (1968)
Eridge Park	1877		66′ × 7′ 6″ (1971)
Eridge Park	1896		85′ × 7′ 1″ (1971)
Eridge Park	1901		56′ × 5′ 5″ (1971)
Speech House	1921		64′ × 4′ 2″ (1963)

in the 1932 Report ("Heron Court") only one probable tree remains but another larger tree not far away is probably of the same date.

Recognition. The scaling orange-red bark in the upper crown is seen in only two other two-needle pines—*P. densiflora* and *P. resinosa*. The glaucous blue-grey short leaves of Scots pine distinguish it from these, also the leaves are much more sparse, more spreading, much thicker and stiffer than in either of these two species.

General. The ease of establishment, availability, and tolerance of many soils, even for many years thin soils over chalk, led to the Scots pine becoming the major coniferous forest tree for a long time. With more species available, and the present emphasis on high volume-production, the tree is little used now except in areas to which it is particularly suited and other species are less so. Thus it remains important on light soils and in exposed areas in the hills of Northumberland, Central Scotland, Moray and Nairnshire particularly. On the southern heaths it is being replaced by the Corsican pine whose production of volume is very much greater.

cv. Aurea. (pre-1876, Germany?). A slow-growing tree of less formal shape when small, in which the leaves are a sickly yellowish grey-green in summer and autumn. In late winter they turn a good golden colour and fade again before growth starts in mid-May.

Table 91. Notable examples of Pinus sylvestris aurea

Locality		*Dimensions*
Smeaton House	8′ (1931 as "globosa")	43′ × 3′ 2″ (1966)
Westonbirt House	12′ × 1′ 2″ (1931)	15′ × 2′ 1″ (1967)
Westonbirt Arboretum		39′ × 2′ 5″ (1970)
Hergest Croft		25′ × 3′ 5″ (1963)
Stonehurst		32′ × 2′ 10″ (1964)
Castlewellan		47′ × 5′ 4″ (1970)

cv. Fastigiata. A form which occurs occasionally in wild populations on the Continent. It is a very neat and attractive tree, regrettably extremely rare. The branches are erect long and slender, making a slender column.

Madresfield Court, 40ft × 2ft 10in (1964); Wisley Royal Horticultural Society Gardens, 21ft × 1ft 0in (1968).

Pinus tabuliformis Carriere. Chinese pine.

China and Korea. Introduced in 1862. Rare; in only a few large collections in each country.

BARK. Grey-pink or grey-orange, early and coarsely fissured vertically.

CROWN. Dense and domed with long level branches, the shoots standing out above them at right angles, in "plates" especially on older trees. (Hence, presumably *tabuliformis.*)

FOLIAGE. Shoot smooth pink-brown, bloomed white in places, becoming yellow-brown.

BUD. Broad bulbous base with narrowly conic sharp point, dark red brown with some white free scale-tips.

LEAVES. Usually in pairs but may be in threes, thick, shiny grey-green, 10–15 cm long, the pairs remain close but are widely spread perpendicular to the shoot.

CONES. Broadly ovoid-conic 5–6 × 3·5 cm, dark shiny green, turning through pale grey-brown to dark brown, with orange-brown centres to the scales and a minute prickle.

GROWTH. Young trees seem to be very vigorous but over a period it is a slow-growing tree.

TABLE 92. SPECIMENS OF PINUS TABULIFORMIS

Locality	*Date Planted*	*Dimensions*	
Borde Hill (Gores Wood)		24′ × 1′ 3″ (1931)	44′ × 2′ 10″ (1960)
Borde Hill (Gores Wood) W8815			44′ × 2′ 0″ (1970)
Borde Hill (Tolls)			48′ × 2′ 9″ (1958)
Bells Wood, Bayford		20′ × 2′ 0″ (1931)	45′ × 3′ 5″ (1962)
Edinburgh R.B.G.			28′ × 2′ 2″ (1970)
Edinburgh R.B.G. (W 1639)			36′ × 2′ 1″ (1967)
Bedgebury	1928		30′ × 2′ 2″ (1969)[1]
Birr Castle	1944		33′ × 2′ 2″ (1966)

[1] Measured at 2 feet

RECOGNITION. Distinguished from *P. densiflora* by the bark, the light brown shoot and longer, more spreading needles.

var. yunnanensis (Franchet) Shaw. Szechuan and Yunnan. 1909. Differs from the type in stout, shining pink shoots; buds with white-fringed basal scales but dark acute-tipped upper scales; reddish scaly bark and long leaves, 15–20 cm or more, drooping. A strong-growing, sturdy young tree with stout shoots and branches. Original trees are at Kew, and probably at Borde Hill.

TABLE 93. NOTABLE TREES OF PINUS TABULIFORMIS YUNNANENSIS

Locality	*Date Planted*	*Dimensions*
Kew R.B.G.	1910	36′ × 3′ 6″ (1969)
Kew R.B.G.	1910	36′ × 4′ 2″ (1969)
Kew R.B.G.	1945	25′ × 2′ 0″ (1969)
Borde Hill (Tolls)		50′ × 4′ 0″ (1957)
Borde Hill (Warren)		37′ × 1′ 4″ (1968)
Borde Hill (Gores Wood)		44′ × 2′ 6″ (1968)
Powerscourt		51′ × 3′ 5″ (1966)
Bedgebury		18′ × 1′ 6″ (1969)

Pinus taeda Linnaeus. Loblolly pine.

South East United States, from New Jersey to Texas. Introduced in 1713. Very rare and confined to a few collections and one old park, in South England.

BARK. Grey, pinkish, brownish or slightly purplish, with fine, deep vertical cracks, and scaly ridges at the base.

CROWN. Rather irregularly conic, becoming domed, with a mass of fine, shining brown branchlets.

FOLIAGE. Shoot olive-brown, slender, glossy; second year orange-brown, bare of leaves but roughened by recurved scales; third year orange.

BUD. Cylindric-conic light red-brown; scales chestnut red with free, straight tips.

LEAVES. In threes, very slender and flexible, 15–17 cm long ending in a minute curved point; light grey-green, somewhat sparse; basal sheaths red-brown at base, pinkish grey outer part, 1 cm long. Resin from broken shoots smells strongly of turpentine.

CONE. Long-ovoid, 8–12 cm long, light brown with stoutly based, curved spines.

GROWTH. In the two, rather young trees of known date, growth has been rapid in girth and moderate in height. It seems a hardy species and it is a pity that it has not been more planted.

RECOGNITION. The tree most resembles *P. radiata*, but differs in the much less dense leaves which are grey-green and in the smoother bark and prickly cone, also the glossy yellowish green-brown shoot.

TABLE 94. SPECIMENS OF PINUS TAEDA

Locality	*Date Planted*	*Dimensions*	
Blackmoor	1912	30′ × 2′ 6″ (1931)	60′ × 6′ 7″ (1968)
Wakehurst Place	1915	17′ × 1′ 7″ (1931)	58′ × 5′ 1″ (1970)
Wakehurst Place			33′ × 4′ 2″ (1964)
Bicton			55′ × 5′ 3″ (1968)
Bicton			55′ × 4′ 0″ (1968)
Headley Park			50′ × 6′ 5″ (1961)
Chiltlee Place			50′ × 6′ 0″ (1961)
Borde Hill		15′ (1931)	45′ × 3′ 0″ (1961)
Leonardslee		27′ × 2′ 3″ (1931)	60′ × 5′ 5″ (1962)
Bedgebury	1925	8′ 3″ (1931)	40′ × 4′ 7″ (1969)
Bedgebury	1925		30′ × 4′ 5″ (1969)

Pinus taiwanensis Hayata.

Formosa. Introduced in about 1930. Very rare. A tree closely allied to *P. densiflora* of Japan. Bark with purplish square scales; shoot green-brown; bud scales with long free tips. Leaves in pairs, 12 cm remaining close, each pair spreading widely from shoot. Cone, globose, 8 cm. Garinish Island (County Cork), 38ft×3ft 0in (1966); Borde Hill, 35ft×1ft 5in; 30ft×1ft 4in (1970).

Pinus teocote Schlechtendal and Chamisso.

Mexico. Introduced before 1826 and in 1839. Formerly several trees in South England and one in Ireland, but only one known in recent years, at Borde Hill (28ft×2ft 1in, 1958). The leaves are usually in threes but may be in pairs, fours or fives; they are spreading and rigid, 10–18 cm long. The cone is only 6 cm long, ovoid-oblong (Dallimore and Jackson).

Pinus thunbergii Parlatore. Japanese black pine

East Japan. Introduced in 1861. Uncommon, but found in many collections and large gardens throughout these countries as far north as South Scotland.

BARK. Dark purplish grey or pink-grey with coarse vertical fissures, deep, rather narrow and interlocking.

CROWN. Most distinctive in old trees, with leaning top and a few, long, level then upcurved slender branches projecting far from the main crown, with close, black, whorled, foliage on them but few side shoots. Young trees conic, upright.

FOLIAGE. Shoot golden-brown, the bare portions between whorls of leaves rough with long scales.

BUD. Cylindric, tapering to a fine point, silky white from broad fringes of white hairs on the scales.

LEAVES. In pairs, not much parted on main shoots, giving a spiky appearance; thick, sharply pointed, slightly twisted, 10 cm long, grey-green (black in the mass) with many fine stomatal lines on the outside, few on the inside. Basal sheaths with long white filaments.

CONE. Borne early in the life of the tree, and often crowded on the main stem below the leaves, sometimes a hundred or so clustered along 6 inches of stem; flat-based-conic, to

6 cm long, reddish brown becoming dark grey, each scale with a transverse ridge and a minute spine.

GROWTH. Young plants are sturdy, handsome and vigorous, with leading shoots of 18 inches or more, but growth becomes slow fairly soon, so that none of even the youngest trees in Table 95 has averaged one foot in a year. Growth in girth is moderately vigorous and fairly well sustained. The larger trees are either leaning or look as if they would easily blow down, and this seems to be the case. None of the five trees given by Elwes and Henry survives today.

RECOGNITION. Young plants are at once known by their golden-brown shoots, light grey-green leaves and silky white buds. They resemble young Corsican pines, but the straight, hard, short, appressed leaves differ as well as minor differences in shoot colour and very different bud. Old trees are unlike any other, with their long, wandering branches and whorled black foliage. Shoots in the hand are identified by the shoot colour and the bud, being otherwise similar to *P. leucodermis*.

Fig. 165
Foliage and cone of *Pinus thunbergii*, Japanese black pine. Some of the fascicles of this specimen contained three needles. The bud has long, fringed, silky-white scales. Cones are frequently borne in clusters of fifty to a hundred or more on the shoots.

TABLE 95. SPECIMEN TREES OF PINUS THUNBERGII

Locality	*Date Planted*	*Dimensions*	
Westonbirt	ca.1876	49′ × 4′ 6″ (1931)	61′ × 5′ 3″ (1971)
Lytchett Heath	1887		65′ × 7′ 4″ (1966)
Lytchett Heath	1887		55′ × 5′ 7″ (1966)
Borde Hill	1890	40′ × 3′ 7″ (1931)	75′ × 5′ 10″ (1968)
Borde Hill	1890	36′ × 3′ 4″ (1931)	48′ × 4′ 5″ (1967)
Bodnant	1902	36′ × 2′ 8″ (1931)	49′ × 5′ 6″ (1966)
Leonardslee	ca.1905	30′ × 2′ (1931)	58′ × 3′ 5″ (1969)
Nymans	ca.1876		62′ × 6′ 1″ (1970)
Pencarrow			79′ × 6′ 1″ (1970)
Curraghmore			65′ × 4′ 6″ (1968)
Clonmannon			48′ × 4′ 9″ (1968)
Glasnevin B.G.			52′ × 5′ 0″ (1966)
St. Clere			55′ × 4′ 9″ (1969)

(*continues*)

Table 96 (*continued*) *Specimen Trees of Pinus thunbergii*

Locality	*Date Planted*		*Dimensions*
Strete Ralegh (Pinetum)			50′ × 3′ 8″ (1964)
Garinish Island			49′ × 5′ 3″ (1966)
Tregothnan		43′ × 4′ (1909)	69′ × 6′ 8″ (1971)
Lanhydrock			72′ × 5′ 9″ (1971)
Wakehurst Place	1918	15′ × 1′ (1931)	37′ × 3′ 0″ (1964)
Fenagh House	1918	14′ (1931)	44′ × 4′ 2′ (1968)
Edinburgh R.B.G.			40′ × 2′ 9″ (1967)
Smeaton House			45′ × 3′ 11″ (1966)
Bedgebury	1925	5′ 2″ (1931)	30′ × 2′ 2″ (1954)
Bedgebury	1926		26′ × 2′ 7″ (1965)
Bedgebury	1930		40′ × 3′ 5″ (1965)

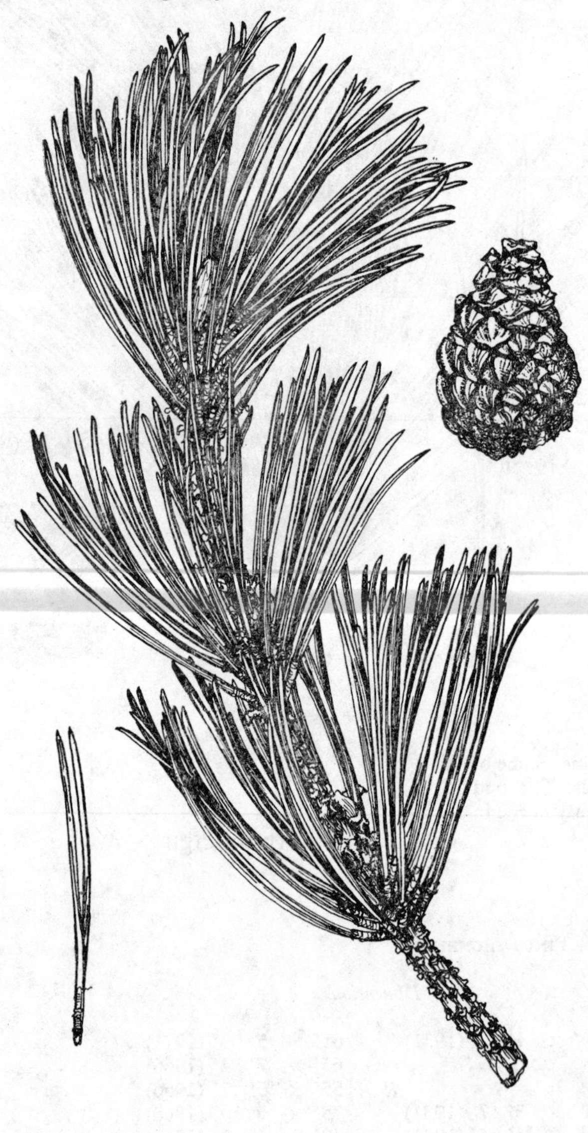

Fig. 166
Foliage and cone of *Pinus uncinata*, the tree form of *P. mugo*, Mountain pine. The hard, dark leaves are in annual whorls separated by lengths bearing abundant male flowers (here long shed). The cone has elongated and down-swept scales on its outer lower parts.

Pinus uncinata Miller. Mountain pine (*P. montana uncinata* Heere; *P. m. rostrata* Hoopes.).

Pyrenees Mountains. Introduction uncertain. Uncommon and confined to a few collections, but more seen in forest-plots or shelterbelts around plots.

BARK. Grey-pink cracked into small squares; usually soon nearly black with square scales lifting away.

CROWN. Sturdy and conic, rather rounded at the top. Resembling an inland form of *P. contorta* superficially, but the short, stiff leaves look black, with grey younger leaves on the outside.

FOLIAGE. Shoot orange-brown, with short bare patches between annual whorls of leaves showing as bare rings for many years, as the leaves remain on a long time.

BUD. 5-8 mm, cylindric, short-pointed, scales appressed, dark red-brown, very resinous.

LEAVES. In pairs, stiff, 6 cm long, dark grey-green; inner surface grooved. Basal sheaths persistent, broad and recurved, dark brown.

FLOWERS AND CONE. Male flowers on every small shoot in squat whorls, shedding pollen in mid-June. Female flowers purple, opening in mid-June. Cone misshapen ovoid, very oblique as basal outer scales have projecting centres bent downwards; 3–5 cm.

GROWTH. A sturdy tree of similar growth to the better inland provenances of *P. contorta* (*latifolia*).

RECOGNITION. Distinguished from the form of *P. contorta* which it resembles, by the bark; the many years of retained foliage divided into whorls by narrow gaps; by the new grey leaves, very dark old leaves, and by the distorted scales on the cones.

TABLE 96. SPECIMENS OF PINUS UNCINATA

Locality	Date Planted	Dimensions	
Cambridge B.G.		41′ × 3′ 5″ (1907)	50′ × 4′ 7″ (1969)
Woburn (Evergreens)			44′ × 5′ 4″ (1970)
Wakehurst Place			50′ × 2′ 4″ (1966)
Castle Milk			35′ × 2′ 11″ (1966)
Powerscourt			43′ × 3′ 5″ (1966)
Bedgebury			43′ × 2′ 8″ (1970)
Findon, Black Isle Forest, Easter Ross	1934		44′ × 2′ 0″ (1964)

Pinus virginiana Miller. Scrub pine

Eastern U.S.A. from New York State to Mississippi and Alabama. Introduced in 1739. Very rare in cultivation in Britain.

BARK. Pink-grey-brown, scaly; young trees very much as Scots pine of similar size.

CROWN. Broad and low, usually leaning, with widely spreading slender branches, bearing old cones.

FOLIAGE. Shoot usually of two or three nodes, and thus with one or two whorls of a few slender, curved shoots spaced along it; pinkish brown, bloomed grey; second year pinkish purple striped with yellow-green. Third year dull purple.

BUD. Slender, cylindric, short-pointed, 1 cm, with some whitish resin.

LEAVES. In pairs, shiny dark mid-green or yellow-green, slightly greyer inner surface, from more prominent lines of stomata; 3–4 cm long, twisted, rather broad. Basal sheath chestnut, 3 mm; second year, dark brown.

CONE. Both narrow cylindric, tapering from near the base, to ovoid, on the same tree; 5–6 cm × 1·5 cm or 3 cm, green, turning shiny dark red-brown, each scale with a flat ridge with a sharp, slender bristle, which may be spreading, or curved upwards or downwards.

GROWTH. Very slow-growing except for the first few years; and rarely making much more than a bush on a stem.

RECOGNITION. The bloomed shoots, later purple, multinodal, and bearing short, broad, paired leaves are unique; but in general it resembles *P. banksiana*.

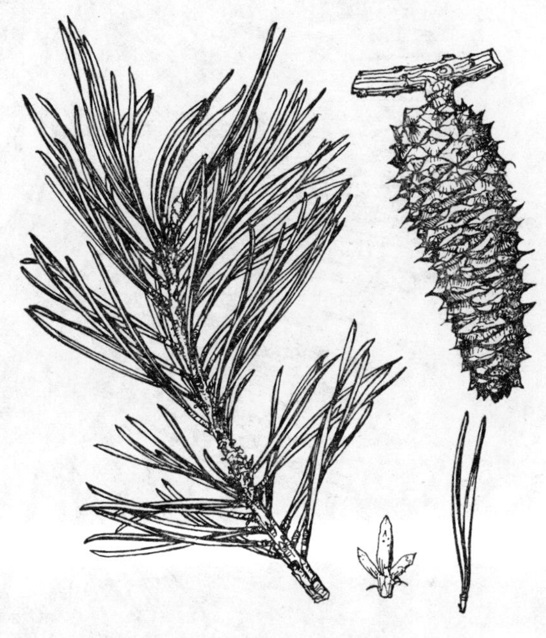

Pinus virginiana

Fig. 167
Foliage and cone of *Pinus virginiana*, a species with short, broad leaves in pairs (lower right); cylindrical resinous buds (lower middle) and spined cone (upper right) varying from cylindrical (as here) to ovoid and smaller on the same tree.

TABLE 97. EXAMPLES OF PINUS VIRGINIANA

Locality	Date Planted	Dimensions	
Borde Hill (Warren)		25′ (1931)	54′ × 3′ 6″ (1957)
Borde Hill (Pinetum)			28′ × 2′ 5″ (1961)
Dropmore			32′ × 2′ 9″ (1957)
Leonardslee			45′ × 3′ 3″ (1960)
Woburn Abbey			30′ × 1′ 8″ (1961)
Arley Castle			20′ × 1′ 1″ (1961)
Alice Holt	1953		20′ × 2′ 0″ (1969)

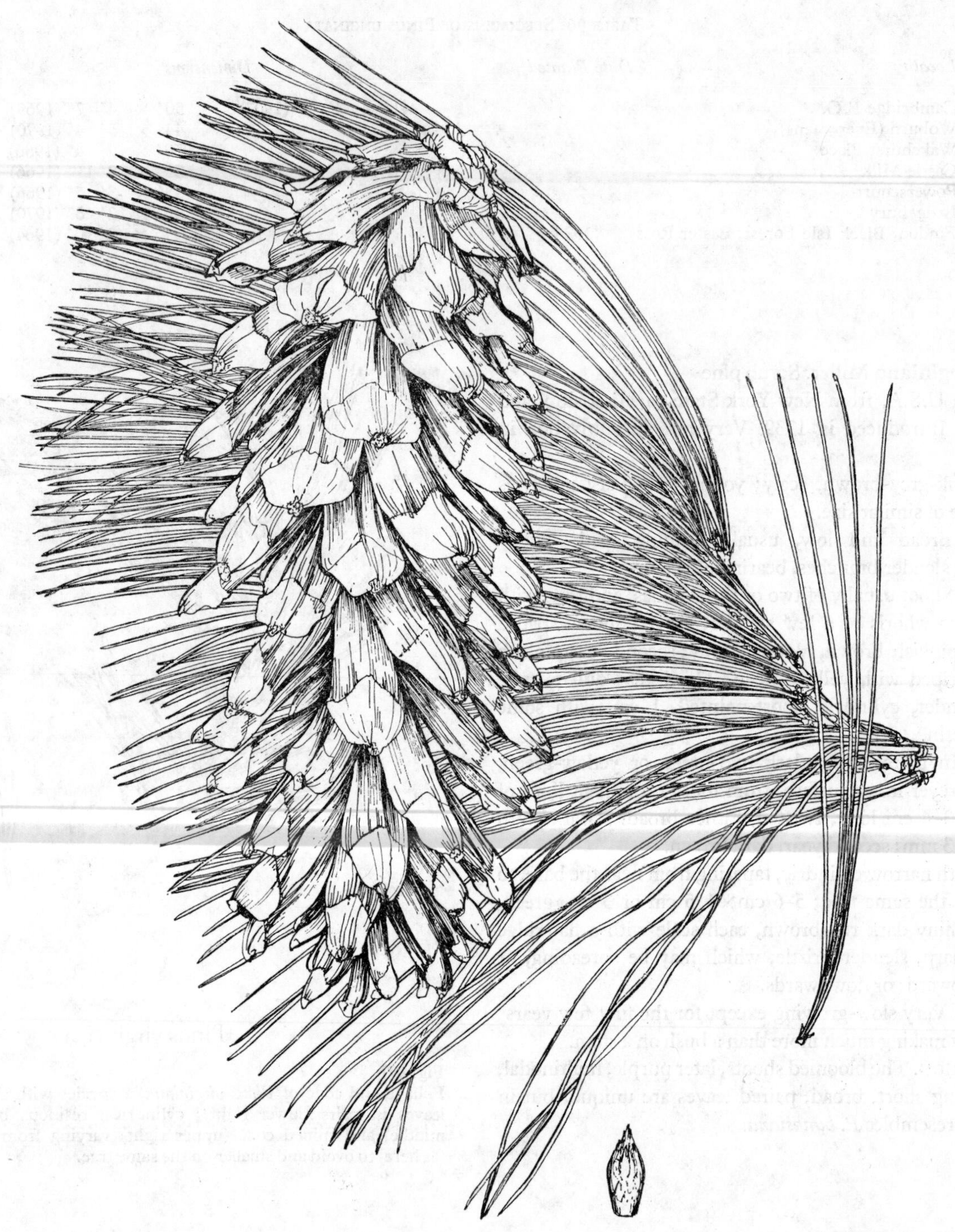

Pinus wallichiana

Fig. 168
Mature cone, young shoot and fascicle of needles, (all × $\frac{1}{3}$) of *Pinus wallichiana*, Bhutan pine. The shoot is bloomed blue-grey, but may be brown on young plants. Bud × $\frac{2}{3}$.

Pinus wallichiana Jackson. Bhutan pine (*P. excelsa* Wallich; *P. griffithii* McClelland).

The Himalaya from Afghanistan to Eastern Nepal. Introduced in 1823. Common. Widely distributed in parks and gardens, quite frequent in old town gardens and churchyards.

BARK. Young trees pewter-grey with some resin blisters. Older trees dark orange-brown or pinkish orange, either lined by very small fissures in smooth folds or shallowly and widely fissured into wide, scaly grey-pink plates.

CROWN. At all ages strongly whorled and very open. Young trees conic, old trees broad-columnar, the large low branches descending gently and curving up on the outside; upper branches curving widely upwards making a flat top. Oldest trees with heavy, high branches much shattered, and many with dead tops. Foliage in the mass is pale blue-grey. One tree (The Frythe, Welwyn) has well-layered branches, as it had in 1906, and is probably the only layered pine in the country.

FOLIAGE. Shoot stout, pale grey, bloomed lilac or finely speckled white, glabrous. Main shoots always long and strong even on the oldest trees. Second year green-grey.

BUD. Cylindric; terminal buds on horizontal shoots bent in a vertical cluster; buds of side-shoots pointed; scales orange with erect free tips.

LEAVES. In fives, lying forwards on the shoot then drooping, arched down each side in a curtain, spraying out from and below the ascending outer shoots; slender, 18–20 cm long, all five in a bundle often sharply curved or crinkled parallel to each other in the basal half; outer surface bright, light, green finely lined with a few stomatal lines; the inner surface with a broad white band. Basal sheath pale red-brown, 1·5 cm lanceolate; soon shed.

FLOWERS AND CONE. Male flowers ovoid, scattered rather thinly on the basal length of new shoots, a few more isolated up to a third of the distance to the tip; pale yellow, shedding pollen in mid-June. Female flowers near the tips of emerging shoots, long, cylindric-ovoids, dull purple in June, remaining as long-stalked club-shaped conelets during the summer. They enlarge next summer into long, drooping, banana-shaped cones, pale green, often shining with resin or silvery as it dries, and purple tinted and ripen pale yellow-brown in December. Fully ripe cones 15–30 $\times$ 3–5 cm, pale brown, the basal ring of scales short, thick and often curved sharply backwards.

GROWTH. Young trees grow very rapidly for at least 20 years, often making shoots 3 feet long and by the end of 30 years the tree can be over 60 feet tall. Growth in height diminishes rapidly after 80 feet has been reached and, due to the brittle branches and dislike of exposure at that height, few grow much beyond that point. Growth in girth is usually well in excess of one inch a year until height-growth ceases, but becomes very slow indeed in old trees. These features of growth are well shown by the figures in Table 98. Shoot-growth starts early in April, reaches a peak of at least 5 inches in a week in vigorous plants, in mid-June and stops in mid-July.

SPECIMENS. The tree on the island at Hewell Grange may possibly be from the original seed, but none other so old is known. Several of the biggest have died back more than half their height and only those of known previous history are, in that case, given in the table. Note the rapid growth of the young trees, especially those at Albury Park.

RECOGNITION. This tree is often confused with *P. strobus* but is different in every detail. From a distance the orange-brown or grey bark and stout shoots with long spreading pendulous leaves identify *P. wallichiana.* Most trees of both species bear many cones and this species has conspicuous bunches like bananas. The foliage is most like *P. ayacahuite* and *P. armandii.* The glabrous and bloomed shoots distinguish it, whilst the tree differs in both bark and cones. *P. armandii* has glabrous but not bloomed shoots and its cones are very different; its leaves are also paler, shorter and thicker, and the second-year shoot is shiny orange-brown.

TABLE 98. SOME SPECIMENS OF PINUS WALLICHIANA

Locality	*Date Planted*	*Dimensions*	
Hewell Grange	prob.1831	93′ × 8′ 4″ (1909)	90′ × 10′ 8″ (1963)
Adare Manor	1843	50′ × 7′ 2″ (1891)	90′ × 10′ 2″ (1968)[1]
Dropmore	1843	90′ × 6′ 6″ (1931)	90′ × 8′ 0″ (1970)
Dropmore	1845		81′ × 8′ 4″ (1958)
The Frythe	1846	60′ × 7′ (1906)	70′ × 8′ 2″ (1969)
Fota	1847		85′ × 13′ 8″ (1966)[2]
Albury Park (1)	1851	91′ × 8′ 3″ (1931)	75′ × 8′ 7″ (1961)
Pampisford	1851	78′ × 7′ 8″ (1931)	70′ × 8′ 4″ (1969)
Bicton			112′ × 15′ 9″ (1968)[3]
Bicton			99′ × 11′ 9″ (1968)
Abbeyleix		40′ × 4′ 6″ (1891)	100′ × 10′ 5″ (1968)
Kilmacurragh			72′ × 11′ 0″ (1966)
Powerscourt			95′ × 10′ 9″ (1966)
Frogmore			90′ × 10′ 10″ (1967)
Highnam		63′ × 8′ 5″ (1906)	74′ × 10′ 5″ (1970)
Wilton House		77′ × 8′ 3″ (1906)	97′ × 10′ 6″ (1971)[1]
Monk Hopton			100′ × 10′ 0″ (1971)
Borde Hill		71′ × 9′ 5″ (1931)	75′ × 10′ 8″ (1968)
Pitt House		71′ × 10′ 3″ (1931)	85′ × 11′ 8″ (1960)
Ochtertyre (Crieff)	1885		85′ × 7′ 3″ (1970)
Redleaf House			105′ × 8′ 10″ (1963)[4]
Smeaton House			91′ × 9′ 4″ (1966)
Sidbury Manor		40′ × 3′ 9″ (1925)	60′ × 8′ 4″ (1959)
Kew R.B.G.		61′ × 5′ 3″ (1931)	66′ × 9′ 6″ (1963)
Fenagh House	1911		50′ × 5′ 7″ (1968)
Fenagh House	1911		50′ × 5′ 6″ (1968)
Albury Park (2)	1921	72′ × 4′ 2″ (1954)	93′ × 5′ 7″ (1968)
Albury Park	1921	60′ × 3′ 9″ (1954)	79′ × 5′ 4″ (1968)
Speech House	1921		57′ × 5′ 5″ (1968)
Powis Castle	1925		54′ × 4′ 5″ (1961)
Dropmore (2)	1929		62′ × 7′ 2″ (1970)
Bells Wood	1928		54′ × 6′ 0″ (1962)

[1] Dying back
[2] Measured at 3 feet
[3] Measured at 5 feet 6 inches
[4] Main stem

Podocarpus L'Heritier ex Persoon (Podocarpaceae)

The largest genus of conifers and taxads, with 115 species. They are mostly found in the Tropics with a big concentration of species on the islands of the South West Pacific, and fewer in Africa and Central and South America. Their foliage is very variable but the leaves are usually strap-shaped, and leathery or hard, broad and spiny. They are mostly dioecious. The seed is borne in a swollen, fleshy, often edible and brightly coloured receptacle, but fruiting in this country occurs only in 2 species. Several species are low shrubs (e.g. *P. alpinus*, *P. nivalis*) not included here. One species (*P. andinus*) is fairly widely planted but the remainder are almost entirely plants of the mildest southern and western areas.

Podocarpus acutifolius Kirk. Sharp-leaved yellow wood New Zealand.

A plant at Castlewellan 20ft × 2ft 0in (1970). Shoot, dull olive-green, slightly ridged; grey-buff by 4th year. Leaves perpendicular, some recurved; narrow base, parallel sides to acuminate, spined tip; hard, spiny, but flexible; 1·5–2·0 × 0·2 cm, bronzed dull grey-green, becoming grey-green by second year; 2 indistinct grey bands beneath. Bedgebury 5ft.

Podocarpus andinus Poeppigg ex-Endlicher. Plum-fruited yew. (*Prumnopitys elegans* Philippi).

The Andes Mountains of Southern Chile. Introduced in 1860. Uncommon, but seen in collections and large gardens in England, Wales and Ireland, rare in North and East England; not noted in Scotland recently. Seen rarely as a hedge.

BARK. Smooth and black with a few horizontal wrinkles, becoming dark copper-grey at the base and then on the bole and branches.

CROWN. An ovoid, pointed upswept bush, often on many stems; rarely a rather slender conic tree. Upper shoots project, arching out nearly level, with long unbranched sections between whorls of small bunched shoots.

FOLIAGE. Shoots slender and green for two years.

BUD. Minute ovoid, green, with a few free scale-tips.

LEAVES. Vary with age and position. Main shoots and young plants: falcate, upswept, 2–3 cm × 0·2 cm, soft; older trees and side-shoots: more or less pectinate, lying 45° forward; 1–2 cm × 0·2 cm; upper side shiny, dark, slightly bluish-green; underside with two broad pale grey-blue bands; the leaf ending with a short, acute tip.

FLOWERS AND FRUIT. Seldom seen. Male flowers cylindrical, blunt, in terminal and axillary clusters (Dallimore and Jackson). Female flowers on a scaly stalk springing from the upper leaf-axes. Fruit yellowish white, plum-shaped (Dallimore and Jackson).

GROWTH. Very slow-growing, slightly less so in West Ireland and in Cornwall.

TABLE 99. SPECIMENS OF PODOCARPUS ANDINUS

Locality	*Date Planted*	*Dimensions*	
Tortworth Court	1866	24′ 7″ (1931)	35′ (1964)
Trebah			49′ × 8′ 7″ (1959)[1]
Scorrier House	1878	29′ (1928)	45′ × 3′ 4″ (1959)[1]
Woodhouse		45′ (1931)	54′ × 3′ 9″ (1957)[2]
Tregrehan		30′ × 3′ 6″ (1931)	57′ × 4′ 7″ (1957)[3]
Tregrehan		25′ × 2′ 9″ (1931)	62′ × 4′ 1″ (1957)
Westonbirt		23′ × 2′ 7″ (1931)	50′ × 3′ 1″ (1967)[1]
Bicton			71′ × 4′ 4″ (1968)
Bicton			44′ × 2′ 7″ (1968)
Wakehurst Place			44′ × 2′ 4″ (1957)[1]
Ashbourne House			49′ × 3′ 8″ (1966)[1]
Bodnant			35′ × 2′ 6″ (1959)[1]
Lamellan			40′ × 2′ 5″ (1963)[1]
Kew R.B.G.			36′ × 3′ 10″ (1965)
Thursley Church			35′ × 5′ 7″ (1967)[4]
Kilmacurragh			40′ × 3′ 4″ (1966)
Cambridge B.G.			29′ × 3′ 2″ (1969)
Mount Usher			35′ × 4′ 7″ (1966)[2]
Borde Hill		16′ (1931)	20′ × 1′ 0″ (1958)
Fota	1916		36′ × 2′ 10″ (1966)

[1] Largest stem of many
[2] Measured at 2 feet
[3] Measured at 3 feet
[4] Measured at 1 foot

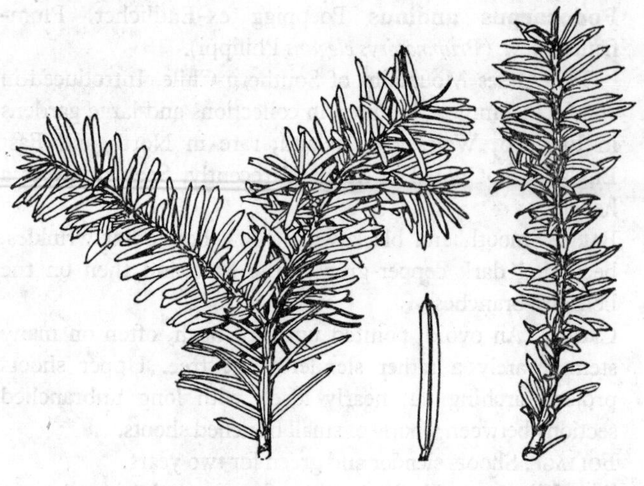

Fig. 169
Adult foliage of *Podocarpus andinus* (left) with single leaf (middle ×1⅓) from beneath, and (right) juvenile foliage.

SPECIMENS. The tree at Tortworth Court must be an original tree, and judging by the girth that at Trebah is either an original or a remarkably vigorous tree.
RECOGNITION. Faintly yew-like; the slender, projecting shoots and an overall bluish green colour, together with softer leaves, banded blue-grey beneath, distinguish *P. andinus* easily. It is more often confused with *Saxegothaea* but separable by the bark, the non-pendulous foliage, and soft, non-prickly leaves less white beneath, less curved, and brighter coloured.
NAME. There is some danger that the name will soon be returned to *Prumnopitys elegans.*

Podocarpus dacrydioides Richard. Kahikatea. New Zealand.

A 9 foot plant at Castlewellan (1966). Shoot with close, long-acuminate, 2 mm scales; side-shoots with minute, pectinate, decurrent leaves, 2 mm long, with an abrupt, curved mucro. Shoot dark grey-pink then deep purple; long and slender, forward in the spray.

Podocarpus hallii Kirk. Hall's totara. (*P. totara* var. *hallii* (Kirk) Pelger).

New Zealand. Introduction not recorded. A form of *P. totara* or a closely allied species whose distinctive features are poorly reported and reside mainly in the length of leaf and shape of seed. The small plants growing under this name have among them several differences from *P. totara* but these are not constant. At Bedgebury the shoot in the second year is a striking black-purple then pale grey-buff until in the sixth year it is mahogany purple. The leaves are $3 \times 0 \cdot 5$ cm, matt yellow-green above, slightly shiny below, tapering from half-way to a sharp spine. They are nearly pectinate and straight. At Grayswood Hill the leaves are as long as $9 \times 0 \cdot 6$ cm, slightly shiny and ridged above very pale and matt below and they spread all round the stem which is apple-green for two years and then gradually turns brown. (See *P. totara* for general description).

Tregrehan, 30ft × 2ft 8in (1971); Grayswood Hill, 5 feet 6 inches (1969); Bedgebury two plants, 4 feet (1969); Bicton, 16ft × 1ft 4in (1968).

Podocarpus macrophyllus (Thunberg) D. Don. Kusamaki.

China and Japan. Introduced in 1861. Rare and confined to collections and a few gardens, in South and South West England and in Ireland.
CROWN. An upright, narrow bush or small tree.
FOLIAGE. Shoot green for two years, then light orange-brown.
BUD. Minute, orange or purple-brown with minute leaves protruding from the tip.
LEAVES. Spiralled all round the shoot (which is vertical) 7–9 cm × 0·8–1·0 cm, tapering from near the middle to the stalk at the base and to the abruptly rounded or acute tip; dark glossy green, often yellowish above, with a raised midrib, pale yellow-green below, also with a raised midrib; leathery and pliant.
GROWTH. Annual shoots seem to range only up to about 8 inches.
RECOGNITION. The leaf is much bigger than that of any other *Podocarpus* grown here (the only "*P. latifolius*" seen is indistinguishable and is now agreed to be the same species) and the habit is also distinct.

TABLE 100. SPECIMENS OF PODOCARPUS MACROPHYLLUS

Locality	*Date Planted*	*Dimensions*		
Tregrehan		15′ × 1″	(1931)	15′ × 1′ 3½″ (1971)
Killerton				12′ × 10″ (1959)
Heligan				13′ 6″ (1959)
Scorrier House				6′ 0″ (1959)
Scorrier House	1924			5′ 6″ × 1′ 0″ (1959)
Bicton	1939			16′ (1968)
Jermyn's House				6′ 6″ (1969)
Clare Lodge				6′ (1959)
Castlewellan				3′ (1966)

Podocarpus nubigenus Lindley. Manio.

Chile and South Argentina. Introduced in 1847. Rare and confined to collections in the far south of England and in Ireland.

BARK. Purple-brown, stripping in spirals.

CROWN. Ovoid and bushy, bright green.

FOLIAGE. Shoot brownish green above, bright yellow-green beneath.

BUD. 1 mm conic, dark purple-brown with long scales pressed together at the tip, their minute free points extending the other side.

LEAVES. Below the shoot spreading and pointing strongly forwards, those above spreading perpendicular to the shoot, vertical along the mid-line, 2–4 cm long, usually 3 cm; 0·3–0·5 cm broad, broadest in the middle, slightly curved, stiff, acute to a fine spine; bright dark green or yellowish green above with a sunken midrib, and two broad white bands beneath, separated by a midrib which is narrowed in the outer half.

GROWTH. In Cornwall and Ireland, a vigorous tree with quite a rapid growth in girth but slow in height. Elsewhere a slow bush. The roots bear nodules.

RECOGNITION. The bright green foliage distinguishes this tree at a distance from *P. totara* which is the only one with which it is likely to be confused.

TABLE 101. EXAMPLES OF PODOCARPUS NUBIGENUS

Locality	*Date Planted*	*Dimensions*		
Scorrier House	1878	45′ × 5′ 3″	(1928)	49′ × 9′ 4″ (1965)[1]
Kilmacurragh				38′ × 7′ 5″ (1966)
Kilmacurragh				47′ × 7′ 2″ (1966)
Pencarrow	1908			36′ × 3′ 7″ (1970)
Headfort	1930			22′ × 2′ 0″ (1966)
Mount Usher				17′ × 1′ 4″ (1966)
Borde Hill		5′	(1931)	17′ × 1′ 0″ (1970)
Werrington Park				16′ × 1′ 9″ (1969)
Bedgebury				3′ (1969)

[1] Measured at 2 feet

Podocarpus salignus D. Don. Willowleaf podocarpus. (*P. chilinus* Richard).

Chile. Introduced in 1849 or 1853. Fairly frequent in collections and large gardens as far north as Argyll but rare in East England.

BARK. Red-brown, stripping coarsely and vertically, the strips purplish and sometimes ashen-grey.

CROWN. Usually a many-stemmed bushy tree or with a single sinuous bole and irregularly conic, fairly narrow crown, but a few have good straight boles. Branches slender.

FOLIAGE. Shoot slender, green for two years, then dull brown.

BUD. A minute thickening of the stem; few green scales with slender dark brown filaments from base.

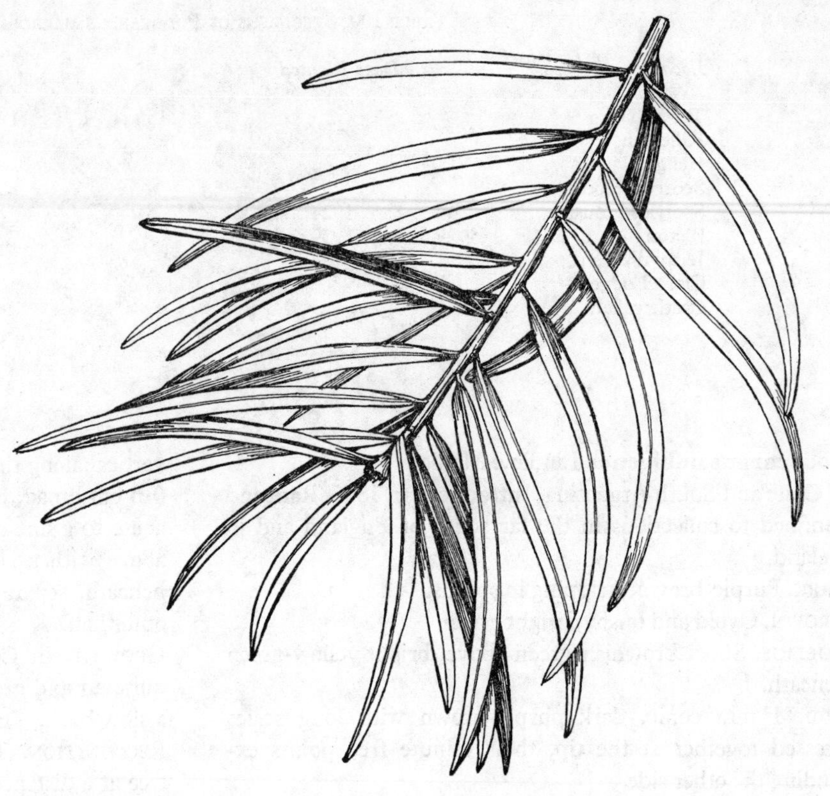

Fig. 170
Spray of *Podocarpus salignus*, a Chilean species with leaves 8–11 cm long, matt yellow-green beneath and glossy deep green above. It is usually a many-stemmed plant.

Podocarpus salignus

TABLE 102. LARGE TREES OF PODOCARPUS SALIGNUS

Locality	*Date Planted*	*Dimensions*		
Ardnagashel				64′ × 9′ 1″ (1966)
Kilmacurragh				40′ × 7′ 8″ (1966)[1]
Tregrehan		28′	(1931)	59′ × 5′ 1″ (1971)
Penjerrick		30′	(1914)	44′ × 4′ 9″ (1965)[1]
Bicton				62′ × 3′ 6″ (1968)
Bicton				47′ × 4′ 8″ (1968)
Powerscourt				46′ × 7′ 1″ (1966)[2]
Fota				45′ × 6′ 2″ (1966)[3]
Beauport Park		25′	(1931)	40′ × 3′ 0″ (1965)[1]
Blackmoor	1897	16′ × 1′ 3″	(1931)	30′ × 2′ 3″ (1968)
Glendurgan		20′	(1928)	44′ × 2′ 9″ (1959)
Stonefield		26′ × 2′ 1″	(1931)	41′ × 3′ 6″ (1969)
Abbotsbury				40′ × 3′ 5″ (1957)
Scorrier House				40′ × 3′ 10″ (1965)
Pencarrow	1906			46′ × 3′ 10″ (1970)
Mount Usher				34′ × 4′ 1″ (1966)
Ashford Castle				42′ × 3′ 5″ (1968)[1]
Annesgrove				42′ × 3′ 2″ (1968)[3]
Benenden				36′ × 2′ 10″ (1970)
Inistioge				47′ × 2′ 9″ (1966)
Borde Hill				34′ × 1′ 10″ (1958)

[1] Largest stem
[2] Measured at 2 feet
[3] Measured at 1 foot

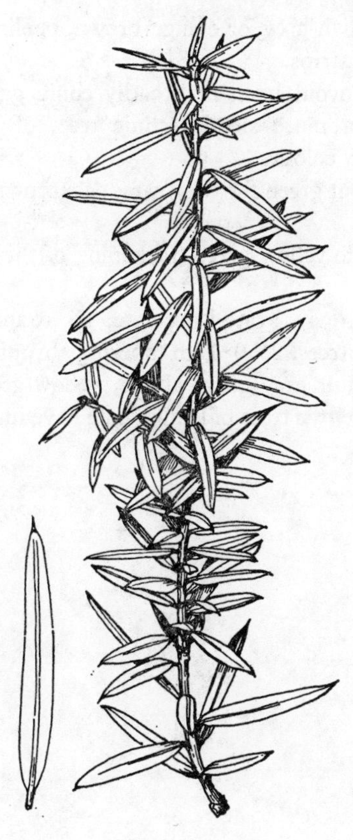

Podocarpus totara

Fig. 171
Shoot and ($\times 1\frac{1}{3}$) single leaf of *Podocarpus totara.* The hard, spined leaves are grey-green above with broad yellow-green bands beneath.

LEAVES. Long, strap-shaped, 8–11 cm, from short stalk, curved to acute or blunt apex, shiny deep green above; pale beneath with raised midrib, yellow.
GROWTH. Only two trees of known date have been found, but many have been measured at intervals of from a few years to 40 years and growth is usually slow. A few individuals in Cornwall have shown moderate growth, and in Ireland it is evident that growth is normally fairly rapid. Seedlings are found near several of the older specimens.
SPECIMENS. The outstanding specimen is the tree at Ardnagashel, near Glengariff, in County Cork. It has a remarkable, single bole. The slender tree near the Museum at Bicton is noteworthy for a good clean bole as well as its height.
RECOGNITION. The shiny dark green, thick slender leaves are unlike any others. In crown form, colour and leaves there is a strong distant resemblance to *Sciadopitys* but from nearer the great differences in shoot and leaves are apparent.

Podocarpus spicatus R. Br. Matai. New Zealand.

A 5 foot plant at Castlewellan (1966). Slender, whip-like shoots, pink-brown and purple. Leaves remote, spirally set, forward 2 mm scales, or flat-pectinate 5–6×2 mm, out-curved broad, blunt apex, pale green above, 2 broad white bands beneath, separated by purple midrib.

Podocarpus totara D. Don ex Lambert. Totara. (*P. cunninghamii* Colenso).

New Zealand. Date of introduction unrecorded. Rare and confined to collections, but in these found in Suffolk and Argyll as well as in the west, and south. Trees of more than the stature of bushes are found only in Cornwall and Ireland.

TABLE 103. SPECIMENS OF PODOCARPUS TOTARA

Locality	*Date Planted*	*Dimensions*	
Trebah		35′ × 6′ 8″ (1928)	53′ × 8′ 5″ (1959)
Enys		35′ × 2′ 7″ (1929)	59′ × 5′ 1″ (1962)
Killiow		20′–25′ (1928)	39′ × 4′ 1″ (1959)
Tregrehan (1)		35′ × 2′ 6″ (1931)	56′ × 5′ 3″ (1971)
Lamellan			38′ × 5′ 1″ (1963)[1]
Garinish Island (County Cork)			30′ × 4′ 8″ (1966)[2]
Garinish Island (County Kerry)			29′ × 2′ 5″ (1966)
Fota			27′ × 2′ 10″ (1966)
Kilmacurragh			33′ × 3′ 3″ (1966)
Tregrehan (2)			66′ × 4′ 7″ (1971)
Exbury			18′ (1969)
Dunloe Castle			27′ (1968)
Crarae			15′ × 1′ 3″ (1969)
Birr Castle	1938		16′ × 11″ (1966)
Wakehurst Place			17′ × 9″ (1969)

1 Measured at 3 feet
2 Measured at 0 feet

BARK. Brownish-grey, or orange-brown, peeling coarsely in grey spiralled strips.
CROWN. An ovoid bush or broadly conic gaunt tree but occasionally a more slender conic tree, of a distinctive yellowish-grey colour.
FOLIAGE. Shoot green for two years, pale brown in the third year.
BUD. A minute yellow-green thickening of the shoot, ovoid and smooth.
LEAVES. Narrowly ovate-lanceolate, all round the shoot, sparse on old trees, 2×0·4 cm tapering abruptly to a spine, stiff, hard; dull grey-green above, yellow-green beneath.
GROWTH. The two trees of known date have made very slow growth although both are in Ireland. It is evident from the few trees remeasured that growth in Cornwall can be moderately rapid and no doubt some of the Irish trees have grown at least as fast.
SPECIMENS. The tree at Trebah is outstanding. It was climbed to over 40 feet in order to measure the height, and the branches at that height were stout enough for safety. The tree at Enys is slender with a clean bole.
RECOGNITION. Bushy plants look like grey, small-leaved *Araucarias* and are distinguished from *P. nubigenus* sufficiently by this colour and the yellowish underside to the leaf. The more distant foliage on trees is distinct in its colour (See also *Podocarpus acutifolius*).

Pseudolarix Gordon (Pinaceae)

A single species closely related to the larches, differing in the cones breaking up when ripe and the spur-shoots lengthening annually.

Fig. 172
Spray of *Pseudolarix amabilis*, Golden larch from China, with spirally set new leaves and second-year wood with whorled leaves on spurs. Single leaf shows broad pale green bands beneath.

Pseudolarix amabilis (Nelson) Rehder. Golden larch

Chekiang and Kiangsi Provinces, East China. Introduced in 1853, but live plants sent in 1854 were the first, as the seed failed to germinate, and until 1860 only one batch out of many yielded plants. Rare and predominantly southern and western in distribution.

Bark. Grey, pale or brownish, deeply cracked into thick square plates; rarely purplish and coarsely scaling.

Crown. Broadly conic; branches level or curved upwards at the tips, long-spurred.

Foliage. Shoot pale yellow-brown ripening pink-buff and purple.

Bud. Small, ovoid; terminals brown, surrounded by fine filamented free scales; side-buds yellowish-green.

Leaves. From May to November; on new shoots all round, lying forwards, gently curved, those on top fully forward; those beneath twisting above the shoot; rosette-leaves on long curved spurs, wrinkled by annual growth-rings, about 15 leaves spread widely 3–5 (7)×0·3 cm, rich grass-green above, with pale edges; beneath with two broad pale green bands; narrowing to acute point. The leaves turn pale then bright yellow in the second half of October and by November in some parts of the crown they are a bright foxy brown.

Flowers and Cone. Borne by some of the older trees; male flowers small ovoids bunched on the ends of some of the spurs; cone ovoid, 5 cm–6 cm×4–5 cm with large, pointed, triangular, hard, leathery, bright pale green scales slightly opened, leaving a sunken centre, ripening pink-brown then brown and woody, falling to pieces on the tree. Abundant after hot summers.

Growth. Young plants are slow to establish and liable to die in the winter. Once established growth is moderate. Medium-sized trees grow very slowly in height but quite rapidly in girth, although probably never quite achieving an annual increase of one inch.

Recognition. The long, curved spurs are unique among conifers. The true larches have short, straight spurs, and more numerous, finer leaves, also the terminal buds of *Pseudolarix* have slender, long free scales around the base.

TABLE 104. LARGE TREES OF PSEUDOLARIX AMABILIS

Locality	*Date Planted*	*Dimensions*	
Scorrier House	1872	30′ × 3′ (1911)	60′ × 7′ 10″ (1965)
Carclew		40′ × 5′ 2″ (1910)	64′ × 7′ 9″ (1962)
Kew R.B.G.			56′ × 5′ 8″ (1970)
Leonardslee			45′ × 6′ 1″ (1969)
Sheffield Park			46′ × 5′ 0″ (1968)
Sheffield Park			48′ × 4′ 8″ (1960)
Wakehurst Place (Drive)			20′ × 4′ 5″ (1971)
Wakehurst Place (Lawn)			18′ × 4′ 6″ (1965)
Wakehurst Place (Valley)			26′ × 4′ 2″ (1965)
Woburn Park (Nursery)			25′ × 3′ 10″ (1962)
Endsleigh			44′ × 4′ 0″ (1963)
Lydhurst			46′ × 3′ 9″ (1971)
Edinburgh R.B.G.	1908		28′ × 3′ 4″ (1967)
Mount Usher			20′ × 2′ 6″ (1966)
Garinish Island			27′ × 2′ 6″ (1966)
Avondale			31′ × 2′ 11″ (1968)
Headfort	1921		18′ × 2′ 3″ (1966)

Pseudotsuga Carriere (Pinaceae)

Trees related to silver-firs, occurring in Western North America, China, Japan and Formosa. They have been divided into 20 species, but only six are generally recognised. The buds are slender and pointed, the leaves mostly soft (hard in *Ps. macrocarpa*) and the cones have 3-pointed, exserted bracts.

Pseudotsuga flahaultii Floris. Mexico. 1962.

Generally regarded as grading into var. *glauca* but young plants from Mexican seed are at present distinct in the following features:

Shoot shiny green-brown or buff-pink, glabrous but roughened; pulvini purple. Bud red-brown, scales not fringed but orange at tips. Leaves along the upper side of the shoot frequently bent forwards showing the underside which has two broad pale blue-white bands; slender, 2 cm, finely pointed with yellow, clear spine; light bluish grey-green above. Crushed foliage has a sweet verbena scent. The leaves immediately below the buds spread perpendicular to the shoot. Growth is vigorous; one two years planted has a shoot 1 foot 10 inches long.

Another batch of seed was received from Mexico as *Pseudotsuga macrolepis* Floris. The plants produced were noticeably bluer as transplants than those of *Ps. flahaultii* and now they differ only in the very broad blue-white bands beneath giving a white appearance as the midrib and margins are narrow and obscure; and a strong, sweet lemon scent.

Pseudotsuga japonica (Shirasawa) Beissner. Japanese Douglas fir

South East Japan. Introduced in 1910. Very rare and found in only a few of the larger collections.

BARK. Dark grey-pink, irregularly cracked.

CROWN. A slender tree with conic, but usually bent or flattened crown; small level branches and fine, dense shoots in upright sprays from them.

FOLIAGE. Shoot glabrous, pale whitish green-brown.

BUD. Shining brown, pointed ovoid, leaving chaffy brown and white scales on the node of the previous year.

LEAVES. All round the upright shoots, more or less parted on long shoots; soft; light green, 2·5 cm long, blunt and notched at the tip; two broad bright white bands below. Crushed foliage has no scent.

CONE. Few-scaled, each convex, smooth, rounded margin; the whole cone ovoid, narrow-pointed, 5 cm long, opening to 3 cm across, dark grey-brown, bracts exserted and spreading, slightly deflexed.

GROWTH. Survival of the early trees has been poor and growth is very slow but in Ireland the only tree seen must have grown quite rapidly.

SPECIMENS. The biggest tree is at Powerscourt where it has run into the branches of an oak tree, but is 60ft × 5ft 10in (1966). Others are: Leonardslee, 30ft × 2ft 8in (1962); Borde Hill (The Tolls), 34ft × 1ft 8in (1968); Wakehurst Place, 30ft × 2ft 3in (1965); Albury Park, 15ft × 1ft 0in (1966) and Bedgebury, planted 1925, 33ft × 1ft 6in; planted 1932, 12ft × 1ft 0in (1968).

RECOGNITION. Distinguished from the other species seen in cultivation by the blunt, notched leaves, and from the other Asiatic species with similar leaves and possibly to be found cultivated, by the broad and bright white bands on the underside and shorter leaves. Also distinguished from those without notched leaves by the glabrous shoot.

Pseudotsuga macrocarpa Mayr. Large-coned Douglas fir

South-west California. Introduced in 1910. An original tree survives at Bayfordbury. Very rare and all specimens seen, except one, are in large collections in South England or in Ireland.

BARK. Dull grey with wide, vertical orange fissures.

CROWN. Broadly conic with level branches.

FOLIAGE. Shoot: one of various shades of fawn, pinks and olive-browns, pale; second year dull brown. Strong shoots greenish grey. All shoots finely pubescent.

BUD. Ovoid-conic, pointed, 8 mm, red-brown with pale brown apex.

LEAVES. Widely spaced, all round the shoot, lying forwards; hard, somewhat stiff; arising from a short slender stalk and ending in an abrupt, acute point, 4–5 × 0·2 cm; on strong

TABLE 105. SPECIMENS OF PSEUDOTSUGA MACROCARPA

Locality	*Date Planted*	*Dimensions*		
Bayfordbury	1912	11′ 6′	(1931)	38′ × 2′ 2″ (1962)
Borde Hill		7′	(1931)	47′ × 3′ 2″ (1968)
Avondale				53′ × 4′ 8″ (1968)
Castlewellan				38′ × 3′ 0″ (1970)
Bedgebury	Graft.1925			54′ × 4′ 11″ (1970)
Bedgebury	Graft.1925			52′ × 4′ 10″ (1970)
Chandlers Ford				30′ × 1′ 11″ (1967)

shoots 8 cm; dark shiny green above; two grey-white bands beneath. Faint resinous aroma when crushed.
CONE. Ovoid-cylindric 9–12 (18) cm, bracts short exserted and straight. (California.) Not yet seen here.
GROWTH. The surviving original tree has grown very slowly but some young trees are making vigorous growth and the two grafted plants at Bedgebury have grown well.

SPECIMENS.
See Table 105, page 263

RECOGNITION. The hard, sharply pointed long leaves are unlike any other Douglas fir. (They are more like *Abies bracteata* and the bud is not unlike that species also, but shorter, more ovoid and redder.)

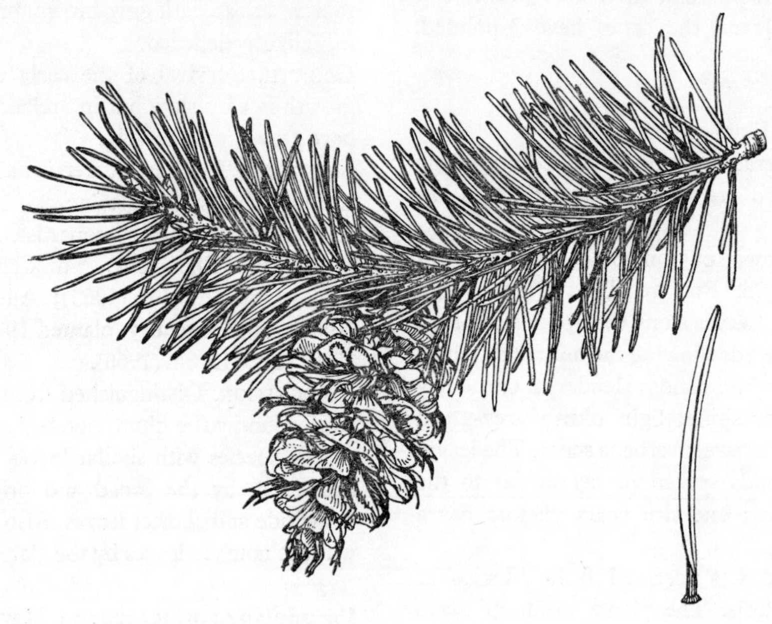

Pseudotsuga menziesii

Fig. 173
Spray and opening cone of *Pseudotsuga menziesii*, Douglas fir. The long, fusiform terminal bud can just be seen. The leaf ($\times 1\frac{1}{3}$) has a very small sucker-like base, and broad white bands beneath.

Pseudotsuga menziesii (Mirbel) Franco. Douglas fir; Green Douglas fir

Western Rocky Mountains from north of Vancouver Island to the Santa Lucia Mountains, Monterey Co., California; the Eastern Rocky Mountains being occupied by var. *caesia* in British Columbia and var. *glauca* south to Mexico. Introduced in late 1827. Several original trees still standing. Very common in most regions in almost all large gardens, estates and parks, especially common in policies in Scotland; in smaller gardens and parks in areas of sandy soils; as plantations on the sides of the lower slopes of valleys and in flat land on heavy or light soils, and as shelterbelts in moderate exposure.

BARK. Young trees smooth, dark grey-green with resin-blisters: small trees, purplish-brown minutely cracked vertically. Larger trees if vigorous, dark grey-brown, widely fissured reddish-brown and corky; if not vigorous, smooth, blistered still, and grey with algae. Old trees variable in corkiness, some pale brown, very corky, with deep, wide fissures; others dark purple-brown with narrow black fissures.

CROWN. Young trees with very open, broadly conic crowns, the leading shoot long with a tuft of shoots and a slight bend some six inches from the top; the side-shoots long and variably ascending. Older trees narrowly conic and dense. Very old trees, wide, heavily branched, often shedding big branches or shattered at the top; the small shoots long-pendulous; foliage very heavy. A tree at Rossie Priory has many branches layered.

FOLIAGE. Shoot yellow-green; short-pubescent.

Bud. Slender, pointed ovoid-conic, pale brown on strong shoots and clustered towards the tip; bright deep red on side shoots of old trees; often purple-red-brown paling to an orange apex; smooth with appressed and unfringed scales.
Leaves. More or less pectinate, in many ranks, spreading beneath, some forwards above, soft, tapering to a blunt but not notched tip, arising from a purplish pulvinus; 2–2·5 cm sometimes much longer, always densely set; dull bluish or yellow-green first year, second year shiny and less blue; two grey-green bands beneath. Strong, sweet, fruity aroma.
Flowers and Cone. Male flowers below and on the terminal length of the new shoot, conic, shedding pollen in late March to April. Female flowers singly or in whorls of 2–3 near the tips of old shoots as the new buds expand; at the sides or below, dark red ovoid, as bud; opening and bending to vertical, green and brown or green and pink, long bracts, in late March, more usually mid April. Conelets soon green and closed when they bend downwards and lengthen to green fusiform cones. Ripe cones fusiform, dull brown, until open when glossy dark brown, 8×2·5 cm with bracts three-pronged and exserted straight, vertically, 1–1·5 cm long, 5 mm across at base.
Growth. On suitable sites growth is very vigorous after a few years and remains so until the trees are of great size. Trees planted three years will often make shoots three feet long and some over four feet. Growth starts in early May and stops in early July.

A few trees have exceeded 100 feet in height in 30 years or even less, and many are 150 feet in 70 years or less. In any but sheltered places, however, the top twenty feet or so is liable to be blown out and the height thereafter does not exceed about 100 feet. Growth in girth is relatively somewhat less vigorous. Many trees have a mean annual increment of about 2 inches but few much more than that, and many of the old trees have grown very slowly since 1931. Many examples of these features of growth can be seen in Table 106.
Specimens. Very large trees are so numerous that only the very tallest and stoutest can be mentioned, often only two out of a group, stand or avenue of dozens similar. This is even the case on one or two estates with original trees, i.e. those with planting dates up to 1840 and a few beyond, where these are numerous.
General. Douglas fir timber is strong and of good quality, so the species has been much planted on the sites to which it is suited. These are well-drained mineral soils, moist or receiving a good rainfall, and sheltered. It is thus planted along the lower slopes in valleys and underplanted in old broadleaved woodland. It will establish well in light shade but soon needs to have this removed or growth becomes slow and severe attacks from the aphid *Adelges cooleyi* develop. This species has suffered from fashions in planting, more than most, and is currently somewhat out of favour, but its great potential growth should ensure that it is always being planted somewhere. When fast-growing stands are at their first thinning stage they frequently lose a lot of foliage and become thin in the crown and cause alarm. Growth hardly suffers, however, and after some years they make a full recovery.

Table 106. Outstanding Specimens of Pseudotsuga menziesii

Locality	*Date Planted*	*Dimensions*	
Dropmore	1828	110′ × 12′ 0″ (1908)	102′ × 12′ 9″ (1970)
Jardine Hall	1828	91′ × 13′ 1″ (1931)	101′ × 14′ 0″ (1954)
Coul	1829		113′ × 16′ 6″ (1956)
Raith	1829		93′ × 14′ 8″ (1966)
Longleat	ca.1830		125′ × 15′ 11″ (1959)[1]
Corehouse	1831		150′ × 12′ 5″ (1954)
Corehouse	1831		120′ × 15′ 4″ (1954)
Drumlanrig	1832	90′ × 11′ 4″ (1904)	117′ × 15′ 7″ (1970)
Scone Palace	1834		115′ × 13′ 9″ (1970)
Dawyck	1835	113′ × 15′ 6″ (1930)	141′ × 16′ 11″ (1970)
Dawyck	1835		145′ × 14′ 5″ (1966)
Eggesford	1837	128′ × 18′ 6″ (1908)	124′ × 20′ 3″ (1970)[1,2]
Penrhyn Castle	1841	87′ × 14′ 8″ (1931)	90′ × 16′ 7″ (1959)
Penrhyn Castle	1841	108′ × 13′ 3″ (1931)	110′ × 14′ 3″ (1959)
Durris House	1841	106′ × 12′ 0″ (1904)	154′ × 16′ 11″ (1970)
Walcot Hall	1842	114′ × 14′ 2″ (1908)	125′ × 18′ 8″ (1962)
Balmacaan			141′ × 15′ 3″ (1970)
Powis Castle	1842	130′ × 9′ 10″ (1908)	180′ × 13′ 6″ (1970)
Stanage Park	1845	132′ × 13′ 3″ (1931)	129′ × 14′ 8″ (1970)
Dunkeld Cathedral	1846	101′ × 17′ (1931)	120′ × 20′ 10″ (1970)
Pencarrow	1847	110′ × 9′ 2″ (1927)	90′ × 13′ 2″ (1970)

[1] Dying back
[2] At 6 feet

(*continues*)

Table 107 (*continued*) *Outstanding Specimens of Pseudotsuga menziesii*

Locality	*Date Planted*	*Dimensions*	
Keir House	1849	93′ × 9′ 2″ (1931)	— × 16′ 0″ (1970)
Endsleigh			140′ × 17′ 2″ (1963)
Endsleigh			140′ × 16′ 11″ (1963)
Tregrehan		100′ × 13′ 7″ (1927)	100′ × 17′ 7″ (1971)
Westonbirt		104′ × 14′ 2″ (1931)	110′ × 16′ 2″ (1969)
Fonthill			145′ × 17′ 4″ (1963)
Fonthill			123′ × 16′ 6″ (1960)
Mamhead			97′ × 17′ 0″ (1970)
Hermitage, Inver. (1)			151′ × 13′ 1″ (1970)
Powerscourt			115′ × 16′ 5″ (1966)
Powerscourt			155′ × 14′ 3″ (1966)
Taymouth Castle			157′ × 15′ 10″ (1970)
Murthly Castle	1850		167′ × 10′ 9″ (1970)
Althorp	1851	109′ × 11′ 5″ (1931)	105′ × 12′ 1″ (1964)
Blairquhan	1855	87′ × 13′ 10″ (1931)	108′ × 15′ 3″ (1970)
Fenagh House	ca.1855	94′ × 10′ 4″ (1931)	126′ × 13′ 10″ (1968)
Castle Kennedy	1856	74′ × 8′ 1″ (1926)	82′ × 12′ 4″ (1967)
Winsford Rectory	ca.1857		104′ × 15′ 10″ (1959)
Bolderwood	1859		153′ × 12′ 1″ (1970)
Ochtertyre	1859	97′ × 10′ 2″ (1931)	134′ × 13′ 0″ (1970)
Kilravock Castle			131′ × 16′ 2″ (1970)
Puck Pits	ca.1860		150′ × 15′ 0″ (1969)
Rhinefield Drive	1861		144′ × 14′ 6″ (1970)
Powis Castle (2)			148′ × 15′ 6″ (1970)
Lanrick			138′ × 15′ 4″ (1970)
Lanrick			148′ × 12′ 2″ (1970)
Dunans			166′ × 16′ 0″ (1969)
Dunans			170′ × 13′ 1″ (1969)
Dunans			165′ × 14′ 6″ (1969)
Glenlee Park			148′ × 15′ 10″ (1970)
Glenlee Park			155′ × 15′ 7″ (1970)
Glenlee Park			151′ × 16′ 2″ (1970)
Belladrum			151′ × 18′ 0″ (1970)
Belladrum			149′ × 17′ 6″ (1970)
Glamis Castle	1864	108′ × 11′ 2″ (1931)	143′ × 16′ 1″ (1970)
Blackmoor	1867	101′ × 9′ 6″ (1931)	130′ × 12′ 6″ (1968)
Alnwick Castle		124′ × 12′ 6″ (1931)	146′ × 13′ 0″ (1958)
Castle Milk	1869	83′ × 13′ 0″ (1931)	110′ × 17′ 4″ (1966)
Irvine House	1872	110′ × 13′ 7″ (1931)	105′ × 15′ 0″ (1954)
Blair Atholl	1872	98′ × 9′ 0″ (1931)	154′ × 11′ 7″ (1970)
Blair Atholl			157′ × 11′ 5″ (1970)
Blair Atholl			154′ × 11′ 10″ (1970)
Brahan			121′ × 17′ 7″ (1970)
Dunster (Broadwood)	1874		150′ × 13′ 2″ (1957)
Kirkennan	1876	126′ × 9′ 10″ (1931)	138′ × 11′ 11″ (1970)
Crogen	1879		155′ × 10′ 1″ (1965)
Escot			110′ × 15′ 6″ (1965)
Dupplin Castle (Pinetum)			144′ × 13′ 9″ (1970)
Dupplin Castle (Pinetum)			124′ × 15′ 6″ (1970)
Castle Forbes		110′ × 12′ 4″ (1931)	125′ × 14′ 7″ (1968)
Coollattin		85′ × 9′ (1906)	130′ × 13′ 6″ (1968)
Stradbally House		80′ × 8′ 3″ (1907)	115′ × 14′ 8″ (1968)
Ardkinglas (Strone)			152′ × 12′ 3″ (1969)
Cortachy Castle			126′ × 16′ 2″ (1962)
Cragside			153′ × 12′ 11″ (1958)
(N. Devon)			130′ × 16′ 9″ (1970)
Barcaldine			90′ × 17′ 5″ (1956)
Doune House			151′ × 15′ 1″ (1970)
Doune House			138′ × 16′ 4″ (1970)
Fairburn (Drive)			128′ × 15′ 11″ (1970)
Fairburn (Burial Ground)			157′ × 12′ 0″ (1970)
Barcaldine			160′ × 9′ 10″ (1956)
West Dean			156′ × 11′ 2″ (1970)
Munches	1880	124′ × 11′ 3″ (1931)	105′ × 13′ 3″ (1970)
Inveraray (Dubh Loch)	1881		162′ × 11′ 6″ (1969)
Darnaway	1882		154′ × 11′ 2″ (1955)
Reelig (Moniack Glen)	1882		167′ × 9′ 3″ (1970)
Dunkeld (Duke's Seat)		96′ × 8′ 6″ (1931)	141′ × 12′ 2″ (1970)
The Hermitage	ca.1887		173′ × 11′ 9″ (1970)

Locality	*Date Planted*	*Dimensions*	
Lake Vyrnwy	1887		150′ × 7′ 0″ (1960)
Stonefield	1888	112′ × 11′ 0″ (1931)	125′ × 12′ 7″ (1969)
Bodnant	1888		133′ × 10′ 8″ (1966)
Benmore (Glen Massan)			167′ × 13′ 1″ (1970)
Harpford Wood	1894		147′ × 12′ 0″ (1964)
Dunkeld Cathedral	1897	74′ × 6′ 11″ (1931)	128′ × 10′ 8″ (1962)
Gregynog	1898		144′ × 8′ 4″ (1960)
Culloden Forest	1906		117′ × 6′ 6″ (1952)
Vivod House			160′ × 8′ 6″ (1964)
Abbotswood (Dean)	1925		123′ × 6′ 10″ (1964)
Ffrwdgrech	1931		105′ × 4′ 2″ (1960)

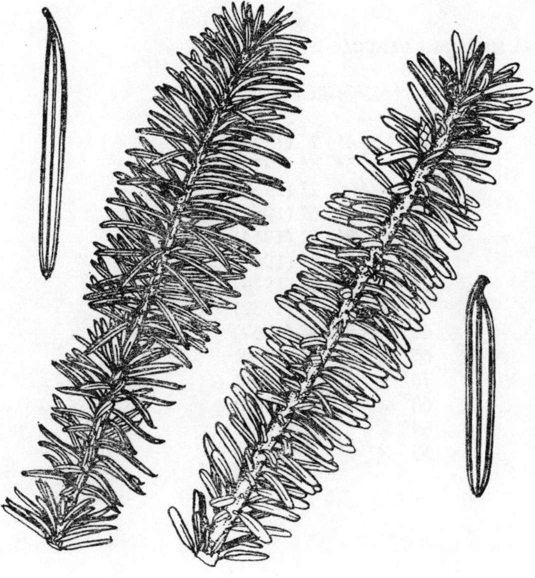

Pseudotsuga menziesii cv. Brevifolia
Pseudotsuga menziesii cv. Fretsii

Fig. 174
Two small-foliaged cultivars of Douglas fir. *Pseudotsuga menziesii* cv. Brevifolia is the less frequent (left). *Ps. menziesii* cv. Fretsii can be a tree of 40 ft. Single leaves × 2.

cv. Brevifolia (Pre-1891). A small, bushy tree with yellow-brown underside to the shoot, dark brown above, purplish above in later years, and slender, short, radiating leaves, those on the upper side recurved; 1·2 cm × 0·2 cm tapering to a round apex or abrupt spine, dark yellow-green above, two grey bands beneath. A very rare plant, distinguished from cv. Fretsii by the slender shoot and slender, curved-back leaves.

var. caesia. (Schwerin) Franco. Fraser River Douglas fir. Inland British Columbia grading southwards into var. *glauca.* Uncommon but frequent in some areas, differing from the type in a smoother, greyer bark, blackish-green leaves, less parted, and small cones like var. *glauca* and with bracts exserted as far but not reflexed at all.

cv. Fretsii (Holland, about 1905). (See figure 174).

A rare semi-dwarf form found in a few collections. It has occurred spontaneously at Avondale several times in seed from normal trees. It has a stout shoot, blackish purple above, green-brown beneath, short pubescent. The leaves are nearly pectinate below but radiate above, slightly leaning forwards, thick, broad, very short, 1 × 0·3 cm straight, dark grey-green above with two broad bright white bands beneath. Avondale, planted 1921, 41ft × 3ft 11in (1965); Dawyck, planted 1919, 18ft × 2ft 7in (1966); Wisley Royal Horticultural Society Gardens, 41ft × 3ft 2in (1969); Wakehurst Place, 32ft × 2ft 8in (1970).

var. glauca (Mayr) Franco. Colorado Douglas fir; Blue Douglas fir. Eastern Rocky Mountains from Montana to Mexico. Introduced in about 1885. Uncommon as a whole, being found in rather few collections and large gardens, but in some areas, like South-west Surrey, frequent in small gardens and roadside plantings.

Bark. Dull pewter-grey or blackish, and very scaly.

Crown. Narrowly conic, dense with many small, level branches.

Foliage. Shoot grey-green, with scattered pubescence.

Bud. Dull purple-brown pale at the tip from the long ciliate scales; ovoid-conic, 1 cm.

Leaves. Spreading all round the shoot and standing perpendicular on the upper side on pale pink petioles and pulvini; thick, 2–2·5 cm long, rounded at the tip, blue-grey above, with two blue-grey bands beneath. Crushed foliage has little scent.

Flowers and Cone. Male flowers numerous, dull purple-brown conic-ovoid and very pointed in bud, with ciliate scales, 7 mm long crowded among the leaves on the lower side of the shoot. Female flowers often abundant, bright dark red. Cone fusiform 5 × 2 cm ripening light copper-brown; bracts exserted 1·2–1·4 mm, bent level, the base 6 mm across.

Growth. A much less vigorous tree than the type and often subject to a leaf-cast caused by the fungus *Rhabdocline pseudotsugae.* It is therefore not planted in forests. Individual trees have, however, shown quite good growth, and as this variety is resistant to the aphid *Adelges cooleyi* it may look healthy where the type is covered in insects. Well-grown trees are handsome in their blue-grey foliage, particularly when the red flowers are open. Some growth-rates are shown in Table 107.

RECOGNITION. There are all stages of intermediates between the type and var. *glauca* (see var. *caesia*) but the proper Colorado tree is very distinct, in bark, bud, leaves, flowers and cones (q.v.).

cv. Stairii (Castle Kennedy, pre-1871). Very rare. A short, broad, bushy tree, or thin, tall and gaunt in which the foliage is rather small and the new leaves are pale yellow. The two trees in the nursery at Castle Kennedy are not the original tree, but their date is not known.

Castle Kennedy, 20ft×3ft 4in at 3 feet; 25ft×2ft 8in (1967); Little Hall, planted 1906, 37ft×2ft 8in (1961); Ilnacullin (Garinish Island), 20 feet (1966); Munches, 66ft ×5ft 1in; 66ft×3ft 9in (1970); Dupplin Castle, 55ft×4ft 3in (1970).

TABLE 107. SPECIMENS OF PSEUDOTSUGA MENZIESII GLAUCA

Locality	*Date Planted*	*Dimensions*
Warnham Court		94′ × 4′ 7″ (1971)
Dropmore (1)	1906	74′ × 5′ 4″ (1970)
Hergest Croft		74′ × 6′ 2″ (1963)
Monzie Castle		81′ × 4′ 6″ (1962)
Welford Park		68′ × 6′ 3″ (1964)
Vernon Holme	1910	65′ × 4′ 9″ (1961)
Dropmore	1913	71′ × 4′ 6″ (1970)
Nymans		71′ × 4′ 1″ (1957)
Bagshot Park		60′ × 3′ 11″ (1957)
Cynywd Forest		65′ × 5′ 1″ (1964)
Werrington Park		70′ × 4′ 9″ (1969)
Fenagh House		68′ × 4′ 10″ (1968)
Wakehurst Place		64′ × 3′ 2″ (1964)
Holkham Hall	1921	55′ × 3′ 3″ (1968)

Saxegothaea Lindley (Podocarpaceae)

A genus of a single species, connected with both *Podocarpus* and *Araucariaceae*.

Saxegothaea conspicua

Fig. 175
Foliage of *Saxegothaea conspicua*, Prince Albert's yew. The leaves are hard, and spined, with white bands on the underside (detail ×1⅓) and many are curved.

Saxegothaea conspicua Lindley. Prince Albert's yew

Chile and South-west Argentina. Introduced in 1847. Rare and confined to collections in Southern England and in Ireland, apparently absent from all the eastern side of England and from Scotland except for one in Edinburgh and one in Argyll.

BARK. Purple-brown, liable to have deep cavities and flutes; smooth; large scales falling cleanly leaving smooth areas of red-brown.

CROWN. Often bushy but can be a slender, conic, slightly bent tree; branches descending, sometimes to the ground, (and layered at Fota), branchlets pendulous, the long shoots hanging with whorls of 3–5 shoots at long intervals.

FOLIAGE. Shoot bright grey-green for 3–4 years, roughened by pegs left where the leaves are shed, and banded white from the long decurrent base of each leaf; fifth year pale reddish-brown.

BUD. Minute, globose and green.

LEAVES. Somewhat sparse and irregular in arrangement, slanted forwards but curving downwards or backwards, 1·5–3·0 cm×0·2 cm, parallel sided, the tip tapering abruptly to a sharp point; slightly ridged above and dark matt grey-green, slightly bloomed; concave below with two broad bright white bands. The leaves are rather hard and slightly prickly.

FLOWERS AND CONE. Male flowers small ovoids, stalked, in pairs at the bases of the leaves. Cone, on the same tree, at the end of a small branchlet, bright powdery blue-grey, flat ovoid 5×10 mm with outspread and downcurved triangular, thick scales. Freely borne at all times of the year.

GROWTH. An extraordinarily slow-growing tree even in Ireland and Cornwall, in height and in girth. The only data are given in Table 108. The tree at Woodhouse is outstandingly fine.

RECOGNITION. Distinguished from all yews by the curved leaf with white bands beneath, but much more like, and confused with *Podocarpus andinus*. It differs from that species in the scaly bark, pendulous shoots, hard, sparser foliage and the bright white underneath the curved leaves.

TABLE 108. SPECIMENS OF SAXEGOTHAEA CONSPICUA

Locality	*Date Planted*	*Dimensions*	
Coldrennick		35′ (1911)	35′ × 4′ 2″ (1957)
Woodhouse		40′ × 3′ 4″ (1912)	55′ × 5′ 2″ (1970)
Fota	1856		30′ × 2′ 10″ (1966)
Kilmacurragh			39′ × 4′ 8″ (1966)
Kilmacurragh			40′ × 4′ 2″ (1966)
Blackmoor	1897	8′ (1931)	10′ (1961)
Edinburgh R.B.G.	1902		9′ × 1′ 1″ (1967)[1]
Wakehurst Place	1914	14′ × 5″ (1931)	29′ × 2′ 0″ (1969)
Wakehurst Place			28′ × 1′ 3″ (1970)
Leonardslee		18′ (1931)	36′ × 2′ 2″ (1969)
Bedgebury	1925		23′ × 1′ 7″ (1969)[2]
Tregullow			31′ (1959)
Crarae			12′ × 1′ 4″ (1969)
Killerton			26′ × 1′ 6″ (1970)

[1] Measured at 3 feet
[2] Main stem

Sciadopitys Siebold and Zuccarini (Taxodiaceae)

A genus of a single species, unique in its whorls of leaves in united pairs.

Sciadopitys verticillata (Thunberg) Siebold and Zuccarini. Japanese umbrella "pine"

Central Honshiu, Japan. Introduced in 1853 as a plant from Buitenzong Botanic Garden, Java. This died and the next plants were raised from Japanese seed sent in 1861. Uncommon, but in many large gardens in all parts except East Anglia.

BARK. Dark red-brown, peeling in narrow vertical plates.

CROWN. Single-stemmed trees upright, irregularly narrow conic, rarely with a long slender spire, sometimes broadly columnar. Many-stemmed plants, perhaps more frequent, broadly conic.

FOLIAGE. Shoot buff-brown, slightly ridged and striped darker, with little bud-like dark brown knobs. Second year yellow-brown; third year pale fawn.

BUD. On main shoots, a small rich red-brown hump with loose outer scales; on minor shoots pale brown and nearly flat.

LEAVES. In big, distant whorls about 3·5 cm apart, each whorl well buttressed by pale brown scale-leaves; each big leaf in the whorl 10–14 cm × 3–4 mm, parallel sided broadly grooved above and below to a notch at the blunt tip; thick; rich, dark, glossy green above, yellowish green beneath with the groove yellow.

FLOWERS AND CONE. Male flowers in terminal clusters of 10–15 on small shoots, bright yellow when shedding pollen in late May. Cones on the same tree, terminal on small shoots, green, ripening to dark brown, broadly ovoid, 6 × 5 cm with loose flexible scales, the lower parts deeply grooved up to the margin from a roll-like transverse fold; the margin decurving broadly when ripe.

GROWTH. Although some trees have grown slowly, most of the many dated trees have not been as slow as is often thought. A few have made mean annual shoots of 1 foot for long periods and many have increased their girth by more than a mean of 1 inch per year. See Table 109.

SPECIMENS. The outstanding tree is at Benenden where it towers in a slender spire out of some rhododendrons. It was the only specimen thought worthy of mention and a portrait by Elwes and Henry in 1905 and it is still by far the tallest and best in shape.

RECOGNITION. No other tree can really be confused with this.

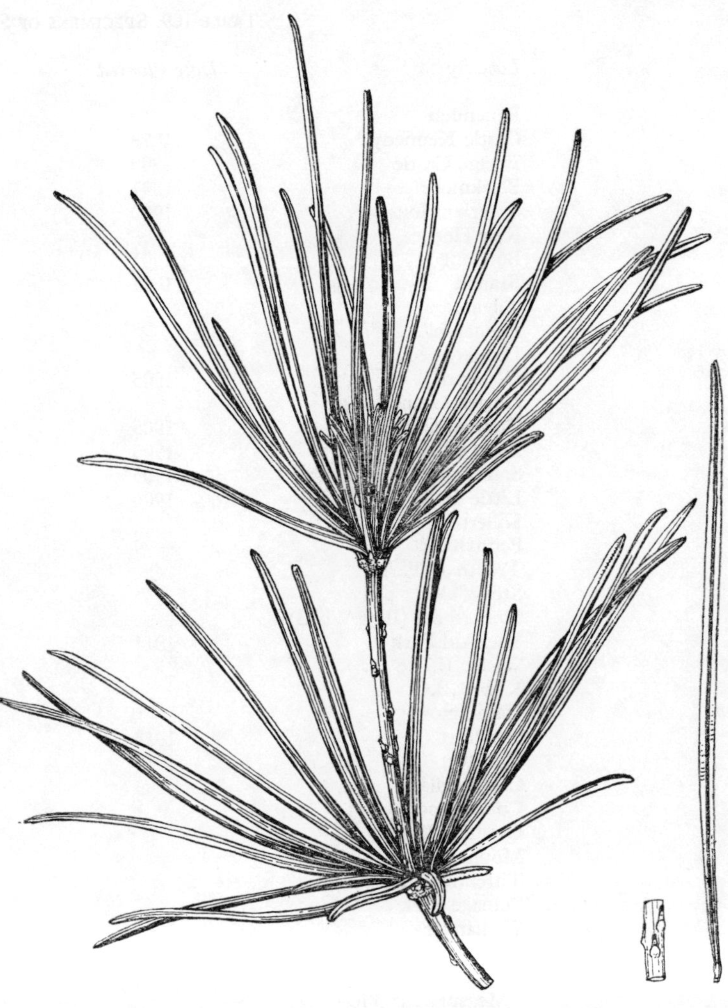

Sciadopitys verticillata

Fig. 176
Shoot and foliage of *Sciadopitys verticillata*, Japanese umbrella "pine". The shoot is clothed in scale-like, appressed leaves (small drawing lower right) the ends of which form small bumps. The apparently normal leaf (far right) is two leaves fused together.

TABLE 109. SPECIMENS OF SCIADOPITYS VERTICILLATA

Locality	*Date Planted*	*Dimensions*	
Benenden		38′ × 2′ 0″ (1905)	74′ × 4′ 8″ (1970)
Castle Kennedy	1878	28′ × 2′ 3″ (1931)	40′ × 2′ 9″ (1967)
Eridge Castle	1885		36′ × 4′ 0″ (1971)
Blackmoor	1897	15′ × 10″ (1931)	31′ × 2′ 8″ (1961)
Scorrier House	1900	30′ (1927)	45′ × 5′ 3″ (1959)[1]
Keir House			46′ × 3′ 9″ (1970)
Bodnant	1901	32′ × 2′ 2″ (1937)	55′ × 4′ 1″ (1966)
Brahan	1901		26′ × 2′ 8″ (1970)
Tilgate		28′ (1931)	47′ × 4′ 4″ (1964)
Leonardslee		27′ × 1′ 4″ (1931)	55′ × 3′ 3″ (1969)
Leonardslee			50′ × 2′ 8″ (1969)
Glenapp	1905	21′ × 1′ 4″ (1931)	35′ × 2′ 9″ (1961)
Hewell Grange		27′ × 3′ (1931)	30′ × 4′ 10″ (1963)[2]
Culzean Castle	1905	25′ × 1′ 1″ (1931)	46′ × 2′ 7″ (1970)
Land of Nod	1905		24′ × 2′ 7″ (1964)
Sandling Park	ca.1905		30′ × 3′ 2″ (1965)
Little Hall	1906	20′ × 0′ 9″ (1931)	25′ × 2′ 8″ (1961)
Killerton			41′ × 4′ 10″ (1970)
Pennyhill			45′ × 5′ 4″ (1960)[1]
Trentham Park			44′ × 3′ 9″ (1968)
Stonefield			43′ × 4′ 6″ (1969)
Sindlesham (Bear Wood)			47′ × 3′ 3″ (1970)
Sheffield Park	1911		46′ × 4′ 0″ (1968)
Wisley R.H.S.G.			49′ × 2′ 10″ (1971)[1]
Kew R.B.G.			34′ × 2′ 1″ (1956)
Hafodunos			34′ × 4′ 1″ (1960)
Headfort	1914		39′ × 2′ 3″ (1966)
Headfort	1916		30′ × 4′ 3″ (1966)
Castlewellan			30′ × 4′ 4″ (1970)
Curraghmore		16′ × 10″ (1931)	40′ × 5′ 2″ (1968)
Garinish Island			37′ × 2′ 8″ (1966)
Mount Usher			44′ × 2′ 2″ (1966)
Tittenhurst Park			39′ × 2′ 7″ (1963)
Stanage Park			38′ × 3′ 4″ (1959)
Wishanger			36′ × 2′ 2″ (1963)

[1] Main stem
[2] Measured at 3 feet

Sequoia Endlicher (Taxodiaceae)

A single species, confined to the 'fog belt' on the Californian coast, in the northern part of which specimens of over 300 feet in height have been found. The tallest tree in the world is one of these, now thought to be 367 feet tall, the 'Howard Libby Tree' at Redwood Creek Grove. This genus is separated from *Sequoiadendron* mainly by bearing two different kinds of leaves, and buds with many loose scales.

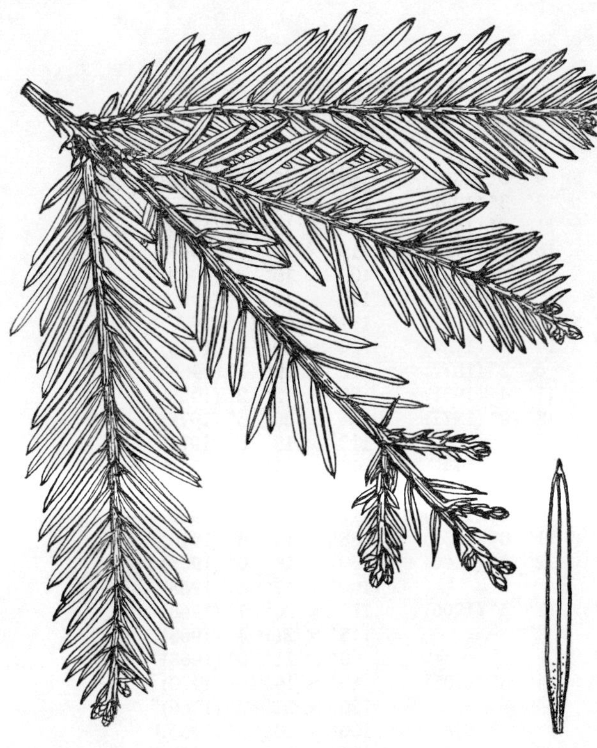

Sequoia sempervirens

Fig. 177
Spray of *Sequoia sempervirens*, Coast redwood, foliage and ($\times 1\frac{1}{3}$) underside of leaf showing broad white stomatal bands. The scale-like leaves which are also grown can be seen on the second-year wood (top left).

Sequoia sempervirens (D. Don) Endlicher. Coast redwood

From Brookings in the extreme south-west of Oregon, along the Californian coast some 450 miles south to Monterey but extending no more than 20 miles in width. Introduced from Fort Ross via Russia in 1843. A few original trees survive. Quite common in large gardens, estates and parks in every region although less so in the east and in North Scotland. Also seen in some small gardens and parks in or near towns.

Bark. Young trees bright orange-brown, loosely stringy. Older trees the same where exposed to erosion by cattle or the public, but where undisturbed; thick, intertwined ridges develop, very dark brown with fraying stringy edges.

Crown. Young trees conic, with widely-spaced, slender branches level, upcurved near their tips. Old trees columnar, pointed or flat-topped, often rather open, showing the long branches sweeping down at a flat angle in a distinctive manner. The most vigorous trees have regularly columnar crowns, less open and very level branches. Huge burrs occur at the base of a few trees, from 3 to 8 feet high, covered in normally ridged bark. Vigorous vertical sprouts arise from the base of some trees.

Foliage. Leading shoots and strong branches on young trees are pinkish green-brown with patches of orange-red lower down, becoming deep red-brown stripes on grey. These leading shoots have widely spaced scale-leaves set spirally, narrowly triangular 6–8 mm long. Side shoots and main shoots in the lower crown of big trees are green, finely speckled with white stomata and winged with fine ridges. They arise from basal rosettes of several layers of dark brown acute bud-scales. Second year shoots bright rusty brown with adherent scale-leaves also brown, or brown in the lower half.

Bud. Terminal buds pinkish-green on leading-shoots, with loose free scales, slender pointed and abruptly incurved at their tips. Other buds nodding, pale green with red-brown tipped free scales.

Leaves. On the inner half of vigorous young side-shoots, intermediate between scale-leaves and normal; spirally set, 1·5–2 cm, hard, short-spined, pale green, often indigo at the tips; a band of scattered white stomata each side of the midrib above; two broad greenish white bands beneath. Ordinary shoots have scale leaves 8–10 mm long, spirally set, and normal leaves pectinate on side-shoots, 1–1·5 cm oblong, abruptly short-pointed, deep shining green; white stomata scattered over the upper side, two pale blue-white or greenish bands beneath. The foliage is hard and slightly prickly. When crushed it has a scent of candle-wax.

Flowers and Cone. Male flowers terminal or sub-terminal, 1 to 4 on most side-shoots, visible from early autumn, globular, 4 mm whitish yellow speckled green, shedding pollen in February unless delayed by cold weather until early April. Frosts just before or during pollination destroy the flowers, turning them white then brown. Female flower terminal on short shoot, nodding, green, ripening in one year to a dark brown cone, ovoid, 2–3 cm long, with wrinkled, leathery scales.

Growth. Height growth starts in mid-May, is at maximum during late June and ends towards the end of September.

Growth, particularly in the far west and south west is extremely vigorous and annual shoots of four feet are made; in Devon a plot 20 years old had a mean height of nearly 70 feet. Growth in girth is equally vigorous and young trees with an average annual increase of 3 inches are known in many places, and over 4 inches in Ireland.

Such growth demands a damp but well-drained site in deep soils and a sheltered situation. As in many *Abies* species, maximum growth is confined to areas with cool, moist summers. The best trees are in Devon, Wiltshire, Ireland and Perthshire.

Growth as coppice from stumps is normal when stands are thinned and can be seen at Montacute House where several trees bordering the drive were felled and coppice shoots form dense, round thickets, to 20 feet high (1971).

SPECIMENS. There are so many trees larger than 100ft × 16ft that smaller specimens can be included only when they are of a very early planting or are young trees of exceptional growth. The table (110) includes all those found which have known planting dates before 1850 and all but a few smaller trees from those which were planted before 1870. It also includes any others of exceptional size or in regions where there are few, and the most vigorous young trees. A remarkably high proportion of the trees given by Elwes and Henry, and nearly all those in the 1932 Report have been found.

TABLE 110. OLD OR OUTSTANDING SPECIMENS OF SEQUOIA SEMPERVIRENS

Locality	*Date Planted*	*Dimensions*	
Smeaton House	1844	57′ × 9′ 0″ (1902)	63′ × 12′ 0″ (1966)
Bury Hill	1844	111′ × 12′ 3″ (1931)	108′ × 14′ 3″ (1971)
Dropmore	1845	94′ × 11′ 0″ (1907)	108′ × 15′ 8″ (1970)
Bowood	ca.1845	91′ × 16′ 0″ (1931)	115′ × 19′ 9″ (1968)
Bowood	ca.1845		109′ × 19′ 6″ (1968)
Bowood	ca.1845		110′ × 19′ 3″ (1968)
Rossie Priory	ca.1845	83′ × 13′ 5″ (1931)	131′ × 20′ 10″ (1970)
Stourhead	ca.1845	90′ × 14′ 7″ (1931)	124′ × 19′ 9″ (1970)
Stratfield Saye	1848	64′ × 6′ 2″ (1877)	112′ × 19′ 1″ (1968)
Falloden	1848	85′ × 11′ 4″ (1931)	85′ × 12′ 2″ (1958)
Longleat		63′ × 8′ 0″ (1877)	124′ × 20′ 5″ (1971)
Longleat			113′ × 19′ 8″ (1971)
Althorp	1851	94′ × 14′ 2″ (1931)	95′ × 15′ 9″ (1964)
Pampisford	1851	98′ × 8′ 9″ (1931)	74′ × 11′ 8″ (1968)
Fulmodestone	1851	67′ × 8′ 6″ (1904)	117′ × 18′ 3″ (1969)
Glenapp	1851	69′ × 11′ 0″ (1931)	88′ × 14′ 5″ (1970)
Whitfield	1851	95′ × 12′ 0″ (1906)	130′ × 16′ 0″ (1963)
Whitfield	1851		100′ × 17′ 4″ (1963)
Coollattin	1851	75′ × 11′ 5″ (1906)	113′ × 20′ 7″ (1968)
Coollattin	1851		115′ × 21′ 4″ (1968)
Coollattin	1851		90′ × 21′ 0″ (1968)
Boconnoc	1851	68′ × 14′ 6″ (1905)	86′ × 19′ 10″ (1970)
Inistioge			120′ × 22′ 2″ (1966)
Inistioge			100′ × 20′ 3″ (1966)[1]
Fota			105′ × 20′ 5″ (1966)[1]
Curraghmore		79′ × 15′ 0″ (1931)	103′ × 20′ 5″ (1968)
Taymouth Castle		73′ × 16′ 4″ (1931)	136′ × 21′ 5″ (1970)
Taymouth Castle			131′ × 21′ 7″ (1970)
Melbury			121′ × 21′ 4″ (1971)
Minterne			129′ × 15′ 3″ (1970)
Herriard Park	1852		112′ × 16′ 10″ (1961)
Cuffnells	1855	98′ × 15′ 0″ (1906)	121′ × 19′ 10″ (1970)
Cuffnells	1855	105′ × 10′ 10″ (1906)	128′ × 16′ 6″ (1970)
Inveraray (Lime Kilns)	1856	78′ × 14′ 9″ (1931)	104′ × 16′ 11″ (1969)
Leighton Hall	1856		104′ × 15′ 11″ (1970)
Biel		50′ × 3′ 0″ (1877)	111′ × 15′ 0″ (1967)
Penrhyn Castle	1857	90′ × 12′ 3″ (1906)	108′ × 17′ 2″ (1959)
Moncrieffe House	1857	65′ × 9′ 0″ (1907)	96′ × 15′ 7″ (1957)
Dupplin Castle	1859	93′ × 13′ 8″ (1931)	124′ × 19′ 3″ (1970)
Bolderwood	1861	90′ × 13′ 7″ (1931)	115′ × 16′ 5″ (1970)
Powis Castle			121′ × 16′ 3″ (1970)
Windsor Great Park			122′ × 18′ 8″ (1970)
Kinfauns			118′ × 18′ 0″ (1970)
Woodhouse			134′ × 10′ 0″ (1970)[2]

[1] Measured at 6 feet 6 inches to avoid burrs
[2] 3 other stems

Locality	*Date Planted*	*Dimension*	
Whiteways			110′ × 18′ 11″ (1964)
Parkhatch			100′ × 17′ 7″ (1970)
Escot			100′ × 18′ 1″ (1965)
Killerton			115′ × 17′ 1″ (1970)
Birr Castle			72′ × 18′ 2″ (1966)
Abercairny	1864	60′ × 14′ 1″ (1931)	116′ × 17′ 1″ (1962)
Bicton		86′ × 9′ 9″ (1877)	100′ × 19′ 0″ (1968)
Coppid Hall	1864	73′ × 9′ 5″ (1905)	105′ × 15′ 11″ (1968)
Claremont		95′ × 12′ 0″ (1903)	118′ × 17′ 1″ (1965)
Eastnor Castle		106′ × 16′ 6″ (1931)	115′ × 18′ 8″ (1970)
Leaton Knolls		103′ × 13′ 1″ (1931)	121′ × 15′ 5″ (1970)
Leaton Knolls			133′ × 15′ 5″ (1970)
Powerscourt	1866		130′ × 13′ 11″ (1966)
Blackmoor	1867	71′ × 14′ 10″ (1931)	75′ × 19′ 11″ (1968)
West Lavington			120′ × 16′ 5″ (1968)
Sindlesham (Bear Wood)			118′ × 17′ 9″ (1970)
(N. Devon)			105′ × 17′ 1″ (1970)
(N. Devon)			138′ × 11′ 11″ (1970)
(N. Devon)			133′ × 13′ 10″ (1970)
Oakley Park			133′ × 17′ 9″ (1971)
Monk Hopton			115′ × 17′ 9″ (1971)
Eridge Castle	1885		90′ × 16′ 11″ (1971)
Bodnant	1887		115′ × 14′ 3″ (1966)
Patshull	1898	60′ × 5′ 8″ (1931)	98′ × 10′ 8″ (1970)
Nymans	1898	72′ × 7′ 3″ (1931)	98′ × 13′ 3″ (1970)
Boconnoc	1902	40′ × 8′ 7″ (1927)	80′ × 15′ 5″ (1970)
Headfort	1915		70′ × 14′ 9″ (1966)
Blackmoor	1915	100′ × 9′ 11″ (1961)	105′ × 11′ 1″ (1968)
Wakehurst Place	ca.1916		92′ × 11′ 6″ (1970)
Gurteen le Poer	1925		95′ × 13′ 7″ (1968)
Clonmannon	1926		79′ × 12′ 11″ (1968)
Bedgebury	1926	12′ 6″ (1931)	76′ × 10′ 2″ (1970)
Ffrwdgrech	1931		80′ × 4′ 1″ (1960)
Bedgebury (Plot)	1932		54′ × 5′ 0″ (1968)
Dartington	1934		82′ × 5′ 7″ (1964)
Dartington	1944		69′ × 3′ 11″ (1964)
Queenswood	1953		46′ × 4′ 3″ (1970)

cv. Adpressa (Angers, France, pre-1865) 'Albo-spica'. A rare tree, in a few collections and gardens, in which the new shoot is creamy white and becomes glaucous grey-blue. The leaves are spirally set scale-leaves 1 cm long. Sometimes grown as a dwarf, the figures below show that this is, in the long term unwise, but there is a well known prostrate form.

Pampisford, planted 1877, 63ft×5ft 10in (1969); Grayswood Hill, 73ft×8ft 5in (1971); Leonardslee, 50ft×4ft 1in (1962); Ryston, 20ft×2ft 0in main stem (1969).

cv. Glauca. Leaves short, 6–8 mm glaucous grey blue. Rare.

Warnham Court, 75ft×6ft 9in (1971); Nymans, 69ft×6ft 1in (1970).

RECOGNITION. This tree does not resemble closely any other. The blue-white bands beneath the leaves and winged, white-spotted shoots preclude confusion with yews.

Sequoiadendron Buchholz (Taxodiaceae)

Sequoiadendron giganteum (Lindley) Buchholz. Wellingtonia, Big tree, Mammoth tree.

A single species which has produced the biggest trees in the world. Trees have been felled which were 365 feet tall and about 4,000 years old. The largest now standing is "General Sherman", 272 feet 4 inches tall, 79 feet 1 inch in girth at 5 feet (101ft round at the base). "General Grant" is 267ft 4ins × 79·7ft. The weight of "General Sherman" has been estimated to be 2,145 tons. *Sequoiadendron* has been separated from *Sequoia*, very reasonably, as a tree of quite different aspect, with naked buds, only scale-type leaves and larger cones which take two years to ripen. In growth in girth it is quite unrivalled by any other conifer in these countries. Now restricted as a native to 72 groves on the western slopes of the Sierra Nevada, California. Introduced in 1853, from the Calaveros Grove, to Gourdiehill, Perth (August) and to the Exeter Nurseries (December). Common everywhere except in areas remote from habitation. In lowland areas this tree is prominent in any wide view. It is found on almost every estate in the land, as park, avenue or policy tree, and in churchyards, cemeteries, many parks and in gardens on the outskirts of towns. Rare in Western and Midland Ireland.

Sequoiadendron giganteum

Fig. 178
Foliage and one-year old cones of *Sequoiadendron giganteum*, wellingtonia, with male flowers on shoot (right) and detail of shoot (lower left, ×2⅔). The male flowers shed pollen in February if they escape damage from frost as they open.

Bark. Young trees soon dark brown and shredding. Old trees broadly of two different kinds, 1) boles tapering sharply for 3–4 feet and deeply fluted—bark dark brown, stringy, deeply fissured, blackish as if burned in places. 2) boles little tapered and smoothly circular in cross-section—bark rich red-brown, with shallow, inter-weaving ridges.

Crown. Conic with concave sides from a base which becomes broad, but the apex is long and narrowly pointed. This shape is maintained by some trees more than 150 feet tall and by most trees in Scotland and Ireland, but in Eastern England constant strikes by lightning cause the tops to become rounded and often to carry dead wood. The lower branches descend from the stem and curve upwards at their ends. Although the foliage on each branch is dense, the branches are often sufficiently separated for daylight to be seen through parts of the upper crown. The lower branches of some old trees have been allowed to layer.

Foliage. Shoot pale or grey-green finely speckled with white stomatal spots; curved upwards; second year, (also curved), green scale-leaves on dark red-brown. Shoots at all angles on the branches and branchlets; ultimate shoots unbranched for as much as 8 cm. Whole branchlet systems swept in a curve towards the exterior of the crown; strongly forwards, spreading.

Leaves. Long-triangular, 4–7 mm, pointing forwards, slightly incurved, matt grey-green at first, speckled all over with stomata; dark green and shining by the third year. The foliage is hard and harsh to the touch and readily emits a scent of aniseed.

Flowers and Cone. Male flowers visible before October as whitish ovoids on the ends of all the minor shoots on some branches. Pollen is shed in dry sunny weather in March or April but the flowers are frequently destroyed by frosts during that period. Cones solitary but appear bunched, green for a year and ripen in the second year (in California live seed is held for 30 years); blunt ovoids, 4·5×3 cm, ripening dark brown; the scales flat diamond-shaped, thick, wrinkled, with a fold along the centre-line.

GROWTH. In these countries, growth in height is not spectacular, but it is sustained, until the tree is 150 feet tall on some sheltered sites. (In Northern Italy a tree 17 years old is reported to have grown to 72ft×9ft 2in.) The usual annual increase in height over long periods from the date of planting is about one and a half to two feet. In girth, however, growth is usually extraordinarily rapid and mean annual increases over long periods are commonly two to three inches and sometimes over four inches. An original tree at Castle Menzies, Perthshire had a girth of 21 feet when it was 49 years old. When it was 73 years old its girth was 26 feet but unfortunately it was then in a poor state of health and died soon afterwards. Table 111 includes a number of young trees of very rapid growth and some older trees which have increased in girth recently by more than two inches a year.

SPECIMENS. The first seed came by steam-packet and arrived fresh and produced great numbers of plants, both at Gourdiehill and other estates in the Errol district of Perthshire, and at Exeter. Plants were still being sold that were raised from it, in 1860, or later. It is therefore not possible to say that any tree must, to be an original tree, have been planted before any particular date. The tree had been given great publicity and was much in demand. The plants were available. This tree never blows down and dead specimens are rarely observed. The result is that original trees or probable original trees are on estates in almost every county. There are also very many equally huge and fine trees of later plantings and of unknown dates. A very restricted list of the largest of these together with some young trees is given in Table 111.

TABLE 111. OUTSTANDING TREES OF SEQUOIADENDRON GIGANTEUM

Locality	*Date Planted*	*Dimensions*	
Taymouth Castle	1854	114′ × 17′ 0″ (1931)	157′ × 23′ 2″ (1970)
Castle Leod	1854		150′ × 25′ 11″ (1966)
Smeaton House	1855	78′ × 12′ 9″ (1905)	110′ × 20′ 11″ (1966)
Bradfield House	1855		94′ × 21′ 3″ (1959)
Ombersley Court	1855		124′ × 21′ 3″ (1964)
Penrhyn Castle	1856	108′ × 18′ 9″ (1931)	115′ × 23′ 8″ (1959)
Cuffnells	1856		135′ × 19′ 9″ (1970)
Durris House	1856	92′ × 16′ 0″ (1931)	121′ × 23′ 0″ (1970)
Holme Lacey	1856		120′ × 22′ 8″ (1962)
Blairquhan	1856		95′ × 21′ 0″ (1970)
Fassaro House	ca.1856		95′ × 22′ 2″ (1968)
Dunkeld House	1857	91′ × 16′ 0″ (1931)	149′ × 22′ 0″ (1970)
Poltalloch		110′ × 20′ 0″ (1931)	120′ × 26′ 5″ (1969)
Keir House	1857	84′ × 17′ 0″ (1931)	128′ × 20′ 6″ (1970)
Highclere		97′ × 13′ 0″ (1906)	115′ × 23′ 10″ (1968)
Stratfield Saye	1857	85′ × 12′ 0″ (1903)	118′ × 24′ 4″ (1968)
Buchanan Castle	1857	71′ × 9′ 3″ (1900)	124′ × 19′ 2″ (1971)
Woodhouse		120′ × 15′ 9″ (1931)	158′ × 22′ 2″ (1970)
Powis Castle			112′ × 28′ 3″ (1970)
Crichel House			112′ × 29′ 5″ (1971)
Kinnettles	1859	75′ × 16′ 0″ (1931)	98′ × 22′ 4″ (1970)
Dropmore	1859		111′ × 19′ 7″ (1970)
Glenlee Park			160′ × 22′ 3″ (1970)
Dupplin Castle	1859	96′ × 16′ 6″ (1931)	138′ × 23′ 1″ (1970)
Endsleigh		90–100′ × 13′ 6″ (1931)	165′ × 22′ 0″ (1970)
Endsleigh			152′ × 18′ 8″ (1970)
Glendoick (Matthew's Seed)	1860	83′ × 15′ 3″ (1931)	118′ × 19′ 6″ (1970)
Westonbirt			145′ × 21′ 1″ (1971)
Melbury			124′ × 21′ 5″ (1970)
Rhinefield (near)	1861		153′ × 23′ 4″ (1970)
Bolderwood	1861		153′ × 23′ 4″ (1968)[1]
Glamis Castle	1861	100′ × 11′ 0″ (1931)	133′ × 16′ 3″ (1970)
Powerscourt	1861		130′ × 23′ 5″ (1966)
Powerscourt	1861		124′ × 25′ 10″ (1966)
Dropmore	1862		118′ × 24′ 6″ (1970)
Scone Palace		93′ × 16′ 7″ (1931)	115′ × 26′ 8″ (1970)
Woburn	1863	104′ × 18′ 0″ (1931)	121′ × 23′ 2″ (1970)
Woburn	1863		124′ × 20′ 2″ (1970)
Shirley Hall			110′ × 24′ 9″ (1968)
Kilkerran			128′ × 20′ 3″ (1970)

[1] In summer 1970 the top 25 feet died back

(*continues*)

Table 111 (*continued*) *Outstanding Trees of Sequoiadendron giganteum*

Locality	*Date Planted*		*Dimensions*
Castlewellan			111′ × 25′ 11″ (1970)
Munches			100′ × 22′ 9″ (1970)
Balmacaan House			95′ × 27′ 0″ (1970)
Achamore, Killin			131′ × 22′ 9″ (1970)
Doune House			144′ × 22′ 3″ (1970)
Whiteways House			108′ × 24′ 10″ (1965)
Eridge Castle	1868		138′ × 20′ 5″ (1970)
Stourhead			131′ × 19′ 5″ (1970)
Crowthorne Avenue	1869		108′ × 22′ 9″ (1969)
Cowdray Park	1870	103′ × 18′ 0″ (1931)	105′ × 26′ 2″ (1967)
Curraghmore	1871	106′ × 19′ 8″ (1931)	120′ × 22′ 0″ (1968)
Curraghmore			135′ × 19′ 2″ (1968)
Kilravock Castle			128′ × 21′ 10″ (1970)
Dupplin (Gardens)		94′ × 11′ 6″ (1931)	144′ × 18′ 3″ (1970)
Sindlesham (Bear Wood)			98′ × 24′ 0″ (1970)
Rossie Priory			134′ × 16′ 6″ (1970)
Knightshayes			136′ × 21′ 0″ (1970)
Cortachy Castle	1872		134′ × 22′ 5″ (1970)
Oakley Park			111′ × 24′ 11″ (1971)
Nuneham Court			122′ × 19′ 9″ (1970)
Sheffield Park			120′ × 22′ 2″ (1968)
Tilgate Forest Lodge			104′ × 23′ 5″ (1961)
Escot			134′ × 21′ 0″ (1965)
Engelfield House			120′ × 22′ 2″ (1968)
Leighton Park			136′ × 18′ 2″ (1967)
Mells Park			126′ × 20′ 2″ (1962)
Achnagarry			124′ × 24′ 8″ (1962)
Queen's Spinney			137′ × 20′ 0″ (1967)
Stratfield Saye	1875		105′ × 19′ 3″ (1968)
Bodnant	1888		132′ × 15′ 8″ (1966)
Abercairny	1888		115′ × 17′ 7″ (1962)
Kirkennan	1890	90′ × 12′ 9″ (1931)	130′ × 18′ 5″ (1970)
Land of Nod	1905		90′ × 16′ 5″ (1964)
Little Hall	1910	44′ × 4′ 6″ (1931)	70′ × 10′ 4″ (1961)
Clonmannon	1926		78′ × 9′ 5″ (1968)
Bedgebury	1926	65′ × 12′ 2″ (1965)	76′ × 13′ 8″ (1969)
Sidbury Manor	1936		49′ × 7′ 4″ (1966)
Alice Holt	1951	36′ × 3′ 6″ (1965)	49′ × 5′ 3″ (1970)
Fairburn			131′ × 20′ 11″ (1970)
Fairburn			124′ × 21′ 8″ (1970)
Benmore (Avenue)			133′ × 20′ 0″ (1970)
Benmore (Avenue)			146′ × 17′ 10″ (1970)
Nettlecombe			111′ × 21′ 6″ (1971)

cv. Aureum (Cork 1856). A slow-growing form with dull yellow new shoots, upswept in rather dense bunches. Very rare.

Pampisford, 53ft × 6ft 2in (1969); Batsford Park, 66ft × 4ft 3in (1964).

cv. Pendulum (Nantes 1863. Distributed 1873). The branches are inserted almost vertically downwards and their foliage lies closely around the stem. A few retain a vertical axis but many bend over in a hoop, when a few branches will rise vertically from the upper parts. Rare.

Bodnant, planted 1890, 92ft × 6ft 10in (1966); Brooklands House, 49ft × 7ft 2in (1959) arches out 14 yards; Inveraray Castle, 75ft × 6ft 6in (1969); Tittenhurst Park, 50ft × 3ft 11in (1963); Highnam, 36ft × 4ft 4in (1970).

Taiwania Hayata (Taxodiaceae)

One or two species from Formosa and China, closest to *Cryptomeria* in foliage but to *Cunninghamia* in the cone.

Taiwania cryptomerioides

Fig. 179
Foliage of *Taiwania cryptomerioides* is blue-grey when new and remains glaucous tinted as each face of the deeply keeled leaf has a broad band of bluish-white. The branchlets are pendulous. Detail ×1½.

Taiwania cryptomerioides Hayata.

Formosa, China and Northern Burma. Introduced in 1920. Rare; confined to collections mainly in the south and west and in Ireland.

BARK. Pale reddish-brown; scaly.

CROWN. A small, gaunt tree with few branches, level then curved downwards, with pendulous foliage.

FOLIAGE. Leaves spirally set, on hanging shoots, with rather more in one plane than the other, broad-based, covering the shoot; tapering regularly then sharply to a fine, spined point, pointing slightly forward, some curved, 1–1·5 cm pale green with a broad band of bluish-white stomata each side.

SPECIMENS. Killerton, 44ft × 1ft 7in (1970); Bodnant, 27ft × 2ft 1in died back to 17ft (1966) and 26ft × 1ft 2in (1959); Sidbury Manor, 24ft × 1ft 1in (1959); Embley Park, 31ft × 2ft 7in (1971); Garinish Island, 36ft × 2ft 5in; 26ft × 1ft 4in (1966); Headfort, planted 1928, 26ft × 2ft 6in (1966); Holkham, 26ft × 1ft 2in (1968); Wakehurst Place, 24ft × 1ft (1970); Tregrehan, 26ft × 1ft 6in (1971).

RECOGNITION. A gaunt, pendulous spiny sort of *Cryptomeria* with glaucous leaves.

Taiwania flousiana Gaussen.

Formosa. As grown at Jermyn's House, this form differs from *T. cryptomerioides* in softer, less spiny foliage which is grassy-green, not glaucous, as the stomatal bands each side are thin and grey-green. The leaves are pectinate in one plane—mostly on one side of the shoot; 1·5 cm.

Taxodium Richard (Taxodiaceae)

Two or three closely related deciduous or semi-evergreen trees from Southern U.SA. and Mexico. Short lateral branchlets have no terminal nor axillary buds and are deciduous as in *Metasequoia.* The leaves of the persistent shoots are radially set and scale like; those of the deciduous shoots are pectinate and linear. All leaves and branches are alternate or spiral not opposite as they are in *Metasequoia.*

Taxodium ascendens Brongniart. Pond cypress

South-east United States; Virginia to Alabama. Introduced in 1789. Rare. Confined to collections in southern England and in Ireland.

BARK. Dull brown, vertically fissured into short ridges.
CROWN. Narrowly conic, domed at the apex; branches small, level.
FOLIAGE. Deciduous shoots arise from all round quite stout branchlets, in erect sprays 10–13 cm long with small leaves, bright green, minutely pointed, 5–10 mm long, appressed all round each shoot. Otherwise as in *T. distichum.*
SPECIMENS. Blackmoor, planted 1871, 50 feet (1968); Knaphill Nurseries, 53ft×6ft 10in; 51ft×5ft 7in (1961); Valentines Park, 73ft×6ft 2in (1954); Lydhurst, 38ft×3ft 7in (1965); Syon House, 78ft×8ft 6in (1967); Sheffield Park, 53ft×3ft 7in (1968); Nymans, 46ft×3ft 4in (1970); Glasnevin Botanic Garden, 44ft×3ft 9in (1966); Woburn Abbey, 51ft×5ft 2in (1970); Bury Hill, 46ft×5ft 11in (1971).

cv. Nutans. Apparently occurring within the population of *T. ascendens* and introduced with the type in 1789. This plant has a history of nomenclatural confusion, being grown sometimes as *Glyptostrobus pendulus* and long known as *T. distichum pendulum.* It differs from *T. ascendens* in having a more dense crown of paler foliage which begins to droop in mid-season, especially the shoots at the ends of the branches. The branch ends arch downward. The leaves are smaller, 4–5 mm closely appressed except at the apex.

Pencarrow, planted 1841, 31ft (broken)×4ft 7in 1970; Kew Royal Botanic Gardens, 52ft×4ft 0in (1970); Grayswood Hill, 34ft×3ft 2in (1971); Wakehurst Place, 37ft×1ft 8in (1964); Garinish Island (County Kerry), 31ft×1ft 5in (1966); Blackmoor, 50ft×3ft 6in (1968).

In these islands this form suffers more from spring frosts than does the type, and many have suffered frequent loss of their leading shoot causing a twiggy, domed apex to form, with negligible increase in height over many years. On the Continent, however, it is reported to be very hardy.

Taxodium distichum

Fig. 180
Foliage and cone of *Taxodium distichum,* Swamp cypress. Many trees bear male catkins but cones are less often seen. The side-shoots are shed with the leaves in late November or December. The slender, thin leaves (left×1⅓) have broad bands on the underside slightly paler green than is the upper surface.

Taxodium distichum (Linnaeus) Richards. Swamp, or Bald cypress

From New Jersey along the coast to Texas and up the Mississippi Valley to Indiana. Introduced in 1640. Common in South England, in parks and large gardens, especially in and near London; rare in North England, South Scotland and in Ireland; not seen north of Perth.

BARK. Dull reddish brown, shallowly ridged in a diagonal network, or smooth but stripping in fine, stringy threads. Frequently deeply fluted.
CROWN. Variable but basically conic; some slender conic to a pointed apex; others broadly conic to a domed apex; some columnar in the lower half; some irregular and broad. Usually densely branched and densely twigged but some quite sparse. Many old trees have heavy low, upswept branches.
FOLIAGE. Persistent shoots green, turning pink-brown then dark purple-brown. Deciduous shoots green, to 10 cm long with 80–100 alternately set leaves, pectinate 1×0·2 cm parallel-sided, abruptly acute; pale green both sides; two broad slightly paler bands beneath. The leaves emerge

TABLE 112. SOME SPECIMEN TREES OF TAXODIUM DISTICHUM

Locality	*Date Planted*	*Dimensions*	
Dean Court, Wimborne			100′ × 17′ 8″ (1968)[1]
Burwood Park			105′ × 17′ 7″ (1965)
The Rectory, Much Hadham			90′ × 15′ 5″ (1964)
Syon House (Duke's Walk)	ca.1750	85′ × 10′ 3″ (1905)	98′ × 12′ 9″ (1969)
Syon House (Lake, South)	ca.1750	90′ × 12′ 0″ (1903)	96′ × 14′ 6″ (1967)[2]
Syon House (Park)	ca.1750		90′ × 14′ 6″ (1967)
Stratfield Saye		63′ × 9′ 0″ (1903)	82′ × 12′ 10″ (1968)[3]
Broadlands			117′ × 14′ 9″ (1968)
Pusey House			85′ × 14′ 1″ (1968)
Wootton House (Dorset)	ca.1790		87′ × 13′ 1″ (1959)
Briggens	ca.1795		70′ × 10′ 10″ (1969)
Longford Castle		× 8′ 10″ (1904)	112′ × 12′ 0″ (1962)
Oxenford Grange			72′ × 12′ 1″ (1959)
Blenheim Park			105′ × 13′ 1″ (1965)
Stocklinch Manor			97′ × 12′ 10″ (1965)
St. Annes Court			77′ × 14′ 2″ (1965)
St. Annes Court			100′ × 10′ 8″ (1965)
Lytchett Minster School			78′ × 12′ 5″ (1968)
Silvermere			88′ × 13′ 0″ (1968)
Fawley Court			77′ × 13′ 0″ (1968)
Bowood			90′ × 13′ 4″ (1953)
Bowood		72′ × 9′ 0″ (1931)	83′ × 10′ 8″ (1957)
Knaphill Nurseries		85′ × 9′ 4″ (1931)	78′ × 10′ 5″ (1962)
Frogmore		80′ × 8′ 6″ (1905)	90′ × 10′ 3″ (1967)
Kenwood House			90′ × 11′ 1″ (1964)
West Harling			81′ × 11′ 10″ (1963)
Munden			80′ × 11′ 2″ (1968)
Springfield Court			70′ × 11′ 8″ (1968)
Hurn Court			90′ × 10′ 9″ (1968)
Ash Cottage, Dulwich			87′ × 10′ 5″ (1957)
Fairlawne			90′ × 10′ 6″ (1965)
Arnos Park			90′ × 10′ 3″ (1954)
Oxford Botanic Garden	1840		72′ × 8′ 5″ (1970)
Dropmore	1843	60′ × 5′ 9″ (1904)	93′ × 8′ 11″ (1970)
Whiteknights			85′ × 10′ 3″ (1971)
Whiteknights			84′ × 10′ 1″ (1971)
Holme Lacey			68′ × 10′ 6″ (1962)
Woburn Abbey			69′ × 10′ 3″ (1970)
Kinfauns			57′ × 7′ 6″ (1970)
Wilton House	1904	28′ × 3′ 4″ (1931)	49′ × 7′ 2″ (1961)
Castle Kennedy	1906	24′ × 1′ 3″ (1926)	52′ × 6′ 0″ (1967)
Bedgebury	1929	4′ 6″ (1931)	45′ × 4′ 2″ (1969)
Bedgebury	1929		49′ × 3′ 10″ (1969)
Tower Court	ca.1935		42′ × 2′ 10″ (1965)
Westonbirt	1929		55′ × 4′ 0″ (1971)

[1] Measured at 6 feet
[2] Measured at 4 feet
[3] Main stem. Other × 7′ 2″

enough to give the crown a soft haze of green by mid-May, although some shoots show green in South West England sometimes as early as March; but the tree is fully in leaf only by June. The leaves turn bright rusty red in late October and darker to a deep russet during November. They may remain on the tree until the end of the year. Pneumatophores ("knees") arise from the roots of many trees growing beside water, but not from all such trees. They may arise in wet hollows 20 yards away from the water, but rarely in land, however poorly drained, unless adjacent to standing water.

GROWTH. Growth in height starts in early June (rarely in very early seasons, in early May) and continues until late August or mid-September. Shoots seldom exceed 1 foot 6 inches and growth is far from rapid. Mean annual increases in girth can exceed 1½ inches but is less than one inch in old trees. Some of the finest trees are growing far removed from open water and whilst many of these are in the old flood-plains of rivers, a few are well above.

This is a very healthy species, rarely seen in anything but thriving condition even if not of great vigour. No dead tree has been found, and the specimens known to be more than

200 years old are as healthy as any. It must be a very long-lived tree.

FLOWERS AND CONE. Male flowers often prominent throughout the winter as 3–4 thick catkins at the ends of all minor shoots. These lengthen from 5–6 cm to 10–30 cm when shedding pollen in April, the flowers being spread down the catkin, scattered at the top end, ovoid, 2 mm, yellow and green until ripe. Cone on a short stalk, globular, 3×2·5 cm, light green until ripe, few scales, with slightly thickened edges and obscure central spines. Cones are borne on the same trees as male flowers, but many flowering trees rarely produce a cone.

SPECIMENS. The two trees first in the table are so much larger than any others including those of "Capability" Brown's planting at Syon (ca.1750) that it is tempting to think that they could be original trees from the seed sent in 1640. They are remarkably similar in size and appearance. There are no trees with known exact dates of planting before 1843 and few with any sort of dating, from which to judge, but those of 1750–1795 are much smaller.

RECOGNITION. *Taxodium* is at all times distinguishable from *Metasequoia* by the alternate buds and twigs with close pink-brown bark not flaking away. In leaf the much narrower and smaller leaves are also alternately placed and the buds are axillary, not beneath the shoots.

cv. Aureum Bright golden foliage. Woburn Abbey, 66ft× 6ft 9in (1970); Poles, 53ft×5ft (1969). Not hitherto reported.

Taxodium mucronatum Tenore. Mexican cypress (*T. distichum* var. *mucronatum*).

Mexico.

The remarkable tree at Santa Maria del Tule, famed for its size and age was, in 1949, 120ft×112ft. (The figure of 150 feet for the girth is obtained by the totally illegitimate practice of pushing the tape into every flute). It has been shown by D. L. Clarke that the age of this tree lies between 750 and 1000 years. Introduction not recorded. One tree at Kew in 1956 was 57ft×4ft 4in. A few other small plants are known. The foliage does not differ from that of *T. distichum* in any constant way except that it remains green until the New Year or the next Spring. Flowers open in autumn.

Taxus Linnaeus (Taxaceae)

A genus of closely related species, spread across the northern hemisphere and divisible into 8 or 9 species as much by their geographical position in some cases, as by differences in foliage. Bushy trees or shrubs, distinguished by the seeds borne in scarlet fleshy cups. They are dioecious.

Taxus baccata

Fig. 181
Foliage and flowers of *Taxus baccata*, Common yew; male flower pollinating (upper right ×6⅓), with foliage of female plant (right), female flower (upper left ×4) and fruit (lower right ×4).

Taxus baccata Linnaeus. Common yew

Algeria, Northern Persia and Europe, including Britain. A few ancient native yew-woods survive on the chalklands as at Kingley Vale in the South Downs and some patches on the Marlborough Downs. Abundant on or near chalk and limestone areas as understorey in broadleaved woods and in hedgerows. Common in gardens with old shrubberies and as shelter-belts or screens, also as clipped hedges. The classic plant for topiary work and for the tall hedge behind a herbaceous border. Almost universal in churchyards and cemeteries. Old parish churches in English and Welsh villages have a unique assemblage of the biggest yews known in Europe. With the exception of a few in Middlesex and Derbyshire, all the biggest and most famous lie within a crescent shaped region from Kent, Surrey and Sussex through Hampshire, Wiltshire, Somerset and part of Devon, north through Gloucestershire and Monmouthshire to Herefordshire, then a gap to Merionethshire, Denbighshire and Flint. Of the many reasons for growing yews in churchyards, the placing of bow-stave trees out of the way of cattle who might be poisoned by browsing them, is the least satisfactory. English yews give short, knotty timber and bow-staves were imported from the Iberian Peninsula with sherry and other wines. The view of Cornish that they were planted to give the best shelter from the South-west winds to resting pall-bearers, especially near the church porch and the path to it, seems most often to be correct.

Bark. Dark purplish-brown, smooth and scaling away to leave pale red-brown, yellowish and purple patches; in oldest trees sometimes stringy and usually deeply fluted, often much burred, may be with dense clusters of sprouts.

Crown. Young trees broadly and obtusely conic, open, with level, wide-spreading branches. Old trees irregular and broadly domed, frequently on many stems from the base or from very low on the bole.

Foliage. Shoot dark green, often brownish above, grooved by leaf-bases; second year partly striped pinkish-brown; third year light pinkish-brown.

Bud. Minute greenish-brown ovoid, 2–3 mm.

Leaves. Pectinate above and below, pointing well forwards, some lying along the shoot in many trees; of mixed lengths, usually 2–3 cm some to 4·5 cm; 3 mm broad, with a broad central rib; deep shining green above, very matt pale or yellowish green beneath with darker midrib and margins; parallel sided to a sharp, short point. The buds leave rosettes of pink-brown scales at the base of the year's growth.

Flowers and Fruit. Male flowers minute and globular along the underside of new shoots, shedding pollen in sometimes visible clouds, in February or March. Female flowers on separate trees, dark green minute, one or two per shoot in the axils of leaves near the the shoot-tip. These ripen into bright red fleshy cups each with a deep cavity; 1×0·6 cm.

Growth. Early height-growth is 8in–12in a year but this is not long maintained and during the many hundreds of years of maturity no increase in height is normally made. Growth in girth can be one inch per year for about one hundred years but after that it decreases, and continues to decrease for many hundreds of years, except where sprouts on the bole are incorporated into the bole. One clean-boled tree cut in a Somerset churchyard showed 500 rings; the outer one and a half inches showed 110 rings, a girth increase of 1 inch each 11½ years. Many of the biggest yews have been measured on a number of occasions and this ought to provide a splendid guide to the rates of increase, and thus the ages of old yews. Unfortunately the measurements are hopelessly unreliable and usually decrease at subsequent visits. Many trees are several feet less in girth now than was claimed in 1883 and almost none of the earlier data can therefore be used. A notable exception is Gilbert White's figure for the Selborne yew, 23 feet at 3 feet in 1789. This tree is now 25 feet 10 inches at 3 feet, an addition of 34 inches in 180 years, or less than one inch each five years.

That the yew is the tree living to the greatest age in Britain is not seriously challenged. It is astonishingly tenacious of life, hardy and tough in every way. All the trees above about 15 feet in girth are hollow. The biggest are enormously hollow and may have been so for 500 years, but their perimeters and crowns grow with undiminished vigour. There are a few trees with clean boles 30 feet round at 5 feet. Even if these could have a mean annual growth of one inch in two years, they need to be 750 years old. In fact it is certain that their more recent growth has been very much slower, about one third of that rate, and they must be more than 1000 years old. Even where sprouts have been incorporated, this can increase the rate only if it happens regularly, and then not by a great amount, for these too grow very slowly indeed.

SPECIMENS. The only trees of known date are given first in Table 113, to show the rates of growth in early life.

TABLE 113. TREES OF KNOWN DATE OF TAXUS BACCATA

Locality	*Date Planted*	*Dimensions*
Waltham St. Lawrence	1655	× 12′ 10″ (1966)
Sutton Church, Sussex	1660	× 12′ 3″ (1966)
Edinburgh R.B.G.	1789 (1824)	× 8′ 8″ (1967)[1]
Middle Woodford Rectory	1832	30′ × 10′ 6″ (1967)

[1] This was "Sutherland's Yew", moved from the Old Botanic Garden in 1824. It blew over in January 1968

The aberrations of past measurements of yews are beyond belief. For example, the tree at Tisbury has a well-defined, clean, if irregular, bole at least 5 feet long. It has been found to have a girth which has dilated and shrunk in the following way:—37 feet (1834 Loudon), 30 feet 6 inches (1892 Lowe), 35 feet (1903 Elwes and Henry), 29 feet 8 inches (1924 E. Swanton), 31 feet 0 inches (1959 Mitchell). A yew with a ten-feet bole at Icklesham, Sussex had girths of 15 feet 6 inches (1896), 19 feet (1944) and 13 feet 11 inches (1965). Even the yew with the cleanest and smoothest 10 feet of bole in any churchyard, at Stowting, Kent has been given as 20 feet 8 inches in 1895, 22 feet 6 inches in 1944 and 20 feet 4 inches in 1965. Earlier measurements have therefore been omitted except for a few rather arbitrarily accepted as likely to have been somewhere near correct, and at the same height on the bole as the recent one given, and also those of the 1932 Report as these seem to be accurate and show the growth made since then.

Many inflated figures can easily be ascribed to measuring at 3 or 5 feet on trees with many stems springing apart near the base. In these trees, the girth should be taken only at the point of minimum girth, whether at 2 feet, 1 foot or even at ground level. Often a large burr needs to be avoided and prevents measurement at 5 feet. All but two of the trees listed in Table 114 stand in churchyards.

The famous tree at Fortingall, Perthshire lives, but can no longer be measured for any useful comparisons. A hulk which was perhaps a tenth of the complete bole bears a large and healthy crown. The original ground-plan can be partly seen and accords roughly with the figure of 52 feet girth given in 1769 by the Hon. Daines Barrington. In the same year it was given as 56 feet by Pennant. From what has been stated here it would obviously be unwise to accept these figures as relating to a good bole at 5 feet from the ground. Even if, however, they were taken at ground-level and were a foot or two on the optimistic side, it seems improbable that a yew could reach this size in less than some 1300 years. The tree can now be regarded as some 1500 years old and thus by a wide margin the oldest tree living in the country.

Tall yews, in woods and gardens. There are remarkable groups of tall yews at Lowther Castle, at Fairlawne and the avenues of the Close Walks, Midhurst. The largest tree in the natural wood at Kingley Vale is 35ft × 18ft 2in (at 3 feet).

Table 114. Trees of Exceptional Girth; Taxus baccata

A. Measured at 5 feet on the bole

Locality	*Dimensions*		*Remarks*
Tandridge, Surrey		45′ × 33′ 4″ (1959)	Female. 3 stems
Cold Waltham, Sussex		40′ × 30′ 11″ (1959)	Very hollow
Hambledon, Surrey		40′ × 30′ 11″ (1959)	Very hollow
Loose, Maidstone, Kent		45′ × 30′ 10″ (1961)	Male. Gaps in bole
Tisbury, Wilts		35′ × 31′ 0″ (1959)	
Crowhurst, Surrey		35′ × 30′ 4″ (1959)	
Farringdon, Hants		40′ × 29′ 6″ (1958)	Male
Gresford, Denbigh	× 27′ 6″ (1878)	35′ × 29′ 6″ (1961)	Male. Fine tree
Keffolds, Haslemere, Surrey		48′ × 29′ 0″ (1961)	Female. Bole 9ft Splendid tree
Lockerley, Hants	× 23′ 4″ (1896)	45′ × 26′ 6″ (1960)	
Selborne, Hants		65′ × 26′ 4″ (1963)	Fine, but short, bole
Boarhunt, Hants		30′ × 25′ 7″ (1961)	Male. × 27ft 10in at 1ft
Crowhurst, Sussex	× 26′ 9″ (1896)	38′ × 27′ 10″ (1965)	Female. Fine tree
Priors Dean, Hants		53′ × 24′ 9″ (1961)	Female. Two stems
Itchen Abbas, Hants		35′ × 24′ 6″ (1960)	
Broadwell, Glos.		45′ × 24′ 0″ (1960)	
Dartington, Devon		30′ × 23′ 6″ (1962)	
Durley, Hants		45′ × 23′ 5″ (1963)	
Church Preen, Salop	× 19′ (1789)	45′ × 22′ 6″ (1962)	Bole 8ft Fine tree
Stowting, Kent		47′ × 20′ 4″ (1965)	Bole 10ft clear

B. Measured at 4 feet on the bole

Locality	*Dimensions*		*Remarks*
Linton, Hereford		× 33′ 8″ (1965)	
Much Marcle, Hereford		× 30′ 6″ (1965)	Seat around the inside

C. Measured at 3 feet on the bole

Locality	*Dimensions*		*Remarks*
South Hayling, Hants	× 32′ 4″ (1896)	32′ × 33′ 6″ (1961)	Fine tree
Woolland, Dorset		55′ × 29′ 1″ (1963)	Large limb out. Fine tree
Cudham, Kent		35′ × 27′ 6″ (1965)	
Ulcombe, Kent	× 26′ 3″ (1889)	40′ × 27′ 1″ (1965)	
Brockenhurst, Hants	× 18′ (1896)	50′ × 19′ 2″ (1963)	Female. Fine tree

D. Measured at 1 foot on the bole

Locality	*Dimensions*		*Remarks*
Braemore, Hants		25′ × 34′ 6″ (1962)	Female. Enormous crown
Stedham, Kent		30′ × 30′ 6″ (1961)	Male

E. Measured at 6 inches on the bole

Locality	*Dimensions*		*Remarks*
Mamhilad, Monmouth		30′ × 31′ 0″ (1959)	

F. Measured at Ground Level

Locality	*Dimensions*		*Remarks*
Ulcombe, Kent		35′ × 32′ 1″ (1965)	Male
Mamhead, Devon		50′ × 32′ 2″ (1970)	Male. Cup shaped crown

Table 115. Tall Trees and Woodland Trees of Taxus baccata

Locality	*Dimensions*	
Close Walks, Midhurst		85′ × 8′ 3″ (1967)
Close Walks, Midhurst		83′ × 6′ 1″ (1967)
Close Walks, Midhurst		72′ × 10′ 6″ (1967)
Fairlawne		74′ × 7′ 11″ (1965)
Lowther Castle		71′ × 10′ 10″ (1967)
Lowther Castle		71′ × 12′ 11″ (1967)
Pusey House		75′ × 7′ 1″ (1968)
Muncaster Castle		73′ × 8′ 6″ (1955)
Enys	75′ × 8′ 0″ (1928)	75′ × 9′ 0″ (1962)
Westonbirt House	× 12′ 11″ (1931)	51′ × 13′ 7″ (1965) at 3′ 6″
Dunloe Castle	49′ × 11′ 7″ (1931)	42′ × 12′ 10″ (1968)
Walcombe		75′ × 8′ 10″ (1964)
Clonmannon		55′ × 15′ 9″ (1968)

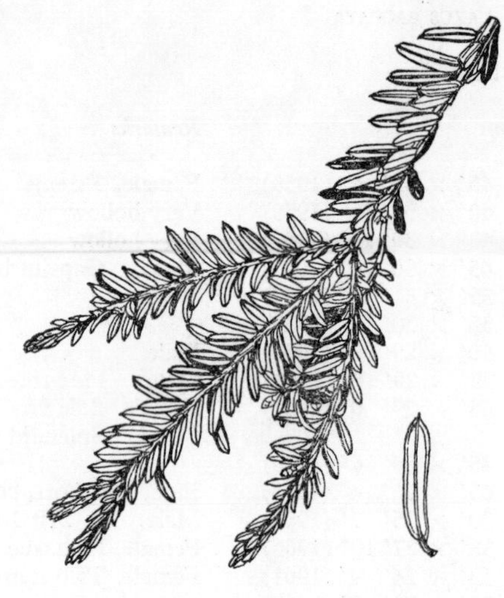

Taxus baccata cv. Adpressa

Fig. 182
The neat, short-leafed foliage of *Taxus baccata* cv. Adpressa, with the underside of a leaf (×1½) showing yellowish-green stomatal bands. A gold-leafed form of this plant is lower and more bushy but is very attractive.

cv. Adpressa (Chester 1828). A widely-spreading obtuse-topped female bush with very small leaves on short, elegant, hanging shoots. The shoots are yellow-brown above and the petioles red-brown. The leaves vary on the same shoot from 6 to 14 mm; 3 mm broad with an abrupt yellow point and pale midrib, the rest dark yellow-green. Thirty-three feet at Westonbirt (Broad Drive).

cv. Adpressa aurea (Sheffield, 1885). A slow-growing, low bush-form of the above with new foliage rich gold and old foliage a good pale gold. Very effective shrub.

cv. Dovastoniana (Westfelton, Salop. 1777). A most striking and distinct plant with straight, single central stem and a wide crown of level branches, each year's new shoots arched slightly; the branches trailing long curtains of hanging, nearly black foliage. It is soon broader than it is tall and will cover a large area of ground. Not common but in many gardens.

cv. Fastigiata (County Fermanagh, ca. 1778). Irish yew. Abundant; in almost every churchyard in the land, and in most formal gardens. Upright with a broad top made up of numerous narrow spires, each long and narrow in the far west where it thrives best, from Cornwall to Argyll; broader and shorter elsewhere. The vertical shoots have small 1 cm slightly curled leaves radiating all round them, and minor shoots from the main ones are very short and also have radial foliage. The two original trees were female and nearly all those seen derive from one of these, but male forms have been found in this century in Norfolk and in West Sussex.

Munches, 54 feet (1970); Pencarrow, 52 feet (1970); Taymouth Castle, 52 feet (1970); Lostwithiel, 46 feet (1957); Lamellan, 44 feet (1962); Blairquhan, 46 feet (1970); Gurteen le Poer, 45 feet (1968); Newton St. Cyr, 42 feet (1967); Strachur, 41 feet (1969); Bedgebury, planted 1928, 12 feet (1967).

RECOGNITION. The form and colour resemble *Cephalotaxus harringtonia* cv. Fastigiata but the leaves are very much smaller, not whorled with age and the shoots are much more branched.

cv. Fastigiata Aureomarginata (Sheffield, 1880). A form with bright golden new growth fading to light green. This appears to be a vigorous, if rare form, for a tree at Westonbirt House is 58ft × 7ft 5in (1967).

Taxus baccata cv. Fastigiata

Fig. 183
Foliage of *Taxus baccata* cv. Fastigiata, the Irish yew, a dark, upright bushy tree found in nearly every churchyard.

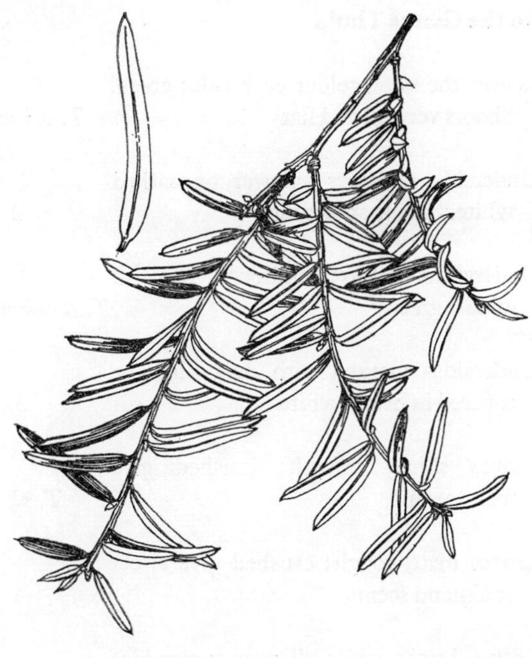

Taxus celebica

Fig. 184
Taxus celebica, Chinese yew, a rare species with distant leaves, irregularly set and much curved backwards. The leaves are yellow-green both sides, paler and very matt beneath (top left, $\times 1\frac{1}{3}$).

Taxus cuspidata

Fig. 185
Fruiting spray and foliage of *Taxus cuspidata,* Japanese yew. The fruit are closely bunched and the leaves held well above the shoot. The underside of the leaf (right $\times 1\frac{1}{3}$) is a bright golden-brown and there is a small spine at the tip.

Taxus celebica (Warburg) Li. Chinese yew

China. Introduced in 1908. Very rare, in a few collections. A broad shrub with an open crown of level branches from a many-stemmed centre. Shoot slender, pale green with bare lengths; second year light brown and ribbed. Leaves very sparse 1–2×0·3 cm, pectinate, curved, some curving backwards in a flat plane, abruptly narrowed to a short spine, shiny pale green above, matt yellowish green below with green midrib. Male flowers sparse, 2 mm ovoids on 1 mm stalk. Fruit 2–3 together 5×5 mm remaining green in this country, with dark olive caps. Bedgebury, 3 plants 15–20 feet tall, Bicton, 16ft×11in (1968).

RECOGNITION. The thin, sparse, pale foliage is unique.

Taxus cuspidata Siebold and Zuccarini. Japanese yew

Japan. Introduced in 1855. Rare; in a few collections. A large shrub. Shoot green until the third year when the decurrent leaf bases are still green but the rest of the shoot is pink-brown. Leaves curved up or straight up like dove's wings or *Cephalotaxus harringtonia* var. *drupacea*, with a 1 mm petiole, 2–3·5 cm×0·3 cm, hard, stiff, tapering to a sharp, often hooked spine; slightly shiny blackish green with a broad central ridge; yellow-green to golden-green beneath. Female plants fruit densely in bunches, pink-green with deep grey-green ends, 7–8 mm; ripening pale scarlet.

Borde Hill, 18ft×1ft 11in (1958); Bedgebury, 25ft×1ft 5in (1969).

cv. Nigra. A very rare male form with more densely set, smaller (1·5 cm) leaves, more or less pectinate, some laid forwards but not raised as in the type.

Bedgebury, planted 1935, 12 feet (1969).

RECOGNITION. Despite an understandable caution in identifying yews as species, when *T. baccata* is so variable, this species is easily identified. The upstanding hard, spiny leaves with curious golden-green undersides are sufficient, but female plants in fruit are even more evident. Only the next species could cause confusion, but the differences in leaves above still hold.

Taxus × media (Massachusetts, ca. 1900) *T. baccata* × *T. cuspidata.*

A hybrid intermediate between the parents. Rare and mostly seen as—

cv. Hicksii (New Jersey, ca. 1900). An upright shrub, like a larger-leaved Irish yew but with short spines on the 2 cm leaves; pale green beneath the leaf, and abundant big, shining, bright scarlet fruit 1×1 cm.

Thuja Linnaeus (Cupressaceae)

Six species from North America and East Asia, with scale-leaves in four ranks of two opposite sets and, mostly, highly aromatic foliage. Small lateral branchlets are shed after several years. Cones small, fusiform with few leathery scales.

Thuja koraiensis

Fig. 186
Foliage of *Thuja koraiensis*, which is either blue-grey or yellow-green above, extensively silvered beneath, and has a rich almond-flavoured fragrance. Below are a seed (×13⅓); detail of shoot, underside (×4); opening cone (×4) and male flowers, on nodding shoots (×⅜), with female flowers at base, seen from beneath.

Key to the Genus Thuja

1. Leaves the same colour each side; green. Shoots vertical and flat — *T. orientalis*

1. Undersides of leaves yellower, or marked white. Shoots spreading — 2

2. Undersides of leaves uniform yellowish or pale green — *T. occidentalis*

2. Undersides marked with dull white or covered in bright white — 3

3. Leaves shiny, smooth; crushed give fruity aroma — *T. plicata*

3. Leaves matt, rough; crushed give sweet or almond scents — 4

4. Leaves bright white all over underside; scent of almonds — *T. koraiensis*

Leaves with small dull white marks beneath; scent of oil of citrinella — *T. standishii*

Thuja koraiensis Nakai. Korean thuja

Korea. Introduced in 1918. Rare but in many large collections.

BARK. Pinkish-brown, peeling away in thin scales.

CROWN. Usually narrowly conic with rather few branches level then curved up at their ends, but can be a low mound; either pale bright green or silvery blue-green.

FOLIAGE. Shoots stout, soon coppery-orange then brown. Leaves flat, broad, in flat sprays, matt soft pale grey-green, often tipped with white stomata, new leaves often bloomed bluish-white or deep blue-green; undersides thickly crusted in bright white often obscuring the midrib and margins. Crushed foliage gives a scent of rich fruit-cake with plenty of almonds. Minor sprays are crowded and overlap.

FLOWERS. Male flowers quite frequent, at the tips of down-curled ultimate shoots, globular, 1 mm, green tipped black.

GROWTH. Over most of the country this grows very slowly; only a few inches a year; but in areas of the west with a high rainfall, annual shoots may exceed one foot.

RECOGNITION. The only *Thuja* with a fully silvered underside, or a scent of almonds.

TABLE 116. NOTEWORTHY TREES OF THUJA KORAIENSIS

Locality	*Date Planted*	*Dimensions*
Borde Hill. W.9244		19′ × 10″ (1968)
Westonbirt (Off Willesley Drive)	1937	27′ × 1′ 1″ (1970)
Wakehurst Place		17′ × 8″ (1970)
Bicton		32′ × 1′ 10″ (1968)
Dawyck		25′ × 1′ 5″ (1961)
Hergest Croft	1925	33′ × 1′ 11″ (1963)
Hergest Croft	1925	30′ × 1′ 9″ (1961)
Bedgebury	1925	21′ × 1′ 3″ (1970)
Bedgebury	1925	22′ × 11″ (1970)
Garinish Island		21′ × 1′ 3″ (1966)
Headfort		23′ × 2′ 3″ (1966)

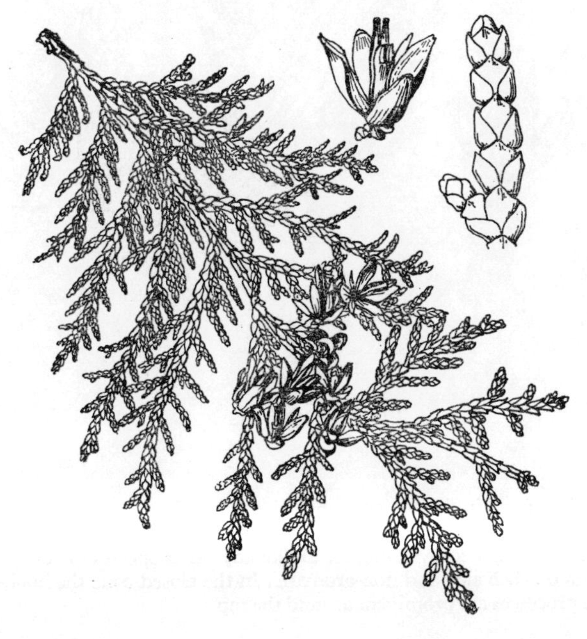

Thuja occidentalis

Fig. 187
Spray with cones of *Thuja occidentalis* from Eastern North America. The foliage is strongly fragrant of apples (cooked) and is uniformly matt yellow-green beneath. (Upper right × 4). The open cones (upper × 1⅓) adhere to the shoot for many months.

Thuja occidentalis Linnaeus. White cedar

Nova Scotia east to Saskatchewan, south to Minnesota and Tennessee. Introduced in 1536 (the first tree from America) or, possibly, 1596. Common nearly everywhere, often as one of the many cultivars, or as a hedge; rare as a specimen tree; very rare in Ireland.

BARK. Orange-brown, fissured into parallel ridges which shred vertically—resembles that of *Cryptomeria*.

CROWN. Slightly rounded conic, open and often gaunt in older trees. Branches descend slightly near the bole then curve gently upwards. Older trees usually bent or leaning, often many stemmed and splayed out. Foliage thin, hanging —tree may look nearly dead.

FOLIAGE. Shoot slender, soon pale brown; "C" shoots broad and spread widely nearly perpendicular to shoot. Leaves thick, flat, dark green above; uniformly yellowish green beneath, (under lens midrib shows unspeckled). Crushed foliage has a strong scent of apples. Young trees hold their shoots partly vertically and curved.

FLOWERS AND CONE. Male flowers black-tipped ovoids, 1 mm on down-curved ends of smallest shoots. Cone upright, yellow-green, 1 cm ripening brown.

GROWTH. A slow-growing and very short-lived species, seldom looking really healthy, except some of the cultivars. It is a useful plant in very ill-drained soils.

SPECIMENS. Only two good specimens have been found in the country; robust trees with good stems. These are at Trawscoed, 63ft × 7ft 2in (1969) and Carey, 68ft × 5ft 11in (1968). The best of the remainder are thin, straggly plants:— Eridge Castle, 60ft × 3ft 3in (1971); Holkham Hall, 35ft × 4ft 1in (1968); Warnham Court, 45ft × 3ft 1in (1962); Tubney Wood, planted 1906, 38ft × 2ft 2in (1966).

RECOGNITION. The way in which young trees hold their shoots curved but vertically is quite distinct. The apple-scent of the foliage is very similar to that of *T. plicata* but the uniform pale or yellowish underside is distinct.

CULTIVARS. There are numerous cultivars which are mostly dwarf or semi-dwarf. Only the tall-growing ones are given here, and the true identity of some specimens is very difficult to determine.

cv. Fastigiata. Conic bush; flame-shaped tree, with nearly erect branches and twisted shoots, holding the foliage partly vertically. The leaves are a bright pale green on both sides and retain their colour through the winter.

cv. Filiformis. Tall-growing mound with distantly branched sprays, nodes 4 cm, apart; shoots flattened with a scalloped edge, pale green above, paler still beneath, hanging in slender sprays. Bedgebury, planted 1926, 25 feet (1969).

cv. Lutea. The strongest growing and best of all *Th. occidentalis,* far superior to the type. Strong branches with upswept ends bear golden foliage contrasting with green older foliage.

Brooklands, 52ft × 5ft 0in (1959); Tilgate, planted 1905, 34ft × 2ft 8in (1961); Little Hall, planted 1906, 50ft × 4ft 1in (1961); Bedgebury, planted 1926, 34ft × 3ft 2in (1969).

cv. Lutescens. A smaller, less bright form of the preceding.

Bedgebury, planted 1947, 23ft × 1ft 3in (1969).

cv. Spiralis. An extremely desirable narrowly columnar, pointed tree with very short, level branches, upturned at the ends of main branches, and short dense shoots. Each spray is oblong, pointed, flat and crowded with short flat side-shoots, very like those of *Chamaecyparis obtusa* 'Filicoides' but not pendulous; deep green above, bright pale green beneath; the upper surface browning rather in winter. Often grown as *pyramidalis* or *fastigiata* and doubtless mixed with *Douglasii pyramidalis* which sounds to be similar except for some cristate foliage. Cv. Spiralis is rare except in South-west Surrey.

Lythe Hill, 38ft × 1ft 10in (1969); Wishanger, 30ft × 2ft 2in; 26ft × 2ft 0in (1963); Wisley Royal Horticultural Society Gardens, 26ft × 1ft 4in (1964); Westonbirt, 25ft × 1ft 3in (1967); Bedgebury, 36ft × 3ft 0in (1969); Busbridge Hall, 20ft × 1ft (1963).

cv. Vervaeneana (Belgium, ca.1860). Conic, finely branched, crowded foliage mixed light yellow and light green.

Wakehurst Place, 30 feet.

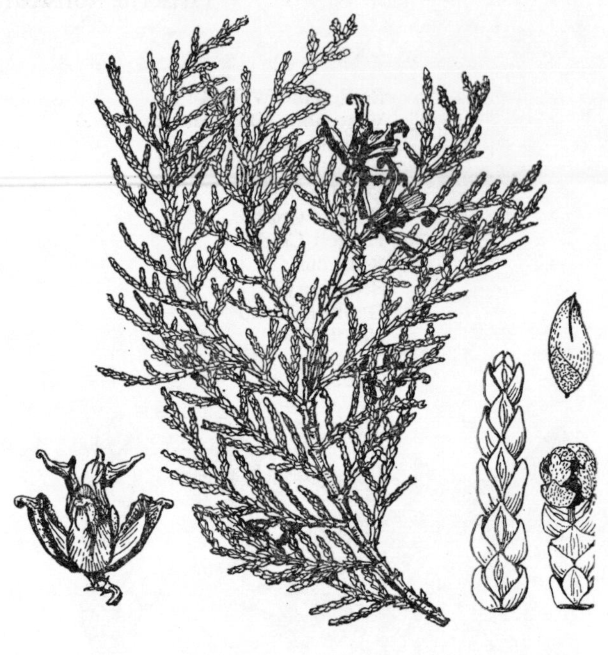

Thuja orientalis

Fig. 188
Thuja orientalis, foliage and opened cones. [Cone, left × 2 shoot, right + male flower × 4⅔ and, above, seed × 2⅔]. The foliage is in erect, flattened sprays, and, is, unlike any other species of Thuja, green on each side and non-aromatic. In the closed cone the hook-like processes are prominent around the top.

Thuja orientalis Linnaeus. Chinese thuja

North China, Manchuria and Korea. Introduced in 1752. Uncommon; very rare in collections and large gardens but frequent in villages and towns, churchyards and parks, especially in the West Midlands and East Anglia.

BARK. Dull red-brown, in stripping, shallow vertical ridges.

CROWN. Gaunt, upright, irregular but roughly conic and pointed. Few branches, bare for much of their length, upswept; foliage in vertical plates. Young plants flame-shaped.

FOLIAGE. Vertical plates of dull, dark green scale-leaves, the same colour both sides. Leaves triangular, bluntly pointed, grooved.

Crushed foliage, alone amongst the Thujas, has no scent.

CONE. Frequent and often-crowded on the shoots; 2 cm upright, flask-shaped, bloomed grey before ripe, six long scales each with a down-curved hooked tip.

Growth. A very slow-growing tree in all its forms, and often unhealthy. The best trees are in towns or cities like Oxford and in villages or, if in gardens, by terrace-steps and in other sharply drained places.

Recognition. A gaunt and upright tree with little foliage, dark and in upright plates, the same colour each side, without a strong scent when crushed and with curly processes on the cones.

Table 117. Specimens of Thuja orientalis

Locality	*Date Planted*	*Dimensions*
Penjerrick		52′ × 5′ 0″ (1959)
Pencarrow		52′ × 6′ 4″ (1970)[1]
West Suffolk Hospital, Thetford	1865	28′ × 4′ 7″ (1965)[1]
Kew, R.B.G.	1898	42′ × 4′ 7″ (1965)[2]
Highnam		47′ × 6′ 6″ (1970)[1]
Trawscoed		40′ × 3′ 11″ (1969)[1]
Codford Village		45′ (1965)
Lyndon House		36′ × 3′ 1″ (1965)
Blenheim Park		41′ × 5′ 5″ (1965)[1]
Sandon House		35′ × 4′ 4″ (1969)[3]
Cambridge B.G.		35′ (1969)
Poles		34′ × 3′ 2″ (1969)
Park Town, Oxford		36′ × 3′ 6″ (1964)[4]

[1] Measured at 1 foot
[2] Measured at 3 feet
[3] Measured at 4 feet
[4] Main stem

cv. Elegantissima (Tooting, 1858). A very attractive young plant, narrowly flame-shaped and bright gold on the outside in summer, dull yellow and turning green and brown in winter. Old plants are broad with many tops.

Wadhurst Village, ca. 20 feet; Tetbury, 20 feet.

cv. Flagelliformis (Japan, pre-1847). A rounded bush or tree with long, whip-like hanging shoots, dark green, browning in winter.

Cambridge Botanic Garden, 33ft × 1ft 8in (1969); Tortworth Court, 35ft × 5ft 9in at 6 inches (1965).

Thuja plicata

Fig. 189
Spray and green cones of *Thuja plicata* with (below, middle ×2) opening cone, (below left, ×4) detail of shoot from beneath, and (below right ×4) seed. The foliage is highly aromatic and there is a pale yellow-green area at the base of each leaf on the underside.

Thuja plicata D. Don. Western red cedar

Alaska to mid-California, inland to Montana and Idaho. Introduced in 1853. Abundant as hedge-plant and tree in gardens of all kinds; screens, shelter-belts and parks. Used in forestry in underplanting broad-leaved woods on heavy soils or larch woods on lighter soils. Frequent in town-gardens and churchyards. Big trees largely confined to the west and north.

BARK. Dark purplish red-brown, usually deeply fluted; coming away in shallow, narrow strips.

CROWN. Young trees, and usually until 80 feet tall, very narrowly conic with erect leader rather scantily branched with curving shoots; variably dense. Old trees rounding at the apex, lower branches descending and curving up at the tips; some trees with very heavy, sharply up-turned low branches, and many with a ring of layered branches.

FOLIAGE. Shoot soon coppery-brown, then red-brown and purple-brown. Main sprays oblong-obovate, flattened in one plane. Minor sprays narrow lanceolate, forward. Leaves on main shoots scale-like with long incurved spine-tip. Other leaves, flat, scale-like, shorter pointed, closely overlapping, incurved, deep glossy green above, pale beneath with grey-white markings towards the base each side of the midrib.

Even touching the foliage causes it to emit a powerful fruity scent, like pear-drops or cooked apples.

FLOWERS AND CONE. Male flowers minute black ovoids, 1–2 mm on down-curved tips of minor shoots, ripening pale yellow and shedding pollen in late March or early April. Female flowers on short shoots near the tips of sprays, yellow-green, ripening into vertical green cones, 1 cm long, flask-shaped then turning brown and the few scales partially opening.

GROWTH. Young trees in moist soils grow rapidly, with shoots up to 3 feet long. They can exceed 80 feet in 40 years in areas of high rainfall and cool summers. Growth in girth is steady and quite rapid, some of the older trees having mean annual increases of 2 inches for 60 years and most exceeding 30 inches in 30 years.

SPECIMENS. The tree at Dropmore is a known original tree. Its growth has been severely curtailed in this century by large rooted layers competing all round the main stem. The tree at Stourhead had been given a planting date of two years before the species was introduced. It is doubtless an original.

TABLE 118. SOME SPECIMEN TREES OF THUJA PLICATA

Locality	*Date Planted*	*Dimensions*	
Dropmore	1854	68′ × 6′ 10″ (1905)	80′ × 9′ 0″ (1970)
Stourhead	ca.1854	80′ × 11′ 3″ (1931)	124′ × 15′ 11″ (1970)
Scorrier House	1858	66′ × 8′ 11″ (1928)	75′ × 11′ 9″ (1965)
Bicton		70′ × 8′ 2″ (1902)	133′ × 18′ 2″ (1968)
Bicton		103′ × 11′ 5″ (1928)	128′ × 14′ 3″ (1968)
Fonthill	Seed 1860	95′ × 10′ 0″ (1906)	120′ × 14′ 11″ (1963)
Fonthill	Seed 1860		113′ × 12′ 11″ (1963)
Bolderwood	1861	100′ × 11′ 0″ (1931)	115′ × 14′ 0″ (1970)
Rhinefield	1861	91′ × 9′ 0″ (1931)	123′ × 11′ 8″ (1970)
(N. Devon)		122′ × 15′ 1″ (1957)	126′ × 16′ 8″ (1970)
Castle Kennedy	1861	71′ × 9′ 6″ (1931)	90′ × 12′ 2″ (1967)
Munches	1861	80′ × 11′ 0″ (1931)	115′ × 13′ 11″ (1970)
Keir House	1862	80′ × 9′ 9″ (1931)	93′ × 11′ 4″ (1970)
Fulmodestone	1863	67′ × 7′ 0″ (1905)	100′ × 12′ 0″ (1969)
Fulmodestone	1863	61′ × 6′ 8″ (1905)	88′ × 11′ 10″ (1969)
Killerton		68′ × 7′ 10″ (1905)	108′ × 13′ 8″ (1970)
Adare Manor		71′ × 7′ 3″ (1901)	90′ × 12′ 10″ (1968)
Shelton Abbey			106′ × 14′ 3″ (1968)
Coollattin			112′ × 13′ 8″ (1968)
West Dean			124′ × 10′ 3″ (1970)
Dupplin Castle		99′ × 9′ 3″ (1931)	123′ × 12′ 3″ (1970)
Inveraray (Lime Kilns)		90–95′ × 12′ 9″ (1931)	117′ × 15′ 4″ (1969)
Hafodunos		65′ × 9′ 7″ (1904)	90′ × 14′ 7″ (1960)
Poltalloch		65′ × 7′ 2″ (1905)	107′ × 11′ 5″ (1969)
Rossie Priory		70′ × 8′ 10″ (1931)	102′ × 11′ 10″ (1970)
Brahan			90′ × 15′ 7″ (1970)
Glamis Castle			121′ × 12′ 10″ (1970)
Belladrum			115′ × 16′ 4″ (1970)
Golden Grove			98′ × 14′ 4″ (1960)
Fairburn			118′ × 14′ 0″ (1970)
Nettlecombe			105′ × 14′ 4″ (1971)
Endsleigh			105′ × 14′ 8″ (1970)
Endsleigh			117′ × 13′ 2″ (1970)
Duncraig Castle	1868	87′ × 10′ 3″ (1931)	112′ × 12′ 10″ (1970)
Derreen			82′ × 14′ 0″ (1966)
Ardkinglas (Strone)	1875	65′ × 9′ 10″ (1931)	120′ × 15′ 7″ (1971)
Ardkinglas (Strone)	1875		115′ × 13′ 9″ (1969)
Stonefield		132′ × 10′ 4″ (1931)	135′ × 12′ 8″ (1969)
Stonefield			130′ × 11′ 10″ (1969)
Longleat			111′ × 14′ 6″ (1971)
Cultoquhey			115′ × 11′ 9″ (1970)
Inistioge			110′ × 13′ 4″ (1966)
Powerscourt			130′ × 11′ 0″ (1966)
Castle Forbes			95′ × 13′ 8″ (1968)
Trawscoed			93′ × 13′ 0″ (1969)
Holkham (Fox's Covert)			87′ × 13′ 6″ (1968)
Fenagh House	1880		103′ × 12′ 2″ (1968)
Headfort	1881		85′ × 12′ 4″ (1966)
Birr Castle			84′ × 12′ 8″ (1966)
Blairquhan	1893	48′ × 6′ 2″ (1931)	60′ × 11′ 5″ (1970)
Gurteen le Poer			110′ × 12′ 2″ (1968)
Murthly Castle (Avenue)			111′ × 10′ 8″ (1970)
Brahan	1901	65′ × 6′ 8″ (1955)	74′ × 8′ 6″ (1970)
Kyloe Wood	1908		87′ × 5′ 8″ (1958)
Auchacloich	1913		85′ × 4′ 9″ (1953)
Speech House	1916		70′ × 4′ 4″ (1968)
Bedgebury	1926	6′ 9″ (1931)	63′ × 5′ 4″ (1970)
Dropmore	1949		49′ × 4′ 2″ (1970)

cv. Fastigiata. Very rare. Neatly conic, thinly foliaged. Bedgebury 44ft × 2ft 5in (1971).

cv. Aureovariegata ('Zebrina') (?Holland, ca. 1890). A very sturdy, rather vigorous, broadly conic tree with a dense crown of foliage banded variously in greenish yellow, bright gold or whitish yellow. (The Irish specimens are of a different form, as yet un-named, which grows at Bedgebury but is burned there each winter by cold winds. It has a looser habit and much paler, brighter gold foliage with scarcely any green bars.) Common in gardens, even around towns.

TABLE 119. SPECIMENS OF THUJA PLICATA 'AUREOVARIEGATA'

Locality	*Date Planted*	*Dimensions*	
Dropmore	1902		65′ × 6′ 8″ (1970)
Tilgate	1905	28′ (1931)	58′ × 4′ 10″ (1961)
Little Hall	1906	29′ × 1′ 4″ (1931)	55′ × 3′ 7″ (1961)
Stourhead	1906	27′ × 2′ 6″ (1931)	66′ × 8′ 1″ (1970)
Lamellan			61′ × 7′ 3″ (1963)
Bicton			72′ × 6′ 5″ (1968)
Tottenham House			68′ × 6′ 10″ (1967)
Tottenham House			62′ × 5′ 7″ (1967)
(N. Devon)			68′ × 7′ 0″ (1970)
(N. Devon)			65′ × 6′ 8″ (1970)
Tongs Wood			62′ × 6′ 4″ (1968)
Carton			65′ × 6′ 6″ (1968)
Bulstrode Park			66′ × 5′ 2″ (1967)
Grayswood Church			56′ × 5′ 11″ (1964)
Nymans (Magnolia Garden)			61′ × 6′ 1″ (1970)
Nymans (Lower Pinetum)			60′ × 6′ 4″ (1970)
Powerscourt			52′ × 4′ 4″ (1966)
Castlewellan			57′ × 5′ 8″ (1970)
Bedgebury	1926		46′ × 4′ 1″ (1970)
Stradbally House			60′ × 4′ 2″ (1968)
Sindlesham (Bear Wood)			57′ × 5′ 4″ (1970)

This is the best golden conifer where a large tree is required, for only *Cupressus macrocarpa* 'Lutea' will attain an equal size and the Thuja is of better colour and shape. It is almost certain to attain 100 feet within this century.

cv. Semperaurescens. A tree of the same habit and vigour as the type but with a mossy yellowish-green foliage. Whilst not striking, it is unusual and attractive. It seems, however, to be confined to Westonbirt where there are groups dating from about 1900, 1939 and 1946; and to Colesbourne.

Westonbirt, 30ft × 1ft 8in (1931); 59ft × 5ft 4in; 61ft × 4ft 11in; 60ft × 5ft 1in (1969); Colesbourne, 63ft × 6ft 11in (1970).

Thuja standishii

Fig. 190
Typically erect and nodding spray of *Thuja standishii*, Japanese thuja, a species with hard, rounded foliage with a sweet lemon-verbena fragrance. The underside of the shoot (left × 6) showing grey-white area at the base of each leaf.

Thuja standishii (Gordon) Carriere. Japanese thuja

Central Japan. Introduced in 1860. Rare; in collections and a few other gardens.

BARK. Deep red, stripping very coarsely with large plates lifting away and strips hanging from their sides and underneath branches.

CROWN. Broadly conic, with level branches upturned at their ends, the lower branches making a wide "U".

FOLIAGE. Dense sprays, those on branch ends upright, nodding at their tips; hard, rough and thick. Leaves very dull matt dark grey-green or yellow-green, new leaves often bloomed grey-blue; shoots oval in section or rounded upper surface, flat beneath; clad in scale-leaves with spreading obtuse, hard points. Shoot coppery-orange turning red-brown. Crushed foliage yields a very sweet scent, like catchouc, lemon-verbena or oil of citronella.

GROWTH. Height growth is slow everywhere, but growth in girth seems to be quite rapid in Ireland.

SPECIMENS. An original tree grows at Linton Park, and the tree at Tregrehan is possibly another. The biggest tree at Westonbirt is a graft at 1 foot on to *T. plicata*.

RECOGNITION. The broad, conic crown with upright nodding shoots of yellowish or silvery green, is distinct at a distance. The red, shaggy bark is distinct from close to, as well as the details of and scent from the foliage.

TABLE 120. SOME SPECIMENS OF THUJA STANDISHII

Locality	*Date Planted*	*Dimensions*	
Linton Park	1866	49′ × 6′ 2″ (1931)	67′ × 7′ 5″ (1970)
Tregrehan			70′ × 6′ 6″ (1971)
Inistioge			55′ × 8′ 7″ (1966)
Powerscourt			55′ × 8′ 0″ (1966)
Trentham Park			60′ × 4′ 3″ (1968)
Kilmacurragh			46′ × 6′ 3″ (1966)
Westonbirt	1875		63′ × 4′ 0″ (1971)
Longleat			54′ × 6′ 4″ (1971)
Kew R.B.G.	1895		42′ × 2′ 4″ (1965)
Kew R.B.G.	1895		38′ × 3′ 3″ (1965)
Warnham Court			49′ × 3′ 6″ (1971)
Bowood			43′ × 4′ 9″ (1968)
Leonardslee		47′ × 4′ 0″ (1961)	51′ × 4′ 9″ (1969)
Leonardslee		41′ × 3′ 9″ (1961)	49′ × 4′ 4″ (1969)
Leonardslee		50′ × 2′ 6″ (1962)	56′ × 3′ 0″ (1969)
Little Hall	1906		48′ × 4′ 8″ (1961)
Batsford Park			49′ × 4′ 3″ (1963)
Lydhurst			49′ × 4′ 10″ (1971)
Chatsworth			57′ × 4′ 10″ (1971)
Castlewellan			44′ × 5′ 2″ (1966)
Glasnevin B.G.			47′ × 5′ 0″ (1966)
Avondale			38′ × 5′ 11″ (1968)
St. Clere			39′ × 5′ 3″ (1969)
Woburn Abbey			37′ × 4′ 3″ (1970)
Tongs Wood			48′ × 3′ 11″ (1968)
Headfort	1914		32′ × 3′ 4″ (1966)
Bedgebury	1926		30′ × 3′ 1″ (1970)
Birr Castle	1934		29′ × 2′ 10″ (1966)
Edinburgh R.B.G.			37′ × 3′ 2″ (1967)
Riccarton			41′ × 4′ 2″ (1967)
The Shrubberies			45′ × 4′ 5″ (1969)

Thujopsis (L.f.) Siebold and Zuccarini

A single species separated from Thuja largely by differences in the size and flatness of the leaves, and more globose cones.

Thujopsis dolabrata

Fig. 191
Spray with cone of *Thujopsis dolabrata,* showing the broad, hard and glossy green scale-leaves. The underside of the leaf (lower right ×2) has a bold white band, likened to the blade of a hatchet ("dolabra"). The cones open widely (upper left ×1⅓) and adhere to the shoot for a short period.

Thujopsis dolabrata (Linnaeus f.) Siebold and Zuccarini. Hiba.

Japan. Introduced via Java in 1853 as a single plant which died. Later introductions in 1859 and 1861. Reasonably common, especially in the west and northwest where it is found in most large gardens.

BARK. Brown, finely shredding in grey strips as if a cat were always scratching it, and usually in spirals. The less common tree-form may have rich red-purple-brown bark stripping to leave orange.

CROWN. Frequently an obtusely conic multiple canopy on 20–30 very straight, cylindrical, small boles, a few in the centre being taller but of hardly any greater girth than the others. Less commonly a single-boled tree with short, upcurved branches and a long, narrow conic top.

FOLIAGE. Shoot erect; minor shoots arching from it. Leaves; reptilian scales, broad and shining bright green, laterals 4–6×2 mm, triangular, incurved toward minutely mucronate tip; facials obovate, grooved with thickened raised tip; underside solid thick white with shiny dark green margin.

FLOWERS AND CONE. Male flowers ovoid, blackish-green curved down from the ends of small side-shoots. Female flower on the ends of shoots towards the tip of the spray, blue-grey ripening to cones 1–2 cm, opening with thickened woody scales.

GROWTH. A slow tree everywhere, even the fastest not attaining one foot per year. Young plants may grow one inch or so a year for 6 to 10 years. Growth in girth has very rarely equalled one inch a year; is usually less than a third of this and can be one tenth.

cv. Variegata. Whole shoots here and there, white. Very unstable—whitish shoots can be found on many trees and possibly most of them were planted as this cv. In view of this, the list of Specimens contains all the trees, splashed white or not, without distinction.

TABLE 121. SOME OF THE LARGEST TREES OF THUJOPSIS DOLABRATA

Locality	*Date Planted*	*Dimensions*		*Remarks*
Scorrier House	1868	39′ × 2′ 10″ (1928)	52′ × 5′ 1″ (1965)	Tree
Penjerrick			69′ × 3′ 3″ (1965)	Twenty-one stems
Heligan		30′ (1928)	65′ × 3′ 3″ (1959)	Many stems
Tregrehan			69′ × 4′ 2″ (1971)	Tree
Tregrehan			66′ × 7′ 10″ (1971)	Tree (short bole)
Melbury			67′ × 4′ 4″ (1971)	Main stem
Abbotsbury			60′ × 3′ 4″ (1957)	Many stems
Castlewellan			64′ × 2′ 5″ (1966)	Many stems
Powerscourt			60′ × 4′ 10″ (1966)	Many stems
Lydhurst			59′ × 3′ 4″ (1965)	Tree
Woodhouse		27′ × 1′ 6″ (1931)	62′ × 4′ 4″ (1970)	Tree
Minterne			56′ × 2′ 4″ (1970)	Many stems
Benenden			57′ × 2′ 9″ (1970)	One stem left
(N. Devon)			56′ × 4′ 4″ (1970)	Tree
Trebah			56′ × 3′ 8″ (1959)	
Trawscoed			56′ × 3′ 4″ (1969)	Many stems
Bicton			57′ (1968)	Many stems
Stonefield			56′ × 4′ 11″ (1969)	Tree
Stonefield			45′ × 5′ 3″ (1969)	Tree
Kilmacurragh			55′ × 3′ 5″ (1966)	Many stems
Inistioge			54′ × 3′ 9″ (1966)	Tree
Sheffield Park			51′ × 3′ 2″ (1968)	
Golden Grove			53′ × 2′ 9″ (1960)	30 stems
Golden Grove			50′ × 4′ 6″ (1960)	Tree
Stourhead	1881	36′ (1931)	59′ × 4′ 0″ (1970)	Two main stems
Arlington Court	ca.1882		51′ × 2′ 10″ (1959)	70 Layered stems
Lamellan			53′ × 5′ 9″ (1963)	Tree
Boconnoc			64′ × 4′ 10″ (1970)	Tree
Boconnoc		35′ × 3′ 9″ (1927)	67′ × 6′ 4″ (1970)	Tree
Killerton		35′ × 2′ 4″ (1906)	55′ × 3′ 5″ (1970)	17 stems 15yd diameter
Killerton			56′ × 3′ 0″ (1970)	Tree
Pencarrow			56′ × 4′ 4″ (1970)	Tree
Derreen			48′ × 4′ 1″ (1966)	Bole 40ft
Derreen			47′ × 4′ 6″ (1966)	Bole 30ft
Hergest Croft	1915		48′ × 2′ 3″ (1969)	Tree
Capenoch			49′ × 2′ 1″ (1970)	Many stems
Glendurgan			46′ × 4′ 7″ (1965)	Tree

Torreya Arnott (Taxaceae)

A small genus of six species from North America, China and Japan. They have rather open crowns and stiff, hard, linear leaves with spined points. The fruit are plum-like. Only two species make worthwhile growth with us.

Torreya californica

Fig. 192
Foliage of *Torreya californica*, California nutmeg, showing leaves slightly curved upwards. Some specimens have more sparse, less regularly arranged leaves.

Torreya californica Torrey. California nutmeg

California, near the coast in the north, and along the western foothills of the Sierra Nevada. Introduced in 1857; one original tree known. Rare but in collections in all parts except North East Scotland.

BARK. Red-brown with a fine, shallow lattice of stringy ridges.

CROWN. Broadly conic; very open with whorls of level branches and sparse, hanging shoots. Usually tall with a good spire-top but occasionally a large bush.

FOLIAGE. Shoot stout, green; second year largely still green, often with patches of red, sometimes red-brown above, pinkish beneath; third year red-brown.

BUD. Conic, finely pointed, brown above, shining green beneath, leaving brown triangular scales at nodes.

LEAVES. Distant (3 per cm) spreading perpendicularly, irregularly pectinate, curved variably upwards or backwards; broadest just above petiole, tapering gently to spine-point, 3–4 (5)×0·3 cm. Dark yellowish-green and dull above; two narrow whitish bands and bright green margins and midrib below.

FLOWERS AND FRUIT. Male flowers globose, 8 mm in axils of the leaves of terminal shoots (Dallimore and Jackson). Fruit ellipsoid or obovoid, 3–4 cm green streaked purple (Dallimore and Jackson).

GROWTH. Growth in height is steady but rather slow over the years although annual shoots of nearly two feet have been seen. Girth in growth has mostly been about one inch per year.

SPECIMENS.

Table 122. Specimens of Torreya californica

Locality	*Date Planted*	*Dimensions*	
Poles	1858	40′ × 4′ 0″ (1910)	74′ × 6′ 8″ (1969)
Tregothnan		45′ × 6′ 0″ (1911)	69′ × 10′ 4″ (1971)
Scorrier	ca.1880	40′ × 4′ 9″ (1928)	56′ × 8′ 2″ (1965)
Mells		30′ (1931)	67′ × 7′ 5″ (1962)
Stonefield		× 3′ 11″ (1931)	40′ × 6′ 7″ (1969)
Castlewellan		38′ × 3′ 8″ (1931)	55′ × 9′ 8″ (1970)
Stourhead			49′ × 4′ 0″ (1970)
Streatham Hall			51′ × 8′ 8″ (1967)
Streatham Hall			47′ × 7′ 9″ (1967)
Batsford Park			59′ × 7′ 4″ (1971)
Fota			35′ × 10′ 1″ (1966)
Borde Hill			44′ × 3′ 6″ (1970)
Exbury		29′ × 2′ 9″ (1907)	27′ × 4′ 8″ (1968)
Nymans			35′ × 5′ 3″ (1970)
Edinburgh R.B.G.	1898		25′ × 3′ 0″ (1967)
Hergest Croft	1913		34′ × 2′ 3″ (1969)
Headfort	1914		40′ × 4′ 6″ (1966)
Garinish Island			35′ × 4′ 2″ (1966)

cv. Variegata. Seen only at Hergest Croft, now 35ft × 2ft 0in (main stem; 1969); parts of foliage dull greenish yellow.
Recognition. The distant, hard, spiny leaves with whitish bands beneath separate *Torreya* from *Taxus.* The hard, spined leaves and narrow bands beneath separate it from the leathery, broadly banded leaves of *Cephalotaxus. T. nucifera* is the only *Torreya* resembling *T. californica* closely, and it has flatter, shorter, closer, evenly pectinate glossy leaves, bent down, not up. The second year shoot is brighter and more orange in *T. nucifera.*

Torreya grandis Fortune.

Eastern and Central China. Introduced in 1855. Very rare; in a few collections in South England.
Bark. Brown and grey, with shallow, vertical flakes.
Crown. Gaunt, narrow, few branches and thin.
Foliage. Bud 3 mm, bluntly conic, shining brown. Shoot bright green 2 years or more, ribbed by leaf-bases.
Leaves. Sparse and irregularly placed; or pectinate, raised in a 'V' parallel-sided; subsessile; raised midrib, broad, pale green, shiny and roughened above; matt uniform yellowish-white bands close beside the midrib beneath; 3×0·3 cm.
Specimens. Borde Hill, 29ft × 1ft 2in (1968); Kew Royal Botanic Gardens, 25ft × 1ft 11in (1970).

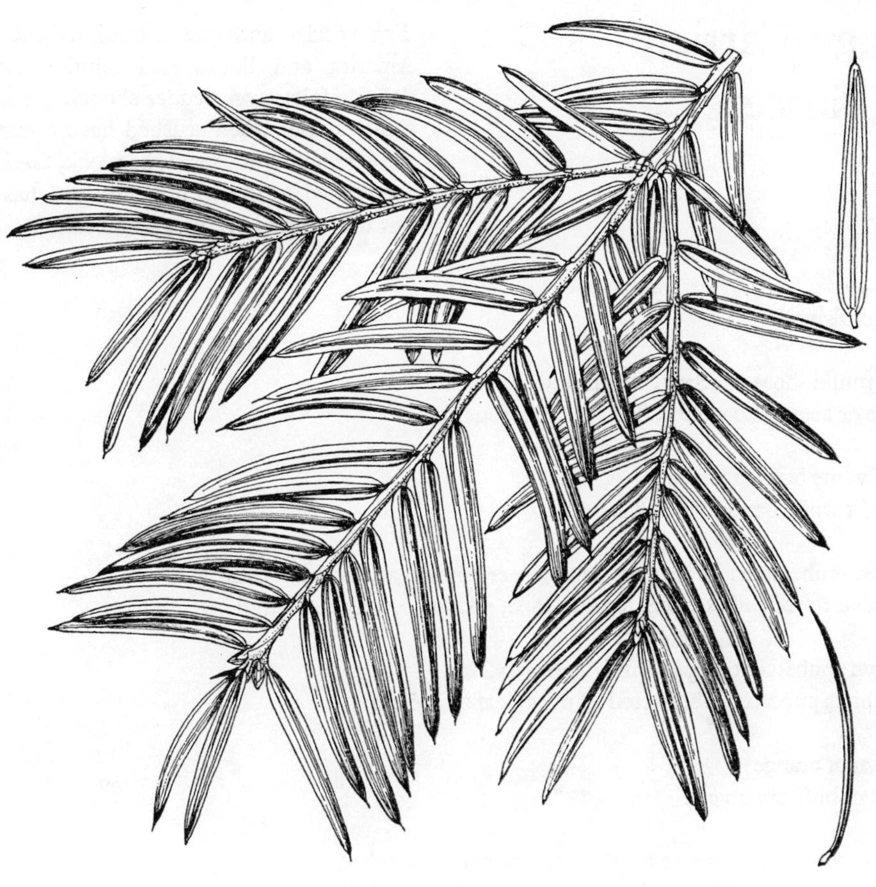

Torreya nucifera

Fig. 193
Torreya nucifera, a Japanese species, with broad, pale-margined leaves, parallel and arched downwards (bottom right) and with glaucous bands broadly margined green beneath (top right) × 1.

Torreya nucifera Siebold and Zuccarini. Kaya.

Central and Southern Japan. Introduced in 1764. Rare; in some collections in South England.

BARK. Pale pinkish-brown and copper-brown with fine shallow greyish ridges in a network.

CROWN. Usually a thinly branched, small, narrow tree.

FOLIAGE. Shoot green, second year still green or bright orange-brown, third year mahogany-purple.

LEAVES. Closely set, 3×0·3 cm with a ridge 2 mm broad and deep glossy green, broad margins brighter green; pectinate, arched, hard; slightly forward; two white bands of the same width as the margins and midrib beneath.

BUD. 2–3 mm ovoid-conic, sharp, shining green, leaving bright orange scales at the base of the first year's shoot.

FLOWERS AND FRUIT. Male flowers about 8 mm long; fruit narrowly obovoid 2–2·5 cm long, green tinged purple (Dallimore and Jackson).

SPECIMENS. Scorrier House, 21ft×1ft 5in (1959); Strete Ralegh (Pinetum), 25ft×3ft 0in (1964); Wakehurst Place, 38ft×2ft 7in (1970); Bicton, 19ft×1ft 4in (1968).

RECOGNITION. Distinguished from *T. californica* by shorter, closer and glossy leaves, parallel and arched down, and bright orange-brown shoots.

Tsuga Carriere (Pinaceae)

Ten species and one natural hybrid, confined to North America and South and South East Asia. They have delicate foliage on slender shoots; the small, linear leaves of some species when crushed have a scent likened to that of the Umbelliferous plant, hemlock, *Conium maculatum*. They are related to the spruces and one has cones like a spruce but the others have very small cones.

Key to the Species of Tsuga

1.	Leaves lying all round shoot; thick; glaucous both surfaces	*mertensiana*
	Leaves pectinate or above shoot only; thin; not glaucous above	2
2.	Leaves greenish white banded beneath	3
	Leaves with bright white bands beneath	5
3.	Shoot long, sparse-pubescent; leaves very slender, perpendicular, some backwards	*jeffreyi*
	Shoot with short scattered pubescence; leaves broad, pectinate, irregular lengths	4
4.	Shoot pink-brown; pubescent on pulvini only, leaf to 2 cm	*forrestii*
	Shoot creamy white; pubescence scattered all over; leaf to 1·5 cm	*chinensis*
5.	Shoot dark brown or orange	6
	Shoot white, fawn, buff, cream etc.	7
6.	Shoot shining red-brown; leaves distant, slender, not flat two-ranked	*caroliniana*
	Shoot bright brown or orange, leaves close, very broad, flat two-ranked	*diversifolia*
7.	Shoot quite glabrous, pale buff	*sieboldii*
	Shoot conspicuously hairy	8
8.	Leaves taper from base or near	9
	Leaves parallel-sided	10
9.	Leaves hard, distant, well forward on shoot, two broad and brilliant white bands beneath	*dumosa*
	Leaves soft, dense except on long shoots, a line lying reversed along and close to shoot, two narrow white bands beneath	*canadensis*
10.	Leaf deep blackish-green after few weeks; two broad blue-white bands beneath; densely set, short mid-shoot leaves irregular, upstanding	*heterophylla*
	Leaf pale shining green; two very broad, very white bands beneath; rather sparse, no upstanding leaves on mid-line	*yunnanensis*

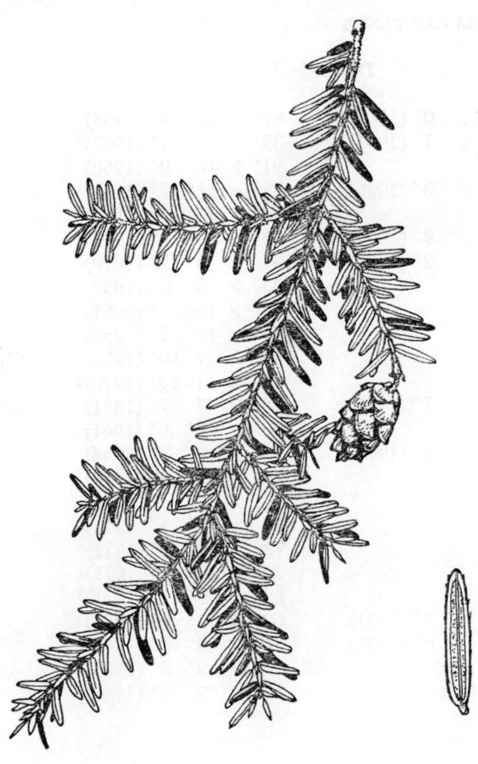

Fig. 194
Foliage and cone of *Tsugac anadensis*, Eastern hemlock, showing the line of leaves reversed over the shoot, their white-banded undersides (right ×2) uppermost.

Tsuga canadensis (Linnaeus) Carriere. Eastern hemlock

Canada from East of the Rocky Mountains to Nova Scotia; U.S.A. Lake States and Appalachian Mountains south to Alabama. Introduced in 1736. Common in collections, large gardens, and frequent in smaller gardens.

BARK. Young trees bright orange-brown with purple-brown scaly ridges. Old trees dark purplish grey with a lattice-work of thick scaly ridges.

CROWN. Young trees broadly conic with obtuse apex and arching slender shoots. Old trees irregularly broad-conic, seldom with a single bole for more than a few feet.

FOLIAGE. Shoot pale brown or cream, with a dense, curly, pale orange pubescence. Second year dark grey or grey-brown.

BUD. Hidden by leaves, broad conic, red-brown.

LEAVES. Pectinate and slightly depressed beneath; above over the shoot and forwards, mid line leaves showing white undersides; broadest at base, tapering slightly to rounded tip. Underside with broad green margins, two white bands and a green midrib which a lens shows to be white centred with a narrow green line each side. Crushed foliage has a sweet lemony scent.

CONE. Ovoid, pendulous, usually numerous, 1·5–2·5 cm, grey-brown; scales rounded, obscurely toothed.

GROWTH. After a fairly rapid start, with shoots to 2 feet or more long, growth in height slows rapidly as the leading shoot tends to lose dominance. There are very few dated trees to show the increase in girth on a single bole but remeasurements show only one approaching one inch per year and the majority less than half this rate. Two dated trees have, however, exceeded one inch per year.

RECOGNITION. The dark, heavily ridged bark and broad crown at once distinguish this from *T. heterophylla.* The foliage is distinguished from all other *Tsugas* by the line of leaves upside-down along the line of the shoot.

CULTIVARS. A great number of cultivars have recently been selected in North America. Many of these are dwarf. Here only the old-established cultivars of tree-dimensions or form are given.

TABLE 123. LARGEST TREES OF TSUGA CANADENSIS

Locality	*Date Planted*	*Dimensions*	
Studley Royal		80′ × 11′ 0″ (1906)	87′ × 12′ 9″ (1958)
Bury Hill	1816	27′ × 4′ 7″ (1931)	35′ × 5′ 7″ (1957)
Fonthill			91′ × 10′ 9″ (1960)
Walcot Hall		60′ × 8′ 8″ (1906)	72′ × 11′ 7″ (1959)
Lowther Castle			80′ × 12′ 3″ (1967)
Patshull House		54′ × 7′ 9″ (1931)	72′ × 10′ 1″ (1970)
Leaton Knolls		85′ × 8′ 2″ (1931)	105′ × 9′ 5″ (1970)
Leaton Knolls			105′ × 8′ 0″ (1957)
Dropmore	1840		55′ × 10′ 9″ (1961)
Dropmore			71′ × 10′ 5″ (1958)
Dropmore	1855		60′ × 7′ 10″ (1958)
Cuffnells	1856		88′ × 11′ 10″ (1970)[2]
Arley Castle		70′ × 6′ 7″ (1906)	74′ × 7′ 7″ (1961)
Arley Castle	1878		60′ × 8′ 6″ (1961)
Hardwicke		60′ × 5′ 10″ (1906)	110′ × 8′ 2″ (1954)
Woburn Abbey			70′ × 11′ 8″ (1970)
Powis Castle			90′ × 9′ 4″ (1970)
Claremont			83′ × 9′ 5″ (1954)
Oakley Park			72′ × 13′ 7″ (1971)
Oakley Park			75′ × 10′ 5″ (1971)[1]
Oakley Park			80′ × 9′ 11″ (1971)[3]
Westonbirt		52′ × 5′ 3″ (1931)	62′ × 7′ 1″ (1964)
Hewell Grange		56′ × 7′ 6″ (1931)	54′ × 8′ 8″ (1963)
Mells Park			70′ × 9′ 2″ (1963)
Marston House			75′ × 8′ 6″ (1967)

[1] Clear bole for 20 feet
[2] At 1 foot
[3] Fork at 40 feet

cv. Albospica (Pre-1884). A slow-growing small tree in which a proportion of the stronger shoots is more or less white and remains so through the winter.

Westonbirt, 46ft × 3ft 6in (1969); Kew Royal Botanic Gardens, 15ft × 1ft 7in (1969).

cv. Fremdii (New York, 1887). A small, spreading tree with dull grey bark cracked into flakes and small leaves, densely set, some standing above the shoot.

Westonbirt, planted 1939, 34ft × 2ft 9in (1967).

cv. Microphylla (pre-1864). A low, bushy tree with dense rather stout shoots, by their fourth year bare and dark grey; leaves dark green 3–6 mm long with two broad bands beneath blue-grey or dull grey (there are several clones). Male flowers 1 mm, in clusters; cones numerous 1·0 × 0·7 cm, dull greyish brown. Buds are prominent, red-brown and ovoid.

Bedgebury, planted 1925, 20ft × 2ft 6in (1969); Nymans, 23ft × 1ft 9in (1966); Kew Royal Botanic Gardens, 11ft × 9in (1969); Borde Hill (Gores Wood), 31 feet (1970).

cv. Milfordiensis. Originally a dwarf form lost to cultivation. A small tree as now re-typified, with sparsely set, long, curved leaves, 1 cm long, dull grey banded beneath; parallel sides, on brown shoots with black pubescence.

Kew, Royal Botanic Gardens, 10 feet.

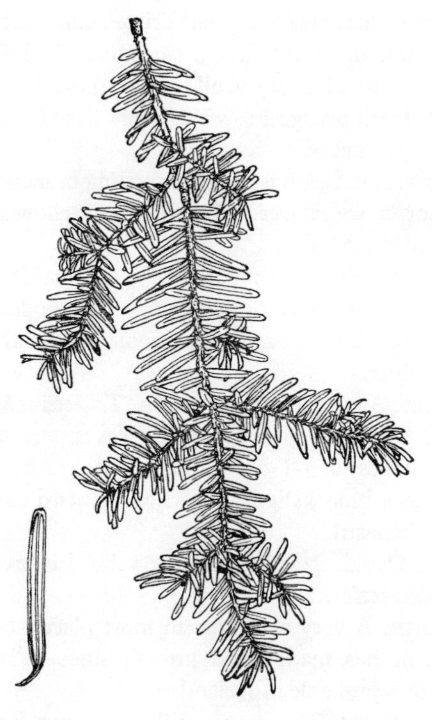

Tsuga caroliniana

Fig. 195
Foliage of *Tsuga caroliniana*, Carolina hemlock. The shoot is a shiny pale or reddish-brown and the slender leaves can be quite distant and spread to make a spiky spray. Single leaf (lower right $\times 1\frac{1}{3}$) showing the broad margins to the white stomatal bands on the underside.

Tsuga caroliniana Engelmann. Carolina hemlock

South-west Virginia to Georgia, South East United States. Introduced in 1886. Very rare, confined to a few collections in South and West England and in Ireland.
BARK. Young trees dark red-brown with large, protruding yellow lenticels. Older trees, purple-grey with wide, shallow, wandering fissures.
CROWN. Open below and inside; densely twigged canopy; irregularly broad-conic or ovoid. The bole has large swellings where the branches arise.
FOLIAGE. Shoot bright red-brown above, pale pink-brown beneath, shining, slightly grooved with pubescence in the grooves. Second year dark red-brown.
BUD. Squat, red-brown, pubescent, 3–4 mm.
LEAVES. Sparse and spiky, slender, distant, many standing well above the shoot; 1–1·2 cm long with blunt, rounded tips and two broad bright white bands beneath; midrib with a shiny white centre; very dark green above.
CONE. Long-ovoid, 1·5–2·5 cm, with tall, thin, rounded orange-brown, striated scales, which spread widely when the cone is mature.
GROWTH. A slow-growing tree, probably rather less slow in the far west and in Ireland.
RECOGNITION. The slender, distant leaves combined with red-brown shining shoot are distinct.

TABLE 124. SPECIMENS OF TSUGA CAROLINIANA

Locality	*Date Planted*	*Dimensions*	
Wakehurst Place	1912	18′ × 1′ 3″ (1931)	45′ × 3′ 6″ (1966)
Bedgebury	1925	5′ (1931)	32′ (1970)
Wisley R.H.S.G.			30′ × 2′ 3″ (1969)
Hergest Croft			35′ × 3′ 0″ (1961)
Windsor Great Park			25′ (1967)
Birr Castle	1934		24′ × 2′ 8″ (1966)
Westonbirt (Morley Drive)	1941		25′ × 1′ 8″ (1969)

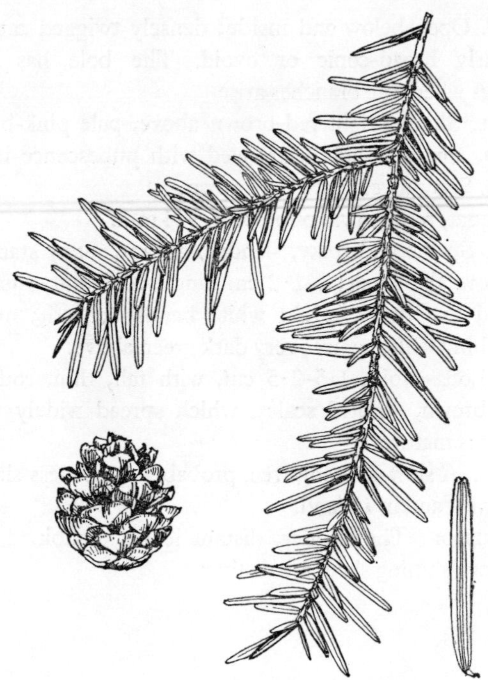

Tsuga chinensis

Fig. 196
Foliage and ripe cone of *Tsuga chinensis*, a Chinese hemlock which differs from the Western hemlock mainly in the pale green upper side of the leaf which has only greenish-white bands beneath. (detail ×1⅓).

Tsuga chinensis (Franchet) Pritzel. Chinese hemlock

Central and West China. Introduced in 1900. Very rare; confined to collections in all parts of these islands.

Bark. Dark orange-brown coarsely flaked with patterns of green-grey flakes.

Crown. A strong bush with ascending branches and vertical axis or a conic tree, of a distinct yellowish-green with protruding shoots.

Foliage. Shoot buff above, shiny cream-white beneath with rich brown pulvini; minutely pubescent, nodding.

Bud. Ovoid, dark red-brown, sometimes with green leaves protruding.

Leaves. Arranged rather as in *T. heterophylla* but distinctively evenly spaced and long leaves separated by several short leaves, 0·5–1·5 cm, light fresh green above, parallel sides to a blunt, slightly notched tip; two narrow greenish bands beneath.

Cone. Ovoid, 2·5 cm, shining yellowish-brown, incurved rounded scales.

Growth. A very slow tree in most places, but the tree at Bodnant has made good growth since 1931 and similar growth is probable in Ireland.

Recognition. The crown differs at once from *T. heterophylla* but the foliage is similar, differing in the apparently glabrous shoot, pale upper surface of the leaf, and, most distinct, the greenish bands beneath. *T. forrestii* (q.v.) is perhaps only a variety.

Table 125. Specimens of Tsuga chinensis

Locality	*Date Planted*	*Dimensions*	
Bodnant		18′ × 1′ 1″ (1931)	41′ × 4′ 0″ (1959)
Borde Hill		5′ 6″ (1931)	22′ × 1′ 7″ (1968)
Woburn Park	1926		10′ (1961)
Wakehurst Place			35′ × 1′ 9″ (1964)
Glasnevin B.G.			28′ × 3′ 4″ (1966)
Headfort			26′ × 3′ 7″ (1966)
Bedgebury	1937		26′ × 1′ 10″ (1970)[2]
Windsor Great Park			39′ × 3′ 3″ (1969)[1]
Windsor Great Park			32′ × 4′ 9″ (1967)[2]

[1] A second stem, ×2 feet 10 inches
[2] Measured at 1 foot

Tsuga diversifolia (Maximowicz) Masters. Northern Japanese hemlock.

Japan, in Central and Southern Honshiu. Introduced in 1861. Rare; confined to collections and a few large gardens.

BARK. Dark orange-brown with pink fissures and with ridges shallowly cracked or flaking vertically.

CROWN. Almost invariably a multitude of straight stems from the ground, forming a broad and very dense, low-domed crown.

FOLIAGE. Shoot orange beneath with fine erect pubescence visible with a lens; second year dull brown. Leaves pectinate below, tips slightly curved down, very regular and closely set on side-shoots, oblong with broad rounded and notched tip, 1×0·2 cm, deep glossy green above; two broad bright white bands beneath with green midrib and margins clearly defined.

FLOWERS AND CONE. Male flowers among the leaves near the tips of side-shoots, bright red-brown as buds. Cone ovoid, 2 cm, shiny brown.

GROWTH. Growth in height is very slow, dated trees averaging little more than 6 inches a year at best. Growth in girth is difficult to assess as single stems are so rare but it is in any case very slow.

RECOGNITION. The short, broad, blunt leaves are similar only to *T. sieboldii*, from which they differ in being broader, more regularly placed, deeper, glossier green above, and whiter beneath. The shoot is also much brighter and darker and minutely pubescent. The crown is broader and more dense and bushy.

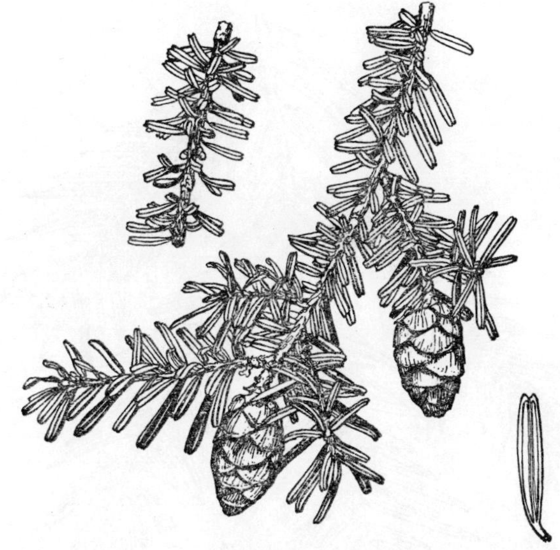

Tsuga diversifolia

Fig. 197
Foliage and cones of *Tsuga diversifolia*, a hemlock from Southern Japan. The shoot is bright orange, very finely pubescent, and from beneath (upper left) contrasts strikingly with the brilliant white of the underside of the leaves (lower right × $1\frac{1}{3}$). The foliage is much brighter, more regular and uniform than that of *T. sieboldii*.

TABLE 126. SPECIMENS OF TSUGA DIVERSIFOLIA

Locality	*Date Planted*	*Dimensions*		
Little Hall	1906			40′ × 3′ 4″ (1961)
Hergest Croft	1916			30′ × 3′ 0″ (1961)
Wakehurst Place				34′ × 3′ 5″ (1966)
Holkham	1920			33′ × 2′ 7″ (1968)
Dropmore				41′ × 3′ 9″ (1970)
Grayswood Hill				43′ × 4′ 4″ (1969)
Headfort	1914	12′	(1931)	33′ × 3′ 5″ (1966)
Bedgebury	1926	6′ 2″	(1931)	26′ × 2′ 4″ (1969)
Glamis Castle				49′ (1970)

Tsuga dumosa

Fig. 198
Tsuga dumosa, Himalayan hemlock, has the largest leaves of all the hemlocks. They are hard, with broad white bands beneath (detail × 1⅓) and the foliage is pendulous.

Tsuga dumosa (D. Don) Eichler. Himalayan hemlock

Himalaya from Kumaon to Bhutan. Introduced in 1838. Two probable original trees have recently died (Boconnoc and Dropmore). Rare. In collections mostly in the extreme South and South West of England and in Ireland.

BARK. Pink-brown and very scaly, becoming in old trees very like that of an old larch; heavily ridged, shallowly fissured, very scaly and pink.

CROWN. Where the tree grows well, a tall, irregular tree with widely spreading branches and several conic tops; the shoots pendulous. Elsewhere an ovoid bush or straggling thin tree.

FOLIAGE. Shoot pale pinkish-brown with a scattered fine pubescence.

BUD. Globose, pubescent.

LEAVES. Distant, hard and rigid, pointing forward along the shoot, all on the upper side; 1–3 cm, long, tapering from near the base or about half way to a rounded end, grooved above; two very broad and very white bands beneath.

CONE. Ovoid, 2–3·5 cm, scales rounded, striated and shining (Dallimore and Jackson).

GROWTH. Dated trees were in South-east England and grew very slowly until 1931 and have not been found since. In the far south west, the big old tree at Boconnoc had been adding an inch a year to its girth and dated trees at Hergest Croft and Headfort have grown reasonably fast.

RECOGNITION. The big, forward-pointing leaves on pendulous shoots are distinctive.

Tsuga forrestii Downie. West China.

Closely allied to *T. chinensis*, differing in pale pink-brown, slender shoot, pubescent only on the pulvini; densely set slender leaves to 2×0·2 cm. A small plant at Jermyn's House.

TABLE 127. SPECIMENS OF TSUGA DUMOSA

Locality	*Date Planted*	*Dimensions*	
Boconnoc		53′ × 12′ 0″ (1905)	77′ × 15′ 10″ (1957)[2]
Dropmore	1848	48′ × 5′ 0″ (1931)	52′ (1956)[2]
Tregrehan		50′ × 5′ 6″ (1931)	65′ × 8′ 0″ (1971)
Borde Hill		12′ (1931)	30′ × 2′ 5″ (1958)[1]
Bicton			31′ × 2′ 8″ (1968)
Fota	1855		62′ × 9′ 7″ (1966)
Inistioge			65′ × 9′ 7″ (1966)
Powerscourt			48′ × 4′ 2″ (1966)
Kilmacurragh			65′ × 7′ 9″ (1966)[1]
Castlewellan		25′ (1931)	43′ × 5′ 11″ (1966)[1]
Mount Usher			50′ × 5′ 11″ (1966)
Headfort	1914	10′ × 1′ 3″ (1931)	38′ × 5′ 9″ (1966)
Hergest Croft	1922		38′ × 3′ 0″ (1961)[1]

[1] Main stem of two
[2] Since died

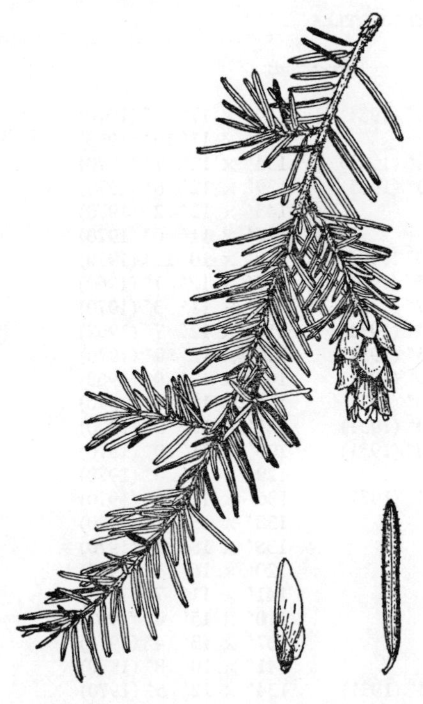

Fig. 199
Foliage and cone of *Tsuga heterophylla*, Western hemlock, with (below) seed ($\times 1\frac{1}{3}$) and underside of leaf ($\times 1\frac{1}{3}$) showing broad white stomatal bands.

Tsuga heterophylla (Rafinesque) Sargent. Western hemlock (*T. albertiana* A. Murray) Sénéclauze.

North-west America from the coast of South West Alaska to Northern California; inland in Southern-central British Columbia. Introduced in 1851. Frequent in most areas in large gardens and some smaller, very common in policies in Scotland; frequent as plantation tree especially under or replacing old hardwoods.

Bark. Young trees reddish purple-brown cracking into circular flakes. The flakes later come away and leave red-purple patches. Old trees: dark purple-brown, sometimes grey; fissured finely into irregular, broken ridges.

Crown. Always distinctively narrow and conic to a slender, gracefully arched and drooping leading shoot. Branches ascending, arching gently out to the tips, with narrow plumes of dense foliage on their undersides partly pendulous; dark and dense.

Foliage. Shoot reddish brown above, creamy-white beneath, ribbed; dense curly, long pale brown pubescence; second year dull brownish grey.

Bud. Hidden by leaves; narrowly conic, pale brown, pubescent. Side-buds in May prominent, globular and white before expanding.

Leaves. In two sets, short nearly upright, 0·5 cm, above the shoot; long 1·5–1·8 cm×0·2 cm, flat pectinate each side of the shoot; parallel-sided to a blunt apex, pale green when fresh, soon blackish-green; two broad blue-white bands beneath almost obscuring midrib; very narrow green margins.

Flowers and Cone. Male flowers clustered among the leaves on the ends of short shoots, crimson before shedding pollen in late April and early May; the pollen abundant often blooms foliage yellow by adhering. Cone 2–2·5 cm long, ovoid, pale green with few scales, ripening dark brown.

Growth. Growth in height is for many years remarkably vigorous on a wide variety of soils from deep neutral loams to dry acid sands. Leading shoots of 4 feet 6 inches are quite frequent. Growth starts downwards from the hanging tip in mid-May; attains 3–5 inches a week in July when most of the growth of the previous year straightens up but leaves the new growth still hanging or at a strongly downward angle. Growth continues until early or mid-September, by which time the basal portion of the new growth is upright. Trees have been found which have grown 60 feet in 20 years, and in Scotland, growth on trees well over 100 feet tall may still be above 1 foot a year. Growth in girth is sometimes extremely rapid. One tree in Table 128 has a mean increase of 3 inches a year for 18 years and many range from $1\frac{1}{2}$ to $2\frac{1}{2}$ inches a year. Older trees remeasured also show some rapid increases and are mostly rather above 1 inch per year.

Specimens. There are so many fine, large trees that Table 128 is restricted to the oldest dated trees, younger dated trees of good growth and a few exceptional trees of unknown dates.

TABLE 128. SOME SPECIMENS OF TSUGA HETEROPHYLLA

Locality	*Date Planted*	*Dimensions*	
Scone Castle	(1863?) 1853	84′ × 12′ 4″ (1931)	124′ × 17′ 5″ (1970)
Boturich Castle	1853		116′ × 11′ 10″ (1953)
Dupplin Castle	1859	99′ × 9′ 4″ (1931)	134′ × 12′ 7″ (1970)
Murthly Castle	1860	70′ × 5′ 0″ (1905)	139′ × 12′ 8″ (1970)
Murthly Castle			143′ × 12′ 2″ (1970)
Dawyck	1860		120′ × 11′ 6″ (1970)
Dropmore	1862	70′ × 6′ 0″ (1905)	88′ × 10′ 11″ (1970)
Hafodunos		94′ × 8′ 5″ (1904)	119′ × 12′ 7″ (1960)
(N. Devon)		90′ × 6′ 7″ (1905)	138′ × 11′ 3″ (1970)
Abercairny	1864	75′ × 10′ 4″ (1931)	116′ × 12′ 7″ (1962)
Glamis Castle	1864	93′ × 9′ 5″ (1931)	134′ × 12′ 9″ (1970)
Buchanan Castle	1865	75′ × 7′ 10″ (1931)	107′ × 12′ 0″ (1962)
Brahan	1865	80′ × 11′ 0″ (1931)	111′ × 13′ 5″ (1970)
Ochtertyre	1865	92′ × 8′ 0″ (1931)	121′ × 10′ 8″ (1970)
Munches	1866	94′ × 9′ 0″ (1931)	108′ × 11′ 10″ (1970)
Durris House			129′ × 11′ 6″ (1970)
Rossie Priory		102′ × 8′ 4″ (1931)	136′ × 11′ 2″ (1970)
Doune Lodge			138′ × 13′ 1″ (1970)
Doune Lodge			138′ × 18′ 4″ (1970)
Golden Grove			120′ × 16′ 8″ (1960)
Dupplin Castle (2)			141′ × 11′ 7″ (1970)
Lowther Castle			110′ × 15′ 0″ (1967)
Lanrick Castle	1870		137′ × 13′ 4″ (1970)
Lanrick Castle	1870		141′ × 10′ 8″ (1970)
Stourhead	1871	100′ × 9′ 4″ (1931)	134′ × 12′ 5″ (1970)
Yester House	1871	100′ × 7′ 10″ (1931)	100′ × 10′ 10″ (1967)
Dunkeld Cathedral	1872	75′ × 8′ 5″ (1931)	124′ × 12′ 4″ (1970)
Ardkinglas (Strone)	1875	90′ × 10′ 2″ (1931)	134′ × 14′ 4″ (1971)
Grayswood Hill	1881		85′ × 14′ 0″ (1970)
Castle Milk	1881	85′ × 8′ 6″ (1931)	100′ × 10′ 11″ (1966)
Castle Milk			102′ × 13′ 1″ (1966)
Bodnant	1887	90′ × 8′ 0″ (1931)	122′ × 12′ 0″ (1966)
Benmore			158′ × 12′ 0″ (1970)
Coldrennick			95′ × 12′ 3″ (1970)
Fonthill			133′ × 7′ 9″ (1963)
Lythe Hill			112′ × 12′ 7″ (1969)
Coollattin		68′ × 7′ 6″ (1931)	100′ × 13′ 0″ (1968)
Shelton Abbey			132′ × 11′ 9″ (1968)
Kilmacurragh			120′ × 10′ 10″ (1966)
Knightshayes			102′ × 12′ 4″ (1970)
Wakehurst Place			124′ × 10′ 1″ (1971)
Cwmllecoediog			130′ × 8′ 11″ (1960)
Monk Coniston			131′ × 12′ 4″ (1971)
Honeyhanger			92′ × 13′ 1″ (1971)
Oakley Park			102′ × 15′ 9″ (1971)
Oakley Park			123′ × 11′ 5″ (1971)
Inveraray (Lime Kilns)			120′ × 11′ 10″ (1969)
Fulmodestone		80′ × 9′ 4″ (1931)	110′ × 12′ 5″ (1969)
Cotehele		75′ × 9′ 7″ (1927)	102′ × 11′ 5″ (1964)
Bicton			92′ × 12′ 6″ (1968)
Dunkeld Cathedral	1897	63′ × 6′ 11″ (1931)	118′ × 11′ 0″ (1970)
Glenapp	1901	60′ × 4′ 7″ (1931) }	108′ × 7′ 10″ (1970)
Glenapp	1901		98′ × 9′ 6″ (1970)
Bodnant	1902		85′ × 6′ 5″ (1959)
Langridge Wood	1904		116′ × 6′ 3″ (1959)
Little Hall	1906	54′ × 3′ 3″ (1931)	71′ × 6′ 5″ (1961)
Smith's Combe	1908		105′ × 4′ 1″ (1959)
Tongs Wood	ca.1908		80′ × 10′ 0″ (1968)
Headfort	1915	46′ × 3′ 10″ (1931)	76′ × 9′ 11″ (1966)
Cortachy Castle	ca.1915		105′ × 9′ 5″ (1962)
Capenoch	1922		80′ × 8′ 1″ (1970)
Bedgebury	1926	7′ 9″ (1931)	73′ × 6′ 3″ (1969)
Speech House	1927		75′ × 6′ 6″ (1963)
Redleaf Wood	1942		66′ × 6′ 3″ (1967)
Gwysaney	1948		49′ × 4′ 0″ (1966)
Dropmore	1949		56′ × 3′ 11″ (1970)

GENERAL. This species establishes most rapidly under light shade. It is able, although it is inadvisable to let it, to grow through over-hanging branches, since the fragile new leading shoot is hanging below and the contact with the branches is made by woody 1–2 year old wood, as part of the leader straightens. Although crops are not particularly stable, individual trees are extraordinarily wind firm. It is not a species to grow in great exposure nor on deep peats, but it will grow in both conditions combined, making bushy, multi-stemmed growth for several years and then a single leading-shoot emerging, and growing steadily if slowly. The tree is susceptible to butt-rot (*Fomes annosus*) and is liable to much loss from this fungus when it is planted in old hardwood areas. There has thus been a recent decrease in such planting.
RECOGNITION. The single-boled, long-spired crown and drooping leading shoot are distinct from all other hemlocks and all other trees, although the very different deodar (*Cedrus deodara*) shares these particular features. The foliage differs in layout from other hemlocks except *T. chinensis*, but unlike that species, the leaves are broadly banded bluish-white beneath.

Tsuga × jeffreyi (Henry) Henry.

Formerly regarded as a variety of *T. mertensiana*, now regarded as a hybrid between *T. mertensiana* and *T. heterophylla*. If this be so, the second parent shows remarkably little in the hybrid; the bark, crown and cone being almost exactly those of *T. mertensiana*. A tree with a curious and doubtful history in cultivation. It was first noticed in Edinburgh Royal Botanic Garden from seed sown in 1851 deriving from near Mount Baker in British Columbia. Another tree was raised there more recently among Rhododendron seeds from the Selkirk Mountains and again one was grown in Ireland from seedlings dug up in Vancouver Island. It was thus unknown in the wild yet occurred three times in the British Isles. In 1967 or 1968 however, Mr. J. Duffield found a hybrid swarm of this parentage growing on the east side of White Pass, south of Mount Rainier, Washington. The origin of the few British specimens is unknown but presumably they were raised from the first tree at Edinburgh. They do not appear to be grafts. There is some variation in these, towards *T. mertensiana*.
BARK. Deep orange-brown or blackish, finely fissured and very scaly.
CROWN. Young plants ovoid, many ascending shoots competing with the leading shoot. Leading shoot bent to one side at the tip. Trees narrowly conic, rather open; descending branches. Layered branches at Lydhurst.
FOLIAGE. Shoot pale brown with a sparse, long pubescence. Leaves nearly pectinate, sparsely set perpendicular to shoot, some pointing backwards, 1–1·5 cm, very slender, and flat, grooved above, light greyish yellow-green both sides.
CONE. Cylindric-oblong to 5 cm (Dallimore and Jackson).
SPECIMENS. Bodnant, 44ft × 2ft 10in (1959); Westonbirt, 34ft × 2ft 6in (1967); Borde Hill (Gores Wood), 30ft × 1ft 6in (1970); Lydhurst, 43ft × 3ft 1in (1971); Edinburgh Royal Botanic Garden, 10ft × 1ft 5in (1967); Windsor Great Park, 10 feet (1967); Bedgebury, planted 1959, 11 feet (1969).
RECOGNITION. A tree like *T. mertensiana* but instead of thick, blue-grey leaves all round the shoot and lying forwards; slender, flat yellowish-grey-green leaves, pectinate, perpendicular and some pointing backwards.

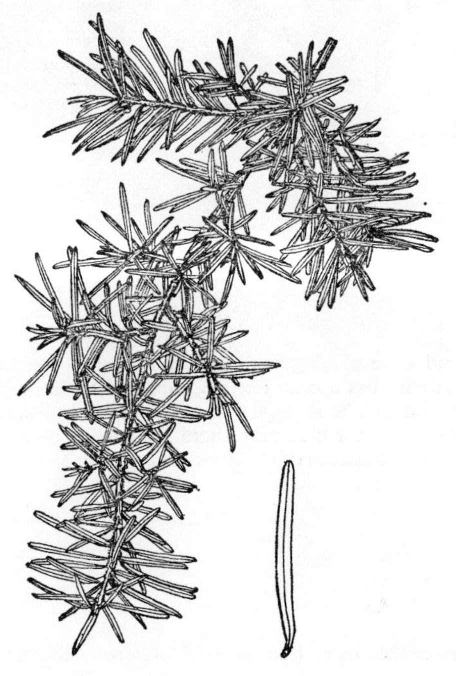

Tsuga x jeffreyi

Fig. 200
The hybrid *Tsuga × jeffreyi*, unknown in the wild until recently, has grey-green leaves, more slender and spreading than those of the one of its parents it most resembles, *T. mertensiana*. They are the same colour both sides and grooved along the upper side (right × $1\frac{1}{3}$).

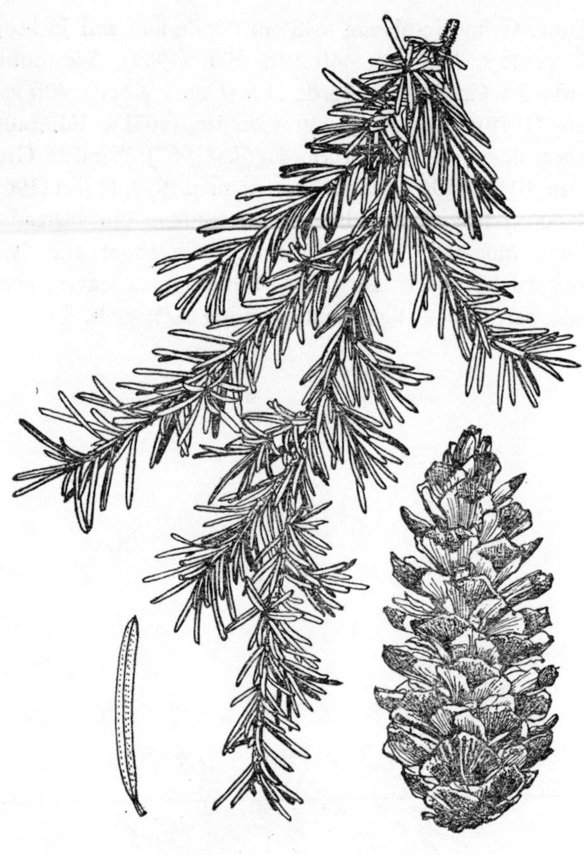

Tsuga mertensiana

Fig. 201
Foliage and cone of *Tsuga mertensiana,* Mountain hemlock. This aberrant species has a cone like a spruce and leaves radiating all round the shoot. The short shoots can look like spurs, and since the leaves are grey or blue-grey, there is a passing resemblance to the foliage of *Cedrus atlantica* 'Glauca'. Inset leaf ×2.

Tsuga mertensiana (Bongard) Carriere. Mountain hemlock (*Tsuga hookeriana* Carriere; *Tsuga pattoniana* Sénéclauze).

Islands and coast of South Alaska and British Columbia; Washington, few in Olympic Mountains; abundant high on the Cascades through Oregon to the Sierra Nevada, California. Introduced in 1854. Uncommon but in many large gardens, particularly in northern parts, and in some small gardens in areas like South West Surrey where many conifers are grown.

BARK. Brownish-orange, fissured finely vertically and flaking into small rectangular scales.

CROWN. Narrowly conic and pointed, usually a bushy base where growth was slow, tending to be narrowly columnar with a long spire where growth has accelerated; short level or depressed branches and variably pendulous pale blue-grey foliage; very dense.

FOLIAGE. Shoot, pale shining brown with a short pubescence; pulvini rich red-brown abruptly changing to greenish-white. Leaves arising all round the shoots and with many short shoots vertical above the spray, the appearance is there like the whorled leaves of a cedar. Leaves lying well forwards, thick, 1·5–2 cm long, parallel sided to a rounded tip, uniformly glaucous but variably blue, all round.

CONE. (ex-California) 7×3·5 cm (open) cylindric, tapered slightly, fawn-pink stained purple, striated. In these countries soon dark brown; clustered around the apex.

GROWTH. At first growth is slow with leading shoots of at most one foot in length and this persists for many years. Later, especially in Scotland, growth is quite rapid and the largest trees are growing rapidly in height and girth. Although a mountain species, the best trees are all on rich soils in lowland arboreta, mainly in damp areas with cool summers, and high altitude plantings whilst remaining healthy, have grown but slowly. In England trees of over 50 feet have tended to be blown over or lean badly in a few places.

RECOGNITION. The narrowly columnar-conic crown of pendulous grey foliage is quite distinct. The thick, grey-blue leaves all round the shoots and pointing forwards are also distinct among all hemlocks (and other trees). The colour of the foliage varies in the whitish blue shade and the brightest are grown as cv. Argentea whilst many almost normally coloured are grown as cv. Glauca but the intermediate colours are too many to establish these as separate cultivars, and occur in adjacent trees in Oregon.

TABLE 129. NOTABLE TREES OF TSUGA MERTENSIANA

Locality	*Date Planted*	*Dimensions*	
Methven Castle	1858	40′ × 7′ 3″ (1931)	71′ × 9′ 3″ (1955)[1]
Murthly Castle	1862	47′ × 3′ 8″ (1906)	94′ × 8′ 3″ (1970)
Murthly Castle	1863	43′ × 4′ 2″ (1906)	85′ × 8′ 6″ (1970)
Murthly Castle		× 6′ 7″ (1906)	84′ × 10′ 8″ (1970)
Murthly Castle			79′ × 10′ 5″ (1970)
Oxenfoord Castle	1871	46′ × 4′ 6″ (1931)	68′ × 5′ 6″ (1967)
Blair Atholl	1872	33′ (1931)	102′ × 7′ 1″ (1970)
Fairburn			102′ × 7′ 5″ (1970)
Fairburn			70′ × 9′ 9″ (1970)
Eridge Castle	1885		54′ × 5′ 9″ (1971)
Keir Estate	1887	36′ × 5′ 0″ (1927)	59′ × 7′ 7″ (1970)
Hallyburton			90′ × 6′ 2″ (1970)
Blair Atholl (St. Brides)			75′ × 5′ 3″ (1970)
Dupplin Castle			82′ × 9′ 4″ (1970)
Dupplin Castle			77′ × 8′ 0″ (1970)
Abercairny		69′ × 7′ 3″ (1955)	77′ × 8′ 0″ (1962)
Heckfield Place			55′ × 7′ 8″ (1969)
Kirkennan			69′ × 4′ 0″ (1970)
Fulmodestone		52′ (1931)	72′ × 5′ 3″ (1969)
Bagshot Park		41′ × 4′ 7″ (1957)	44′ × 5′ 9″ (1969)
Durris House			79′ × 8′ 4″ (1970)
Tilgate	1905	26′ (1931)	45′ × 6′ 7″ (1964)
Little Hall	1906	13′ × 7′ 0″ (1931)	37′ × 1′ 8″ (1961)
Dropmore	1906	27′ × 1′ 6″ (1931)	59′ × 4′ 0″ (1970)
Westonbirt		47′ × 3′ 5″ (1931)	65′ × 3′ 9″ (1967)
St. Clere	ca.1910	37′ × 3′ 4″ (1954)	53′ × 5′ 6″ (1969)
Bedgebury	1925	5′ 3″ (1931)	24′ × 2′ 4″ (1969)[2]

[1] Probably felled since
[2] cv. Argentea

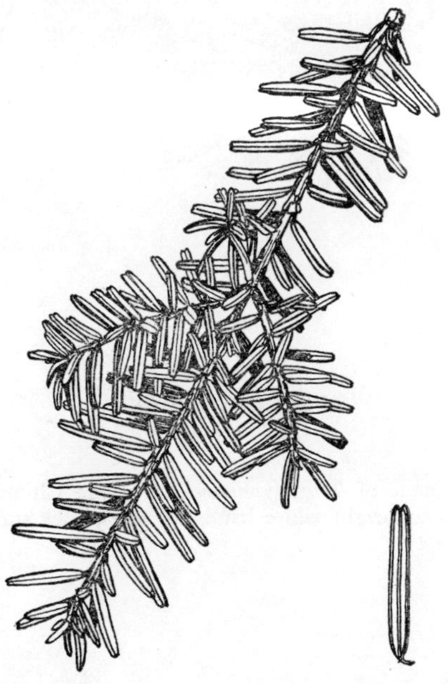

Tsuga sieboldii

Fig. 202
Foliage of *Tsuga sieboldii*, Southern Japanese hemlock, a species in which the length of the leaf and the brightness of the white bands on their undersides (right × $1\frac{1}{3}$) vary much, but they are always longer and less white than in *T. diversifolia*.

Tsuga sieboldii Carriere. Southern Japanese hemlock

South Honshiu and the southern islands of Japan. Introduced in 1861. Uncommon: in collections and many large gardens; more frequent than *T. diversifolia.*

BARK. Dark grey and smooth at first with regular horizontal folds; later cracking vertically, then into pink-grey square scales.

CROWN. Usually multiple stems from the ground and broadly conic but well defined acute apex; more open and pointed than *T. diversifolia.*

FOLIAGE. Shoot shining, glabrous pale buff; pulvini orange-red; second year shoot dull brown.

BUD. Surrounded by small leaves but more visible than in *T. diversifolia*, ovoid, narrow at base; dark orange, convex scales.

LEAVES. Irregularly spreading below shoot; of varied lengths and pectinate above, 0·7–2 cm long 2 mm broad, less regularly arranged but often more dense than *T. diversifolia*, shining dark green and grooved above, rounded and notched at the apex; two broad white bands beneath, less bright than in *T. diversifolia* and sometimes pale.

CONE. Pendulous, 2·3×1·3 cm, blunt ovoid-conic; scales flat-topped, very dark brown.

GROWTH. A taller growing tree than *T. diversifolia* and slightly more rapid in growth, but exact data are few.

TABLE 130. SPECIMENS OF TSUGA SIEBOLDII

Locality	*Date Planted*	*Dimensions*	
Lydhurst			54′ × 4′ 6″ (1971)
Abercairny			49′ × 6′ 4″ (1962)
Blackmoor	1901		37′ × 2′ 4″ (1968)
Little Hall	1906	24′ × 2′ 0″ (1931)	43′ × 2′ 10″ (1961)
Bodnant			35′ × 3′ 7″ (1959)
Leonardslee			43′ × 2′ 1″ (1969)
Wakehurst Place			45′ × 2′ 11″ (1964)
Edinburgh R.B.G.			38′ × 3′ 0″ (1967)
Bedgebury	1926	7′ (1931)	40′ × 2′ 11″ (1969)
Bedgebury	1926		38′ × 3′ 5″ (1969)
Westonbirt	1934		22′ × 2′ 1″ (1969)
Birr Castle	1934		18′ × 2′ 3″ (1966)
Melbury			46′ × 3′ 2″ (1971)

SPECIMENS. Most of the trees given have many stems and the figure applies to the central stem only.

RECOGNITION. Very similar to *T. diversifolia*, differing in the colour of the glabrous shoot, usually narrower leaves less regularly arranged and less white beneath; also in a more open and taller crown.

Tsuga yunnanensis (Franchet) Masters. Yunnan hemlock

Yunnan and West Szechuan, China. Introduced in 1908. Very rare; in a few collections in South England. A small, narrow tree with level branches and foliage similar to *T. dumosa* but less pendulous and often less bright white beneath.

FOLIAGE. Shoot rather stout, pale brown above; cream-white beneath, with patches of dense, curly pubescence.

BUD. Pale brown, 2 mm shiny and lumpy.

LEAVES. Rather sparse, more or less pectinate, of varying length 1–2 cm, 2–3 mm broad (narrower in Borde Hill: W 10293) blunt or slightly acute; pale shining green above; two broad white bands sometimes very white beneath.

CONE. Nodding, 2·3×1·2 cm, green shiny scales with pale edges, broadly rounded; ovoid-cylindric.

SPECIMENS. Borde Hill (W 10293), 30ft×3ft 3in (1968); Chandlers Ford, 18ft×1ft 0in (1961); Jermyn's House, 8 feet.

Tsuga yunnanensis

Fig. 203
Foliage and cone of *Tsuga yunnanensis*, a rare Chinese hemlock with broad and bright white bands on the under surface of the leaf. (Detail × $1\frac{1}{3}$).

Widdringtonia Endlicher (Cupressaceae)

Cypress pines. A small genus from southern and tropical Africa, related to *Callitris*.

The only outdoor plants seen are described below.

Widdringtonia cupressoides (L.) Endlicher. Cypress pine. South Africa, Table Mountain to Drakensberg.

A rather upright ovoid, bushy plant of very fine dark green scale-clad shoots. Each scale-leaf has a long closely appressed slender base and abruptly swollen broad tip which is obtuse, incurved and minutely mucronate. The tips stand out from the very slender shoot and give a serrated appearance. The tips are in pairs 1–4 mm apart along the shoot. Casa di Sole, South Devon, 6 feet.

Widdringtonia juniperoides (L.) Endlicher. Clanwilliam cedar. Cedarberry Mountains, West Cape Province

Only juvenile foliage seen on a small upright bushy plant. Leaves spirally set, spreading nearly perpendicular from shoot, 1·5–1·8 cm long, 1 mm across, shiny grey-green, raised midrib above, slightly decurved margins, matt yellowish green beneath; bluntly tipped and minutely mucronate. Casa di Sole, South Devon, 5 feet 6 inches.

Glossary

Acuminate	Narrowing gradually to a fine point.
Appressed	Closely pressed to.
Assurgent	Rising to nearly or quite vertical.
Backward	Pointing away from the terminal bud, towards the base of the shoot.
Clone	A population of plants raised vegetatively from a single plant and thus genetically identical.
Crenate	With teeth which have rounded shoulders and a central point.
Decurved	Curved down or back (cf 'Recurved').
Dioecious	Male and female flowers on separate trees.
Distant	Widely spaced on shoot.
Epicormic	A shoot or bud arising from interior tissues on old branches or bole.
Exserted	Thrust out from.
F_1	First generation hybrid—i.e. with parents of different species (or populations).
F_2	Second generation hybrid—i.e. raised from F_1 hybrid and thus with both parents similar hybrids.
Flush	Leaf-out; leaves emerging from the bud.
Flute	Longitudinal furrow in a bole.
Forward	Pointing towards the terminal bud.
Free	(Of bud-scales). Clear of the main body of the bud.
Fusiform	Spindle-shaped; tapered each end from an ovoid middle.
Glabrous	Without hairs.
Globose	More or less spherical.
Globular	Spherical.
Lanceolate	Spear-shaped.
Layered	Branches bent to ground, rooted there and growing up.
Leading shoot	Central, terminal shoot.
Linear-lanceolate	Narrowly spear-shaped.
Monoecious	Male and female flowers separate but on the same trees.
Mucro	A minute, abrupt sharp point.
Mucronate	Bearing a mucro.
Node	The point on a stem from which a whorl of shoots arises.
Oblique	Unequal at the base.
Obovoid	Ovoid with greatest width in the outer half.
Ovate	Elongated oval.
Ovoid	Egg-shaped.
Pectinate	Spread each side like the teeth of a comb, flat.
Perpendicular	Of leaves; at right angles to the shoot, in any plane (not necessarily vertical).
Proliferous	(Cone). A cone in which the shoot continues growth beyond the apex as an ordinary leafy shoot.
Pubescent	Bearing fine hairs.
Pulvinus	The swelling from which leaves arise on the stem.
Recurved	Curved upwards or forwards (cf "decurved").
Reflexed	Curved outwards.
Revolute	Curled downwards and under (leaf-margin).
Ribbed	Smoothly grooved and ridged.
Serotinous	Late in season or late to be shed. Of cones—persisting on the tree for several years.
Sessile	Without a stalk.
Subsessile	With scarcely any stalk.
Terete	Smoothly rounded.
Tomentose	Bearing long hairs.
Truncate	Ending abruptly as if cut across.

Index to Estates and Forests mentioned and their Localities

Notes. Where the county is stated in brackets, it is the county at the estate or forest, not of the town given. In all, 527 collections are listed.
** Open to the public at all seasons, either free of charge or on payment.*
† Open seasonally.
Other properties not marked, may be open occasionally.

Estate or Forest	Nearest Town, etc.
Bradfield House	Tiverton, Devon.
*Brandon Park	Thetford, Norfolk. (Forestry Commission).
Brahan	Conon Bridge, Easter Ross-shire.
Briggens	Hundsdon, Ware, Hertfordshire.
Brinkburn Priory	Rothbury, Northumberland.
Brockhall	Weedon, Northamptonshire.
Brocklesby Park	Limber, Lincolnshire.
Brooklands House	Langport, Somerset.
Brownscombe	Shottermill, Haslemere, Surrey.
Broxwood Court	Sarnesfield, Herefordshire.
Buchanan Castle	Drymen, Stirlingshire.
Burnside	Forfar, Angus.
Burwood Park	Walton-on-Thames, Surrey.
Bury Hill	Dorking, Surrey.
Busbridge Hall	Godalming, Surrey.
Busbridge Lakes	Godalming, Surrey.
Butleigh House	Glastonbury, Somerset.
Cairnsmore	Newton Stewart, (Kirkcudbrightshire).
*Cambridge B.G.	Cambridge University Botanic Garden, Trumpington Road, Cambridge.
Canford House	Wimborne, Dorset.
*Cannop	Forest of Dean, Gloucestershire. (Forestry Commission).
Canonbie	Dumfriesshire.
Capenoch	Penpont, Thornhill, Dumfriesshire.
Carclew	Penryn, Falmouth, Cornwall.
Cardross	Menteith, Perthshire.
Carey House	Wareham, Dorset.
Carton House	Maynooth, County Meath, Ireland.
Casa di Sole	Near Salcombe, South Devon.
Castle Forbes	Newtown Forbes, County Longford, Ireland.
†Castle Kennedy	(Lochinch) Stranraer, Wigtownshire.
Castle Leod	Strathpeffer, Dingwall, Ross-shire.
Castle Milk	Lockerbie, Dumfriesshire.
Castle, Old, Wardour	Warminster, Wiltshire.
†Castlewellan	Newcastle, County Down, Northern Ireland.
Cawdor Castle	Cawdor, Nairn.
Cedars, The	Windlesham, Surrey.
Chandlers Ford	Southampton, Hampshire. (Hillier & Sons, Nursery. Now sold.)
Chart Park	Dorking, Surrey.
†Chatsworth	Edensor, Bakewell, Derbyshire.
Chiddingly	West Hoathly, Sussex.
Childrey Rectory	Childrey, Wantage, Berkshire.
Chiltlee Place	Liphook, Hampshire.
*Chiswick House	Chiswick, London.
†Clare College Garden	Queens Road, Cambridge.
Clare Lodge	Rowledge, Farnham, Surrey.
*Claremont	Esher, Surrey. (National Trust).
Clavery House	Ascot, Berkshire.
Clonmannon	Wicklow, County Wicklow, Ireland.
Cobham Hall	Rochester, Kent.
Codford Village	Warminster, Wiltshire.
Coldrennick	Menheniot, Cornwall.
Compton Chamberlayne	Wilton, Wiltshire.
Conon House	Conon, Ross-shire.
Coollattin	Carnew, County Wicklow, Ireland.
Coppid Hall	Stonor, Henley, Oxfordshire.
Corehouse	Lanark, Lanarkshire.
†Corsham Court	Corsham, Wiltshire.
Cortachy Castle	Kirriemuir, Angus.
Coul	Dingwall, Ross and Cromarty.
†Cowdray Park	Midhurst, Sussex.
Cowarne Court	Much Cowarne, Herefordshire.
†Cragside	Rothbury, Northumberland.
Craigdarroch	Moniaive, Dumfries.
Cranford Farm	Hawkhurst, Kent.
†Crarae	Minard, Argyll. (Part Forestry Commission*).
Creech Grange	Wareham, Dorset.
Crichel Down	Wimborne, Dorset.
Cricket St. Thomas	Crewkerne, Somerset.
Crogen	Bala, Merioneth.
Crowthorne	Berkshire.
Crwys Morchard	Tiverton, Devon.
Cuffnells	Lyndhurst, Hampshire.
Cullen House	Cullen, Banffshire.
*Culloden Forest	Inverness. (Forestry Commission).
†Culzean Castle	Maybole, Ayrshire. (National Trust for Scotland).
Curraghmore	Waterford, County Waterford, Ireland.
Cwmllecoediog	Aberangell, Machynlleth, Montgomery.
*Cynwyd Forest	Corwen, Merioneth. (Forestry Commission).
Dalguise House	Dalguise, Dunkeld, Perthshire.
Darnaway	Forres, Moray.
†Dartington Hall	Dartington, Totnes, Devon.
†Dawyck	Stobo, Peebles.
Derreen	Kenmare, County Kerry, Ireland.
Dogmersfield	Odiham, Hampshire.
Doldowlod	Rhayader, Radnorshire.
Dropmore	Burnham, Buckinghamshire.
Drumlanrig Castle	Thornhill, Dumfries.
Drummuir	Dufftoun, Banffshire.
*Drumtochty	Fordoun, Kincardineshire.
Dryderdale	Wolsingham, Durham.
Dubs House	Kirkmichael, Ayrshire.
Dunans	Glendaruel, Argyll.
†Duncombe Park	Helmsley, North Riding, Yorkshire.
Duncraig Castle	Plockton, Kyle of Lochalsh, Wester Ross-shire.
Dungarthill	Dunkeld, Perthshire.
*Dunkeld Cathedral	Dunkeld, Perthshire.
Dunkeld House	Dunkeld, Perthshire.
Dunira House	Comrie, Perthshire.
Dunloe Castle	Dunloe, Killarney, County Kerry, Ireland.
*Dunorlan Park	Tunbridge Wells, Kent.
Duns	Duns, Berwickshire.
*Dunster	Broadwood, Dunster, Somerset.
Dupplin Castle	Forteviot, Perthshire.

Estate or Forest	Nearest Town, etc.
†Hopetoun	Queensferry, West Lothian.
Howick	Alnwick, Northumberland.
Humewood Castle	Kiltegan, County Wicklow, Ireland.
Hurn Court.	Hurn, Christchurch, Hampshire.
Ickworth	Horringer, Bury St. Edmunds, Suffolk.
†Ilnacullin	Garinish Island, Glengarriff, County Cork, Ireland.
Inchmarlo	Banchory, Kincardineshire.
Inistioge	Woodstock, County Kilkenny, Ireland.
†Inveraray Castle	Inveraray, Argyll.
Irvine House	Canonbie, Dumfries.
Jardine Hall	Lockerbie, Dumfries.
Jenkyn Place	Bentley, Alton, Hampshire.
†Jermyn's House	Ampfield, Romsey, Hampshire.
Kailzie	Near Peebles.
Keir House	Dunblane, Perthshire.
†Kenwood House	Hampstead, North London. (Greater London Council).
Kildangan	Kildare, County Kildare, Ireland.
Kidbrooke Park	Forest Row, Sussex.
Kilkerran	Maybole, Ayrshire.
†Killarney House	Killarney, County Kerry, Ireland.
†Killerton	Silverton, Exeter, Devon.
Killiow	St. Kea, Falmouth, Cornwall.
Kilmacurragh	Rathdrum, County Wicklow, Ireland.
*Kilmun	Benmore, Dunoon, Argyll. (Forestry Commission).
Kilravock Castle	Croy, Nairn.
Kinfauns Castle	Perthshire.
Kinloch House	Meigle, Perthshire.
Kinnettles	Glamis, Angus.
Kippendavie	Doune, Perthshire.
Kitlands	Leith Hill, Surrey.
Ladham House	Goudhurst, Kent.
*Lake Vyrnwy	Llanfyllin, Montgomery. (Liverpool Corporation).
Lamellan	St. Tudy, Cornwall.
Land of Nod	Headley Down, Hampshire.
Langholm	Dumfriesshire.
Lanrick Castle	Doune, Perthshire.
Leaton Knolls	Shrewsbury, Shropshire.
Lee Park	Lanark.
Leighton Hall	Welshpool, Montgomery.
Leighton Park	Welshpool, Montgomery.
†Leonardslee	Lower Beeding, Horsham, Sussex.
Lexden Manor	Colchester, Essex.
Lilliesden	Hawkhurst, Kent.
Linley Hall	Lydbury, Shropshire.
Linton Park	Maidstone, Kent.
Little Hall	St. Stephen, Canterbury, Kent.
Little Kingsmill Grange	Gt. Missenden, Buckinghamshire.
Llanfachreth	Pentrefoelas, Denbighshire.
Lochanhead	Dumfries (Kirkcudbrightshire).
Lochnaw	Leswalt, Stranraer, Wigtownshire.

Estate or Forest	Nearest Town, etc.
Lockerley Hall	Romsey, Hampshire.
Lodge, The	Wateringbury, Kent.
Londesborough Hall	Market Weighton, East Riding, Yorkshire.
Longford Castle	Salisbury, Wiltshire.
†Longleat	Warminster, Wiltshire.
Lowther Castle	Penrith, Cumberland.
Lude House	Blair Atholl, Perthshire.
Luscombe Castle	Dawlish, Devon.
Luxborough	Dunster, Somerset.
Lydhurst	Warninglid, Sussex.
Lyndon Hall	Oakham, Rutland.
Lynedoch	Scone, Perthshire.
Lynhales	Kington, Herefordshire.
Lytchett Heath	Poole, Dorset.
Lythe Hill	Haslemere, Surrey.
Madresfield Court	Malvern, Worcestershire.
Maesllwch Castle	Glasbury, Radnor.
Mamhead Park	Exeter, Devon.
Melbury	Evershot, Dorset.
Melfort House	Lochgilphead, Argyll.
Mells Park	Frome, Somerset.
Minard Castle	Minard, Argyll.
Minterne	Evershot, Dorset.
Minto House	Hawick, Roxburgh.
Moncrieffe House	Bridge of Earn, Perthshire.
Monk Coniston	Coniston, Lancashire.
Monk Hopton	Bridgnorth, Shropshire.
†Montacute House	Yeovil, Somerset. (National Trust).
Monymusk	Monymusk, Donside, Aberdeenshire.
Monzie Castle	Crieff, Perthshire.
Moor Park	Farnham, Surrey.
Moor Park	Ludlow, Shropshire.
*Moss's Wood	Leith Hill, Dorking, Surrey. (National Trust).
Mount Edgcumbe	Plymouth (Cornwall).
†Mount Usher	Ashford, County Wicklow, Ireland.
†Muckross Abbey	Killarney, County Kerry, Ireland.
Munches	New Abbey, Dumfries.
Munden	Watford, Hertfordshire.
Murraythwaite	Lockerbie, Dumfries.
Murthly Castle	Murthly, Perthshire.
Nettlecombe Court	Willaton, Somerset.
New Court	Topsham, Exeter, Devon.
Newton St. Cyres	Exeter, Devon.
(N. Devon)	Near Barnstaple, Devon.
North Manor	Crickhowell, Brecon.
Novar	Evanton, Ross-shire.
Nunwick	Hexham, Northumberland.
†Nymans	Handcross, Sussex. (National Trust).
Oakley Park	Ludlow, Shropshire.
Ochtertyre	Crieff, Perthshire.
Ombersley Court	Ombersley, Worcester.
Ormidale	Candahar, Argyll.
†Osborne House	Osborne, Isle of Wight, Hants.

Estate or Forest	Nearest Town, etc.
Oxenford Grange	Elstead, Surrey.
Oxenfoord Castle	Dalkeith, Midlothian.
Pains Hill	Cobham, Surrey.
Pampisford	Pampisford, Cambridge.
Panshanger	Ware, Hertfordshire.
Parkhatch	Hascombe, Godalming, Surrey.
Park Place	Henley, Oxfordshire.
Patshull	Burnhill Green, Wolverhampton, Staffordshire.
Peamore	Exeter, Devon.
Peckover	Wisbech, Cambridgeshire.
Pencarrow	Bodmin, Cornwall.
Penjerrick	Falmouth, Cornwall.
Pennyhill	Bagshot, Surrey.
Penpont	Brecon.
Penrhyn Castle	Bangor, Caernarvonshire.
Penshurst Place	Penshurst, Kent.
Peper Harrow	Elstead, Surrey.
†Petworth House	Petworth, Sussex.
Pitt House	Chudleigh, Exeter.
Poles	Ware, Hertfordshire.
Poltalloch	Kilmartin, Lochgilphead, Argyll.
Poltimore	Exeter, Devon.
Post Green	Lytchett Matravers, Dorset.
†Powderham Castle	Kenton, Exeter, Devon.
†Powerscourt	Enniskerry, County Wicklow, Ireland.
Powis Castle	Welshpool, Montgomeryshire.
Preston House	Linlithgow, West Lothian.
*Puck Pits	New Forest, Lyndhurst, Hampshire. (Forestry Commission).
Pusey House	Faringdon, Berkshire.
Pylewell Park	Lymington, Hampshire.
Queen's Spinney	Ashurst, Kent.
Queenswood	Hope-under-Dinmore, Herefordshire.
Radley College	Abingdon, Berkshire.
Raehills	Moffat, Dumfriesshire.
Raith House	Kirkcaldy, Fife.
Rammerscales	Lockerbie, Dumfriesshire.
Ramster	Chiddingfold, Surrey.
*Ravensbury Park	Mitcham, Surrey.
Rectory, The, Much Hadham	Much Hadham, Hertfordshire.
Redleaf Woods	Chiddingstone Causeway, Kent.
Rednock	Port of Menteith (Stirling).
*Reelig (Moniack Glen)	Beauly, Inverness. (Forestry Commission).
Rendcombe	North Cerney, Gloucestershire.
*Rhinefield Ornamental Drive	New Forest, Lyndhurst, Hampshire. (Forestry Commission).
Riccarton	Currie, Midlothian.
Ripley Castle	Harrogate, Yorkshire.
Rookeries, The	Dorking, Surrey.

Estate or Forest	Nearest Town, etc.
Rossdhu	Luss, Dunbartonshire.
Rossie Priory	Dundee, Angus. (Perthshire).
†Rowallane	Saintfield, County Down, Northern Ireland.
Ryston	Downham Market, Norfolk.
St. Annes Court	Chertsey, Surrey.
St. Clere	Kemsing, Maidstone, Kent.
St. Erth Station	Nr. Penzance, Cornwall.
Sandling Park	Hythe, Kent.
†Savill Gardens	Windsor Great Park, Berkshire. (Commissioners of Crown Lands).
†Scone Castle	Perth.
Scorrier House	Redruth, Cornwall.
†Scotney Castle	Lamberhurst, Kent. (National Trust).
Sharpham House	Totnes, Devon.
†Sheffield Park	Uckfield, Sussex. (National Trust).
Shelton Abbey	Arklow, County Wicklow, Ireland. (Forestry Division, Department of Lands, Eire).
Shirley Hall	Langton Green, Tunbridge Wells, Kent.
Shroner's Hill	Ampfield, Hampshire.
Shrubland	Ipswich, Suffolk.
Sidbury Manor	Sidbury, Devon.
Silia	Presteigne, Radnorshire.
Silvermere	Nr. Cobham, Surrey.
Sindlesham	Wokingham, Berkshire. (Bear Wood).
Skibo Castle	Dornoch, Sutherlandshire.
Smeaton House	East Linton, East Lothian.
Snowdenham House	Bramley, Guildford, Surrey.
*Speech House	Coleford, Forest of Dean, Gloucestershire. (Forestry Commission).
*Speymouth Forest	Fochabers, Moray. (Forestry Commission).
Springfield Court	Seaview, Isle of Wight, Hants.
Springkell	Eaglesfield, Dumfries.
Sprivers	Horsmonden, Kent.
Spye Park	Calne, Wiltshire.
Stanage Park	Knighton, Radnorshire.
Stanway	Winchcombe, Gloucestershire.
Stapehill Nurseries	Stapehill, Wimborne, Dorset.
Stocklinch Manor	Ilminster, Somerset.
Stonefield	Tarbert, Argyll.
†Stourhead	Stourton, Mere, Wiltshire. (National Trust).
Strachur	Loch Fyne, Argyll.
Stradbally House	Stradbally, County Leix, Ireland.
Stratfield Saye	Tadley, Hants.
Strathallan Castle	Dunblane, Perthshire.
Streatham Hall	Exeter (University), Devon.
Strete Ralegh House	Ottery St. Mary, Devon.
*Strete Ralegh Pinetum	Ottery St. Mary, Devon.
Strone	Cairndow, Argyll.
Sunninghill Nurseries	Windlesham, Surrey.
Sutton Place	Guildford, Surrey.
†Syon House	Brentford, Middlesex.

Printed in England for Her Majesty's Stationery Office by McCorquodale (Printers) Ltd. Dd. 501985 K48 2/72

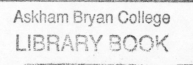